5.95

AUTOMATIC CONTROL ENGINEERING

McGraw-Hill Series in Mechanical Engineering

Jack P. Holman, *Southern Methodist University*
Consulting Editor

Barron: *Cryogenic Systems*
Eckert: *Introduction to Heat and Mass Transfer*
Eckert and Drake: *Analysis of Heat and Mass Transfer*
Eckert and Drake: *Heat and Mass Transfer*
Ham, Crane, and Rogers: *Mechanics of Machinery*
Hartenberg and Denavit: *Kinematic Synthesis of Linkages*
Hinze: *Turbulence*
Jacobsen and Ayre: *Engineering Vibrations*
Juvinall: *Engineering Considerations of Stress, Strain, and Strength*
Kays: *Convective Heat and Mass Transfer*
Lichty: *Combustion Engine Process*
Martin: *Kinematics and Dynamics of Machines*
Phelan: *Dynamics of Machinery*
Phelan: *Fundamentals of Mechanical Design*
Raven: *Automatic Control Engineering*
Schenck: *Theories of Engineering Experimentation*
Schlichting: *Boundary-Layer Theory*
Shigley: *Dynamic Analysis of Machines*
Shigley: *Kinematic Analysis of Mechanics*
Shigley: *Mechanical Engineering Design*
Shigley: *Simulation of Mechanical Systems*
Stoecker: *Refrigeration and Air Conditioning*
Sutton and Sherman: *Engineering Magnetohydrodynamics*

AUTOMATIC CONTROL ENGINEERING

Third Edition

Francis H. Raven
Professor of Mechanical Engineering
University of Notre Dame

INTERNATIONAL STUDENT EDITION

McGRAW-HILL KOGAKUSHA, LTD.

Tokyo Auckland Beirut Bogota Düsseldorf Johannesburg Lisbon London Lucerne Madrid Mexico New Delhi Panama Paris San Juan São Paulo Singapore Sydney

This book was set in Times Roman.
The editors were B. J. Clark and Frances A. Neal;
the production supervisor was Dennis J. Conroy.
New drawings were done by J & R Services, Inc.

AUTOMATIC CONTROL ENGINEERING

INTERNATIONAL STUDENT EDITION

Library of Congress Cataloging in Publication Data

Raven, Francis Harvey, date
Automatic control engineering.

Includes bibliographical references and index.
1. Automatic control. I. Title.
TJ213.R38 1977 629.8'3 77-12005
ISBN 0-07-051228-0

TOSHO PRINTING CO., LTD., TOKYO, JAPAN

To Therese

CONTENTS

Preface xi

1 Introduction to Automatic Controls 1

1.1 Historical Development 1
1.2 Feedback Control Systems 2
1.3 System Representation 3

2 Representation of Control Components 6

2.1 Operational Notation 6
2.2 Mechanical Components 11
2.3 Electrical Components 15
2.4 Series and Parallel Laws 16
2.5 Analogies 24
2.6 Scale Factors 26
2.7 Thermal Systems 30
2.8 Fluid Systems 32

3 Representation of Control Systems 43

3.1 Linearization of Nonlinear Functions 43
3.2 Linearization of Operating Curves 51
3.3 Hydraulic Systems 55
3.4 Pneumatic Systems 61
3.5 DC Motors 64
3.6 AC Motors 69
3.7 Block-Diagram Algebra 72
3.8 Speed Control System 72
3.9 Generalized Feedback Control System 78

4 Steady-State Operation 88

4.1 Steady-State Analysis 88
4.2 Equilibrium 96
4.3 Proportional Control Systems 99
4.4 Integral Control Systems 103
4.5 Proportional Plus Integral Control Systems 106
4.6 Modes of Control 108

5 Laplace Transforms 114

5.1 Classical Methods 114
5.2 Laplace Transformation Method 121
5.3 Transform Properties 126
5.4 Initial Conditions 139
5.5 General Procedures 145
5.6 Piecewise Continuous Functions 151
5.7 Error Coefficients 156

6 Transient Response 164

6.1 Inverse Transformations 165
6.2 Complex Conjugate Zeros 168
6.3 Damping Ratio and Natural Frequency 173
6.4 Transient Response Specifications 178
6.5 General Form of Transient Response 181
6.6 Response to an External Disturbance 183
6.7 Impulse Response 185
6.8 Routh's Stability Criterion 186
6.9 Summary 190

7 The Root-Locus Method 196

7.1 Significance of Root Loci 196
7.2 Construction of Loci 200
7.3 General Procedure 211
7.4 Loci Equations 217
7.5 Variation of Parameters 220
7.6 Sensitivity 225

8 Analog Computers 235

8.1 Computer Operations 236
8.2 Direct Programming 239
8.3 Time Scale 245
8.4 Simulation 250

9 State-Space Methods 260

9.1 System Representation 260
9.2 Signal Flow Graphs 270
9.3 Linear Algebra 277

9.4 Repeated Eigenvalues 291
9.5 Solution of State-Space Equations 296
9.6 Methods of Computing $\Phi(t)$ 300
9.7 Forced Response 308
9.8 Transfer Functions 313
9.9 State-Space Design 318

10 Digital-Control Systems 331

10.1 Sampled-Data Systems 331
10.2 The z Transform 333
10.3 Inverse z Transforms 342
10.4 Block-Diagram Algebra 345
10.5 Transient Response 349
10.6 Filters 356
10.7 Response between Sampling Instants 362
10.8 Discrete Data Systems 366
10.9 Computer-controlled Systems 380

11 Frequency-Response Methods 391

11.1 Frequency Response 392
11.2 Logarithmic Representation 397
11.3 Evaluating the Gain K 406
11.4 Equivalent Unity-Feedback System 408
11.5 Polar Plots 409
11.6 M and α Circles 412
11.7 Correlation between Transient and Frequency Response 416
11.8 Determining the Gain K to Yield a Desired M_p 425

12 System Compensation 439

12.1 Nyquist Stability Criterion 439
12.2 Gain Margin and Phase Margin 448
12.3 Lead Compensation 454
12.4 Lag Compensation 461
12.5 Lag-Lead Compensation 465
12.6 Internal Feedback 467
12.7 Inverse Polar Plots 468
12.8 Stability Criteria in the Inverse Plane 475

13 Describing Functions 485

13.1 The Describing Function 485
13.2 Stability Analysis 490
13.3 Describing Functions with a Phase Shift 496
13.4 Frequency-sensitive Describing Functions 498

14 The Phase-Plane and Liapunov Methods 506

14.1 The Phase-Plane Method 506
14.2 Feedback Systems 515
14.3 Singular Points 520
14.4 Liapunov's Direct Method 530
14.5 Generating Liapunov Functions 535
14.6 The Variable-Gradient Method 539
14.7 The Format Method 542

Appendix I Equilibrium Flow 557

Index 563

PREFACE

In recent years, automatic control systems have been rapidly increasing in importance in all fields of engineering. The applications of control systems cover a very wide range, from the design of precision control devices such as delicate instruments used for inertial guidance to the design of massive equipment such as that used for the manufacture of steel or other industrial processes. New applications for automatic controls are continually being discovered.

This text is the outgrowth of notes developed by the author to teach control engineering at the University of Notre Dame. The author has endeavored to give the principles a thorough presentation and yet make them clear and easy to understand. It is assumed that the reader has the general maturity and background of a third- or fourth-year engineering student, but no previous training in control engineering.

Although the principles of feedback control systems are presented in a manner which is appropriate to the interests of mechanical engineers, this text has also been successfully used to teach students in other fields of engineering. In addition, the author has taught night courses for practicing engineers. In the light of their enthusiastic comments, it is felt that this book will be of much value to the engineer in industry who did not have the opportunity to take such a course while in college.

The study of control engineering is begun by showing how typical control systems may be represented by block diagrams. This is accomplished by first demonstrating how to represent each component or part of a system as a simple block diagram, then explaining how these individual diagrams may be connected to form the overall block diagram, just as the actual components are connected to form the complete control system. Because actual control systems frequently contain nonlinear components, considerable emphasis is given to such components. This material is presented in the first three chapters. In the fourth chapter, it is shown that much important information concerning the basic or inherent operating characteristics of a system may be obtained from knowledge of the steady-state behavior.

This introduction to control theory differs from the usual "black-box" approach, in which the block diagram for a system is given outright. The "black-box" approach permits the introduction of Laplace transforms and other methods of system analysis at an earlier stage. However, it has been the author's experience that students attain deeper understanding of the various techniques used in system analysis if they are first familiarized with the physical significance of feedback controls.

In Chapter 5, it is shown how the linear differential equations which describe the operation of control systems may be solved algebraically by the use of Laplace transforms. It is seen that this method reveals directly much interesting information about systems. General characteristics of transient behavior are described in Chapter 6. It is pointed out that the transient response is governed by the location of the roots of the characteristic equation. In Chapter 7, it is shown how these roots may be ascertained by the root-locus method. Application of the analog computer to simulate control systems is presented in Chapter 8.

State-space methods are presented in Chapter 9. It is shown how the concepts of classical control theory are combined with state-space concepts to yield the "modern" control theory. By seeing how "modern" control theory builds on classical methods, the reader attains both a better understanding of modern methods and a deeper appreciation of the classical formulation. Digital computers and microprocessors are becoming increasingly important as elements of control systems. As is explained in Chapter 10, most of the methods (both classical and modern) used in the design of continuous-data systems may be extended to digital control systems. The term digital control system comprises a broad class of systems, including computer-controlled systems, discrete data systems, sampled-data systems, and timesharing systems. The use of frequency-response techniques to evaluate dynamic performance is explained in Chapters 11 and 12. One of the most versatile methods for handling nonlinear control systems, the describing function, is presented in Chapter 13. Next, Chapter 14 begins by explaining the phase-plane method, which is a general procedure for determining the behavior of second-order nonlinear systems. It is then shown, with the aid of state-space concepts, that in reality the Liapunov method is an extension of the phase-plane method to general higher-order nonlinear systems.

The author wishes to express his appreciation for the many fine suggestions made by teachers who have used the previous editions. These suggestions have been of great value in the preparation of this revised edition. Special gratitude is owed to Professor Frank D'Souza, Illinois Institute of Technology, and Professor Gerald Whitehouse, Louisana State University, who reviewed the entire manuscript for this edition. Students have also been very helpful in their comments. Particular recognition is due to Abraham Ma and Betty Raven.

The author also wishes to express his gratitude for the continued encouragement of his colleagues at the University of Notre Dame, especially to Dr. Kwang-Tzu Yang, chairman of the Department of Aerospace and Mechanical Engineering. Thanks are also due to Ms. Valerie Flanagan, Ms. Kathy Simon, and Ms. Ella Levee for their typing of the numerous revisions of notes from which this text has developed.

The author's wife, Therese, has faithfully worked with him throughout the development of this text. She has made innumerable suggestions and has been a constant source of encouragement.

Francis H. Raven

The author also wishes to express his gratitude for the continued encouragement of his colleagues at the University of Notre Dame, especially to Dr. Kwang-Tzu Yang, chairman of the Department of Aerospace and Mechanical Engineering. Thanks are also due to Ms. [illegible], Ms. Kathy [illegible] and Ms. Ella [illegible] for their typing of the numerous revisions of notes from which this text has developed.

The author's wife, Therese, has faithfully worked with him throughout the development of this text. She has made innumerable suggestions and has been a constant source of encouragement.

Francis H. Raven

AUTOMATIC CONTROL ENGINEERING

CHAPTER
ONE

INTRODUCTION TO AUTOMATIC CONTROLS

1.1 HISTORICAL DEVELOPMENT

Early people had to rely upon their own brute strength or that of beasts of burden to supply energy for doing work. By the use of simple mechanical devices such as wheels and levers, they accomplished such feats as the building of high pyramids and Roman highways and aqueducts. They first supplemented their energy and that of beasts by utilizing power from natural sources, such as the wind for powering sailing vessels and windmills, and waterfalls for turning water wheels. The invention of the steam engine was a milestone in human progress because it provided people with useful power that could be harnessed at will. Since then, people have devised many different means for obtaining abundant and convenient sources of energy. Engineering effort is primarily concerned with the practical applications of using power to serve human purposes. That is, the engineer designs and develops machines and equipment by which people can utilize power.

Early machines and equipment had controls which were predominantly of a manual nature, and the adjustments had to be reset frequently in order to maintain the desired output or performance. The design of newer equipment with greater usefulness and capabilities is bringing about an ever-increasing growth in the development of control equipment. The reason is twofold. First, automatic controls relieve people of many monotonous activities so that they can devote their abilities to other endeavors. Second, modern complex controls can perform functions which are beyond the physical abilities of people to duplicate. For example, an elaborate automatic control system operates the engine of a modern jet airplane with only a minimum amount of the pilot's attention so that the pilot is free to maneuver and fly the airplane.

It is interesting to note that, as the applications and uses for controls have increased, so also have the demands upon the performance of these systems increased. There is no doubt that a major concern of the engineer today, and even more so in the future, is, and will be, the design and development of automatic control systems.

1.2 FEEDBACK CONTROL SYSTEMS

The controlling of temperature is a typical example of a feedback control system. The position of the temperature dial sets the desired temperature (i.e., the reference input). The actual temperature of the system is the controlled variable (i.e., the quantity which is being controlled). The thermostat, or comparator, compares the actual temperature with the desired temperature in order to measure the error. This error signal is the actuating signal, which is then sent to the heating units in order to correct the temperature. For example, if the actual temperature is less than the desired temperature, the actuating signal causes the control elements to supply more heat. If there is no error, the control elements do not change the amount of heat which is being supplied. When the actual temperature is greater than the desired value, then the actuating signal calls for a decrease in the amount of heat.

For a system to be classified as a feedback control system, it is necessary that the controlled variable be fed back and *compared* with the reference input. In addition, the resulting error signal must *actuate* the control elements to change the output so as to minimize the error. A feedback control system is also called a closed-loop system. Any system which incorporates a thermostat to control temperature is a feedback, or closed-loop, system. Well-known examples are electric frying pans, irons, refrigerators, and household furnaces with thermostatic control.

For speed control systems, the device which subtracts the feedback signal from the reference input (i.e., the comparator) is usually a centrifugal governor. The governor serves the same purpose that the thermostat does for temperature controls. That is, the governor compares the actual speed which is to be controlled with the desired value and measures the error. This error signal then actuates the control elements. The same basic concepts apply to all types of feedback control systems, whether the controlled variable be temperature, speed, pressure, flow, position, force, torque, or any other physical quantity.

In an open-loop system there is no comparison of the controlled variable with the desired input. Each setting of the input determines a fixed operating position for the control elements. For example, for a given input temperature setting, the heating units are positioned to supply heat at a fixed rate. (Note that there is no comparator, or thermostat, which measures the error and resets the heating units.) The disadvantage of such a system is illustrated by the fact that if a fixed rate of heat is supplied to a house, the inside temperature will vary appreciably with changes in the outside temperature. Thus, for a given set input to an open-loop system, there may be a big variation of the controlled variable depending on the ambient temperature.

In this example, the ambient temperature is an external disturbance. By an external disturbance is meant something external to the system which acts to change or disturb the controlled variable. A major advantage of employing feedback control is that, because of the comparator, the actuating signal continually changes so that the controlled variable tends to become equal to the reference input regardless of the external disturbance. Another consideration is that with feedback one can generally use relatively inexpensive components and yet obtain better control than is possible with very expensive components in an open-loop system. The primary effort of this text will be devoted to feedback control systems.

1.3 SYSTEM REPRESENTATION

The mathematical relationships of control systems are usually represented by block diagrams. These diagrams have the advantage of indicating more realistically the actual processes which are taking place, as opposed to a purely abstract mathematical representation. In addition, it is easy to form the overall block diagram for an entire system by merely combining the block diagrams for each component or part of the system.

A comparator subtracts the feedback signal from the reference input r. For the case in which the controlled variable c is fed back directly (i.e., for unity-feedback systems), the signal coming from the comparator is $r - c$, which is equal to the actuating signal e. The mathematical relationship for this operation is

$$e = r - c \tag{1.1}$$

A circle is the symbol which is used to indicate a summing operation, as is illustrated in Fig. 1.1. The arrowheads pointing toward the circle indicate input quantities, while the arrowhead leading away signifies the output. The sign at each input arrowhead indicates whether the quantity is to be added or subtracted.

The relationship between the actuating signal e, which enters the control elements, and the controlled variable c, which is the output of the control, is expressed by the equation

$$c = G(D)e \tag{1.2}$$

where $G(D)$ represents the operation of the control elements. In Chaps. 2 and 3, it is shown how the actual values of $G(D)$ for specific control systems are obtained. The block-diagram representation for the preceding equation is shown in Fig. 1.2.

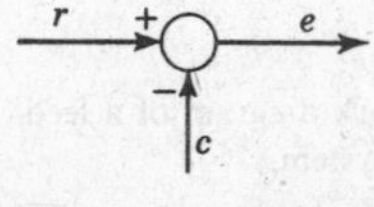

Figure 1.1 Block diagram of a comparator.

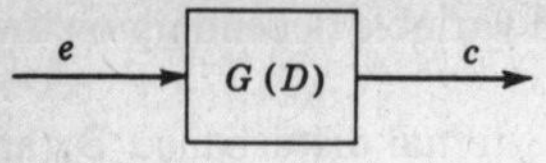

Figure 1.2 Block diagram of the control elements.

A box is the symbol for multiplication. In this case, the input quantity e is multiplied by the function in the box $G(D)$ to obtain the output c. With circles indicating summing points and with boxes, or blocks, indicating multiplication, any linear mathematical expression may be represented by block-diagram notation.

The complete block diagram for an elementary unity-feedback control system is obtained by combining Figs. 1.1 and 1.2 to yield Fig. 1.3. This diagram shows the controlled variable c being fed back to the summing point, where it is compared with the reference input r. This diagram pictorially shows why a feedback control system is also called a closed-loop system.

When the controlled variable is fed back to the comparator, it is usually necessary to convert the form of the controlled variable to a form that is suitable for the comparator. For example, in a temperature control system the controlled temperature is generally converted to a proportional force or position for use in the comparator. This conversion is accomplished by feedback elements $H(D)$. The block-diagram representation for this more general case of a feedback control system is shown in Fig. 1.4. The signal which is fed back is

$$b = H(D)c \tag{1.3}$$

The elements represented by $H(D)$ are called the feedback elements because they are located in the feedback portion of the control. The control elements represented by $G(D)$ are the feedforward elements because of their location in the feedforward portion of the loop. The actuating signal e is now $r - b$. This actuating signal e is a measure or indication of the error.

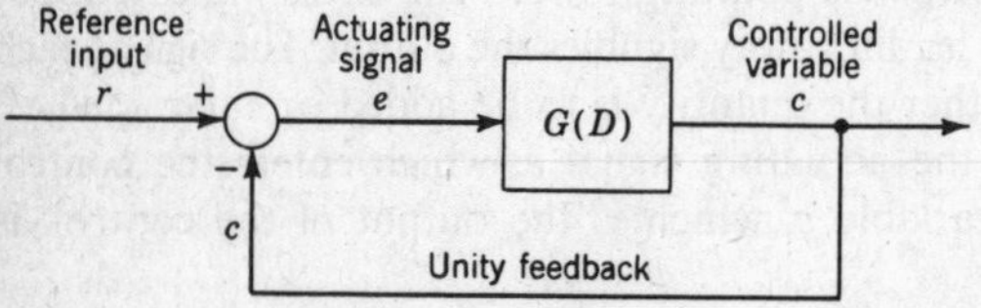

Figure 1.3 Block diagram of a unity-feedback control system.

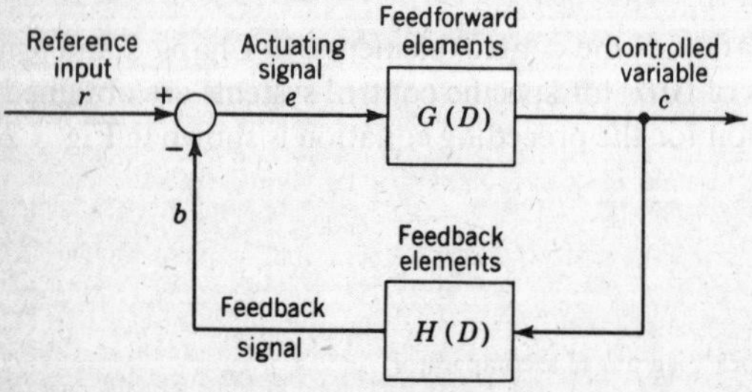

Figure 1.4 Block diagram of a feedback control system.

The term "feedback control system" is a general term which applies to any system in which the controlled variable is measured and fed back to be compared with the reference input. The terms "servomechanism" and "regulator" are distinguished as follows: A servomechanism is a particular type of feedback control system in which the controlled variable is a mechanical position (e.g., the angular position of a shaft). A regulator is distinguished as a feedback control system in which the reference input, although adjustable, is held fixed, or constant, for long periods of time (e.g., most temperature controllers).

CHAPTER

TWO

REPRESENTATION OF CONTROL COMPONENTS

To investigate the performance of control systems, it is necessary to obtain the mathematical relationship $G(D)$ relating the controlled variable c and the actuating signal e of the feedforward elements. This is accomplished by first obtaining the mathematical representation for each component between the actuating signal and the controlled variable and then expressing each of these equations as a block diagram. The combination of the block diagrams for each component yields the desired representation for $G(D)$. The value of $H(D)$ is obtained by applying the same technique to the components in the feedback portion of the control.

The quantity $G(D)$ could be obtained by writing the mathematical equation describing the operation of each component between e and c and then combining these individual equations algebraically to obtain the overall relationship between e and c. However, for all but the simplest systems, this procedure proves cumbersome because of the interaction between the various components in a typical control system. In addition, the block-diagram method gives one a better understanding of the system because of its visual representation.

The obtaining of block diagrams for typical elements used in control devices is illustrated in this chapter. In the next chapter, it is shown how these individual diagrams are combined to form entire control systems.

2.1 OPERATIONAL NOTATION

In writing equations for control systems, it is convenient to use the operational notation

$$D^n = \frac{d^n}{dt^n} \qquad n = 1, 2, 3, \ldots \tag{2.1}$$

The operator D is a symbol which indicates differentiation with respect to time. For example, if x and y are functions of time, then

$$D(x+y)=\frac{d}{dt}(x+y)=\frac{dx}{dt}+\frac{dy}{dt}=Dx+Dy$$

This shows that the operator D obeys the distributive law, that is,

$$D(x+y)=Dx+Dy$$

It may also be shown that if a and b are constants, then

$$\begin{aligned}(D+a)(D+b)y &= (D+a)\left(\frac{dy}{dt}+by\right)\\ &= \frac{d}{dt}\left(\frac{dy}{dt}+by\right)+a\left(\frac{dy}{dt}+by\right)\\ &= \frac{d^2y}{dt^2}+(a+b)\frac{dy}{dt}+aby\\ &= [D^2+(a+b)D+ab]y\end{aligned}$$

Thus, the commutative law also holds. That is

$$(D+a)(D+b)y=(D+b)(D+a)y$$

Consider the differential equation

$$\frac{d}{dt}x(t)+ax(t)=f(t)$$

In operational notation, this differential equation is

$$(D+a)x(t)=f(t) \tag{2.2}$$

To solve the differential equation, first multiply through both sides by e^{at}. That is,

$$e^{at}\left[\frac{d}{dt}x(t)+ax(t)\right]=\frac{d}{dt}[e^{at}x(t)]=e^{at}f(t)$$

Integration yields

$$e^{at}x(t)=\int f(t)e^{at}\,dt+C$$

where C is the constant of integration. Solving the preceding for the function $x(t)$ which satisfies the differential equation gives

$$x(t)=e^{-at}\left[\int f(t)e^{at}\,dt+C\right] \tag{2.3}$$

To check that this function $x(t)$ does satisfy the differential equation, note that

$$Dx(t)=\frac{d}{dt}x(t)=-ae^{-at}\left[\int f(t)e^{at}\,dt+C\right]+e^{-at}[f(t)e^{at}]$$

and that

$$ax(t) = ae^{-at}\left[\int f(t)e^{at}\,dt + C\right]$$

Adding verifies that $Dx(t) + ax(t) = f(t)$. Cross multiplying the operator in Eq. (2.2) yields the form

$$x(t) = \frac{1}{D+a} f(t) \tag{2.4}$$

Because Eqs. (2.2) and (2.4) are equivalent forms of the same differential equation, $x(t)$ as given by Eq. (2.3) must satisfy Eq. (2.4) as well as Eq. (2.2). That is,

$$\frac{1}{D+a} f(t) = e^{-at}\left[\int f(t)e^{at}\,dt + C\right] \tag{2.5}$$

It has previously been shown that the derivative d/dt of the right side plus a times the right side yields $f(t)$. Thus, operating on both sides of Eq. (2.5) by $D + a$ yields

$$(D+a)\frac{1}{D+a} f(t) = f(t) \tag{2.6}$$

Since the right side is $f(t)$, it follows that the operators on the left side may be canceled. In general, it may be shown that

$$(D+a)^n \frac{1}{(D+a)^m} f(t) = (D+a)^{n-m} f(t) \tag{2.7}$$

where m and n are positive integers.

The meaning of the reciprocal of D is obtained by noting that the integral of the derivative of a function is

$$y(t) = \int [Df(t)]\,dt = \int f'(t)\,dt = f(t) + C \tag{2.8}$$

where C is the constant of integration. The derivative of both sides with respect to time is

$$Dy(t) = Df(t)$$

Solving for $y(t)$ gives

$$y(t) = \frac{1}{D}[Df(t)] \tag{2.9}$$

Comparison of Eqs. (2.8) and (2.9) shows that

$$\frac{1}{D}[Df(t)] = \int [Df(t)]\,dt = f(t) + C$$

Therefore, the symbol $1/D$ indicates integration.

The constant of integration is determined by evaluating Eq. (2.8) at some convenient initial time t_0. Thus, it is found that

$$C = y(t_0) - f(t_0)$$

Substitution of this result back into Eq. (2.8) shows that

$$y(t) = \int f'(t)\, dt = f(t) - f(t_0) + y(t_0) \tag{2.10}$$

The cancellation of operators in Eq. (2.9) would yield the erroneous result $y(t) = f(t)$. The algebraic cancellation of operators in Eq. (2.9) does not take into account the constant of integration that arises from the integration indicated by the $1/D$ term. Operators cannot be canceled when integration is the last operation to be performed unless there is no constant of integration, as is the case when all initial conditions are zero or $y(t_0) = f(t_0)$. The form of Eq. (2.9) that results after cancellation of operators is $y(t) = f(t)$. Note that when $y(t_0) = f(t_0)$, the initial conditions are such as to satisfy this form that results after cancellation.

In general, it may be shown that the cancellation

$$y(t) = \frac{1}{D^m} D^n f(t) = D^{n-m} f(t)$$

is valid if the initial conditions are such as to satisfy the expression that results after cancellation. For $n > m$, this form is $y(t_0) = D^{n-m} f(t_0)$. For $n = m$, this form is $y(t_0) = f(t_0)$. For $m > n$, this form is $D^{m-n} y(t_0) = f(t_0)$. The resulting form is automatically satisfied when all the initial conditions are zero.

The process of differentiating an integral may be expressed in the form

$$y(t) = D^n \frac{1}{D^m} f(t) = D^{n-m} f(t) \tag{2.11}$$

Because no initial-condition terms arise from the differentiation process, one may always cancel operators when differentiating an integral.

Illustrative example 1 For the operational relationship

$$y(t) = \frac{1}{D} D^2 f(t)$$

determine the initial conditions required for cancellation of operators to be valid. For $f(t)$ use the function $f(t) = t^2 + 3t + 5$.

SOLUTION The form that results after cancellation is

$$y(t) = \frac{1}{D} D^2 f(t) = Df(t) = f'(t) = 2t + 3$$

Evaluation at $t = 0$ yields the necessary initial condition

$$y(0) = f'(0) = (2t + 3)\Big|_{t=0} = 3$$

This result is substantiated by performing the indicated operations. That is,

$$y(t) = \frac{1}{D} D^2 f(t) = \frac{1}{D} f''(t) = f'(t) + C$$

Evaluation at $t = 0$ shows that $C = y(0) - f'(0)$. In order that $y(t) = f'(t)$, it is necessary that $y(0) = f'(0) = (2t + 3)|_{t=0} = 3$, so that $C = 0$.

Illustrative example 2 For the operational relationship

$$y(t) = \frac{1}{D^2} Df(t)$$

determine the initial conditions necessary for cancellation of operators to be valid. For $f(t)$ use the function $f(t) = 3t^2 + 2t + 1$.

SOLUTION The form that results after cancellation is

$$y(t) = \frac{1}{D^2} Df(t) = \frac{1}{D} f(t)$$

or $\quad Dy(t) = f(t)$

Evaluation at $t = 0$ yields

$$y'(0) = f(0) = (3t^2 + 2t + 1)\Big|_{t=0} = 1$$

To substantiate this result by performing the indicated operations, note that

$$y(t) = \frac{1}{D^2} Df(t) = \frac{1}{D} \int f'(t)\, dt = \frac{1}{D}[f(t) + C]$$

Hence

$$y'(t) = f(t) + C$$

Evaluation at time $t = 0$ shows that $C = y'(0) - f(0)$. In order that $y'(t) = f(t)$, it is necessary that $y'(0) = f(0) = 1$, so that $C = 0$.

The operator $1/(D + a)$ has properties similar to those of $1/D$. To show this, consider the differential form

$$y(t) = \frac{1}{D + a}(D + a)f(t) = \frac{1}{D + a} f'(t) + \frac{1}{D + a} af(t)$$

Application of Eq. (2.5) shows that

$$y(t) = e^{-at}\left[\int f'(t)e^{at}\, dt + C_1\right] + ae^{-at}\left[\int f(t)e^{at}\, dt + C_2\right]$$

Integration by parts [$\int u\,dv = uv - \int v\,du$] in which $u = e^{at}$, $du = ae^{at}\,dt$, $v = f(t)$, and $dv = f'(t)\,dt$ gives

$$y(t) = e^{-at}\left[f(t)e^{at} - a\int f(t)e^{at}\,dt + C_1\right] + ae^{-at}\left[\int f(t)e^{at}\,dt + C_2\right]$$

$$= f(t) + Ce^{-at}$$

where $C = C_1 + aC_2$. Evaluation at some convenient initial time t_0 gives $C = [y(t_0) - f(t_0)]e^{at_0}$. Substitution of this result back into the preceding expression shows that

$$y(t) = f(t) + [y(t_0) - f(t_0)]e^{-a(t-t_0)}$$

The term $1/(D + a)$ indicates integration. As is the case with the operator $1/D$, operators cannot be canceled when integration is the last operation to be performed unless there is no constant of integration. The constant of integration vanishes when the initial conditions are such as to satisfy the form that results after cancellation. For the preceding example this resulting form is $y(t) = f(t)$. When $y(t_0) = f(t_0)$, then $C = [y(t_0) - f(t_0)]e^{-a(t-t_0)} = 0$.

In general it may be shown that the cancellation

$$y(t) = \frac{1}{(D + a)^m}(D + a)^n f(t) = (D + a)^{n-m} f(t) \tag{2.12}$$

is valid if the initial conditions are such as to satisfy the expression that results after cancellation.

In summary, the operators D and $D + a$ have similar properties. As indicated by Eqs. (2.7) and (2.11), cancellation of operators is always valid when differentiation is the last operation to be performed. As indicated by Eqs. (2.10) and (2.12), when integration is the last operation to be performed, cancellation is valid if the initial conditions are such as to satisfy the expression that results after cancellation. This resulting expression is automatically satisfied when all the initial conditions are zero.

2.2 MECHANICAL COMPONENTS

The load-deflection characteristics for a mechanical spring are shown in Fig. 2.1*a*. The spring force F_s required to deflect a spring a distance X from its free length is given by the equation

$$F_s = KX \tag{2.13}$$

where K, the spring rate, is a constant which is equal to the slope of the curve of the load F_s versus deflection X. The input to a spring is usually the force F_s, and the output is the deflection X, so that the block-diagram representation for Eq. (2.13) is as shown in Fig. 2.1*b*.

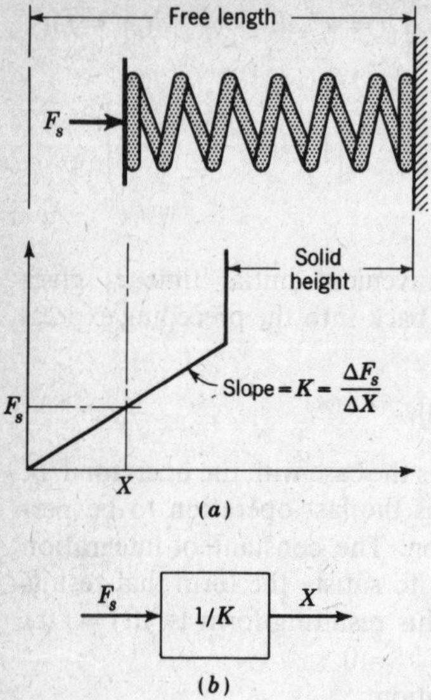

Figure 2.1 Spring characteristics.

For a viscous damper as illustrated in Fig. 2.2*a*, the force F_d required to move one end of the dashpot at a velocity V relative to the other end is equal to the product of the damping coefficient B and the velocity. That is,

$$F_d = BV = B\frac{dX}{dt}$$

The substitution of the operator symbol $D = d/dt$ into the preceding expression yields

$$F_d = BDX \tag{2.14}$$

With the force F_d as the input and the displacement X as the output, the block-diagram representation for Eq. (2.14) is shown in Fig. 2.2*b*.

By Newton's second law of motion, it follows that the summation of the external forces $\sum F_e$ acting on a mass is equal to the product of the mass and acceleration.

$$\sum F_e = MA = M\frac{d^2X}{dt^2} = MD^2X$$

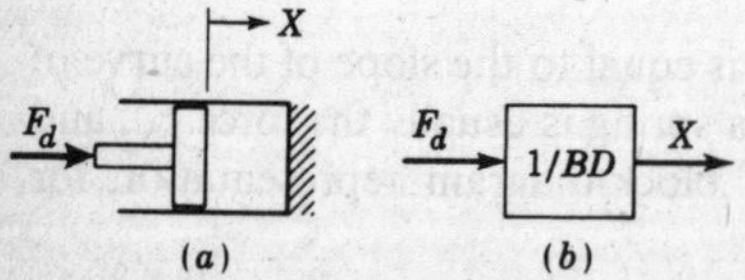

Figure 2.2 Viscous damper.

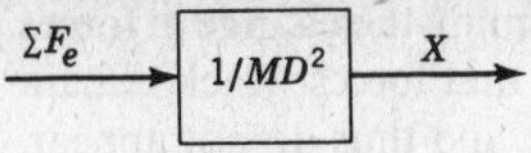

Figure 2.3 Acceleration of a mass.

The displacement X is given by the equation

$$X = \frac{1}{MD^2} \sum F_e \tag{2.15}$$

This is represented diagrammatically in Fig. 2.3.

For the mass-spring-damper combination shown in Fig. 2.4*a*, the spring force and damper force are opposed to, or resist, the motion caused by the applied load F. The summation of the forces acting on the mass is

$$\sum F_e = F + Mg - F_s - F_d = MD^2X$$

or

$$F = (MD^2 + BD + K)X - Mg \tag{2.16}$$

This is the equation for the total forces acting on the system. For control work, it is usually more convenient to make measurements with respect to some reference operating point. A lowercase letter is used to designate the variation or change in displacement x from the reference position X_i, so that $x = X - X_i$. The force equation at the reference operating condition is

$$F_i = KX_i - Mg$$

where F_i is the force required to maintain the mass in equilibrium at the reference position X_i. Subtracting the equation for the forces at the reference position from that for the total forces gives the equation of operation for changes about the reference position. That is,

$$F - F_i = (MD^2 + BD)X + K(X - X_i)$$

If lowercase letters are used to represent changes about the reference position, then the change in force is $f = F - F_i$ and similarly the change in displacement is $x = X - X_i$. Because X_i is a constant, $DX = D(X_i + x) = Dx$ and $D^2X = D^2x$. As would be expected, velocity and acceleration are independent of the reference position from which displacement is measured. The preceding equation of operation with respect to the reference position may thus be written in the form

$$f = (MD^2 + BD + K)x \tag{2.17}$$

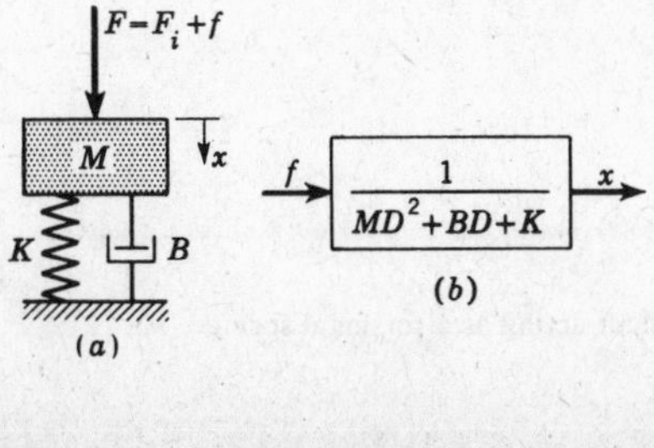

Figure 2.4 Series mass-spring-damper combination.

This result could have been obtained directly by summing the change in forces from the reference operating condition. It is to be noted that forces which remain constant, such as the gravitational force, have no change and thus do not appear.

Although x and f are measured from the reference operating point, Eq. (2.17) is a general equation describing the dynamic behavior of the system. It is not necessary that the system be initially at this reference operating point or that the system be initially at rest. As is later explained, it is usually much easier to obtain the equation of operation with respect to some convenient reference point rather than using total values. When total values are desired, it is an easy matter to add the reference value to the variation. The block diagram for Eq. (2.17) is shown in Fig. 2.4*b*.

Rotational Mechanical Components

A torsional spring is characterized by the equation

$$T_s = K_s \theta \tag{2.18}$$

where T_s = torque tending to twist spring
K_s = torsional spring rate
θ = angular displacement of spring

A well-known example of a torsional spring is a shaft as shown in Fig. 2.5. The right end of the shaft is displaced an angle θ with respect to the left end because of the twisting torque T_s. For a straight shaft, the torsional spring rate is

$$K_s = \frac{\pi d^4 G}{32L}$$

where G = modulus of elasticity in shear
d = diameter of shaft
L = length of shaft

The torque T_d required to overcome viscous friction of a rotating member is

$$T_d = B_v \omega = B_v \frac{d\theta}{dt} = B_v D\theta \tag{2.19}$$

where B_v = coefficient of viscous friction
ω = angular velocity

A disk rotating in a viscous medium and supported by a shaft is shown in

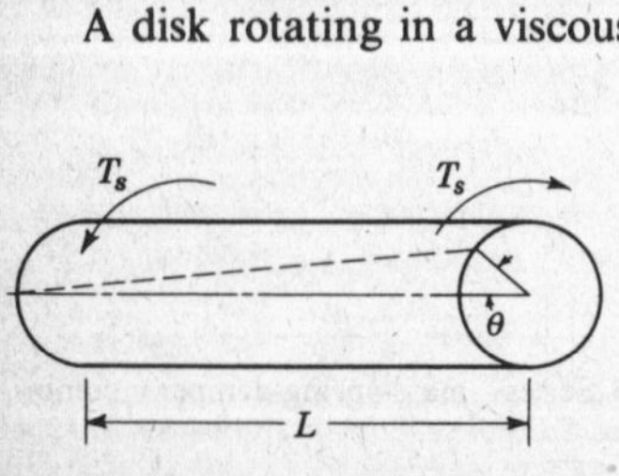

Figure 2.5 Shaft acting as a torsional spring.

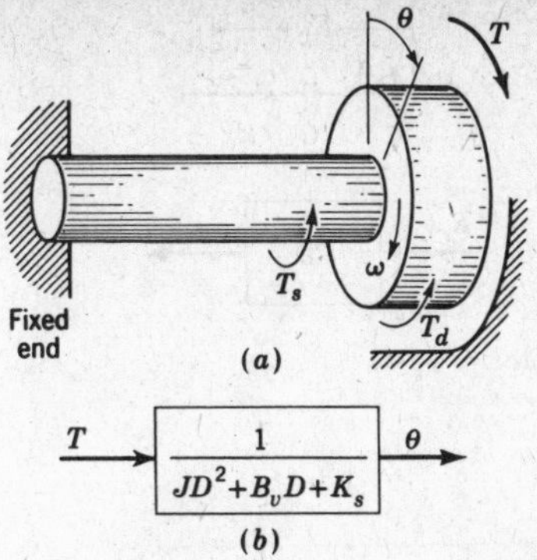

Figure 2.6 Torsional inertia-spring-damper combination.

Fig. 2.6*a*. The applied torque tending to rotate the disk is T. The shaft torque and viscous friction oppose the motion, so that

$$\sum T_e = T - T_s - T_d = J\alpha = JD^2\theta \tag{2.20}$$

where $\sum T_e$ is the summation of external torques acting on the disk. The substitution of T_s from Eq. (2.18) and T_d from Eq. (2.19) into Eq. (2.20) yields

$$T = (JD^2 + B_vD + K_s)\theta \tag{2.21}$$

The block-diagram representation for this system is shown in Fig. 2.6*b*.

2.3 ELECTRICAL COMPONENTS

The resistor, inductor, and capacitor are the three basic components of electric circuits. The equation for the voltage drop E_R across a resistor is

$$E_R = RI \tag{2.22}$$

where R is the resistance in ohms and I is the current flowing through the resistor in amperes.

For an inductor, the voltage drop E_L is given by the equation

$$E_L = L\frac{dI}{dt} = LDI \tag{2.23}$$

where L is the inductance in henrys.

Similarly, the voltage drop E_C across a capacitor is

$$E_C = \frac{1}{CD}I \tag{2.24}$$

where C is the capacitance in farads.

The diagrammatic representations of Eqs. (2.22) to (2.24) are shown in Fig. 2.7.

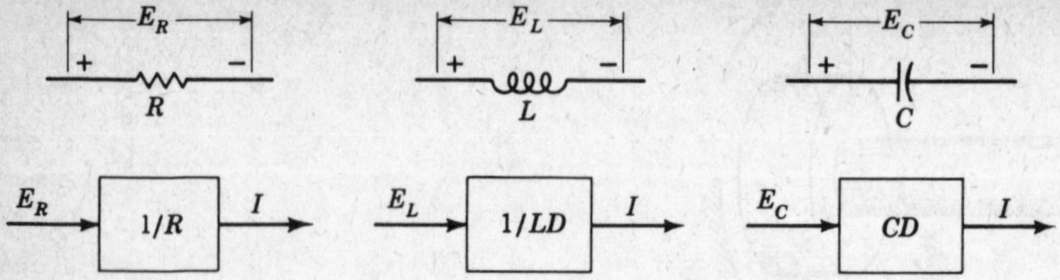

Figure 2.7 Representation of resistor, inductor, and capacitor.

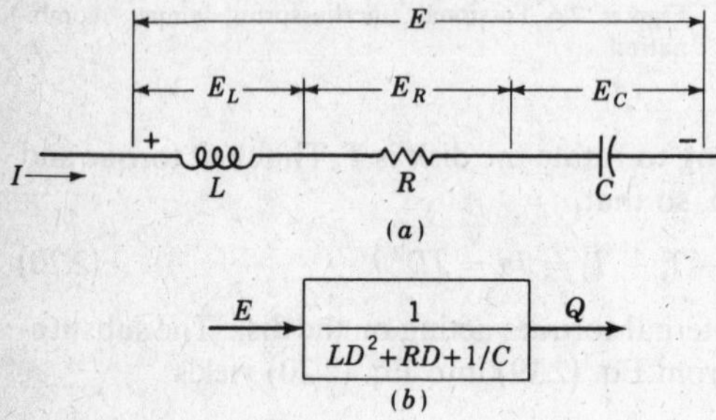

Figure 2.8 *RLC* series circuit.

For the series *RLC* circuit shown in Fig. 2.8*a*, the total voltage drop E is the sum of the voltage drop across the inductor E_L, plus that across the resistor E_R and that across the capacitor E_C.

$$E = E_L + E_R + E_C = \left(LD + R + \frac{1}{CD}\right)I \tag{2.25}$$

The charge Q is the time integral of the current, that is, $Q = (1/D)I$ or $I = DQ$. By noting that $LDI = LD^2Q$, $RI = RDQ$, $(1/CD)I = (1/C)Q$, Eq. (2.25) becomes

$$E = \left(LD^2 + RD + \frac{1}{C}\right)Q \tag{2.26}$$

The overall block-diagram representation for this *RLC* circuit is shown in Fig. 2.8*b*.

2.4 SERIES AND PARALLEL LAWS

Elements are usually connected in either a series or a parallel arrangement. Arriving at the equation for such systems can be greatly simplified by the use of the laws for series and the laws for parallel combinations.

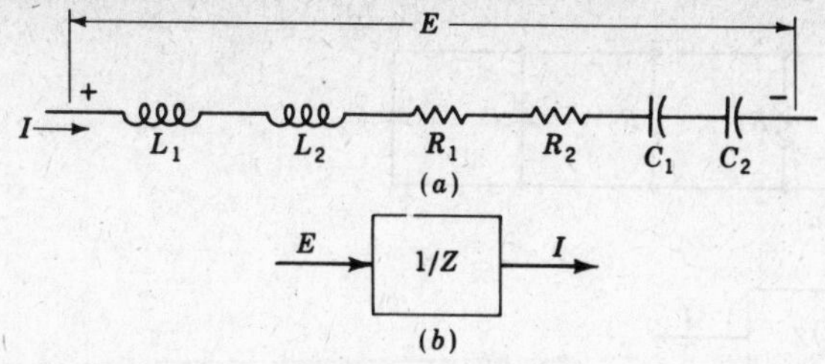

Figure 2.9 General series circuit.

Series Electric Circuits

A general series circuit is shown in Fig. 2.9*a*. In a series circuit, *the total voltage drop E is the sum of the individual voltage drops across each element*, and *the same current I flows through each element*. The equation for the summation of the voltage drops is

$$E = \left(L_1 D + L_2 D + R_1 + R_2 + \frac{1}{C_1 D} + \frac{1}{C_2 D}\right) I = ZI \qquad (2.27)$$

The equivalent impedance Z for elements in series is

$$Z = L_1 D + L_2 D + R_1 + R_2 + \frac{1}{C_1 D} + \frac{1}{C_2 D} \qquad (2.28)$$

The block-diagram representation is shown in Fig. 2.9*b*.

Parallel Electric Circuits

A general combination of electrical elements in parallel is shown in Fig. 2.10*a*. The distinguishing features of a parallel arrangement are that *the voltage drop E across each element is the same*, and *the total current I flowing into the system is the sum of the currents flowing through each element*. Thus

$$I = \frac{E}{L_1 D} + \frac{E}{L_2 D} + \frac{E}{R_1} + \frac{E}{R_2} + \frac{E}{1/C_1 D} + \frac{E}{1/C_2 D} \qquad (2.29)$$

or

$$E = \frac{1}{1/L_1 D + 1/L_2 D + 1/R_1 + 1/R_2 + C_1 D + C_2 D} I = ZI$$

The equivalent impedance Z for elements in parallel is

$$Z = \frac{1}{1/L_1 D + 1/L_2 D + 1/R_1 + 1/R_2 + C_1 D + C_2 D} \qquad (2.30)$$

The block-diagram representation is shown in Fig. 2.10*b*.

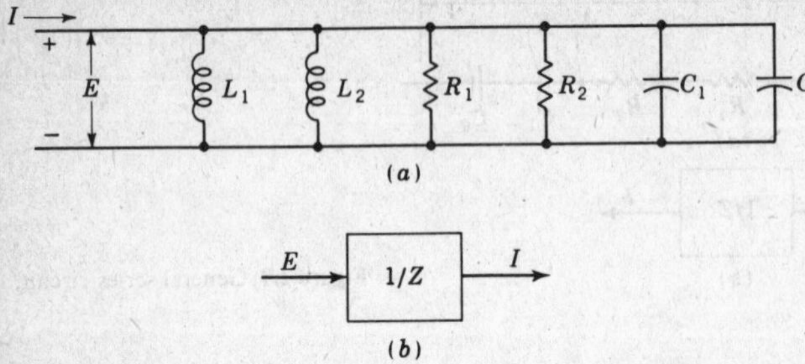

Figure 2.10 General parallel circuit.

Illustrative example 1 For the circuit shown in Fig. 2.11, let it be desired to determine the equation relating the output voltage E_2 to the input voltage E_1.

SOLUTION The parallel combination of R_1 and C_1 is in series with R_2, so that the total impedance Z is

$$Z = Z_1 + R_2 = \frac{1}{1/R_1 + C_1 D} + R_2 = \frac{R_1}{1 + R_1 C_1 D} + R_2 \tag{2.31}$$

The voltage E_1 is given by the equation

$$E_1 = ZI = \frac{R_1 + R_2 + R_1 R_2 C_1 D}{1 + R_1 C_1 D} I \tag{2.32}$$

Similarly E_2 is

$$E_2 = R_2 I \tag{2.33}$$

The substitution of I from Eq. (2.32) into Eq. (2.33) yields the desired answer:

$$E_2 = \frac{R_2(1 + R_1 C_1 D)}{R_1 + R_2 + R_1 R_2 C_1 D} E_1 \tag{2.34}$$

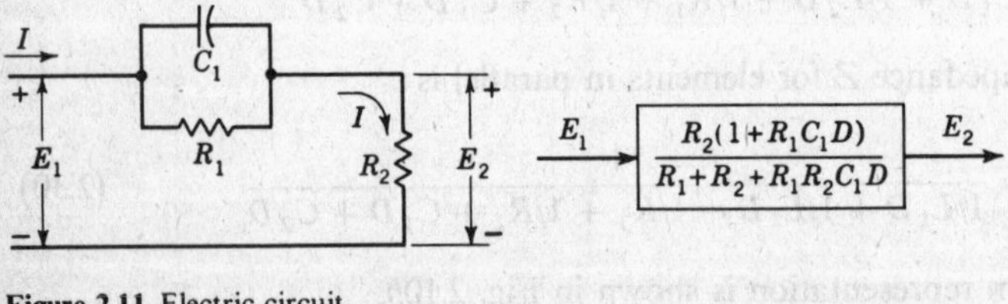

Figure 2.11 Electric circuit.

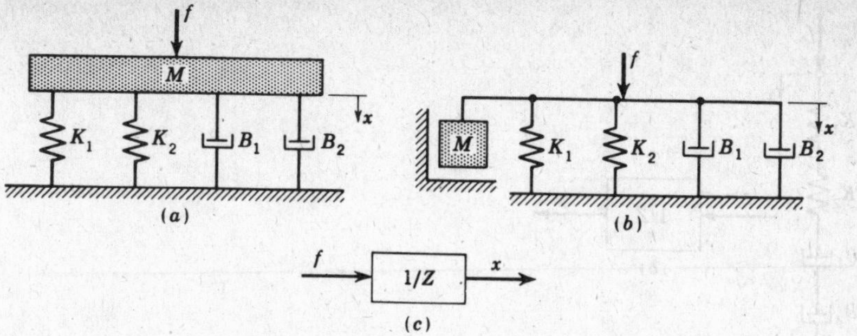

Figure 2.12 Mechanical elements in series.

Series Mechanical Elements

A series arrangement of linear mechanical elements is shown in Fig. 2.12*a*. In general, it is better to use the equivalent "grounded-chair" representation for a mass, as shown in Fig. 2.12*b*, rather than the more common representation of Fig. 2.12*a*. The fact that the mass is in series with the other elements is more readily seen from Fig. 2.12*b* than from Fig. 2.12*a*. In determining inertia force, the acceleration of a mass is always taken with respect to ground. Thus, providing the grounded-chair to indicate motion relative to ground is a more justifiable representation than Fig. 2.12*a*, which shows better the actual physical arrangement of the elements in the system. For series mechanical elements, *the force f is equal to the summation of the forces acting on each individual component*, and *each element undergoes the same displacement*. Thus

$$f = (K_1 + K_2 + B_1 D + B_2 D + MD^2)x = Zx \tag{2.35}$$

where x and f are measured from a convenient reference operating point. The equivalent impedance for mechanical elements in series is

$$Z = K_1 + K_2 + B_1 D + B_2 D + MD^2 \tag{2.36}$$

The block-diagram representation for this system is shown in Fig. 2.12*c*.

Parallel Mechanical Elements

A parallel combination of mechanical elements is shown in Fig. 2.13*a*. For parallel elements, *the same force f is transmitted through each element*. In addition, *the total deflection x is seen to be the sum of the individual deflections of each element*. Thus

$$x = \frac{f}{K_1} + \frac{f}{K_2} + \frac{f}{B_1 D} + \frac{f}{B_2 D} \tag{2.37}$$

or

$$f = \frac{1}{1/K_1 + 1/K_2 + 1/B_1 D + 1/B_2 D} x = Zx$$

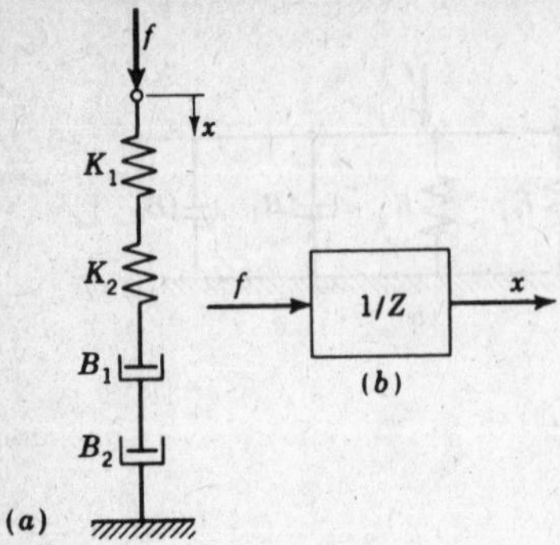

Figure 2.13 Mechanical elements in parallel.

The equivalent impedance for mechanical elements in parallel is

$$Z = \frac{1}{1/K_1 + 1/K_2 + 1/B_1 D + 1/B_2 D} \tag{2.38}$$

The block-diagram representation is shown in Fig. 2.13*b*.

A necessary condition for parallel elements is that the same force be transmitted through each element. Springs and dampers satisfy this condition because the force is the same on both sides. However, this is not the case for a mass such as

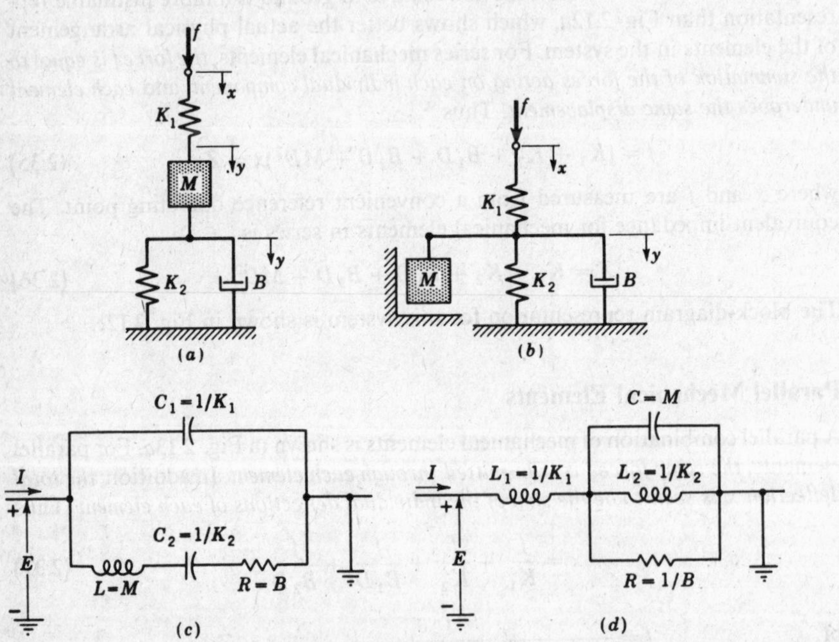

Figure 2.14 Mechanical system.

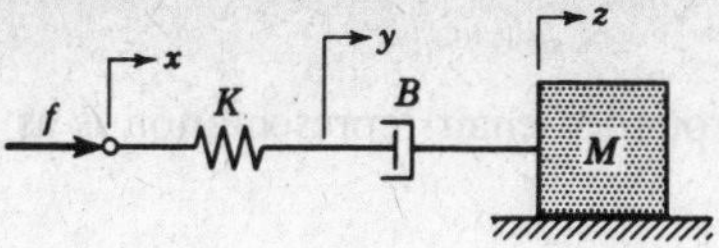

Figure 2.15 Parallel mass-spring-damper combination.

that shown in Fig. 2.14*a* because the difference in forces acting on both sides of a mass is utilized in acceleration. Thus, a mass located between other elements cannot be in parallel with them. A mass can be in parallel only if it is the last element, as shown in Fig. 2.15. For this system, the displacement x is

$$x = (x - y) + (y - z) + z = \left(\frac{1}{K} + \frac{1}{BD} + \frac{1}{MD^2}\right) f$$

Thus,

$$f = \frac{1}{1/K + 1/BD + 1/MD^2} x \tag{2.39}$$

Parallel and series laws for rotational mechanical components may also be developed by extending the preceding techniques.

Illustrative example 2 For the mass-spring-damper combination shown in Fig. 2.14*a*, determine the equation relating f and x, the equation relating f and y, and the equation relating x and y.

SOLUTION The first step is to draw the equivalent grounded-chair system, in which the motion of the mass with respect to ground is clearly indicated as shown in Fig. 2.14*b*. The spring K_1 is in parallel with the series combination of M, K_2, and B. Application of the laws for parallel and series elements gives

$$f = Zx = \frac{1}{1/K_1 + 1/Z_2} x = \frac{K_1 Z_2}{K_1 + Z_2} x \tag{2.40}$$

where $Z_2 = MD^2 + BD + K_2$

Thus,

$$f = \frac{K_1(MD^2 + BD + K_2)}{MD^2 + BD + K_1 + K_2} x \tag{2.41}$$

The force f is transmitted through the spring K_1 and acts upon the series combination of M, K_2, and B. Thus, the equation of motion for this part of the system which relates f and y is

$$f = (MD^2 + BD + K_2)y \tag{2.42}$$

Equating (2.41) and (2.42) yields the desired relationship between x and y. That is,

$$y = \frac{K_1}{MD^2 + BD + K_1 + K_2} x \tag{2.43}$$

Grounded-Chair Representation

The general procedure for constructing the grounded-chair representation is as follows:

1. Draw coordinates such that the coordinate at which the force acts is at the top and ground is at the bottom.
2. Insert each element in its correct orientation with respect to these coordinates.

For the system shown in Fig. 2.16*a*, the coordinates are x, y, and ground. Step 1 is carried out by drawing the coordinates as shown in Fig. 2.16*b*. To do step 2 we must note that for the spring K_1 and mass M_1 the coordinates are x and ground, for the spring K and damper B the coordinates are x and y, and finally for the mass M_2 and spring K_2 the coordinates are y and ground. Inserting these elements between the proper coordinates as shown in Fig. 2.16*c* completes the grounded-chair representation. The series and parallel combinations are now recognized directly from this grounded-chair representation. The equation for the force f is

$$f = \left[M_1 D^2 + K_1 + \frac{1}{1/(K + BD) + 1/(K_2 + M_2 D^2)} \right] x$$

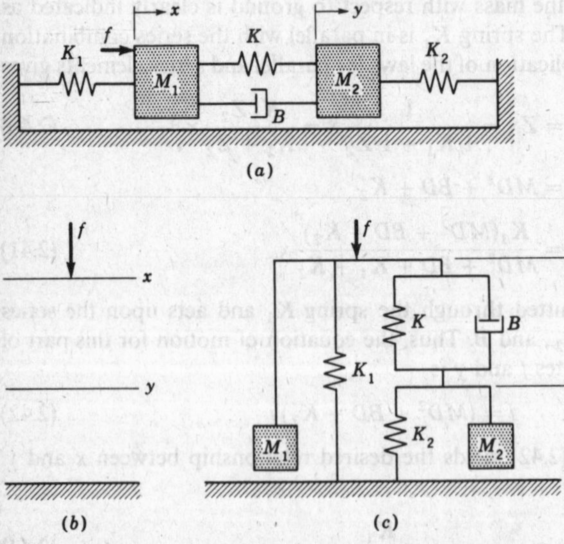

Figure 2.16 General mechanical system.

Degrees of Freedom

By degrees of freedom is meant the number of coordinates required to specify the position of all the elements in a mechanical system. Thus, the system shown in Fig. 2.14 has two degrees of freedom, while that shown in Fig. 2.15 has three degrees of freedom.

Rather than using the series and parallel laws, an alternative method of determining the equation of operation of mechanical systems is to write the force balance at each coordinate. For example, the force equation at the x coordinate of Fig. 2.14b is

$$K_1(x - y) = f \tag{2.44}$$

The compression of the spring K_1 is $x - y$; as x increases, so does the spring force, but as y increases, the spring force decreases. The force balance at the y coordinate is

$$K_1(x - y) - K_2 y - BDy = MD^2 y \tag{2.45}$$

The two preceding force equations may be written in the form

$$\begin{aligned} K_1 x \qquad\qquad\qquad\qquad - K_1 y &= f \\ K_1 x - (K_1 + K_2 + BD + MD^2)y &= 0 \end{aligned} \tag{2.46}$$

These two equations may be solved simultaneously to yield any of the desired relationships between x, y, and f. For example, solving for y gives

$$\begin{aligned} y &= \frac{\begin{vmatrix} K_1 & f \\ K_1 & 0 \end{vmatrix}}{\begin{vmatrix} K_1 & -K_1 \\ K_1 & -(K_1 + K_2 + BD + MD^2) \end{vmatrix}} \\ &= \frac{K_1 f}{K_1[(K_1 + K_2 + BD + MD^2) - K_1]} = \frac{f}{K_2 + BD + MD^2} \end{aligned} \tag{2.47}$$

Suppose that it is desired to consider y positive for upward motion rather than for downward motion. (Downward motion is shown in Fig. 2.14.) This reversal would change the sign of each y term in Eqs. (2.44) and (2.45), which would change the sign of y in the resultant expression given by Eq. (2.47). In effect, reversing the positive sense of a coordinate merely changes its sign.

In applying the series or parallel laws to mechanical elements, care must be exercised to take the positive sense of motion of each coordinate (this is indicated by the arrow at each coordinate) in the same direction as that of the applied force. It is a simple matter to later change the positive sense of a coordinate by merely changing the sign of the corresponding term in the derived equation.

2.5 ANALOGIES

The equation of operation for the series mechanical system of Fig. 2.4*a* is given by Eq. (2.17), and the equation for the series electric circuit of Fig. 2.8*a* is given by Eq. (2.26). Comparison of corresponding terms in Eqs. (2.17) and (2.26) shows that the differential equation of operation for each system has the same form. The terms which occupy corresponding positions are called analogous quantities. This particular analog is referred to as the direct analog. The analogous quantities for a direct analog are shown in Table 2.1.

The total force acting on a group of mechanical elements in series is equal to the sum of the forces exerted on each element. Similarly, the total voltage drop across a group of electrical elements in series is equal to the sum of the voltage drops across each element. Thus, in constructing a direct analog, series mechanical elements are replaced by analogous series electrical elements.

For parallel mechanical elements, the force acting on each element is the same, and for parallel electrical elements the voltage drop across each element is the same. Thus, in a direct analog, parallel mechanical elements should be replaced by equivalent electrical elements in parallel. A direct analog is also called a force-voltage analog in that force and voltage are analogous quantities.

The other type of analog is the inverse analog. To construct an inverse analog, it should first be noted that the *total current* flowing through a group of electrical elements in parallel is the *sum* of the currents in each element. This is analogous to the fact that the *total force* acting on a group of mechanical elements in series is the *sum* of the forces acting on each element. Thus, to construct an inverse analog, series mechanical elements must be replaced by parallel electrical elements. Similarly, in an inverse analog, it may be shown that parallel mechanical elements should be replaced by series electrical elements. Thus, the arrangement of series and parallel elements is inverted in constructing an inverse analog (i.e., series elements are replaced by parallel elements and vice versa). An inverse analog is also called a force-current analog in that force and current are analogous quantities.

Analogous quantities for an inverse analog may be determined by comparing

Table 2.1 Analogous quantities in a direct (force-voltage) analog

Translational mechanical system	Force f	Mass M	Viscous damping coefficient B	Spring constant K	Displacement x	Velocity $\dot{x} = Dx$
Electrical system	Voltage E	Inductance L	Resistance R	Reciprocal of capacitance $\frac{1}{C}$	Charge Q	Current $I = DQ$

the equation of operation for the parallel mechanical system of Fig. 2.15 with that for the series electrical system of Fig. 2.8*a*. The equation of operation for the parallel mechanical system of Fig. 2.15 is given by Eq. (2.39). Multiplication of both sides of Eq. (2.39) by D gives

$$\dot{x} = \left(\frac{D}{K} + \frac{1}{B} + \frac{1}{MD}\right) f \tag{2.48}$$

The operation of the series electric circuit of Fig. 2.8*a* is described by Eq. (2.25), which has the same form as Eq. (2.48). Comparison of corresponding terms in Eqs. (2.25) and (2.48) yields the analogous quantities for an inverse analog that are shown in Table 2.2.

Illustrative example Let it be desired to determine the electrical analog for the mechanical system of Fig. 2.14*b* by using (1) the direct analog, (2) the inverse analog.

Solution (1) The direct analog for the mechanical system of Fig. 2.14*b* is shown in Fig. 2.14*c*. Note that the capacitor C_1 is in parallel with the series combination of L, C_2, and R, just as the spring K_1 of Fig. 2.14*b* is in parallel with the series combination of M, K_2, and B. The equation of operation for the electric circuit of Fig. 2.14*c* is

$$E = ZI = \frac{1}{\dfrac{1}{1/C_1 D} + \dfrac{1}{LD + R + 1/C_2 D}} I$$

or

$$E = \frac{(1/C_1)(LD^2 + RD + 1/C_2)}{LD^2 + RD + (1/C_1 + 1/C_2)} Q \tag{2.41a}$$

Comparison of corresponding terms in Eqs. (2.41) and (2.41*a*) verifies the analogous quantities given in Table 2.1.

(2) The resulting inverse analog for Fig. 2.14*b* is shown in Fig. 2.14*d*. In Fig. 2.14*d*, it is to be noted that the inductor L_1 is in series with the parallel combination of C, L_2, and R, whereas in Fig. 2.14*b* the spring K_1 is in parallel

Table 2.2 Analogous quantities in an inverse (force-current) analog

Translational mechanical system	Force	Velocity	Spring constant	Damping coefficient	Mass
	f	$\dot{x}$	K	B	M
Electrical system	Current	Voltage	Reciprocal of inductance	Reciprocal of resistance	Capacitance
	I	E	$\dfrac{1}{L}$	$\dfrac{1}{R}$	C

with the series combination of M, K_2, and B. The equation of operation for the electric circuit of Fig. 2.14d is

$$E = ZI = \left(L_1 D + \frac{1}{CD + 1/R + 1/L_2 D}\right) I$$

or

$$I = \frac{(1/L_1)[CD^2 + (1/R)D + 1/L_2]}{CD^2 + (1/R)D + (1/L_1 + 1/L_2)} \frac{E}{D} \tag{2.41b}$$

Comparison of corresponding terms in Eqs. (2.41) and (2.41b) verifies the analogous quantities given in Table 2.2. In the inverse analog, velocity is analogous to voltage, and thus displacement is analogous to the integral of voltage.

Comparison of corresponding terms in Eqs. (2.17) and (2.21) shows that a direct (torque-force) analog may be developed in which series translational mechanical elements are replaced by series rotational elements. Similarly, parallel translational elements should be replaced by parallel rotational elements.

2.6 SCALE FACTORS

Because of the convenience of working with electrical equipment, ordinarily an electrical analog is constructed for some other system. Scale factors ensure that the values of the voltages and currents in the electrical analog will be reasonable. For example, in a direct analog, analogous quantities are force-voltage and velocity-current; hence

$$f = k_E E \tag{2.49}$$

$$\frac{dx}{dt} = k_I I \tag{2.50}$$

Thus, if the maximum value of f is 1000 lb and the maximum desired voltage is 100 V, then

$$k_E = \frac{f}{E} = 10 \text{ lb/V}$$

In this case, one volt corresponds to 10 lb of force.

To determine the other analogous relationships, first write the force equations for a mass, a damper, and a spring. That is,

$$f = M \frac{d}{dt}\left(\frac{dx}{dt}\right) \tag{2.51}$$

$$f = B \frac{dx}{dt} \tag{2.52}$$

$$f = Kx \qquad \text{or} \qquad \frac{df}{dt} = K \frac{dx}{dt} \tag{2.53}$$

The voltage equations for an inductor, resistor, and capacitor are

$$E = L\frac{d}{dt}I \qquad E = RI \qquad \frac{dE}{dt} = \frac{1}{C}I$$

The preceding expressions may be written in the form

$$k_E E = \frac{k_E}{k_I} L \frac{d}{dt} k_I I \tag{2.54}$$

$$k_E E = \frac{k_E}{k_I} R k_I I \tag{2.55}$$

$$\frac{d}{dt} k_E E = \frac{k_E}{k_I} \frac{1}{C} k_I I \tag{2.56}$$

From a comparison of Eqs. (2.51) and (2.54), it follows that to have $f = k_E E$ and $dx/dt = k_I I$, then $M = (k_E/k_I)L$ or

$$L = kM \tag{2.57}$$

where $k = k_I/k_E$.

Comparison of Eqs. (2.52) and (2.55) shows that

$$R = kB \tag{2.58}$$

Comparison of Eqs. (2.53) and (2.56) yields

$$C = \frac{1}{kK} \tag{2.59}$$

For the case in which $k = 1$, the preceding analogous relationships are the same as those given in Table 2.1.

Time Scale

For systems which are extremely fast acting, it may be desired to slow down the solution on the electric analog. Similarly, for extremely slow systems it may be desired to speed up the solution. By letting t represent actual time for a phenomenon to occur in the actual system and τ represent the time for the corresponding phenomenon to take place in the analog, then

$$\tau = at \tag{2.60}$$

where t = actual time of phenomenon
τ = time in analog

If a phenomenon takes 1 s to complete in actual time t and if $a = 10$, then $\tau = at = 10$, or the solution has been slowed down on the analog by a factor of 10. Hence, for $a > 1$ the solution is slowed down and for $a < 1$ the solution is speeded up.

When a time scale change is effected, events in the electric analog occur in analog time τ; hence, writing Eqs. (2.54), (2.55), and (2.56) in terms of τ gives

$$k_E E = \frac{L}{k}\frac{d}{d\tau} k_I I$$

$$k_E E = \frac{R}{k} k_I I$$

$$\frac{d}{d\tau} k_E E = \frac{1}{kC} k_I I$$

Differentiation of Eq. (2.60) shows that $d\tau/dt = a$; hence

$$\frac{dI}{d\tau} = \frac{dt}{d\tau}\frac{dI}{dt} = \frac{1}{a}\frac{dI}{dt} \qquad \text{and} \qquad \frac{dE}{d\tau} = \frac{1}{a}\frac{dE}{dt}$$

Expressing the equations for the electrical elements in terms of time t gives

$$k_E E = \frac{L}{ka}\frac{d}{dt} k_I I \tag{2.61}$$

$$k_E E = \frac{R}{k} k_I I \tag{2.62}$$

$$\frac{d}{dt} k_E E = \frac{a}{kC} k_I I \tag{2.63}$$

From a comparison of Eqs. (2.51) and (2.61), it follows that to have $f = k_E E$ and $dx/dt = k_I I$, then $M = L/ka$ or

$$L = akM \tag{2.64}$$

Comparison of Eqs. (2.52) and (2.62) shows that

$$R = kB \tag{2.65}$$

Comparison of Eqs. (2.53) and (2.63) shows that

$$C = \frac{a}{k}\frac{1}{K} \tag{2.66}$$

For the case in which $a = 1$ and $k = 1$ the preceding results are identical to those given in Table 2.1.

The corresponding relationships for an inverse analog are developed in a similar manner. In this analog, force and current are analogous quantities, as are voltage and velocity; hence, the desired scale factors are

$$f = k_I I \tag{2.67}$$

$$\frac{dx}{dt} = k_E E \tag{2.68}$$

Equations (2.61), (2.62), and (2.63) are modified forms of the basic relationships for an inductor, resistor, and capacitor, respectively. Solving Eqs. (2.61), (2.62), and (2.63) for $k_I I$ gives

$$\frac{d}{dt} k_I I = \frac{ka}{L} k_E E \tag{2.69}$$

$$k_I I = \frac{k}{R} k_E E \tag{2.70}$$

$$k_I I = \frac{kC}{a} \frac{d}{dt} k_E E \tag{2.71}$$

Comparison of Eqs. (2.53) and (2.69) reveals that to have $f = k_I I$ and $dx/dt = k_E E$, then $K = ka/L$ or

$$L = ak \frac{1}{K} \tag{2.72}$$

Similarly, comparing Eq. (2.52) with (2.70) and comparing Eq. (2.51) with (2.71) shows that

$$R = k \frac{1}{B} \tag{2.73}$$

$$C = \frac{a}{k} M \tag{2.74}$$

For the case in which $a = 1$ and $k = 1$, these relationships become identical to those given in Table 2.2.

Units

In the British gravitational system, force is measured in pounds (lb_f), length in feet (ft), time in seconds (s), and mass in slugs. From Newton's equation of motion ($f = ma$), it follows that the unit relationship is

$$\text{lb}_f = \text{slug·ft/s}^2$$

For a direct analog, the units of k_E are lb_f/V and the units of k_I are (ft/s)/A. Thus, $k = k_I/k_E$ has units of $\text{ft·V/lb}_f\text{·A·s}$. From Eq. (2.64), the resulting units for $L = akM$ are

$$L = \left(\frac{\text{ft·V}}{\text{lb}_f\text{·A·s}}\right)\left(\frac{\text{lb}_f\text{·s}^2}{\text{ft}}\right) = \frac{\text{V·s}}{\text{A}}$$

Substitution of units into the relationship $E = L(dI/dt)$ shows that inductance L has units of V·s/A, which are called henrys. Similarly, from Eq. (2.65) it is found that resistance R has units of V/A, which are ohms. From Eq. (2.66) it is found that capacitance C has units of A·s/V, which are farads. For the inverse analog, k_I

has units of lb_f/A and k_E has units of (ft/s)/V. The resulting units for $k = k_I/k_E$ are $\text{lb}_f\cdot\text{V}\cdot\text{s/ft}\cdot\text{A}$. From Eq. (2.72), the resulting units for $L = ak/K$ are

$$L = \left(\frac{\text{lb}_f\cdot\text{V}\cdot\text{s}}{\text{ft}\cdot\text{A}}\right) \Big/ \left(\frac{\text{lb}_f}{\text{ft}}\right) = \frac{\text{V}\cdot\text{s}}{\text{A}}$$

These are the units for henrys. Similarly, Eqs. (2.73) and (2.74) yield the proper units for R and C, respectively.

In the SI system, force is measured in newtons (N), mass in kilograms (kg), length in meters (m), and time in seconds (s). The relationship among the units in the SI system is

$$\text{N} = \frac{\text{kg}\cdot\text{m}}{\text{s}^2}$$

The use of SI units in the preceding analysis yields the same results as those obtained with the British gravitational system. The only difference is that ft is replaced by m, lb_f is replaced by N, and $\text{slug} = \text{lb}_f\cdot\text{s}^2/\text{ft}$ is replaced by $\text{kg} = \text{N}\cdot\text{s}^2/\text{m}$.

2.7 THERMAL SYSTEMS

For small temperature differences, the rate of heat transferred into a body is proportional to the temperature difference across the body.

$$Q = hA(T_1 - T) = \frac{T_1 - T}{R_T} \tag{2.75}$$

where Q = rate of heat flow
h = coefficient of heat transfer of the surface of the body
A = surface area
T = the temperature of the body
T_1 = temperature of the surrounding medium

and the symbol $R_T = 1/hA$ means equivalent thermal resistance and will soon be shown to be analogous to the electrical resistance R.

The rate of change of temperature of the body dT/dt is related to the rate of heat transfer into the body by the expression

$$Q = Mc\frac{dT}{dt} = C_T DT \tag{2.76}$$

where c = average specific heat of the body
M = mass
$C_T = Mc$ is the equivalent thermal capacitance

The equation for a resistor and a capacitor may be written in the form

$$I = \frac{1}{R}E \tag{2.77}$$

and

$$I = CDE \tag{2.78}$$

Comparison of Eq. (2.77) with Eq. (2.75) and of Eq. (2.78) with Eq. (2.76) shows the following quantities to be analogous.

$$T \sim E \qquad Q \sim I$$
$$R_T \sim R \qquad C_T \sim C \tag{2.79}$$

This is the direct, or temperature-voltage, analog.

In Fig. 2.17*a* is shown an insulated container. The liquid is stirred so that the temperature T of the liquid is constant throughout. The equation for the heat transfer into the liquid is given by Eq. (2.75). Because this equation has the same form as the resistor equation, it is represented as a thermal resistor R_T in the equivalent thermal circuit of Fig. 2.17*b*. Similarly, the equation for the heat stored in the liquid is given by Eq. (2.76). Because this equation has the same form as the capacitor equation, it is represented as a thermal reservoir in Fig. 2.17*b*. The equation of operation for this thermal circuit is

$$Q = \frac{T_1 - T}{R_T} = C_T DT$$

Solving for T gives

$$T = \frac{T_1}{1 + (R_T C_T)D} \tag{2.80}$$

The electric circuit which is the direct analog of the thermal circuit is shown in Fig. 2.17*c*. The equation of operation for the electric circuit is

$$I = \frac{E_1 - E}{R} = CDE$$

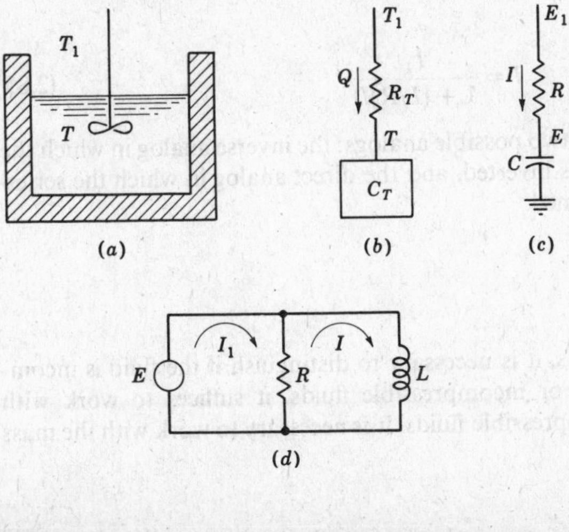

Figure 2.17 Thermal system.

Solving for E gives

$$E = \frac{E_1}{1 + (RC)D} \tag{2.81}$$

In the direct analog, series thermal elements are replaced by analogous electrical elements in series. Similarly, parallel thermal elements are replaced by analogous electrical elements in parallel. For thermal systems, there are only two elements.

The inverse, or temperature-current, analog is developed by first writing the equation for a resistor and inductor in the form

$$E = RI \tag{2.82}$$

$$E = LDI \tag{2.83}$$

Comparison with Eqs. (2.75) and (2.76) reveals the following analogous relationships:

$$T \sim I \qquad Q \sim E \tag{2.84}$$

$$R_T \sim \frac{1}{R} \qquad C_T \sim L$$

The inverse analog of Fig. 2.17*b* is constructed by replacing the thermal resistor R_T and thermal capacitor C_T, which are in series, by an electrical resistor R and inductor L as shown in Fig. 2.17*d*. Because the thermal elements R_T and C_T have the same rate of heat flow Q, each electrical element R and C must have the same voltage E. The temperature of the thermal reservoir is T, and thus the inductor current is I. Similarly, the temperature difference across the thermal resistor is $T_1 - T$, and the electric resistor current is $I_1 - I$. The equation of operation for the inverse analog, Fig. 2.17*d*, is

$$E = R(I_1 - I) = LDI$$

Solving for I gives

$$I = \frac{I_1}{1 + (L/R)D} \tag{2.85}$$

For any circuit, there are but two possible analogs: the inverse analog in which the series-parallel arrangement is inverted, and the direct analog in which the series-parallel arrangement is retained.

2.8 FLUID SYSTEMS

In working with fluid systems, it is necessary to distinguish if the fluid is incompressible or compressible. For incompressible fluids, it suffices to work with volume rate of flow. For compressible fluids, it is necessary to work with the mass rate of flow.

Incompressible Fluids

When the pressure difference across a flow restriction is small, the volume rate of flow Q is proportional to the pressure drop $P_1 - P$ across the restriction.

$$Q = \frac{P_1 - P}{R_F} \tag{2.86}$$

where R_F is the equivalent fluid resistance.

The rate of flow into a tank, such as that shown in Fig. 2.18*a*, is equal to the cross-sectional area A of the tank times the rate of change of height. Thus

$$Q = ADH = \frac{A}{\rho} DP = C_F DP \tag{2.87}$$

where $P = \rho H$, in which ρ is the density of the fluid

H = the head

$C_F = A/\rho$ = equivalent fluid capacitance

The equation of operation for the fluid system of Fig. 2.18*a* is

$$Q = \frac{P_1 - P}{R_F} = C_F DP$$

Solving for P gives

$$P = \frac{P_1}{1 + (R_F C_F)D} \tag{2.88}$$

Replacing P by ρH yields the equation for the head H. In Fig. 2.18*b* is shown the fluid circuit representation for this system.

Comparison of Eqs. (2.86) and (2.87) with Eqs. (2.77) and (2.78) shows the following quantities to be analogous.

$$\begin{aligned} P &\sim E \qquad & Q &\sim I \\ R_F &\sim R \qquad & C_F &\sim C \end{aligned} \tag{2.89}$$

These are analogous quantities for the direct, or pressure-voltage, analog. The electric circuit which is the direct analog for the fluid system of Fig. 2.18*b* is the same as that shown in Fig. 2.17*c*.

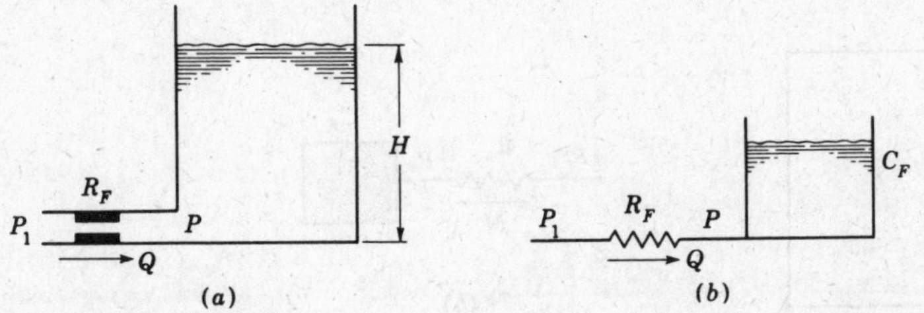

Figure 2.18 Fluid system.

Comparison of Eqs. (2.86) and (2.87) with Eqs. (2.82) and (2.83) yields the analogous relationships for the inverse, or pressure-current, analog. Thus,

$$P \sim I \qquad Q \sim E \tag{2.90}$$

$$R_F \sim \frac{1}{R} \qquad C_F \sim L$$

The inverse analog for the fluid system of Fig. 2.18*b* is the same as that shown in Fig. 2.17*d*.

Compressible Fluids

For small pressure differences, the mass rate of flow M through a restriction is proportional to the pressure difference $P_1 - P$.

$$M = \frac{P_1 - P}{R_F} \tag{2.91}$$

where R_F is the equivalent fluid resistance. In Fig. 2.19*a* is shown a tank of constant volume V. The equation of state for the fluid in the tank is

$$PV = WRT$$

The flow into such a tank is usually isothermal. Thus, differentiating both sides of the equation of state with respect to time and solving for $M = dW/dt$ gives

$$M = \frac{dW}{dt} = \frac{V}{RT}\frac{d}{dt}P = \frac{V}{RT}DP = C_F DP \tag{2.92}$$

where $C_F = V/RT$ is the equivalent fluid capacitance. In Fig. 2.19*b* is shown the fluid circuit representation for this system. The equation of operation is

$$P = \frac{P_1}{1 + (R_F C_F)D} \tag{2.93}$$

The analogous relationships for the direct, or pressure-voltage, analog are the same as those given by Eq. (2.89) except that Q is replaced by M. The electric circuit which is the direct analog is the same as Fig. 2.17*c*.

Similarly, the analogous relationships for the inverse, or pressure-current,

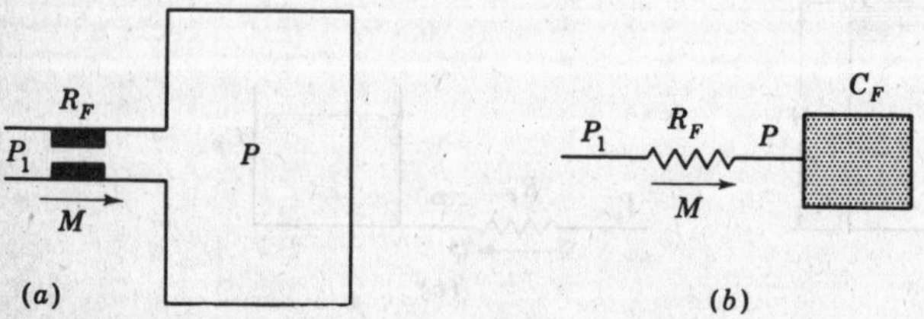

Figure 2.19 Fluid system.

analog are the same as those given by Eq. (2.90) with Q replaced by M, and the electric circuit which is the inverse analog is the same as Fig. 2.17*d*.

A major use of analogs is that often it is easier to study experimentally one type of system rather than another. For example, it may be easier to change a resistor rather than a coefficient of viscous friction. Whenever possible, it is best to work with the system directly rather than to consider the operation of an analogous system. This eliminates the chance of error in construction of the analogy. Also, when carried far enough analogies usually break down because things which are physically possible for one component may be impossible for the analogous component.

PROBLEMS

2.1 For each of the following operational relationships, determine the required initial conditions such that cancellation of operators is valid. For $f(t)$ use the function $f(t) = e^{2t}$.

(*a*) $y(t) = \dfrac{1}{D} Df(t)$

(*b*) $y(t) = \dfrac{1}{D} D^2 f(t)$

(*c*) $y(t) = \dfrac{1}{D+1}(D+1)f(t)$

(*d*) $y(t) = \dfrac{1}{D+1}(D+1)^2 f(t)$

2.2 For each of the mechanical systems shown in Fig. P2.2,

(*a*) Determine the equation which relates f and x.

(*b*) Determine the equation which relates f and y.

(*c*) Determine the equation which relates x and y.

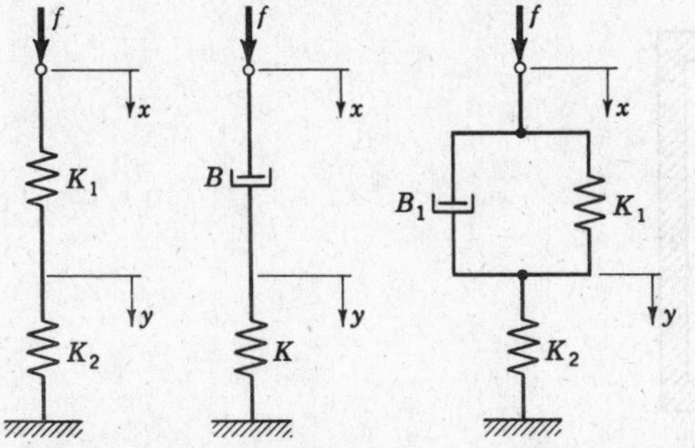

Figure P2.2

2.3 For each of the mechanical systems shown in Fig. P2.3, construct the equivalent grounded-chair representation and

(*a*) Determine the equation which relates f and x.

(*b*) Determine the equation which relates f and y.

(*c*) Determine the equation which relates x and y.

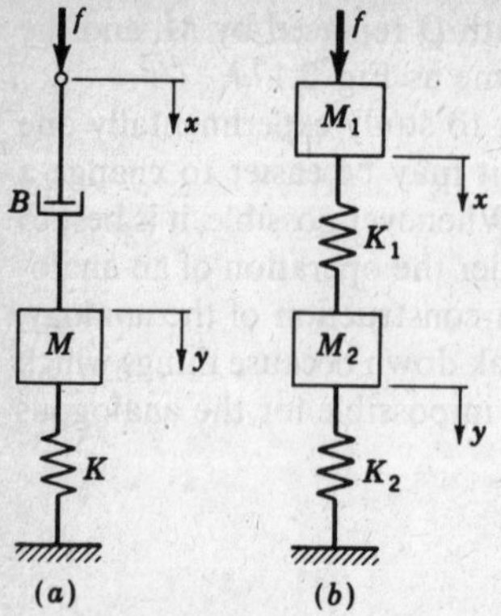

Figure P2.3

2.4 For the electrical networks shown in Fig. P2.4*a* and *b*,

(*a*) Determine the equation which relates E_1 and I.

(*b*) Determine the equation which relates E_1 and E_2.

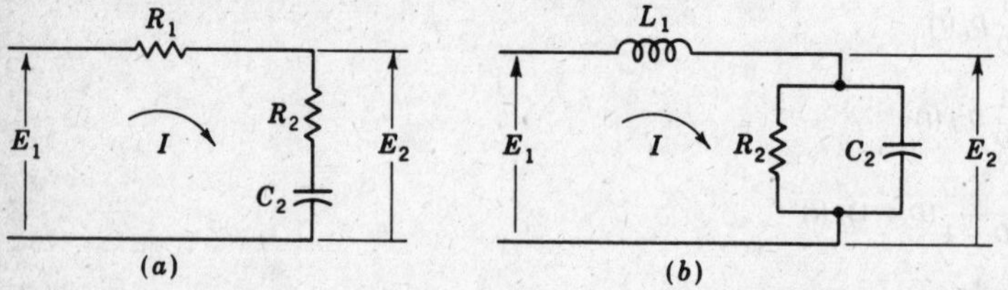

Figure P2.4

2.5 A schematic diagram of an accelerometer for measuring the linear acceleration d^2x/dt^2 is shown in Fig. P2.5. Determine the operational form for the differential equation which relates y (the change in the position of the mass relative to the frame) to the acceleration D^2x of the frame.

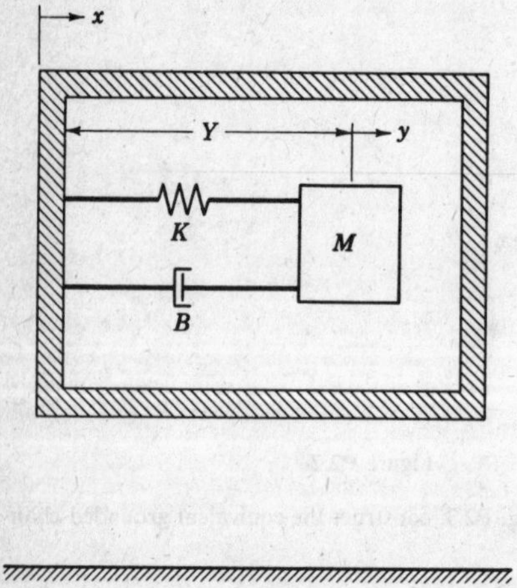

Figure P2.5

2.6 For each of the mechanical systems shown in Fig. P2.6, construct the grounded-chair representation and determine the equation relating f and x.

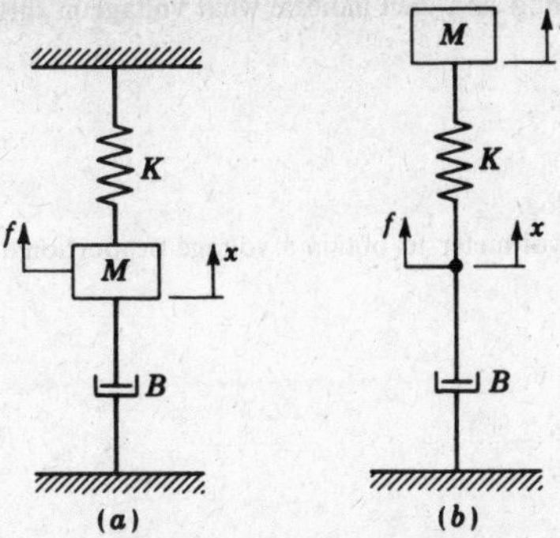

Figure P2.6

2.7 For the mechanical system shown in Fig. P2.2*c*, construct the electric circuit which is the

(*a*) Direct analog. Determine the equation relating E and I of this electrical system, and compare this equation with that relating f and x of Fig. P2.2*c*.

(*b*) Inverse analog. Determine the equation relating E and I of this electrical system, and compare this equation with that relating x and f of Fig. P2.2*c*.

2.8 For the electrical system shown in Fig. P2.4*b*, construct the mechanical circuit which is the

(*a*) Direct analog. Determine the equation relating f and x of this mechanical system, and compare this equation with that relating E_1 and I of Fig. P2.4*b*.

(*b*) Inverse analog. Determine the equation relating x and f of this mechanical system, and compare this equation with that relating E_1 and I of Fig. P2.4*b*.

2.9 For the mechanical system shown in Fig. P2.9,

(*a*) Determine the differential equation relating f and x.

(*b*) Construct the direct (force-voltage) analog.

(*c*) Construct the inverse (force-current) analog.

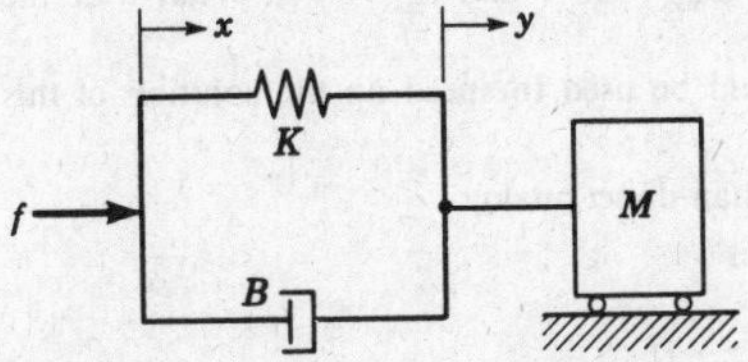

Figure P2.9

2.10 For the mechanical system shown in Fig. P2.10,

(*a*) Construct the grounded-chair representation.

(*b*) Obtain the overall equation relating f and x.

(*c*) Construct the electric circuit which is the direct analog.

(*d*) Indicate what current in the analog corresponds to the velocity of the mass M.

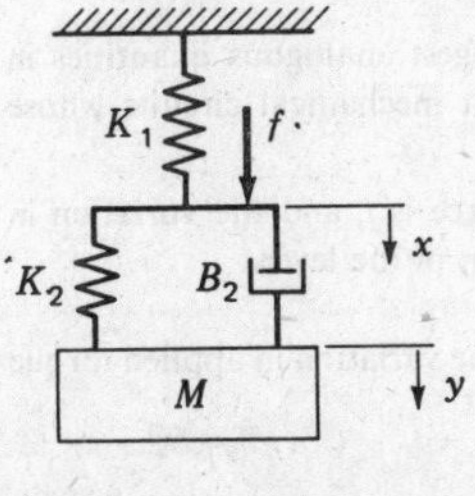

Figure P2.10

2.11 Same as Prob. 2.10, except construct the inverse analog, and then indicate what voltage in this analog corresponds to the velocity of the mass M.

2.12 For the mechanical system shown in Fig. P2.12,

(*a*) Draw the grounded-chair representation.

(*b*) Determine the equation relating f and x.

(*c*) Draw the electric circuit which is the direct analog.

(*d*) On the analog show where you would place a voltmeter to obtain a voltage proportional to the force across the damper B_2.

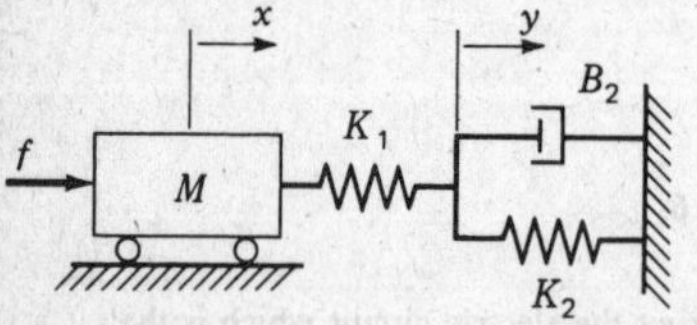

Figure P2.12

2.13 Same as Prob. 2.12, except construct the inverse analog, and then indicate where you would place an ammeter to obtain a current proportional to the force across the damper B_2.

2.14 For the mechanical system shown in Fig. P2.9, determine numerical values for the electrical elements of the direct analog when

(*a*) $M = 0.5$ slugs, $B = 10$ lb$_f$ s/ft, $K = 50$ lb$_f$/ft, $k_E = 2$ lb$_f$/V, and $k_I = 200$ ft/s·A.

(*b*) $M = 0.5$ kg, $B = 10$ N·s/m, $K = 50$ N/m, $k_E = 2$ N/V, and $k_I = 200$ m/s·A.

2.15 For the mechanical system shown in Fig. P2.9, determine numerical values for the electrical elements of the inverse analog when

(*a*) $M = 0.5$ slugs, $B = 10$ lb$_f$·s/ft, $K = 50$ lb$_f$/ft, $k_E = 2$ ft/s·V, and $k_I = 200$ lb$_f$/A.

(*b*) $M = 0.5$ kg, $B = 10$ N·s/m, $K = 50$ N/m, $k_E = 2$ m/s·V, and $k_I = 200$ N/A.

2.16 The parameters for a mechanical system are $M = 10$ slugs, $B = 5000$ lb$_f$ s/ft, and $K = 2500$ lb$_f$/ft. It is estimated that $f_{max} = 500$ lb$_f$ and $\dot{x}_{max} = 5$ ft/s. Determine what size resistor, inductor, and capacitor to use in the direct analog such that $E_{max} = 100$ V and $I_{max} = 10$ A.

After the analog has been made, it is found that $E_{max} = 50$ V and $I_{max} = 4$ A. What were the actual values of f_{max} and $\dot{x}_{max}$?

What size resistor, inductor, and capacitor should be used to speed up the solution of this problem by a factor of 10?

2.17 Same as Prob. 2.16, except for an inverse rather than direct analog.

2.18 The differential equation for a series *RLC* circuit is

$$E = \left(LD + R + \frac{1}{CD}\right)I$$

(*a*) Construct the mechanical circuit which is the direct (force-voltage) analog for the series *RLC* circuit. Determine the equation for the force f as a function of velocity $\dot{x}$. (Label mass M_a, spring K_a, and damper B_a).

(*b*) Construct the mechanical circuit which is the inverse analog for the series *RLC* circuit. Determine the equation for velocity $\dot{x}$ as a function of force f. (Label mass as M_b, spring K_b, and damper B_b.)

(*c*) Compare the results of parts (*a*) and (*b*) above, and then suggest analogous quantities in constructing the dual of a mechanical circuit. (Duals are two different mechanical circuits whose differential equations have the same form.)

2.19 For the lever shown in Fig. P2.19, the variation in the applied force is f, and the variation in spring position is x. The horizontal line represents the reference position of the lever.

(*a*) Determine the equation relating f and x.

(*b*) Determine the relationship between t and θ (where $t = fL_f$ is the variation in applied torque and $x = L_2\theta$).

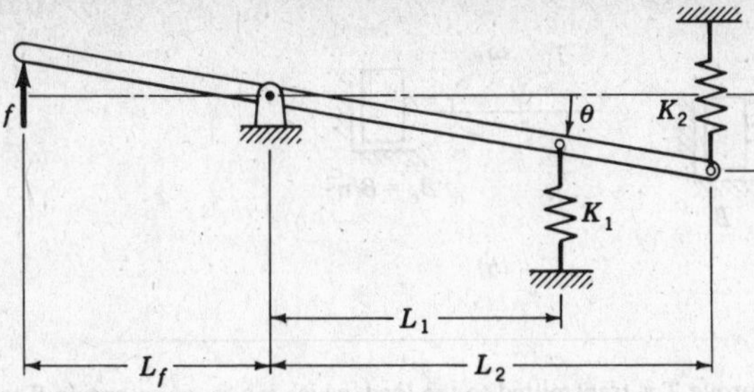

Figure P2.19

2.20 The lever system shown in Fig. P2.20 is drawn in its reference position. The variation in spring position is designated by x. The variation in applied force is designated by f. (f and x are zero at the reference position.)

(*a*) Determine the equation relating f and x.

(*b*) Determine the relationship between t and θ

where $t = fL_f$ and $x = L\theta$.

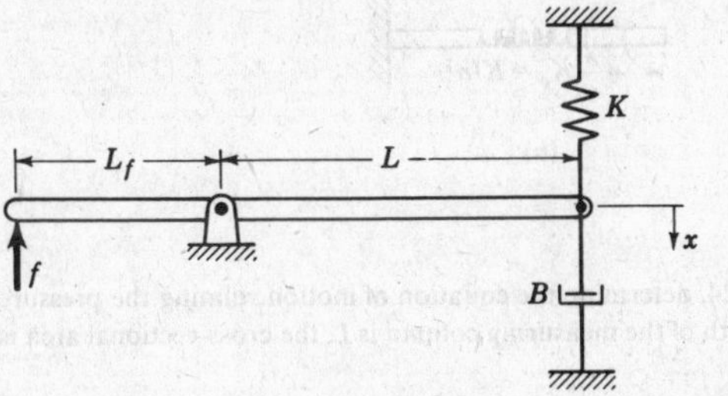

Figure P2.20

2.21 Oftentimes mechanical systems have gearing. Such systems may be represented by equivalent systems without gearing. Figure P2.21*a* shows a geared system, and Fig. P2.21*b* shows an equivalent system without gearing. The gear ratio $n = \omega_1/\omega_2$ is the ratio of the speed of the driving shaft ω_1 to that of the driven shaft ω_2. In order for the systems to be equivalent, the kinetic energy of the system without gearing $J_e\omega_1^2/2$ must be the same as that of the system with gearing $J\omega_2^2/2$. Thus, show that $J_e = J/n^2$.

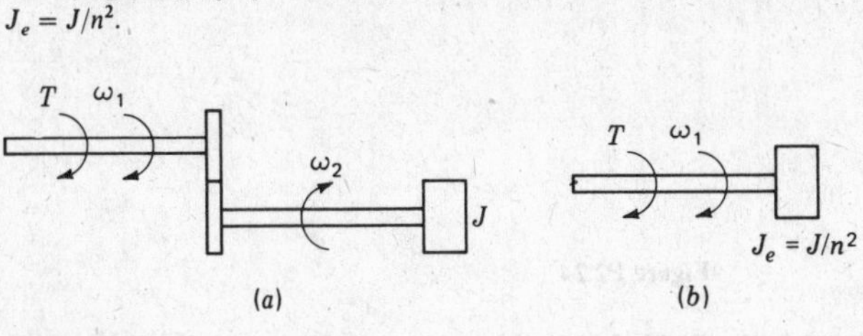

Figure P2.21

2.22 As shown in Fig. P2.22*a*, the torque T is transmitted through gearing to the load, which is viscous friction. The resisting torque due to the viscous friction is $B\omega_2$, where B is the coefficient of viscous friction. The rate at which power is being dissipated is equal to the product of the resisting torque and the angular velocity $P = (B\omega_2)\omega_2 = B\omega_2^2$. The system without gearing is shown in Fig. P2.22*b*. In order for the systems to be equivalent, the rate of power dissipation of the system without gearing $B_e\omega_1^2$ must be the same as that for the system with gearing. Thus, show that $B_e = B/n^2$.

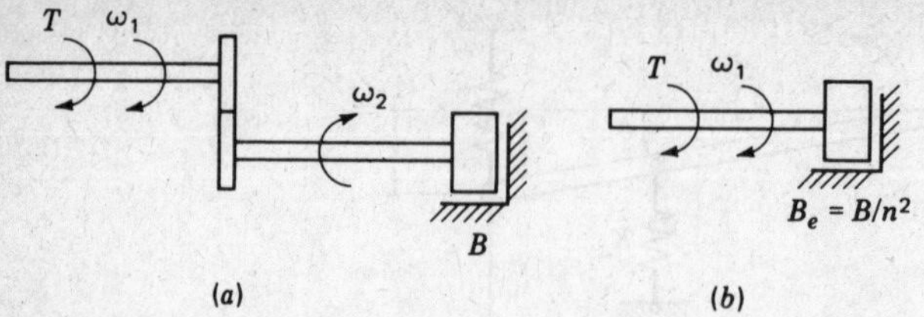

Figure P2.22

2.23 As shown in Fig. P2.23*a*, the torque T is transmitted to the load, which is a torsional spring. The torque applied to the torsional spring is $K\theta_2$, where K is the torsional spring rate and θ is the angle of the twist. The potential energy stored in the spring is $K\theta_2^2/2$. The corresponding system without gearing is shown in Fig. P2.23*b*. In order for the systems to be equivalent, the potential energy stored in the system without gearing $K_e\theta_1^2/2$ must be the same as that for the system with gearing. Thus, show that $K_e = K/n^2$.

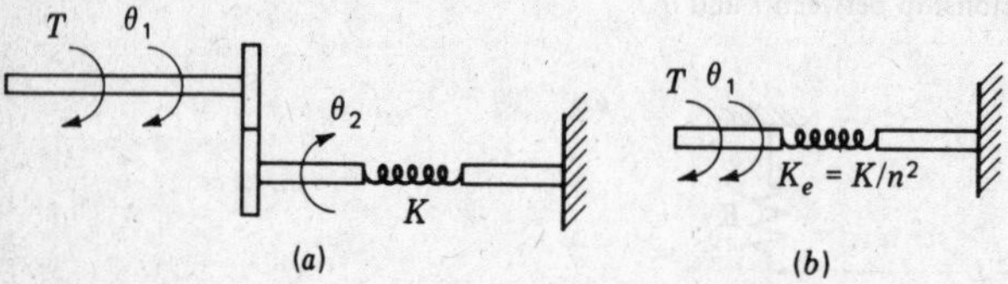

Figure P2.23

2.24 For the manometer shown in Fig. P2.24, determine the equation of motion relating the pressure P at the open end to the position x. The length of the measuring column is L, the cross-sectional area is A, and the density is ρ.

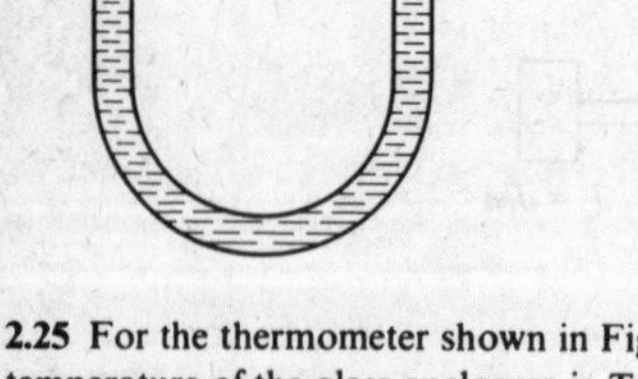

Figure P2.24

2.25 For the thermometer shown in Fig. P2.25, the temperature of the surrounding medium is T_1, the temperature of the glass enclosure is T_2, and the temperature of the fluid in the thermometer is T. The rate of heat flow from the surrounding medium to the glass is $Q_1 = (T_1 - T_2)/R_{T_1}$. The rate of heat flow from the glass to the fluid is $Q_2 = (T_2 - T)/R_{T_2}$.

The rate of temperature change of the glass is $DT_2 = (Q_1 - Q_2)/C_{T_1}$, and the rate of change of temperature of the fluid is $DT = Q_2/C_{T_2}$.

Construct the thermal circuit representation for this system, and then determine the equation for the temperature T of the fluid as a function of the surrounding temperature T_1.

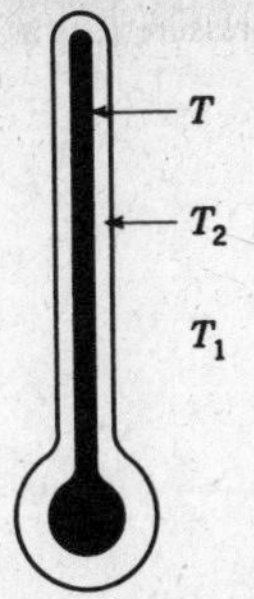

Figure P2.25

2.26 In Fig. P2.26 is shown an oven which is supplied with heat from an electric source. The rate of heat supplied is proportional to the voltage, $Q_s = KE_s$. The rate at which heat is lost through the walls is $Q = (T - T_1)/R_T$. The rate of change of temperature of the oven is

$$DT = \frac{Q_s - Q}{C_T}$$

Construct the thermal circuit representation for this system, and then determine the equation for the temperature T of the oven as a function of the applied voltage E_s and the surrounding temperature T_1.

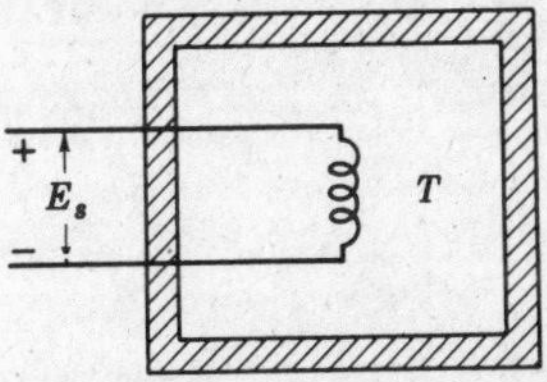

Figure P2.26

2.27 In Fig. P2.27 is shown a fluid system of two tanks in series. Construct the fluid circuit representation for this system. Determine the equation for the pressure P (head $H = P/\rho$) as a function of the inlet pressure P_1 (P_2 should not appear in this equation).

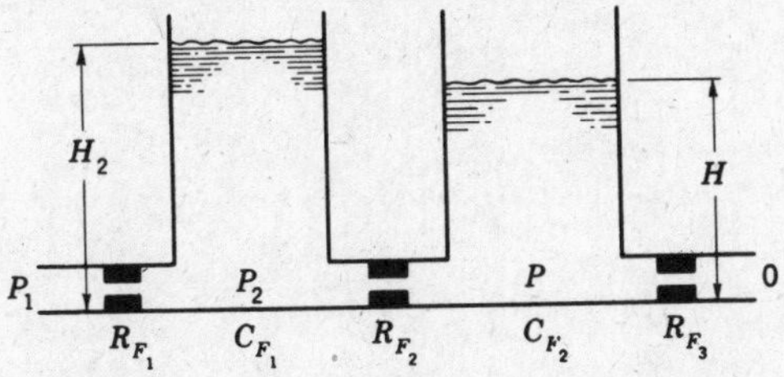

Figure P2.27

2.28 In Fig. P2.28 is shown a tank in which flow is supplied at a rate Q_s. Construct the fluid circuit representation for this system. Determine the equation for the pressure P (head $H = P/\rho$) as a function of P_1 and Q_s.

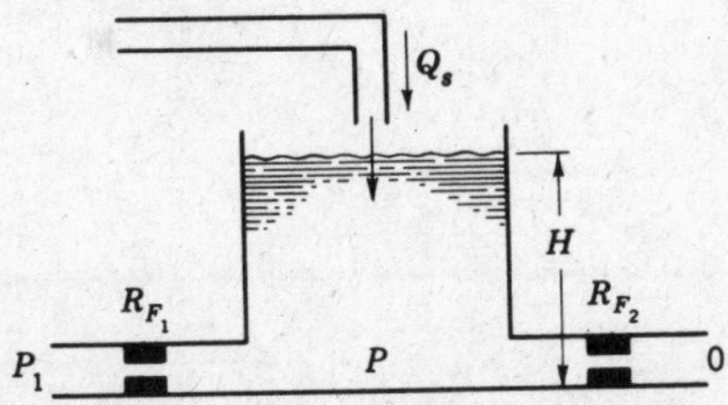

Figure P2.28

2.29 In Fig. P2.29 is shown a tank with two inlets. Determine the equation for the pressure P as a function of P_1 and P_2.

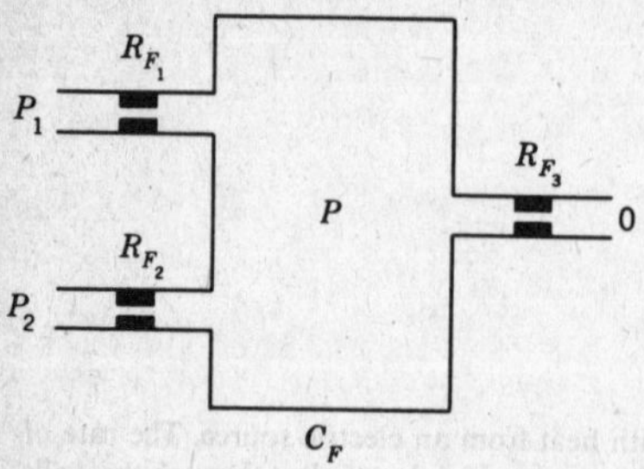

Figure P2.29

2.30 In Fig. P2.30 are shown two tanks in series. Determine the equation for the pressure P as a function of the inlet pressure P_1 (P_2 should not appear in the equation).

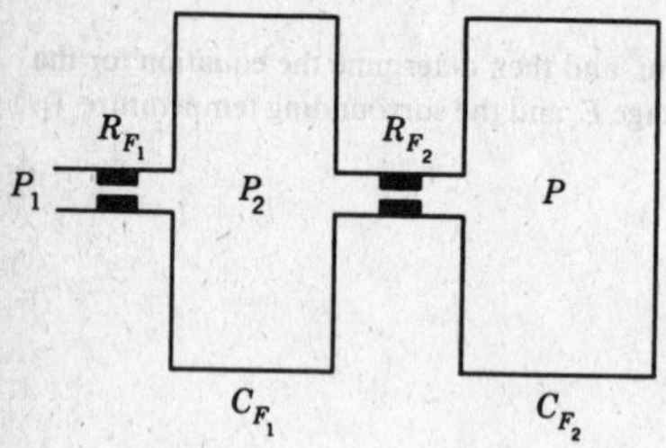

Figure P2.30

CHAPTER

THREE

REPRESENTATION OF CONTROL SYSTEMS

In this chapter it is shown how to obtain the overall block-diagram representation for some typical control systems. In brief, the method employed is to obtain the block diagram for each component or process and then "hook up," or connect, the corresponding inputs and outputs for each diagram to obtain the one overall representation for the system. The techniques which are presented in later chapters for determining the operating characteristics of control systems are based on a knowledge of the overall block-diagram representation for the system.

3.1 LINEARIZATION OF NONLINEAR FUNCTIONS

The most powerful methods of system analysis have been developed for linear control systems. For a linear control system all the relationships between the variables are linear differential equations, usually with constant coefficients. The reason that differential equations rather than algebraic equations are obtained is that in feedback control systems the variables are functions of time. For example, in controlling temperature, the actuating signal causes a change in heat flow, but time is required for this added heat to bring the temperature to its desired value. In speed control systems, the actuating signal causes a change in power of the prime mover, but time is required for the engine to accelerate or decelerate to its desired speed. Similarly, in pressure control systems, it takes time to bring the pressure in a chamber to some desired value.

Actual control systems usually contain some nonlinear elements. Such elements would in turn yield nonlinear differential equations for the system. In the following it is shown how the equations for nonlinear elements may be linearized.

Thus, the resulting differential equation of operation for the system becomes linear.

A plot of the nonlinear relationship

$$Y = X^2 \tag{3.1}$$

is shown in Fig. 3.1. In the vicinity of the point (X_i, Y_i), the function is closely approximated by the tangent. For example, consider the point (X, Y) on the curve of the nonlinear function. The abscissa X is displaced a distance x from X_i. This abscissa X intersects the nonlinear function a vertical distance $y + \varepsilon$ from Y, and it intersects the tangent a distance y from Y_i. The equation for Y is

$$Y = Y_i + y + \varepsilon \approx Y_i + y \tag{3.2}$$

Lowercase letters indicate the variation of the capital-letter parameters from the reference point. From Fig. 3.1, it is seen that the slope of the tangent line is

$$\frac{y}{x} = \left.\frac{dY}{dX}\right|_i = \text{slope at point } (X_i, Y_i)$$

The symbol $|_i$ means that the derivative is to be evaluated at the reference point. Thus

$$y = \left.\frac{dY}{dX}\right|_i x = \left.\frac{d}{dX}(X^2)\right|_i x = 2X_i x \tag{3.3}$$

Substitution of y from Eq. (3.3) into Eq. (3.2) yields the following linear approximation for Y:

$$Y \approx Y_i + 2X_i x \tag{3.4}$$

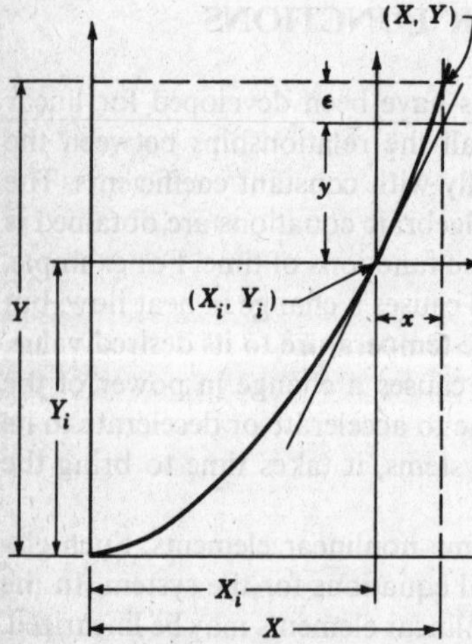

Figure 3.1 Graph of function $Y = X^2$.

Illustrative example 1 Effect a linear approximation for the equation $Y = X^2$ for values of X in the neighborhood of 10, and find the error when using this approximation for $X = 11$.

SOLUTION The reference values are $X_i = 10$ and $Y_i = X_i^2 = 100$. The variation from the reference value is $x = X - X_i = 11 - 10 = 1$. Substitution of these values into Eq. (3.4) yields

$$Y \approx Y_i + 2X_i x = 100 + (2)(10)(1) = 120$$

The exact value is $Y = X^2 = 121$; thus the error is 1 part in 121, or less than 1 percent.

A general procedure for obtaining a linear approximation is to use the expression derived in calculus for approximating the variation ΔY for a function $Y = Y(X_1, X_2, \ldots, X_n)$ of n independent variables. That is,

$$\Delta Y = \frac{\partial Y}{\partial X_1}\bigg|_i \Delta X_1 + \frac{\partial Y}{\partial X_2}\bigg|_i \Delta X_2 + \cdots + \frac{\partial Y}{\partial X_n}\bigg|_i \Delta X_n$$

Using lowercase letters to represent variations from the reference values, then,

$$y = \Delta Y = Y - Y_i$$

$$x_1 = \Delta X_1 = X_1 - X_{1_i}$$

$$x_2 = \Delta X_2 = X_2 - X_{2_i}$$

$$\vdots$$

$$x_n = \Delta X_n = X_n - X_{n_i}$$

Thus, the general expression for obtaining a linear approximation for a nonlinear function is

$$y = C_1 x_1 + C_2 x_2 + \cdots + C_n x_n \tag{3.5}$$

where

$$C_1 = \frac{\partial Y}{\partial X_1}\bigg|_i \qquad C_2 = \frac{\partial Y}{\partial X_2}\bigg|_i \qquad \text{etc.}$$

Evaluation of these partial derivatives at the reference condition yields constants. As is illustrated by Eq. (3.5), in a linear equation each variable term $x_1, x_2, \ldots, x_n$ is of the first power, and the contribution of each term is added independently.

The application of Eq. (3.5) to the nonlinear equation $Y = X^2$ is effected as follows: The independent variable is X, which corresponds to X_1 in the general equation. Thus,

$$C_1 = \frac{\partial Y}{\partial X_1}\bigg|_i = \frac{\partial Y}{\partial X}\bigg|_i = \frac{\partial}{\partial X} X^2\bigg|_i = 2X_i$$

The variation is

$$y = C_1 x = 2X_i x$$

This is the result obtained by the preceding geometric interpretation and given by Eq. (3.3).

The need for linearizing nonlinear relationships is frequently encountered in control engineering. For example, most mechanical speed control systems incorporate a flyball governor for sensing the speed error. This is a centrifugal device, so that a force is obtained which is proportional to the square of the speed. In the design of hydraulic equipment in which the working medium is an incompressible fluid, one encounters the nonlinear equations which govern such fluid flow. Similarly, the working medium for pneumatic equipment is air, whose flow is described by nonlinear relationships.

Illustrative example 2 Effect the linear approximation for P in the equation of state $PV = WRT$. The reference conditions are $P_i = 100\ \text{lb}_f/\text{ft}^2$, $V_i = 100\ \text{ft}^3$, $W_i = 10/53.3\ \text{lb}_m$, and $T_i = 1000°\text{R}$. Determine the percent error in using this approximation for P when $V = 110\ \text{ft}^3$, $T = 1200°\text{R}$, and W remains the same. The constant R is $53.3\ \text{ft} \cdot \text{lb}_f/\text{lb}_m/°\text{R}$.

SOLUTION From the equation of state and the fact that W remains constant, it is seen that P is a function of the independent variables T and V, or $P = P(T, V)$. Application of Eq. (3.5) to obtain the variation p of the pressure from its reference value yields

$$p = \left.\frac{\partial P}{\partial T}\right|_i t + \left.\frac{\partial P}{\partial V}\right|_i v \tag{3.6}$$

The partial derivatives are evaluated from the equation of state as follows:

$$\left.\frac{\partial P}{\partial T}\right|_i = \left.\frac{\partial}{\partial T}\left(\frac{WRT}{V}\right)\right|_i = \left.\frac{WR}{V}\right|_i = \frac{(10)(53.3)}{(53.3)(100)} = 0.10$$

$$\left.\frac{\partial P}{\partial V}\right|_i = \left.\frac{\partial}{\partial V}\left(\frac{WRT}{V}\right)\right|_i = \left.\frac{-WRT}{V^2}\right|_i = -1.0$$

The linearized approximation for P is

$$P \approx P_i + p = P_i + 0.1t - v$$

From the given information, it follows that

$$v = V - V_i = 110 - 100 = 10$$

$$t = T - T_i = 200$$

Thus $$P \approx 100 + (0.1)(200) - (10) = 110\ \text{lb}_f/\text{ft}^2$$

It is convenient to express linear approximations in nondimensional form. This is accomplished by expressing the partial derivatives in terms of the reference value of the function being approximated. For the preceding, the reference value is $P_i = (WRT/V)|_i$. Thus,

$$\left.\frac{\partial P}{\partial V}\right|_i = \left.\frac{WR}{V}\right|_i = \left.\left(\frac{WRT}{V}\right)\right|_i \frac{1}{T_i} = \frac{P_i}{T_i}$$

$$\left.\frac{\partial P}{\partial V}\right|_i = -\left.\frac{WRT}{V^2}\right|_i = -\left.\left(\frac{WRT}{V}\right)\right|_i \frac{1}{V_i} = \frac{-P_i}{V_i}$$

Substitution of these results into Eq. (3.6) gives

$$p = P_i\left(\frac{t}{T_i} - \frac{v}{V_i}\right) \tag{3.7}$$

Note that t/T_i and v/V_i are nondimensional ratios. Evaluation of the resulting linear approximation gives

$$P = P_i + p = 100 + 100(\tfrac{200}{1000} - \tfrac{10}{100}) = 100 + (20 - 10) = 110 \text{ lb}_f/\text{ft}^2$$

This checks the previously attained result. The exact value of P is

$$P = \frac{WRT}{V} = \frac{(10)(53.3)(1200)}{(53.3)(110)} = 109.1$$

Therefore, the percent error is

$$\frac{(110 - 109.1)100}{109.1} = 0.82\%$$

In the SI system, pressure has units of N/m^2, volume has units of m^3, mass has units of kg, and temperature has units of kelvins (K). When using SI units, the value of R in the equation of state ($PV = WRT$) is $R = 287 \text{N} \cdot \text{m/kg} \cdot \text{K}$.

Illustrative example 3 The equation for the flow of an incompressible fluid through a restriction is

$$Q = C_c A\sqrt{\frac{2g_c}{\rho}(P_1 - P_2)} \tag{3.8}$$

where Q = rate of flow, ft^3/s
C_c = coefficient of discharge (dimensionless)
A = area of restriction, ft^2
$P_1 - P_2$ = pressure drop across restriction, lb_f/ft^2
ρ = density of fluid, lb_m/ft^3
g_c = gravitational conversion constant = 32.2

Determine the linear approximation for the variation q. Letting $g_c = (32.2)(12) = 386$ converts the length units in Eq. (3.8) from feet to inches. Thus, the flow units are in^3/s, the area units are in^2, the pressure units are lb_f/in^2, and the density units are lb_m/in^3.

SOLUTION Because Q is a function of the area A and pressure drop $P_1 - P_2$, then

$$Q = Q[A, (P_1 - P_2)]$$

The variation q is

$$q = \frac{\partial Q}{\partial A}\bigg|_i a + \frac{\partial Q}{\partial (P_1 - P_2)}\bigg|_i (p_1 - p_2)$$

The partial derivatives are

$$\frac{\partial Q}{\partial A}\bigg|_i = C_c\sqrt{\frac{2g_c}{\rho}(P_1 - P_2)}\bigg|_i = \frac{Q}{A}\bigg|_i$$

and
$$\frac{\partial Q}{\partial (P_1 - P_2)}\bigg|_i = \frac{C_c A}{2}\sqrt{\frac{2g_c}{\rho}\frac{1}{P_1 - P_2}}\bigg|_i = \frac{1}{2}\frac{Q}{P_1 - P_2}\bigg|_i$$

Thus
$$q = Q_i\left[\frac{a}{A_i} + \frac{1}{2}\frac{p_1 - p_2}{(P_1 - P_2)_i}\right] \tag{3.9}$$

For fluid flow, it is customary to express mass in units of pounds-mass (lb_m) rather than slugs. At sea level the weight ($W = mg$) of a mass of one slug is $W = (1)(32.2)$ slug $\cdot$ ft/s^2 $= 32.2$ ($lb_f \cdot s^2$/ft)(ft/s^2) $= 32.2$ lb_f. The mass of a body in slugs is equal to its mass in pounds-mass divided by 32.2. The units relationship is slug $= lb_m/g_c = lb_m/32.2$ where $g_c = 32.2$ is the gravitational conversion constant. The constant $g_c = 32.2$ is not necessarily the local value of g.

In the flow equation, the kinetic energy term ($mv^2/2$) has units of (slug)(ft/s)^2 $=$ ($lb_f \cdot s^2$/ft)(ft/s)^2 $=$ ft $\cdot$ lb_f. When mass is expressed in units of lb_m, the kinetic energy term is ($mv^2/2g_c$). Note that dividing m by g_c converts mass from pounds-mass to slugs. When using SI units, the g_c term does not appear in Eq. (3.8); thus $Q = C_c A\sqrt{(P_1 - P_2)/\rho}$. Substitution of units into this expression shows that the units of Q are $m^2\sqrt{(N/m^2)/(kg/m^3)} = m^2\sqrt{N \cdot m/kg} = m^2\sqrt{N \cdot m/(N \cdot s^2/m)} = m^2\sqrt{m^2/s^2} = m^3/s$.

Illustrative example 4 For sonic flow of air through a restriction, the mass rate of flow is

$$M = \frac{0.53}{\sqrt{T}} AP \tag{3.10}$$

where M = mass rate of flow, lb_m/s
T = the inlet temperature, °R
A = area of restriction, ft^2
P = inlet pressure, lb_f/ft^2

Determine the linearized approximation for the variation m when the inlet temperature T is constant. It is interesting to note that because the length unit cancels in Eq. (3.10), any unit of length may be used. When using inches, the area is in in^2 and the pressure is in lb_f/in^2.

SOLUTION Because the temperature is constant, the mass rate of flow is a function of A and P. Thus

$$m = \left.\frac{\partial M}{\partial A}\right|_i a + \left.\frac{\partial M}{\partial P}\right|_i p$$

The partial derivatives are

$$\left.\frac{\partial M}{\partial A}\right|_i = \left.\frac{0.53}{\sqrt{T}} P\right|_i = \left.\frac{M}{A}\right|_i$$

and

$$\left.\frac{\partial M}{\partial P}\right|_i = \left.\frac{0.53}{\sqrt{T}} A\right|_i = \left.\frac{M}{P}\right|_i$$

Thus,

$$m = M_i\left(\frac{a}{A_i} + \frac{p}{P_i}\right) \tag{3.11}$$

When using SI units, Eq. (3.10) becomes $M = 0.04AP/\sqrt{T}$. The units for mass rate of flow M are kg/s, the units for area A are m^2, the units for pressure P are N/m^2, and the units for temperature T are kelvins (K).

Illustrative example 5 For subsonic flow of air through a restriction, the mass rate of flow is

$$M = \frac{1.05}{\sqrt{T}} A\sqrt{(P_1 - P_2)P_2} \tag{3.12}$$

where M = mass rate of flow, lb_m/s
T = inlet temperature, °R
A = area of restriction, ft^2
P_1 = inlet pressure, lb_f/ft^2
P_2 = outlet pressure, lb_f/ft^2

Determine the linearized approximation for the variation m when the inlet temperature is constant. As was the case for Eq. (3.10), any unit of length may be used in Eq. (3.12).

SOLUTION The mass rate of flow is a function of A, $P_1 - P_2$, and P_2. Thus

$$m = \left.\frac{\partial M}{\partial A}\right|_i a + \left.\frac{\partial M}{\partial (P_1 - P_2)}\right|_i (p_1 - p_2) + \left.\frac{\partial M}{\partial P_2}\right|_i p_2$$

Evaluating the partial derivatives yields

$$m = \left[\frac{a}{A_i} + \frac{p_1 - p_2}{2(P_1 - P_2)_i} + \frac{p_2}{2(P_2)_i}\right] M_i \tag{3.13}$$

The same result is obtained if P_1 and P_2 are regarded as the variables rather than $P_1 - P_2$ and P_2.

When using SI units, Eq. (3.12) becomes $M = 0.08A\sqrt{(P_1 - P_2)P_2/T}$. The units are kg, m, N, s, and K.

Geometric Interpretation of Error Introduced by a Linear Approximation

From the linear approximation for the area of a rectangle, it is possible to represent geometrically the error which is introduced. In Fig. 3.2 is shown a rectangle in which the reference length is L_i and the width W_i. The area of a rectangle is a function of the length L and width W, so that the variation in the area from its reference size is obtained as follows:

$$A = A(L, W)$$

$$a = \left.\frac{\partial A}{\partial L}\right|_i l + \left.\frac{\partial A}{\partial W}\right|_i w$$

The preceding partial derivatives are evaluated from the equation $A = LW$,

$$\left.\frac{\partial A}{\partial L}\right|_i = W_i \quad \text{and} \quad \left.\frac{\partial A}{\partial W}\right|_i = L_i$$

Thus the linearized expression for the area A is

$$A \approx A_i + a = A_i + W_i l + L_i w \tag{3.14}$$

Each term in the preceding expression is represented by an area in Fig. 3.2. The difference between this approximation and the actual area LW is the small shaded portion lw.

Illustrative example 6 Determine the linearized representation for Eq. (2.16), that is

$$F = (MD^2 + BD + K)X - Mg \tag{2.16}$$

SOLUTION Because F is a function of X, it follows that

$$f = \left.\frac{\partial F}{\partial X}\right|_i x$$

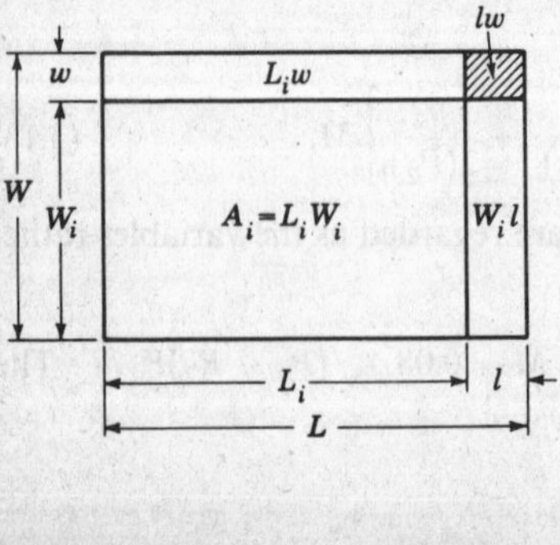

Figure 3.2 Geometric representation of error.

The operator D is not a function of X. Thus, the operator is regarded as a constant in evaluating the preceding partial derivative. That is,

$$\left.\frac{\partial F}{\partial X}\right|_i = MD^2 + BD + K$$

The resulting linearized equation is

$$f = (MD^2 + BD + K)x \tag{2.17}$$

This verifies the linearized form given by Eq. (2.17). As illustrated by this example, for equations which are already linear the substitution of lowercase letters for the capital-letter variable terms and dropping out the constant terms (for example, $-Mg$) yields directly the linear equation of operation about the reference point. Constant terms drop out because the partial derivative of a constant is zero.

3.2 LINEARIZATION OF OPERATING CURVES

In the preceding section, it was shown how equations which are nonlinear could be linearized. For many components encountered in control systems, the operating characteristics are given in the form of general operating curves rather than equations. For example, in Fig. 3.3 is shown a family of curves of constant values of Z (i.e., $Z = 15, 20$, and 25). For $X = 1000$ and $Z = 20$, the corresponding value of Y is 60. This point is indicated by A. The general functional relationship is

$$Y = Y(X, Z)$$

Linearization about a reference point of operation gives

$$y = \left.\frac{\partial Y}{\partial X}\right|_Z x + \left.\frac{\partial Y}{\partial Z}\right|_X z \tag{3.15}$$

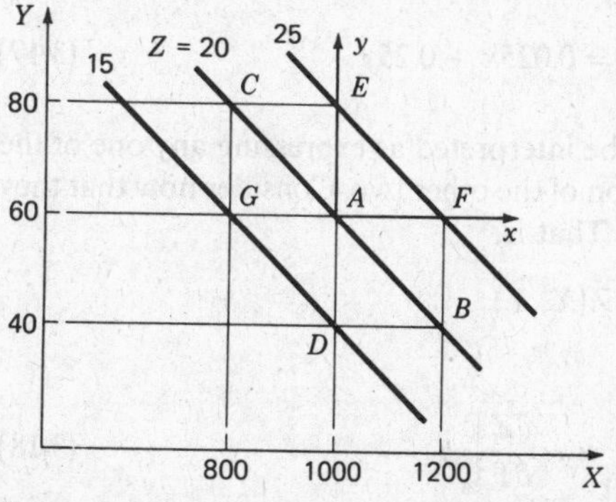

Figure 3.3 General operating curves.

The term $\partial Y/\partial X\,|_Z$ is obtained by dividing changes ΔY by corresponding changes ΔX in which Z is maintained constant at the reference value. For $Z_i = 20$, the value of Y at point B is 40 and the value at point C is 80. Similarly, the value of X at point B is 1200 and the value at point C is 800. Thus

$$\left.\frac{\partial Y}{\partial X}\right|_Z = \left.\frac{\Delta Y}{\Delta X}\right|_Z = \frac{Y_B - Y_C}{X_B - X_C} = \frac{40 - 80}{1200 - 800} = -\frac{40}{400} = -0.10$$

This partial derivative is the slope of the curve $Z_i = 20$ at the reference operating point.

The term $\partial Y/\partial Z\,|_X$ is obtained by dividing changes ΔY by corresponding changes ΔZ in which X is maintained constant at the reference value. For $X_i = 1000$, the value of Y at point D is 40 and the value of Z is 15. Similarly, at point E the value of Y is 80 and the value of Z is 25. Thus

$$\left.\frac{\partial Y}{\partial Z}\right|_X = \left.\frac{\Delta Y}{\Delta Z}\right|_X = \frac{Y_D - Y_E}{Z_D - Z_E} = \frac{40 - 80}{15 - 25} = \frac{-40}{-10} = 4$$

This partial derivative, which is obtained from a vertical (X_i = constant) extrapolation of the curves, determines the vertical spacing. That is,

$$\Delta Y = 4\,\Delta Z$$

As Z changes by 5 units, the vertical distance ΔY between lines of constant Z is $\Delta Y = 4(5) = 20$ units. Substitution of the preceding results into Eq. (3.15) yields

$$y = -0.1x + 4z \tag{3.16}$$

The origin of the (x, y) system is at point A, which is the reference point. Note that $X = X_i + x = 1000 + x$ and $Y = Y_i + y = 60 + y$.

At point B, $x = X - X_i = 1200 - 1000 = 200$ and $z = Z - Z_i = 20 - 20 = 0$. Thus, $y = -0.1(200) + 0 = -20$. The value of Y at point B is $Y = Y_i + y = 60 - 20 = 40$. At point E, $x = 1000 - 1000 = 0$ and $z = 25 - 20 = 5$. Thus, $y = 0 + 4(5) = 20$, and $Y = Y_i + y = 60 + 20 = 80$.

The preceding relationship may be solved for z. That is,

$$z = \frac{0.1x + y}{4} = 0.025x + 0.25y \tag{3.17}$$

The curves shown in Fig. 3.3 may be interpreted as expressing any one of the three variables (X, Y, or Z) as a function of the other two. Consider now that they represent Z as a function of X and Y. That is,

$$Z = Z(X, Y)$$

Linearization gives

$$z = \left.\frac{\partial Z}{\partial X}\right|_Y x + \left.\frac{\partial Z}{\partial Y}\right|_X y \tag{3.18}$$

The term $\partial Z/\partial X\,|_Y$ is obtained by dividing changes in Z by corresponding changes in X in which Y is maintained constant. For $Y_i = 60$, the value of Z at point F is 25 and the value of X is 1200. Similarly, at point G the value of Z is 15 and the value of X is 800. Thus

$$\left.\frac{\partial Z}{\partial X}\right|_Y = \left.\frac{\Delta Z}{\Delta X}\right|_Y = \frac{Z_F - Z_G}{X_F - X_G} = \frac{25-15}{1200-800} = 0.025$$

This partial derivative, which is obtained from a horizontal (Y_i = constant) extrapolation of the curves, determines the horizontal spacing. That is,

$$\Delta X = \frac{1}{0.025}\Delta Z = 40\,\Delta Z$$

As Z changes by 5 units, the horizontal spacing ΔX between lines of constant Z is $\Delta X = 40(5) = 200$ units. The term $\partial Z/\partial Y\,|_X$ is obtained by dividing changes in Z by corresponding changes in Y with X fixed. Thus

$$\left.\frac{\partial Z}{\partial Y}\right|_X = \left.\frac{\Delta Z}{\Delta Y}\right|_X = \frac{15-25}{40-80} = \frac{-10}{-40} = 0.25$$

Note that $\partial Z/\partial Y\,|_X = \frac{1}{4}$ is the reciprocal of $\partial Y/\partial Z\,|_X = 4$, which was previously evaluated. Substitution of the results for $\partial Z/\partial X\,|_Y$ and $\partial Z/\partial Y\,|_X$ into Eq. (3.18) verifies the result given by Eq. (3.17).

The functional relationship between X, Y, and Z represented in Fig. 3.3 may be expressed in the implicit form

$$G(X, Y, Z) = 0$$

From calculus, it is known that for an implicit function of n variables, the product of the n partial derivatives is $(-1)^n$. For this function of the three variables X, Y, and Z, this relationship is

$$\left.\frac{\partial X}{\partial Y}\right|_Z \left.\frac{\partial Y}{\partial Z}\right|_X \left.\frac{\partial Z}{\partial X}\right|_Y = (-1)^3 = -1 \tag{3.19}$$

Substitution of the values $\partial X/\partial Y\,|_Z = 1/(-0.1) = -10$, $\partial Y/\partial Z\,|_X = 4$, and $\partial Z/\partial X\,|_Y = 0.025$ verifies that $(-10)(4)(0.025) = -1$. In effect, if any two of the three quantities: horizontal spacing $\partial X/\partial Z\,|_Y$, vertical spacing $\partial Y/\partial Z\,|_X$, and slope $\partial Y/\partial X\,|_Z$ are known, then the third is known and may be determined in accordance with Eq. (3.19).

A typical family of operating curves for an engine is shown in Fig. 3.4. Usually such curves are determined experimentally, and it would be quite tedious and difficult to express them as equations. The linearized equation for the operation of the engine about some reference operating point is obtained as follows: From Fig. 3.4, it is seen that the speed N is a function of the rate of fuel flow Q and the engine torque T; thus

$$N = N(Q, T)$$

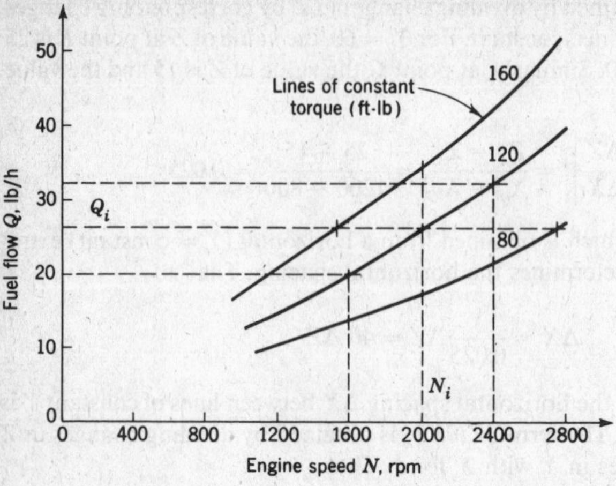

Figure 3.4 Characteristic curves for an engine.

Linearization gives

$$n = \left.\frac{\partial N}{\partial Q}\right|_i q + \left.\frac{\partial N}{\partial T}\right|_i t$$

The term $\partial N/\partial Q\,|_i$ is the change in speed per change in fuel flow with all other parameters held constant (in this case with T constant). This partial derivative is equal to the reciprocal of the slope of the line of constant torque evaluated at the reference point. That is,

$$\left.\frac{\partial N}{\partial Q}\right|_i = \frac{2400 - 1600}{32 - 20} = 66.7$$

The partial derivative $\partial N/\partial T\,|_i$ is the change in speed per change in torque with Q held constant. This is evaluated from a horizontal interpolation of the characteristic operating curves as follows:

$$\left.\frac{\partial N}{\partial T}\right|_i = \frac{2730 - 1530}{80 - 160} = -15$$

The minus sign indicates that for a constant Q the speed decreases as the torque increases. Thus, for operation in the vicinity of the point $N_i = 2000$, $Q_i = 26$, and $T_i = 120$, the linearized approximation for N is

$$N \approx N_i + n = 2000 + 66.7q - 15t$$

The main difference in working with characteristic operating curves for a component rather than equations is that the partial derivatives are evaluated from a physical interpretation of the curves rather than mathematically from the equation.

3.3 HYDRAULIC SYSTEMS

A schematic diagram of a hydraulic amplifier is shown in Fig. 3.5*a*. Such amplifiers are very rapid acting and are capable of producing very large forces. The position of the valve is designated by x, and the position of the large piston which moves the load is y. This type of valve is called a balanced valve because the pressure forces acting on it are all balanced so that it requires little force to change its position. When the valve is moved upward, the supply pressure admits oil to the upper side of the piston, and the fluid in the lower side of the piston is returned to the drain, where it is recirculated in the system through the pump. For the reverse process, the valve is moved downward so that the supply pressure is connected to the bottom side of the big piston. The upper side of this piston is connected to the upper drain to permit return flow to the pump.

When the mass of the load is negligible, the pressure drop across the valve remains constant. For this case the rate of flow to the piston is proportional to the area uncovered by the valve, which is seen to be proportional to the distance x. Thus,

$$q = Cx$$

where q is the rate of flow through the valve to the piston chamber. This rate of flow q into the piston chamber is equal to the rate of change of volume of the chamber, which is equal to the piston velocity Dy times the cross-sectional area A of the piston,

$$q = ADy$$

Equating the preceding expressions for q and solving for y gives

$$y = \frac{C}{AD}x = \frac{C}{A}\frac{1}{D}x \tag{3.20}$$

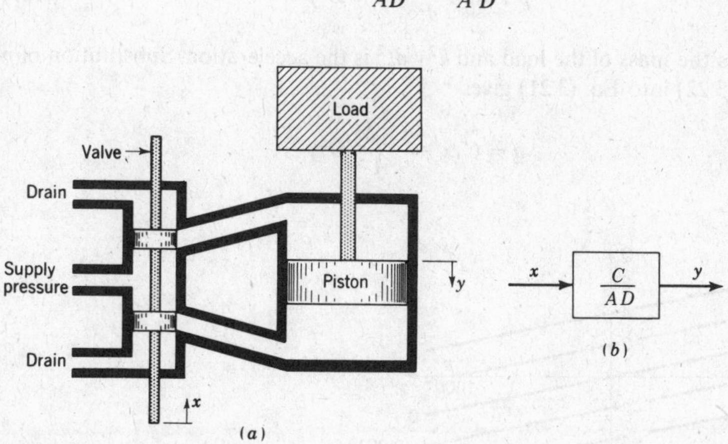

Figure 3.5 Hydraulic amplifier.

The $1/D$ term indicates that this hydraulic valve and piston combination in effect integrates hydraulically. That is, the position y is proportional to the integral of the position x. The block-diagram representation is shown in Fig. 3.5*b*.

The effect of the load M upon the operation of this hydraulic amplifier may be ascertained from the operating curves shown in Fig. 3.6. The rate of flow Q to the cylinder is a function of the valve position X and the pressure drop P across the power piston. That is,

$$Q = Q(X, P)$$

Linearization gives

$$q = \left.\frac{\partial Q}{\partial X}\right|_P x + \left.\frac{\partial Q}{\partial P}\right|_X p = C_1 x - C_2 p \tag{3.21}$$

where $C_1 = \partial Q/\partial X\,|_P$ and $C_2 = -\partial Q/\partial P\,|_X$. The term $\partial Q/\partial X\,|_P$ is obtained from a vertical interpolation of the curves in which P is maintained constant at the reference value. Because Q increases as X increases, $\partial Q/\partial X\,|_P$ is a positive constant. The term $\partial Q/\partial P\,|_X$ is the slope of the curve at the reference value of X. Because Q decreases as P increases (negative slope), the term $\partial Q/\partial P\,|_X$ is negative. The constant $C_2 = -\partial Q/\partial P\,|_X$ is a positive constant. In analyzing control systems, it is desirable that all constants be positive. This enables the control engineer to determine directly from the equations of operation and the resulting block diagrams whether the output increases or decreases when the input undergoes a certain change.

The force transmitted to the load by the power piston is equal to the product of the pressure drop across the piston and the cross-sectional area A of the piston. Thus,

$$pA = M\frac{d^2y}{dt^2} = MD^2y \tag{3.22}$$

where M is the mass of the load and d^2y/dt^2 is the acceleration. Substitution of p from Eq. (3.22) into Eq. (3.21) gives

$$q = C_1 x - \frac{C_2 M}{A} D^2 y$$

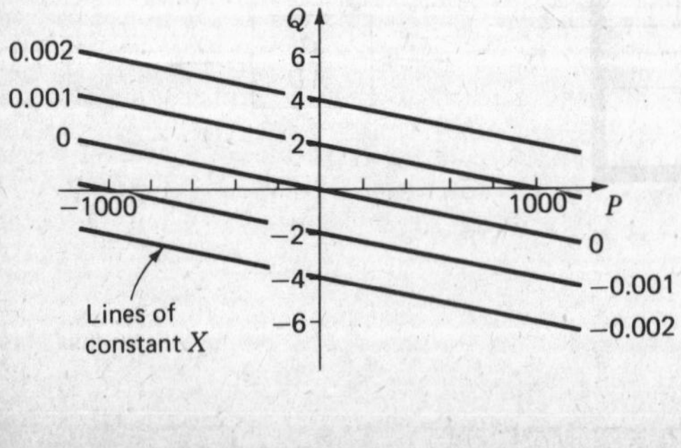

Figure 3.6 Operating curves for a hydraulic amplifier.

The rate of flow q into the cylinder is equal to the rate of change of volume, which is the cross-sectional area A times the velocity dy/dt. Thus

$$q = A\frac{dy}{dt} = ADy$$

Equating the preceding expressions for q and solving for the output position y as a function of the input position x gives

$$y = \frac{(C_1/A)x}{D(1 + \tau D)} \tag{3.23}$$

where $\tau = C_2 M/A^2$. Note that when the load is neglected ($M = 0$), then $\tau = C_2 M/A^2 = 0$ and Eq. (3.23) reduces to Eq. (3.20). Usually C_2 is quite small, so that $\tau \approx 0$. In general the approximation given by Eq. (3.20) is quite good.

Hydraulic Servomotor

A hydraulic servomotor is shown in Fig. 3.7. A linkage called a *walking beam* connects the input position x, the valve position e, and the piston position y. The center line of the lever when the servomotor is in its reference position is indicated in Fig. 3.7. The variations in x, e, and y from their reference positions are also indicated. When e is zero, the valve is "line on line" and no flow can go to or from the big piston.

The operation of this servomotor may be visualized as follows: When the input x is changed from the reference position, the walking beam first pivots about the connection at y because the large forces acting on the piston hold it in place

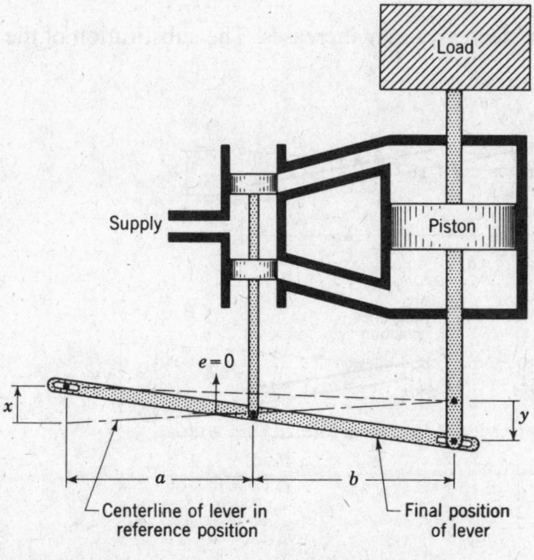

Figure 3.7 Hydraulic servomotor.

temporarily. This position of the walking beam is shown by the dashed line in Fig. 3.7. Because of the corresponding movement of e, the valve now admits fluid to the big piston to move it in the direction which makes e zero. The final position of the walking beam, in which e is again zero and the piston has moved a distance y, is indicated in Fig. 3.7. For steady-state operation ($e = 0$), the relationship between the input x and the output y is

$$\frac{y}{b} = \frac{x}{a} \qquad \text{or} \qquad y = \frac{b}{a}x$$

The overall block diagram which describes the dynamic as well as the steady-state operation of this servomotor is obtained as follows: In Fig. 3.8a is shown the walking-beam linkage. For small variations about the reference position,

$$e = \frac{\partial E}{\partial X}\bigg|_i x + \frac{\partial E}{\partial Y}\bigg|_i y \tag{3.24}$$

The value of $\partial E/\partial X\,|_i$ is obtained by finding the ratio of the change in E for a change in X with all other parameters held constant at the reference condition. Figure 3.8b illustrates the linkage with Y fixed in the reference position. From similar triangles,

$$\frac{\partial E}{\partial X}\bigg|_i = \lim_{\substack{\Delta E \to 0 \\ \Delta X \to 0}} \frac{\Delta E}{\Delta X} = \frac{b}{a+b}$$

Similarly, from Fig. 3.8c, in which X is fixed in the reference position,

$$\frac{\partial E}{\partial Y}\bigg|_i = \lim_{\substack{\Delta E \to 0 \\ \Delta Y \to 0}} \frac{\Delta E}{\Delta Y} = \frac{-a}{a+b}$$

The minus sign arises because e decreases as y increases. The substitution of the

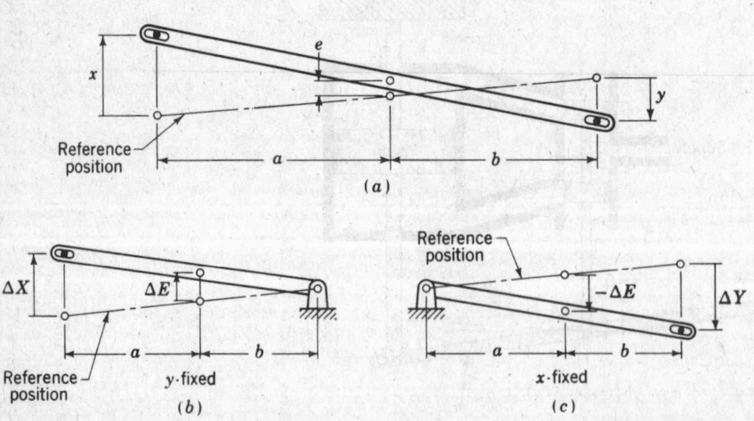

Figure 3.8 Walking-beam linkage.

preceding results into Eq. (3.24) yields the following expression for the walking-beam linkage:

$$e = \frac{b}{a+b}x - \frac{a}{a+b}y \tag{3.25}$$

This equation shows that the walking-beam linkage is actually a comparator or summing point. The preceding result could have been obtained directly by a closer examination of Fig. 3.8*a*. It is apparent that the motion of e is the sum of the contribution due to changing x with y fixed, that is, $[b/(a+b)]x$, and that due to changing y with x fixed, that is, $[-a/(a+b)]y$.

For the case in which $a = b$,

$$e = \frac{x-y}{2} \tag{3.26}$$

The block-diagram representation for Eq. (3.26) is shown in Fig. 3.9*a*.

The equation for the valve-and-piston combination is given by Eq. (3.20), in which x is replaced by e. Thus

$$y = \frac{C}{AD}e \tag{3.27}$$

The block-diagram representation for the preceding expression is shown in Fig. 3.9*b*. Combining Fig. 3.9*a* and *b* yields the overall block diagram for the servomotor as shown in Fig. 3.9*c*.

The overall relationship between the input x and the output y is obtained as follows from the block diagram of Fig. 3.9*c*:

$$(x-y)\frac{C}{2AD} = y$$

or

$$(1+\tau D)y = x \tag{3.28}$$

where

$$\tau = \frac{2A}{C}$$

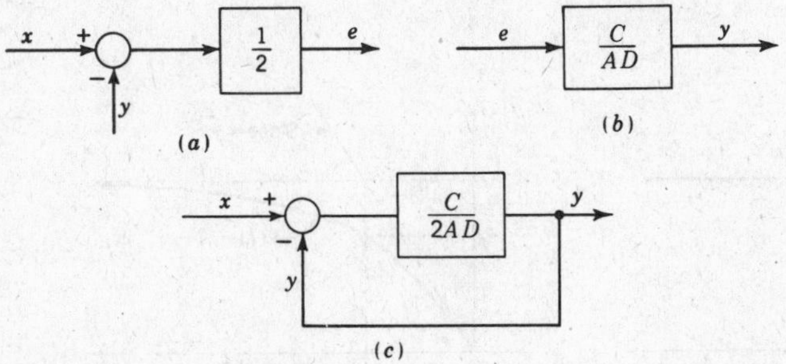

Figure 3.9 (*a*) Block diagram for walking-beam linkage; (*b*) block diagram for valve and piston; (*c*) block diagram for servomotor.

Equation (3.28) is the differential equation relating x and y. For steady-state operation, both x and y are constant. The quantity $Dy = dy/dt$ is zero when y is constant, and thus for steady-state operation Eq. (3.28) becomes

$$y = x$$

To determine the transient response of y for a given change in x, it is necessary to solve Eq. (3.28), which is a first-order linear differential equation with constant coefficients. If, at some arbitrary time $t = 0$, the input x changes instantaneously from its reference position in which $x = 0$ to a new or final position at which $x = x_f$, then a step change, as is illustrated graphically in Fig. 3.10*a*, has occurred.

Dividing through Eq. (3.28) by τ yields the form given by Eq. (2.2). That is,

$$\left(D + \frac{1}{\tau}\right)y(t) = \frac{1}{\tau}x_f$$

The solution of this differential equation is given by Eq. (2.3), in which $a = 1/\tau$ and $f(t) = (1/\tau)x_f$. Thus,

$$y(t) = e^{-t/\tau}\left[\int \frac{x_f}{\tau} e^{t/\tau}\, dt + C\right] = e^{-t/\tau}[x_f e^{t/\tau} + C]$$

$$= x_f + Ce^{-t/\tau}$$

Evaluation at $t = 0$, in which case $y(0) = 0$, shows that $C = -x_f$. The resulting solution of this differential equation is

$$y(t) = (1 - e^{-t/\tau})x_f \qquad (3.29)$$

A graph of the response $y(t)$ is shown in Fig. 3.10*b*. A characteristic feature of such an exponential response curve is that when $t = \tau$, then $y(t)$ has undergone 63.2 percent of its total change. This is proved by letting $t = \tau$ in Eq. (3.29); thus

$$y(\tau) = (1 - e^{-1})x_f = (1 - 0.368)x_f = 0.632x_f$$

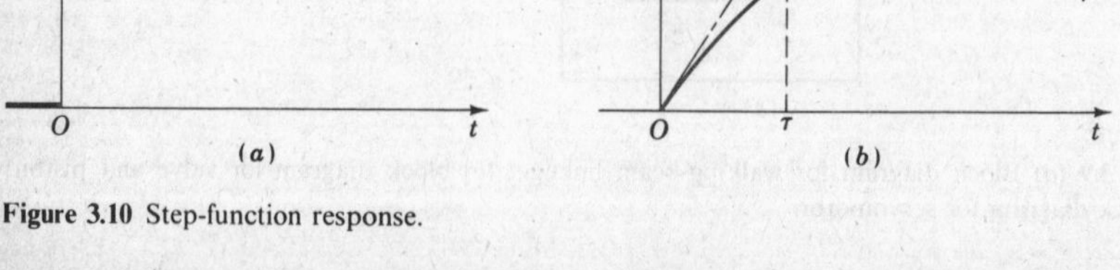

Figure 3.10 Step-function response.

Another unique feature of such an exponential response is that the tangent to the curve at $t = 0$ intersects the final value at time $t = \tau$. This is proved as follows:

$$\left.\frac{dy}{dt}\right|_{t=0} = \left.\frac{1}{\tau} e^{-t/\tau} x_f\right|_{t=0} = \frac{x_f}{\tau}$$

Thus, as shown in Fig. 3.10*b*, the slope of the tangent line is such that it intersects the final value $y(t)_f = x_f$ at $t = \tau$. The term τ is called the time constant and is a measure of the speed of response. When τ is small, the system approaches its new operating condition very fast, and when τ is large, more time is required for the change to occur.

3.4 PNEUMATIC SYSTEMS

A flapper valve, as shown in Fig. 3.11*a*, is one in which small changes in the position X of the flapper cause large variations in the controlled pressure P_2 in the chamber. When the flapper is closed off, the pressure P_2 in the chamber is equal to the supply pressure P_1. If the flapper is opened wide, the chamber pressure approaches the ambient pressure P_a. If a spring-loaded bellows which is free to expand as the chamber pressure changes is attached, this becomes a position control device as well as a pressure controller. An equivalent system which uses a piston rather than a bellows is shown in Fig. 3.11*b*.

Although flapper valves have numerous applications in hydraulic systems, they are more extensively used in pneumatic controls. A major reason for this is that spool valves do not lend themselves to pneumatic applications because of the excessive leakage of air that is the result of the very low viscosity of air. When the flapper valves of Fig. 3.11 are supplied with air, pneumatic amplifiers result.

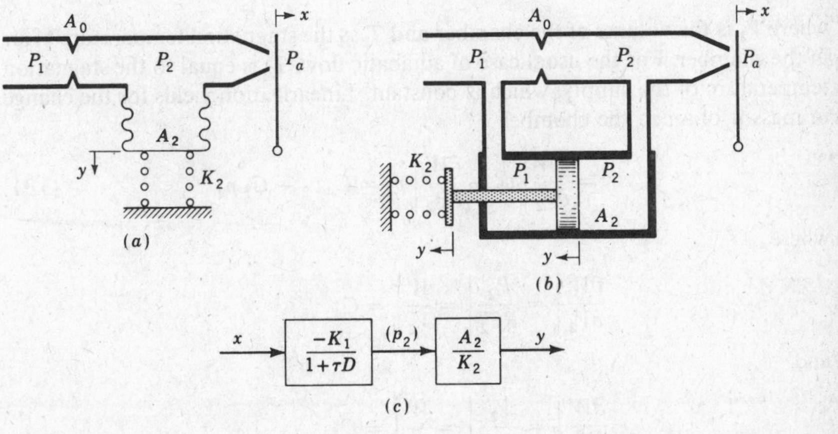

Figure 3.11 Pneumatic amplifier.

The procedure used to obtain the equation of operation for a pneumatic amplifier is similar to that used for a hydraulic amplifier, with the exception that because of compressibility effects, the mass rate of flow must be considered rather than the volume rate. For a constant supply pressure P_1 and fixed inlet orifice, the mass rate of flow into the chamber M_{in} is a function of the chamber pressure P_2 only. Linearization gives

$$m_{\text{in}} = \left.\frac{\partial M_{\text{in}}}{\partial P_2}\right|_i p_2 = -C_1 p_2$$

The minus sign indicates that as p_2 increases, m_{in} decreases. For a constant ambient pressure P_a, the mass rate of flow out from the chamber M_o is a function of X and P_2. Thus,

$$m_o = \left.\frac{\partial M_o}{\partial X}\right|_i x + \left.\frac{\partial M_o}{\partial P_2}\right|_i p_2 = C_2 x + C_3 p_2$$

When the pressure ratio across an orifice is less than 0.528, the flow is sonic, and when it is greater than 0.528, the flow is subsonic. For sonic flow the mass rate of flow is given by Eq. (3.10), and for subsonic flow it is given by Eq. (3.12).

The change in mass w of air in the chamber is the integral of $m_{\text{in}} - m_o$. That is,

$$w = \frac{m_{\text{in}} - m_o}{D} = -\frac{C_1 p_2 - (C_2 x + C_3 p_2)}{D}$$

Multiplying through by D shows that

$$-C_1 p_2 - C_2 x - C_3 p_2 = Dw \tag{3.30}$$

From the equation of state, the total mass W of air in the chamber is

$$W = \frac{P_2 V_2}{RT_2}$$

where V_2 is the volume of the chamber and T_2 is the stagnation temperature of air in the chamber. For the usual case of adiabatic flow, T_2 is equal to the stagnation temperature of the supply, which is constant. Linearization yields for the change in mass w of air in the chamber

$$w = \left.\frac{\partial W}{\partial V_2}\right|_i v_2 + \left.\frac{\partial W}{\partial P_2}\right|_i p_2 = C_4 v_2 + C_5 p_2 \tag{3.31}$$

where

$$\left.\frac{\partial W}{\partial V_2}\right|_i = \left.\frac{P_2}{RT_2}\right|_i = \left.\frac{W}{V_2}\right|_i = C_4$$

and

$$\left.\frac{\partial W}{\partial P_2}\right|_i = \left.\frac{V_2}{RT_2}\right|_i = \left.\frac{W}{P_2}\right|_i = C_5$$

The term $C_4 v_2$ represents the change in mass required to account for the change in volume, and the term $C_5 p_2$ represents the change in mass required to account for the change in pressure. This is the compressibility effect. The change in volume of the chamber is equal to the area A_2 times the change in position

$$v_2 = A_2 y$$

From Fig. 3.11*a*, the summation of forces acting on the bellows is

$$P_2 A_2 = K_2 Y$$

Similarly, from Fig. 3.11*b*, the summation of forces acting on the piston is

$$P_2 A_2 - P_1 A_1 = K_2 Y$$

Because $P_1 A_1$ is constant, linearization of either of the preceding gives the same result. That is,

$$y = \frac{A_2}{K_2} p_2$$

Substituting w from Eq. (3.31) into Eq. (3.30), then using the preceding expressions to eliminate v_2 and y yields the result

$$p_2 = -\frac{K_1}{1 + \tau D} x \tag{3.32}$$

where $K_1 = C_2/(C_1 + C_3)$ and $\tau = (C_5 + A_2^2 C_4/K_2)/(C_1 + C_3)$. The minus sign indicates that as x increases, p_2 decreases. Because $y = (A_2/K_2)p_2$, it follows that

$$y = \frac{A_2}{K_2} \frac{(-K_1)}{1 + \tau D} x \tag{3.33}$$

The block-diagram representation is shown in Fig. 3.11*c*. For most flapper valves the time constant τ may generally be regarded as negligible.

A nondimensional family of curves (Fig. I.1) for determining the equilibrium chamber pressure P_2 is developed in Appendix I. Lines of constant area ratio A_2/A_1 are plotted, where A_1 is the area of the first orifice times its coefficient of discharge and A_2 is the area of the second orifice times its coefficient of discharge. The abscissa is the overall pressure ratio P_1/P_3, where P_1 is the supply pressure and P_3 is the discharge pressure, which is usually the ambient pressure P_a. The ordinate P_2/P_1 is the ratio of the chamber pressure to the supply pressure. If the area ratio A_2/A_1 and the overall pressure ratio P_1/P_3 are known, then the ratio P_2/P_1 may be determined. The desired chamber pressure is equal to this ratio (P_2/P_1) times the supply pressure P_1. A typical plot of P_2 versus X is shown in Fig. 3.12. Note that absolute pressure is used for pneumatic amplifiers, whereas gage pressure is used for hydraulic amplifiers.

For steady-state operation, the right side of Eq. (3.30) vanishes. Thus

$$p_2 = -\frac{C_2}{C_1 + C_3} x = -K_1 x \tag{3.34}$$

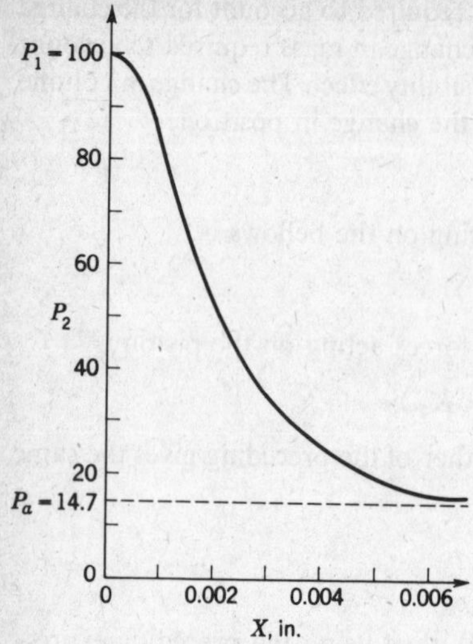

Figure 3.12 Equilibrium curve of P_2 versus X for a pneumatic amplifier.

The constant $(-K_1) = p_2/x$ is the slope of Fig. 3.12 at the reference point of operation. As shown in Fig. 3.12, this slope remains quite constant over a considerable portion of the operating range. Note that it is not necessary to evaluate C_1, C_2, and C_3 individually in order to attain K_1.

3.5 DC MOTORS

A major reason for the use of dc machines in electromechanical control systems is the ease with which speed can be controlled. The polarity of the applied voltage determines the direction of rotation. Also, dc machines are capable of providing large power amplifications.

The field and armature windings of dc motors may be shunt-connected, series-connected, compounded, or separately excited. The motors used in control systems are generally separately excited. There are two types of separate excitation, field control with fixed armature current and armature control with fixed field.

Field Control

A separately excited motor in which the armature current I_a is maintained constant is shown in Fig. 3.13*a*. The constant current I_a may be supplied by a dc generator or from an ac line. The latter method requires the use of transformers and rectifiers to obtain the proper rectification. The voltage E_f applied to the field is obtained from the output of an amplifier in low-power application or from a dc

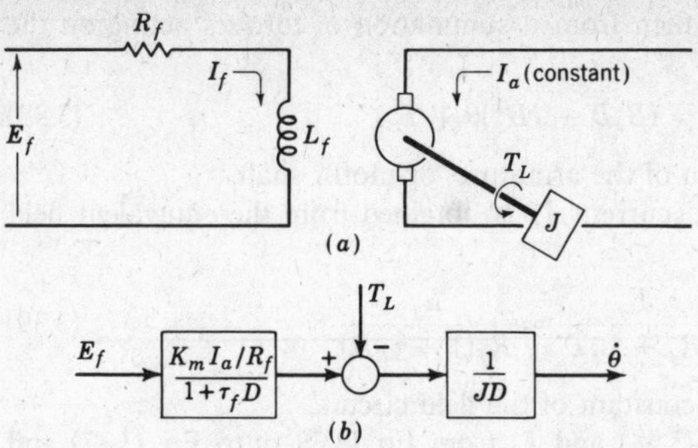

Figure 3.13 Field-controlled dc motor.

generator when greater power is needed. In the field circuit, the resistance of the windings is R_f, and the inductance is designated by L_f. The torque T developed by a motor is proportional to the product of the armature current I_a and the magnetic flux ϕ of the field.

$$T = K_1 \phi I_a \tag{3.35}$$

where K_1 is a constant for any motor and depends upon the total number of armature conductors, the number of field poles, etc.

A typical curve of flux ϕ versus field current I_f is shown in Fig. 3.14. When the field current I_f becomes great enough to cause the iron to saturate, the flux ϕ no longer increases linearly with the current. Motors used in control systems usually operate over the linear portion of this curve, in which case

$$\phi = K_2 I_f \tag{3.36}$$

where K_2 is the slope of the linear portion of the curve as shown in Fig. 3.14. The substitution of the preceding result into Eq. (3.35) yields

$$T = K_1 K_2 I_a I_f = K_m I_a I_f \tag{3.37}$$

where $K_m = K_1 K_2$.

If the moment of inertia of the armature is J, the coefficient of viscous friction

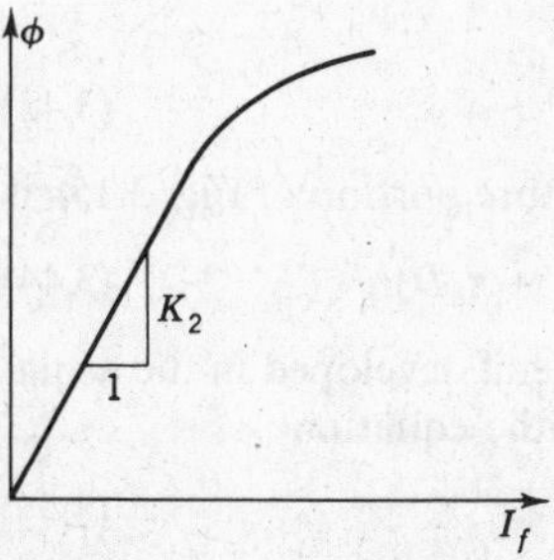

Figure 3.14 Plot of flux versus field current.

B_v, and the load torque T_L, then from a summation of torques acting on the armature it follows that

$$T = (B_v D + JD^2)\theta + T_L \tag{3.38}$$

where θ is the angular position of the armature, or motor shaft.

The equation for the field current I_f is obtained from the equivalent field circuit of Fig. 3.13*a*.

$$I_f = \frac{E_f}{R_f + L_f D} = \frac{E_f}{R_f(1 + \tau_f D)} \tag{3.39}$$

where $\tau_f = L_f / R_f$ is the time constant of the field circuit.

Substituting T from Eq. (3.38) and I_f from Eq. (3.39) into Eq. (3.37) and solving for θ gives

$$\theta = \frac{1}{D(B_v + JD)}\left[\frac{(K_m I_a / R_f)E_f}{1 + \tau_f D} - T_L\right] \tag{3.40}$$

Multiplication of the preceding expression by D gives the angular velocity $\dot{\theta} = D\theta$,

$$\dot{\theta} = \frac{1}{B_v + JD}\left[\frac{(K_m I_a / R_f)E_f}{1 + \tau_f D} - T_L\right] \tag{3.41}$$

Generally, the damping B_v is negligible, so that the block-diagram representation for the speed of this field-controlled dc motor is as shown in Fig. 3.13*b*.

Armature Control

A dc motor with armature control is one in which the speed is controlled by the armature voltage E_a. An armature-controlled motor in which the field current I_f is kept constant is shown in Fig. 3.15*a*. The armature voltage E_a is usually supplied by a generator, which in turn may be supplied by an amplifier. The voltage E_c is the counter emf induced by the rotation of the armature windings in the magnetic field. The counter emf is proportional to the product of the armature speed $\dot{\theta}$ and the field strength ϕ. That is,

$$E_c = K_3 \phi \dot{\theta} \tag{3.42}$$

where K_3 is a constant for any particular motor. The substitution of ϕ from Eq. (3.36) into the preceding gives

$$E_c = K_2 K_3 I_f \dot{\theta} = K_c I_f \dot{\theta} \tag{3.43}$$

where $K_c = K_2 K_3$. The circuit equation for the armature portion of Fig. 3.15*a* is

$$E_a - K_c I_f \dot{\theta} = R_a I_a + L_a D I_a = R_a(1 + \tau_a D)I_a \tag{3.44}$$

where $\tau_a = L_a / R_a$ and the term $K_c I_f \dot{\theta}$ is the counter emf developed in the armature. The torque developed by the motor is given by the equation

$$T = K_m I_f I_a \tag{3.45}$$

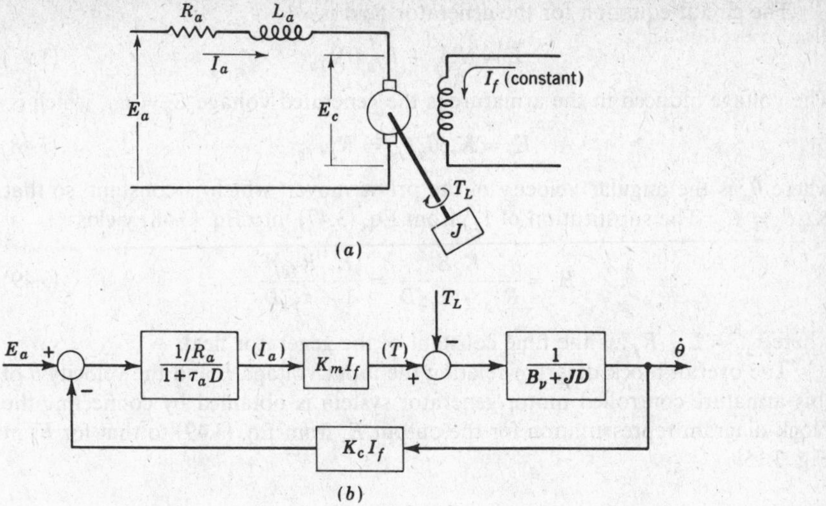

Figure 3.15 Armature-controlled dc motor.

and the torque balance for the output shaft is

$$T = (B_v D + JD^2)\theta + T_L \tag{3.46}$$

The block-diagram representation for this armature-controlled motor is obtained by combining the block-diagram representations for Eqs. (3.44), (3.45), and (3.46) as shown in Fig. 3.15*b*. The counter emf is responsible for the feedback.

A complete generator and armature-controlled motor combination is shown in Fig. 3.16. This is in effect a Ward Leonard system, or motor-generator set. The voltage E supplied to the generator may be quite small, as in the case of that coming from an amplifier. The resistance of the field of the generator is R_{fg}, and the inductance is L_{fg}. The armature of the generator is driven at a constant speed by a prime mover. The output voltage of the generator, E_g, goes directly to the armature of the motor, so that $E_g = E_a$.

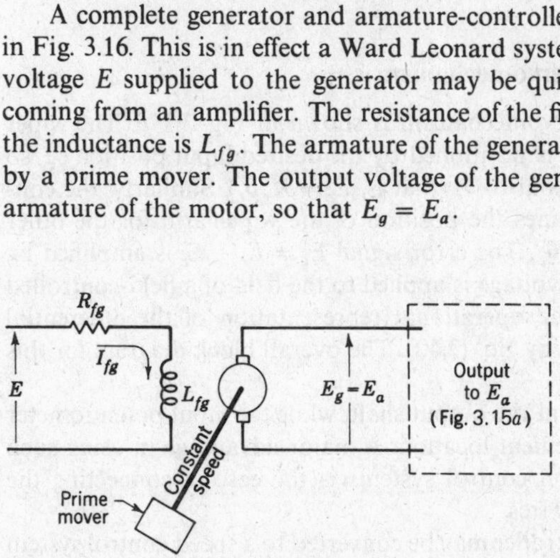

Figure 3.16 Complete generator and armature-controlled motor combination.

The circuit equation for the generator field is

$$E = (R_{fg} + L_{fg}D)I_{fg} \tag{3.47}$$

The voltage induced in the armature is the generated voltage $E_g = E_a$, which is

$$E_a = K_{cg}\dot{\theta}_g I_{fg} = K_c I_{fg} \tag{3.48}$$

where $\dot{\theta}_g$ is the angular velocity of the prime mover, which is constant, so that $K_{cg}\dot{\theta}_g = K_c$. The substitution of I_{fg} from Eq. (3.47) into Eq. (3.48) yields

$$E_a = \frac{K_c E}{R_{fg} + L_{fg}D} = \frac{(K_c/R_{fg})E}{1 + \tau_{fg}D} \tag{3.49}$$

where $\tau_{fg} = L_{fg}/R_{fg}$ is the time constant of the generator field.

The overall block diagram relating the input voltage E and the velocity $\dot{\theta}$ of this armature-controlled motor-generator system is obtained by connecting the block-diagram representation for the output E_a from Eq. (3.49) to that for E_a in Fig. 3.15*b*.

DC Tachometer

A dc tachometer is a generator in which the magnetic flux is supplied by a permanent magnet. Because the flux is maintained constant, the equation of operation for a tachometer is obtained from Eq. (3.42) as follows:

$$E_c = E_g = K_3 \phi \dot{\theta} = K_g \dot{\theta} \tag{3.50}$$

where $K_g = K_3 \phi$ is a constant and E_g is the generated voltage.

Thus a tachometer is seen to supply a voltage E_g which is proportional to the speed at which it is driven.

Remote-Control Positional Servomechanism

A remote-control positional servomechanism is shown in Fig. 3.17*a*. The wiper arm of the input potentiometer is positioned by the desired input position θ_r, so that the voltage E_r is proportional to θ_r (that is, $E_r = K_r \theta_r$). Similarly, the controlled shaft position θ_c determines the position of the wiper arm for the other potentiometer, so that $E_c = K_c \theta_c$. The error signal $E_e = E_r - E_c$ is amplified by the amplifier, and the resultant voltage is applied to the field of a field-controlled motor, so that $E_f = K_1 E_e$. The operational representation of the differential equation for the motor is given by Eq. (3.40). The overall block diagram for this system is shown in Fig. 3.17*b*.

The motor must be located at the output shaft, while the input potentiometer is usually situated in any convenient location. A major advantage in using such electrical equipment for position control systems is the ease of connecting the input and output by means of wires.

The preceding position controller may be converted to a speed control system

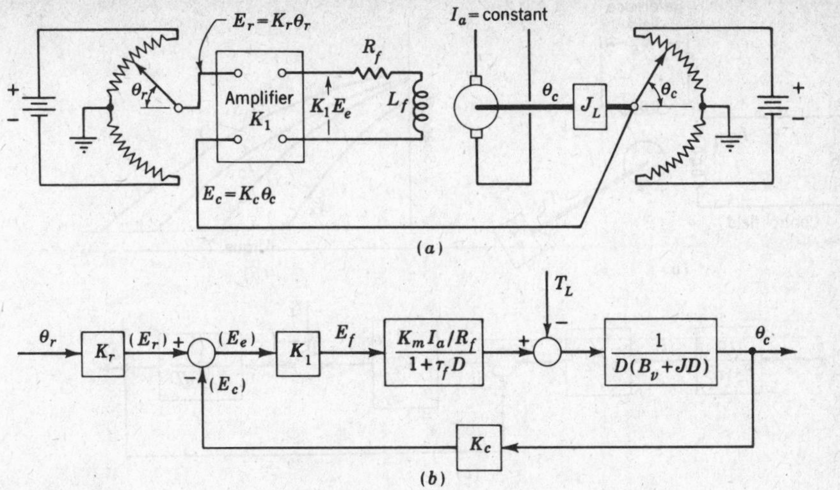

Figure 3.17 Remote-control positional servomechanism.

by connecting the output shaft to a tachometer rather than to a potentiometer. In this case, the voltage signal E_c coming from the tachometer is proportional to the speed $\dot{\theta}_c$ (that is, $E_c = K_c\dot{\theta}_c$). Similarly, each wiper position of the input potentiometer corresponds to a desired speed setting $\dot{\theta}_r$ rather than position θ_r, so that the reference voltage is $E_r = K_r\dot{\theta}_r$.

3.6 AC MOTORS

An ac two-phase motor is used for simple low-power applications. One of the phases is supplied with a fixed ac voltage which acts as the reference voltage. The other phase is connected to the controlled voltage. A schematic representation of a two-phase motor is shown in Fig. 3.18*a*. Because the reference voltage E_R is constant, the speed depends upon the control voltage E. The direction of rotation is reversed by changing the polarity of the control voltage.

As is shown in Fig. 3.18*a* the reference and control windings are displaced by 90° in the stator of the motor. Thus, although the voltage applied to each winding has the same frequency, there is a 90° phase shift of one with respect to the other.

Typical performance curves relating the developed motor torque T and the angular velocity $\dot{\theta}$ for constant values of control current I are shown in Fig. 3.18*b*. The equation describing the operation of a two-phase motor about some equilibrium point of operation is derived as follows: From Fig. 3.18*b* it is to be noticed that the speed is a function of T and I:

$$\dot{\theta} = F(T, I)$$

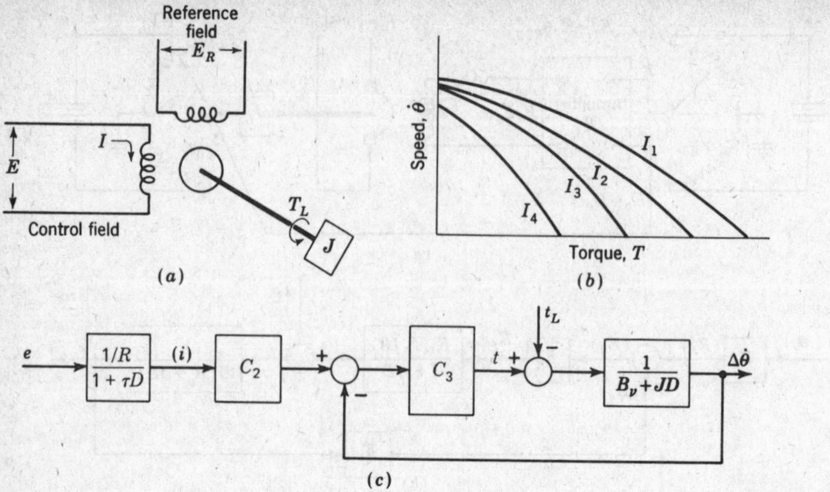

Figure 3.18 (*a*) Two-phase ac motor; (*b*) typical performance curves; (*c*) block-diagram representation.

Linearization about the reference point of operation gives

$$\Delta\dot\theta = \frac{\partial\dot\theta}{\partial T}\bigg|_I t + \frac{\partial\dot\theta}{\partial I}\bigg|_T i = -C_1 t + C_2 i \tag{3.51}$$

where $\Delta\dot\theta$ is the change in speed from the reference value, $C_1 = -\partial\dot\theta/\partial T\,|_I$ and $C_2 = \partial\dot\theta/\partial I\,|_T$. The term $\partial\dot\theta/\partial T\,|_I$ is the slope of the operating curves at the reference operating condition, which is negative. The minus sign converts C_1 to a positive constant. For a given torque, the speed increases as the current increases, so that $C_2 = \partial\dot\theta/\partial I\,|_T$ is positive. Solving Eq. (3.51) for t gives

$$t = \frac{1}{C_1}[C_2 i - \Delta\dot\theta] = C_3(C_2 i - \Delta\dot\theta) \tag{3.52}$$

where $C_3 = 1/C_1 = -\partial T/\partial\dot\theta\,|_I$. The torque balance for the armature is

$$T - T_L = (B_v + JD)\dot\theta$$

For small departures,

$$t - t_L = (B_v + JD)\,\Delta\dot\theta \tag{3.53}$$

The circuit operation for the control windings is

$$E = (R + LD)I = R(1 + \tau D)I$$

where $\tau = L/R$. For small departures, the preceding becomes

$$e = R(1 + \tau D)i \tag{3.54}$$

The block-diagram representation for this two-phase ac motor is obtained from Eqs. (3.52), (3.53), and (3.54) as shown in Fig. 3.18*c*.

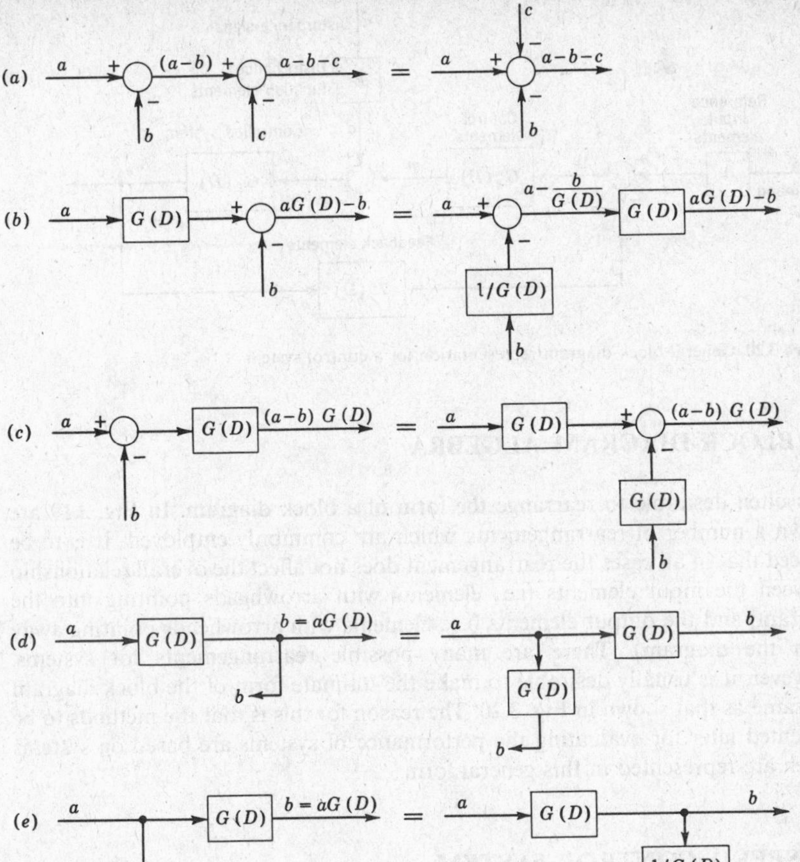

Figure 3.19 Equivalent block diagrams. (*a*) Combining interconnected summing points; (*b*) moving a summing point behind an element; (*c*) moving a summing point ahead of an element; (*d*) moving a take-off point behind an element; (*e*) moving a take-off point ahead of an element; (*f*) eliminating a minor feedback loop.

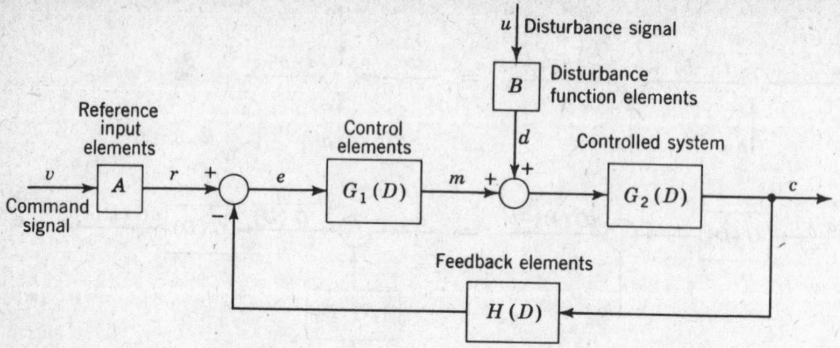

Figure 3.20 General block-diagram representation for a control system.

3.7 BLOCK-DIAGRAM ALGEBRA

It is often desirable to rearrange the form of a block diagram. In Fig. 3.19 are shown a number of rearrangements which are commonly employed. It is to be noticed that in all cases the rearrangement does not affect the overall relationship between the input elements (i.e., elements with arrowheads pointing into the diagram) and the output elements (i.e., elements with arrowheads pointing away from the diagram). There are many possible rearrangements for systems. However, it is usually desirable to make the ultimate form of the block diagram the same as that shown in Fig. 3.20. The reason for this is that the methods to be presented later for evaluating the performance of systems are based on systems which are represented in this general form.

3.8 SPEED CONTROL SYSTEM

Figure 3.21 shows a typical speed control system for gas turbines, steam turbines, or diesel engines. The position of the throttle lever sets the desired speed of the engine. The speed control is drawn in some reference operating position so that the values of all the lowercase parameters are zero. The positive direction of motion of these parameters is indicated by the arrowhead on each.

The center of mass of the flyweights is at a distance $R = R_i + r$ from the center of rotation. The flyweights are geared directly to the output shaft, so that the speed ω of the flyweights is proportional to the output speed. A lever which is pivoted as indicated in Fig. 3.21 transmits the centrifugal force from the flyweights to the bottom of the lower spring seat. The pivot and lever rotate with the flyweights as a unit. If the speed of the engine should drop below its reference value, then the centrifugal force of the flyweights decreases, thus decreasing the force exerted on the bottom of the spring. This causes x to move downward, which in turn moves e downward. Fluid then flows to the bottom of the big piston to increase y and thus

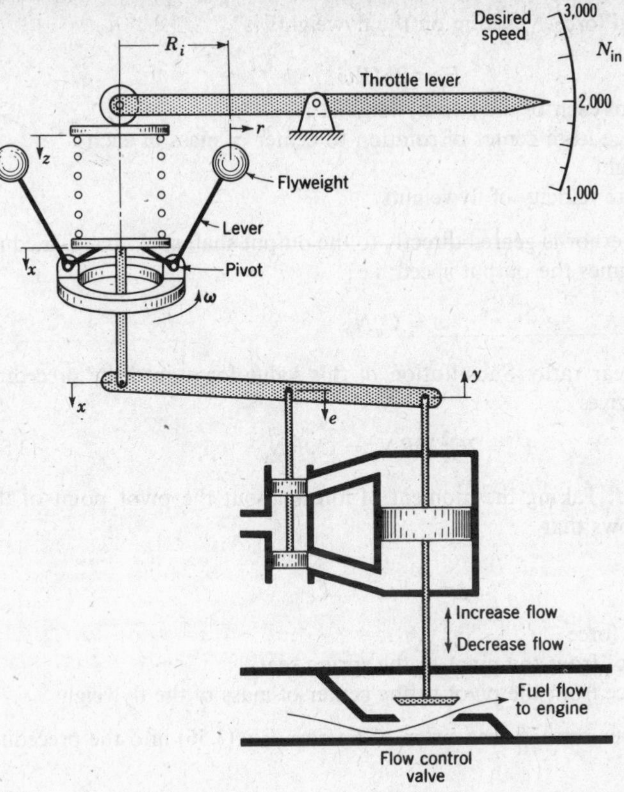

Figure 3.21 Speed control system.

open wider the flow control valve. When more fuel is supplied, the speed of the engine will increase until equilibrium is again reached. For steam turbines, the flow control valve controls the flow of steam rather than fuel as is the case with gas turbines and diesels.

Suppose that the throttle lever is moved to a higher speed setting, which in turn causes z to move downward. This in turn causes x to move downward. As just discussed, moving x downward opens the fuel flow valve, which increases the speed.

The overall block-diagram representation for this system is obtained as follows: The position of the top of the spring is a function of the desired speed only. Thus, the variation of the top of the spring z from its reference position is

$$z = C_2 n_{in} \tag{3.55}$$

where $n_{in} = N_{in} - N_i$ is the change in desired speed and $C_2 = \partial Z/\partial N_{in}|_i$ is the change in position Z per change in desired speed N_{in}.

The centrifugal force F_c acting on the flyweights is

$$F_c = 2MR\omega^2$$

where M = mass of each of the two flyweights
R = distance from center of rotation to center of mass of each flyweight
ω = angular velocity of flyweights

Usually, a governor is geared directly to the output shaft such that ω is equal to the gear ratio times the output speed; i.e.,

$$\omega = C_g N_o$$

where C_g is the gear ratio. Substitution of this value for ω into the preceding expression for F_c gives

$$F_c = 2C_g^2 MRN_o^2 = C_f RN_o^2 \tag{3.56}$$

where $C_f = 2C_g^2 M$. Taking the moment of forces about the pivot point of the flyweight lever shows that

$$F_s = \frac{b}{a} F_c = C_r F_c$$

where F_s = spring force
a = distance from the pivot to the spring seat
b = distance from the pivot to the center of mass of the flyweight

$C_r = b/a$ is the lever ratio. Substitution of F_c from Eq. (3.56) into the preceding expression gives

$$F_s = C_f C_r RN_o^2 \tag{3.57}$$

The two independent variables are R and N_o; linearization gives

$$f_s = C_3 r + C_4 n_o \tag{3.58}$$

where $$C_3 = \left.\frac{\partial F_s}{\partial R}\right|_i = C_f C_r N_i^2$$

and $$C_4 = \left.\frac{\partial F_s}{\partial N_o}\right|_i = 2C_f C_r R_i N_i$$

The compression of the spring from its reference length is $z - x$. Thus, the variation in force exerted by the spring is

$$f_s = K_s(z - x) \tag{3.59}$$

where K_s is the spring constant. Setting Eqs. (3.58) and (3.59) equal,

$$K_s(z - x) = C_3 r + C_4 n_o$$

The geometry of Fig. 3.21 shows that the motions of r and x are related by a lever, so that $r = -C_r x$. The reason for the minus sign is that as r increases, x decreases. Eliminating r from the preceding equation yields

$$K_s z - K_s x = -C_r C_3 x + C_4 n_o$$

or
$$x = \frac{K_s z - C_4 n_o}{K_s - C_r C_3} \tag{3.60}$$

The block-diagram representation for Eqs. (3.55) and (3.60) is given in Fig. 3.22, which is the comparator for the speed control system.

The operation of the servomotor was discussed in Sec. 3.3, and the block diagram was given in Fig. 3.9c.

The flow through the flow control valve is a function of the position Y [that is, $Q = Q(Y)$]. Linearization gives

$$q = \left.\frac{\partial Q}{\partial Y}\right|_i y = C_5 y \tag{3.61}$$

where C_5 is the slope of the curve of Q versus Y evaluated at the reference position.

The speed N_o of an engine is a function of the fuel flow Q supplied to the engine and the engine torque T:

$$N_o = N_o(Q, T)$$

The linearized form of this expression is

$$n_o = \left.\frac{\partial N_o}{\partial Q}\right|_T q + \left.\frac{\partial N_o}{\partial T}\right|_Q t = C_6 q - C_7 t \tag{3.62}$$

where $C_6 = \partial N_o/\partial Q\,|_T$ is the change in speed per change in fuel flow with T maintained at the reference value and $C_7 = -\partial N_o/\partial T\,|_Q$ is the change in speed per change in torque with Q maintained constant at the reference value. For a constant T, the speed N_o increases as Q increases, so that $\partial N_o/\partial Q\,|_T$ is a positive number. For a given Q, the speed decreases as the torque increases, so that $\partial N_o/\partial T\,|_Q$ is a negative number. The minus sign ($C_7 = -\partial N_o/\partial T\,|_Q$) converts C_7 to a positive constant. For convenience in analyzing control systems, it is desirable

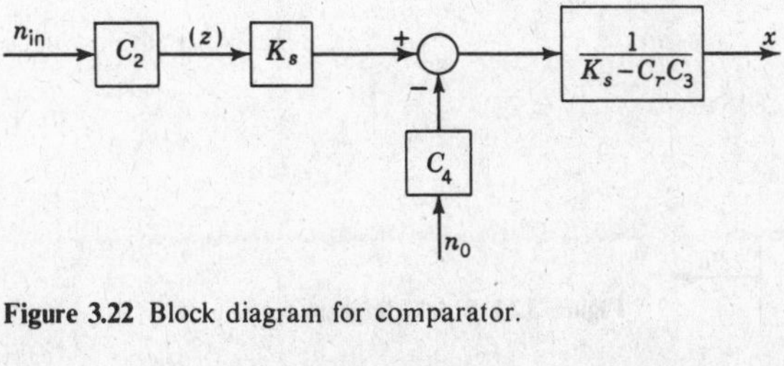

Figure 3.22 Block diagram for comparator.

that all constants be positive numbers. The values of the preceding partial derivatives are obtained from the curve of operating characteristics of the particular engine under consideration. Typical operating characteristics for an engine are shown in Fig. 3.5.

The torque t produced by the engine minus the load torque t_L is the net torque available for acceleration. That is,

$$t - t_L = J\alpha = JDn_o \tag{3.63}$$

where $\alpha = dn_o/dt = Dn_o$ is the angular acceleration of the engine, and J is the rotational inertia of the engine. Substituting t from Eq. (3.63) into Eq. (3.62) gives

$$n_o = C_6 q - C_7 t_L - C_7 JDn_o$$

or

$$n_o = \frac{C_6 q - C_7 t_L}{1 + C_7 JD} = \frac{C_6}{1 + \tau_2 D}(q - C_8 t_L) \tag{3.64}$$

where $\tau_2 = C_7 J$ and $C_8 = \dfrac{C_7}{C_6} = \dfrac{-\partial N_o/\partial T\,|_i}{\partial N_o/\partial Q\,|_i} = \dfrac{\partial Q}{\partial T}\bigg|_i$

By writing $N_o = N_o(Q, T)$ in the implicit form $G(Q, T, N_o) = 0$, then the product of the partial derivatives is

$$\frac{\partial Q}{\partial T}\frac{\partial T}{\partial N_o}\frac{\partial N_o}{\partial Q} = (-1)^3 = -1 \qquad \text{or} \qquad \frac{-\partial N_o/\partial T}{\partial N_o/\partial Q} = \frac{\partial Q}{\partial T} \tag{3.65}$$

The block-diagram representation for Eqs. (3.61) and (3.64) is shown in Fig. 3.23.

The overall block-diagram representation for this speed control system is obtained by combining Figs. 3.22, 3.9c, and 3.23, as is shown in Fig. 3.24, in which $\tau_1 = 2A/C$.

Letting $K_1 = C_5/(K_s - C_r C_3)$ and eliminating the minor feedback loop, Fig. 3.24 may be represented as shown in Fig. 3.25. The operational form of the differential equation relating the output n_o to the input n_{in} and external disturbance t_L for the speed control system represented by the block diagram of Fig. 3.25 is obtained as follows: Subtract the feedback signal $C_4 n_o$ from the reference input $C_2 K_s n_{\text{in}}$, and perform the mathematical operations indicated by the feedforward portion of the block diagram until the output n_o is obtained. That is,

$$\left\{\left[(C_2 K_s n_{\text{in}} - C_4 n_o)\frac{K_1}{1 + \tau_1 D}\right] - C_8 t_L\right\}\frac{C_6}{1 + \tau_2 D} = n_o \tag{3.66}$$

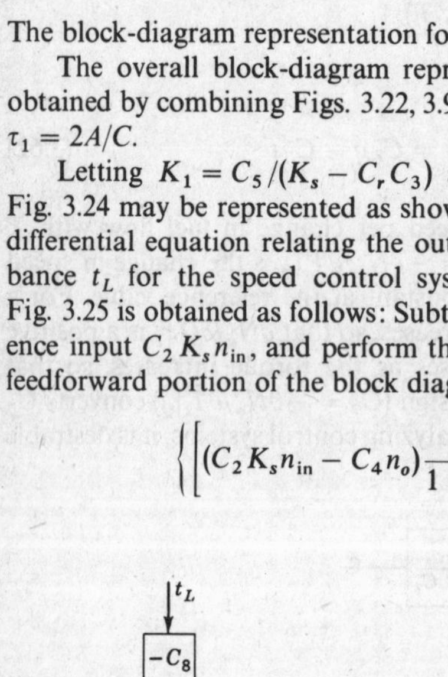

Figure 3.23 Block diagram for engine.

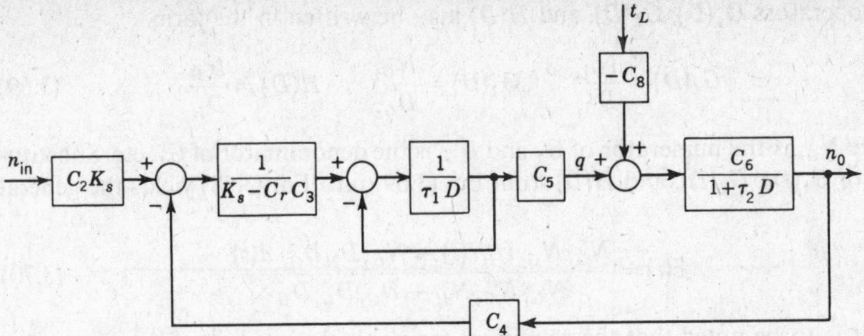

Figure 3.24 Combined block diagram.

Solving for n_o yields

$$n_o = \frac{C_2 C_6 K_1 K_s n_{in} - C_6 C_8 (1 + \tau_1 D) t_L}{(1 + \tau_1 D)(1 + \tau_2 D) + C_4 C_6 K_1} \tag{3.67}$$

In determining the dynamic behavior of a system, one is interested in the variation of the system parameters from some reference condition. This is the type of information that is available from the block-diagram representation shown in Fig. 3.25. If absolute values are desired, it is an easy matter to convert from n_{in} to N_{in} or from n_o to N_o by merely adding the reference value.

In Fig. 3.20 is shown the block-diagram representation for a typical feedback control system. The overall equation of operation is

$$\{[r(t) - H_1(D)c(t)]G_1(D) + d(t)\}G_2(D) = c(t)$$

Solving for the output $c(t)$ gives

$$c(t) = \frac{G_1(D)G_2(D)r(t) + G_2(D)d(t)}{1 + G_1(D)G_2(D)H(D)} \tag{3.68}$$

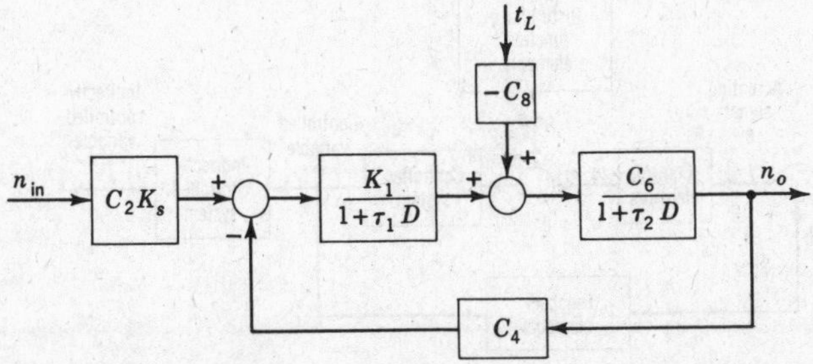

Figure 3.25 Overall block diagram for speed control system.

The operators $G_1(D)$, $G_2(D)$, and $H(D)$ may be written in the form

$$G_1(D) = \frac{N_{G_1}}{D_{G_1}} \qquad G_2(D) = \frac{N_{G_2}}{D_{G_2}} \qquad H(D) = \frac{N_H}{D_H} \tag{3.69}$$

where N_{G_1} is the numerator of G_1 and D_{G_1} is the denominator of G_1, etc. Substitution of $G_1(D)$, $G_2(D)$, and $H(D)$ from Eq. (3.69) into Eq. (3.68) yields the general form

$$c(t) = \frac{N_{G_1} N_{G_2} D_H r(t) + N_{G_2} D_H D_{G_1} d(t)}{N_{G_1} N_{G_2} N_H + D_{G_1} D_{G_2} D_H} \tag{3.70}$$

It is to be noted that the coefficient for $r(t)$ is the product of the numerator terms $N_{G_1} N_{G_2}$ from $r(t)$ to the output and the denominator term D_H from the output back to $r(t)$. Similarly, the coefficient for $d(t)$ is the product of the numerator term N_{G_2} from $d(t)$ to the output and the denominator terms $D_H D_{G_1}$ from the output back to $d(t)$. The denominator for Eq. (3.70) is seen to be the product of all the numerator terms in the loop $(N_{G_1} N_{G_2} N_H)$ plus the product of all the denominator terms $(D_{G_1} D_{G_2} D_H)$. The form given by Eq. (3.70) saves considerable time and effort in obtaining the differential equation of operation for a control system. For example, from Fig. 3.25, it is to be noted that $N_{G_1} = K_1$, $N_{G_2} = C_6$, $N_H = C_4$, $D_{G_1} = (1 + \tau_1 D)$, $D_{G_2} = (1 + \tau_2 D)$, $D_H = 1$, $r(t) = C_2 K_s n_{\text{in}}$, $d(t) = -C_8 t_L$, and $c(t) = n_o$. Substitution of these values into Eq. (3.70) yields directly Eq. (3.67).

3.9 GENERALIZED FEEDBACK CONTROL SYSTEM

A general representation for a feedback control system is shown in Fig. 3.26. It is to be noticed that the command signal, or desired input, does not usually go directly to the comparator but must be converted to a suitable input for this

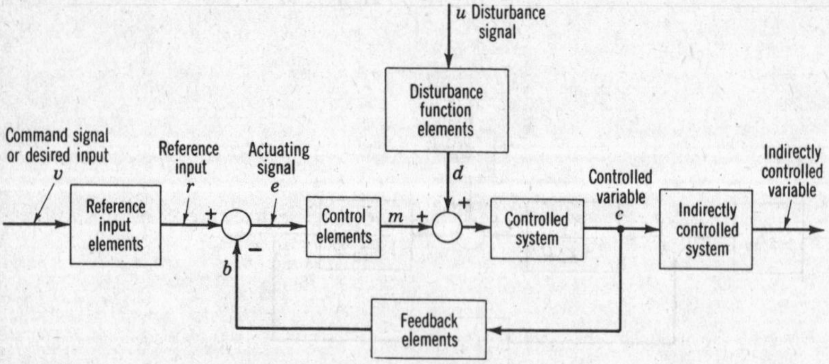

Figure 3.26 Generalized feedback control system.

device. Similarly, the controlled variable, or output, in the general case must also be changed by the feedback elements $H(D)$ before it can be measured by the comparator. The actuating signal e is amplified by the control elements $G_1(D)$ before it enters the system $G_2(D)$ being controlled. An external disturbance, as shown in Fig. 3.26, is a disturbance which acts independently to affect the operation of the system. Although in Fig. 3.26 the external disturbance is shown entering the system between the control elements and the controlled system, in general, the external disturbance may enter the system at any point.

It is also to be noticed from this generalized representation of a control system that the controlled variable is not necessarily the quantity which it is desired to control. For example, a household thermostat controls the temperature of the air around the thermostat, and depending upon the circulation of air in the house, the temperature of other areas may vary considerably. In addition, the idealized purpose of this control is to maintain the comfort of the persons of the household, which depends upon humidity, their clothing, their amount of physical activity, etc. Thus, it is apparent that the controlled variable is not necessarily the ultimate quantity which it is desired to control.

PROBLEMS

3.1 Linearize each of the following equations:

(a) $Y = \sin KX$

(b) $Y = \tan KX$

(c) $Y = e^{KX}$

What is the resulting linearized expression in each case when $X_i = 0$?

3.2 Linearize each of the following equations:

$$(a)\ Z = 0.1X^2 + \frac{100}{Y} \qquad (b)\ Z = X(2Y + 5)$$

If $Y_i = 10$ and $X_i = 20$, what percent error results in each of the above cases when $y = +1$ and $x = -2$?

3.3 The volume V of a sphere is $V = \frac{4}{3}\pi R^3$. Determine the equation for the linear approximation to V. If $R_i = 10$, what percent error results from using this approximation for V when $R = 11$? What is the percent error for $R = 9$?

3.4 The equation for the volume of a cylinder is $V = \pi R^2 H$, where R is the radius of the base and H is the altitude. Determine the equation for the variation v in the volume due to a variation r in the radius and a variation h in the altitude.

3.5 The equation for the area of a triangle may be written in the form

$$A = \tfrac{1}{2}XY \sin \theta$$

where X and Y are the lengths of two adjacent sides and θ is the included angle. Designate variations as a, x, y, and $\Delta\theta$, and then determine the linear approximation for the area for the case in which $X_i = 20$, $Y_i = 10$, and $\theta_i = 30°$.

3.6 The period of oscillation of a simple pendulum is

$$T = 2\pi\sqrt{\frac{L}{g}}$$

for $L_i = 100$ in and $g = 32.2$ ft/s^2. Determine the change in the period due to

(a) An increase in L of 1 in.

(b) A decrease in g of 0.1 ft/s^2.

3.7 Linearize the following equation:

$$V = \frac{D}{T}$$

where V is velocity, D is distance, and T is time.

(a) Determine the linear approximation for V when $V_i = 60$ mph, $D_i = 1$ mi, and $T_i = 60$ s.

(b) With the speedometer indicating 60 mph, it is observed that 62 s are required to travel between successive mile indicator markers on the thruway. Approximately what is the velocity of the vehicle?

3.8 To linearize $V = D/T$ of Prob. 3.7 by the perturbation method, replace V by $V_i + v$, D by $D_i + d$, and T by $T_i + t$. Neglect higher-order variations (differential quantities), and then subtract off the reference condition $V_i T_i = D_i$. Thus, verify the linearized form obtained in Prob. 3.7.

3.9 Given $Y = 1 + \sin X$,

(a) Sketch Y versus X over the period $0 \leq X \leq 2\pi$.

(b) On the same plot, sketch the linear approximation to Y vs. X at $X = \pi$.

(c) Determine the equation for this linear approximation.

3.10 Use linearization procedures to effect a linear approximation for $Y = X^{4/3}$, and then evaluate $(123.5)^{4/3}$. HINT: Let $X_i = 125$.

3.11 Effect a linear approximation for $Y = X^{2/3}$, and then evaluate $(997)^{2/3}$.

3.12 Effect a linear approximation for $Y = \log X$, and then evaluate log 101.

3.13 The volume of a torus ("donut" shaped, Fig. P3.13) is $V = 2\pi^2 R r^2$.

(a) Determine the equation for the variation ΔV in the volume due to a change ΔR in R and a change Δr in r.

(b) The change in volume due to a change in Δr only is $S\,\Delta r$, where S is the surface area. Proceed to determine the equation for the surface area S.

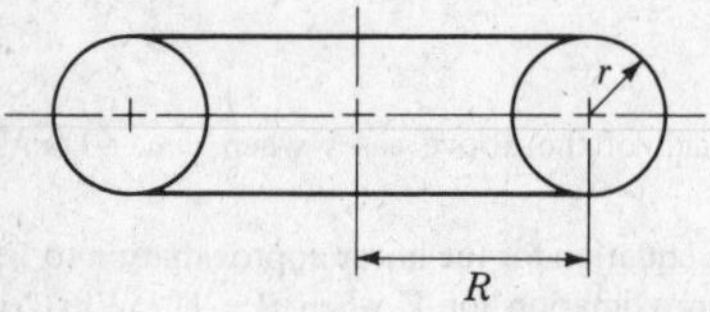

Figure P3.13

3.14 From the law of cosines, it follows that the length of the side Z of a triangle is

$$Z^2 = X^2 + Y^2 - 2XY\cos\theta$$

where θ is the included angle between sides X and Y. Designate variations as x, y, z, and $\Delta\theta$, and proceed to determine the equation for the variation z when $X_i = 50$, $Y_i = 80$, and $\theta_i = 60°$. What is the approximate value of Z when $X = 52$, $Y = 76$, and $\theta = 60°$?

3.15 Typical operating curves for a dc motor are shown in Fig. P3.15. These are curves of torque T versus operating speed N for constant values of voltage E applied to the motor. These curves are a plot of the function $N = N(T, E)$. Effect a linear approximation for N. Evaluate the partial derivatives in this approximation when T_i is 1 in-lb and E_i is 16 V.

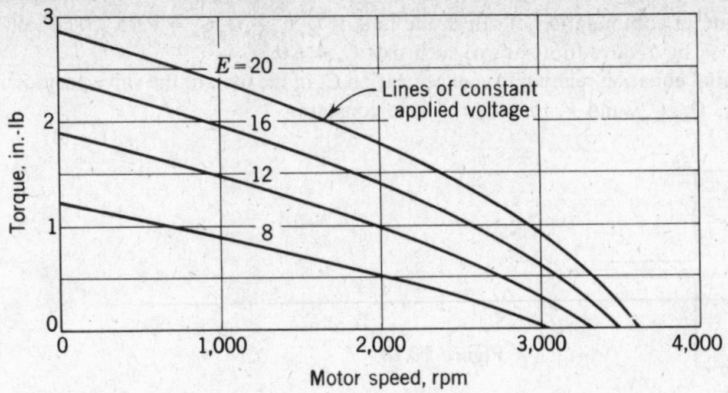

Figure P3.15

3.16 The linearized equation of operation about a typical operating point for a hydraulic amplifier used in a machine tool is

$$f = 2 \times 10^6 e - 5 \times 10^3 \dot{y}$$

where $\dot{y} = Dy$ = velocity of the power piston
f = change in force acting on the piston
e = position of the valve which controls the piston

The load is that due to the tool reactive force f_L and inertia force MD^2y; hence

$$f = f_L + MD^2y$$

The reference position x and controlled position y are connected by a walking-beam linkage such that

$$e = \frac{x - y}{2}$$

Obtain the overall block-diagram representation for this system in which x is the reference input, y the controlled variable, and f_L the external disturbance.

3.17 For the tank shown in Fig. P3.17, Q_{in} is constant. The flow out is a function of the head $Q_o = Q_o(H)$, where $H = H_i + h$. The equilibrium level is such that $Q_{in} = Q_o(H_i)$. The linear approximation for the flow out is $Q_o = Q_o(H_i) + (\partial Q_o/\partial H)_i h = Q_o(H_i) + Ch$, where $C = (\partial Q_o/\partial H)_i$. Show that the differential equation of operation for this tank is $dh/h = -(C/A)dt = -dt/\tau$, where $\tau = A/C$. Integrate both sides of this differential equation, and show that $h = h_0 e^{-t/\tau}$, where h_0 is the value of h at time $t = 0$. Note that as time approaches infinity, the level returns to its equilibrium value $h = 0$.

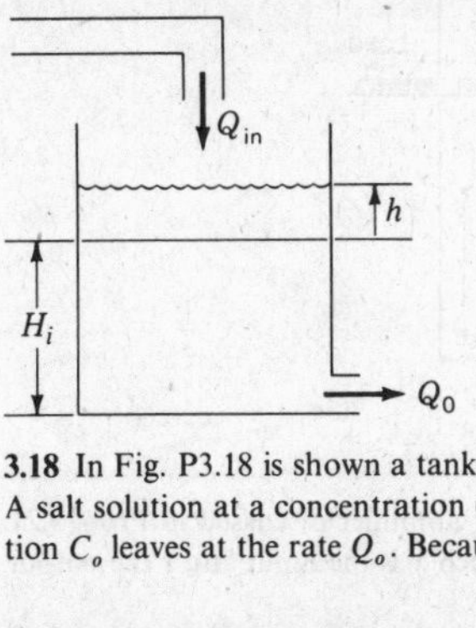

Figure P3.17

3.18 In Fig. P3.18 is shown a tank which is used as a mixer. Pure water flows in at a constant rate Q_w. A salt solution at a concentration C_s flows in at a constant rate Q_s. The mixed solution of concentration C_o leaves at the rate Q_o. Because the volume V of fluid in the tank is kept constant, the outflow Q_o

is equal to $Q_w + Q_s$. The rate of accumulation of salt in the tank is $Q_s C_s - Q_o C_o = VDC_o$. The salt concentration C_s is controlled by a valve (not shown) such that $C_s = K\theta$.

Determine the differential equation relating the concentration C_o of the tank to the valve position θ in terms of the parameters Q_s, Q_w, and V. Identify the time constant.

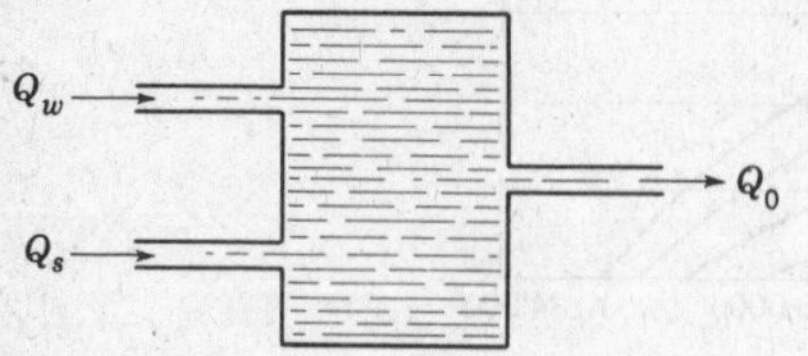

Figure P3.18

3.19 A block of material at temperature T_0 is placed in an oven which is held at the constant temperature T_1. The rate of heat flow q into the material is given by $q = hA(T_1 - T)$, where h is the coefficient of heat transfer of the surface, A is the area of the surface, and T is the temperature of the block. The rate of change of temperature of the block is $dT/dt = q/Mc$, where M is the mass and c is the average specific heat. Determine the differential equation which describes the temperature of the block as a function of time.

3.20 Determine the differential equation relating y and x for the hydraulic system described by the block diagram shown in Fig. P3.20. Identify the time constant and steady-state gain.

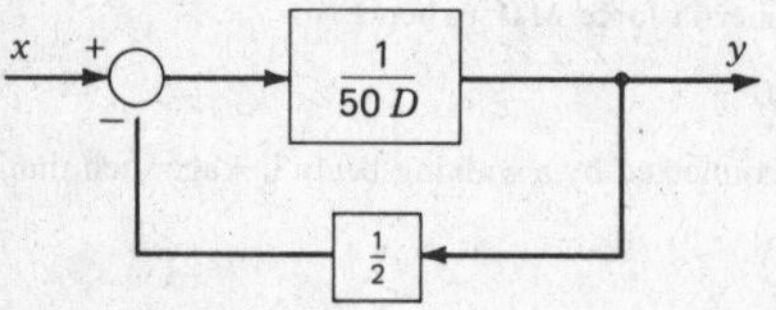

Figure P3.20

3.21 In Fig. P3.21 is shown a hydraulic servomotor which is similar to the power-amplifying device used in power steering units. A movement in the x direction of the valve is seen to open passage 1 to the supply pressure which in turn causes the big piston to move to the right. Because the sleeve is directly connected to this piston, the sleeve also moves to the right to close off flow from the valve. Determine the block diagram relating the input position x to the output y. Identify the time constant.

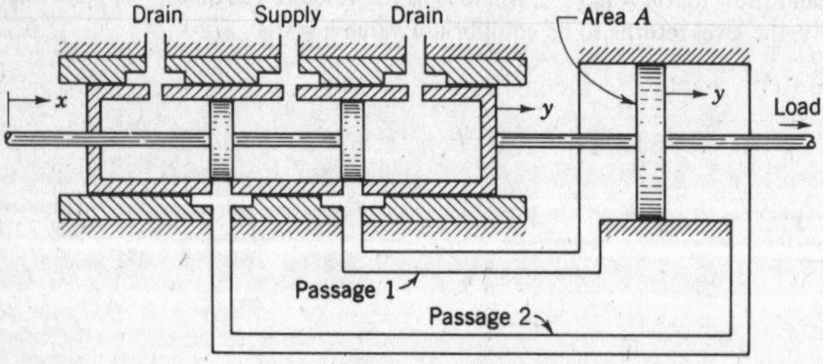

Figure P3.21

3.22 In Fig. P3.22 is shown a modification of the hydraulic power amplifier discussed in Prob. 3.21. Determine the block-diagram representation for this device, in which x is the input and y the output. Note that the position of the sleeve is $[a/(a + b)]y$.

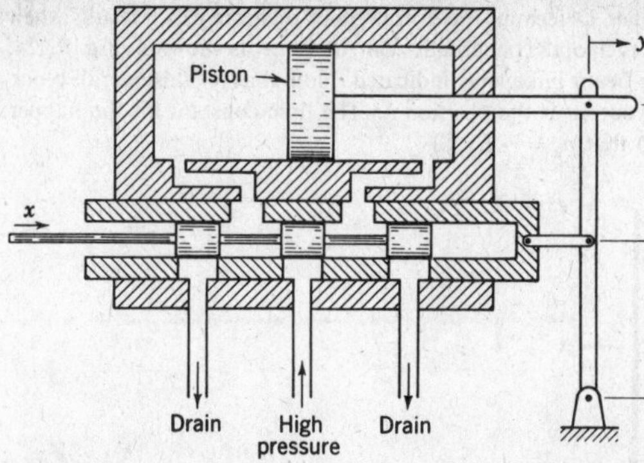

Figure P3.22

3.23 For the hydraulic amplifier shown in Fig. P3.23, determine the block diagram for the walking-beam linkage and also the block diagrams relating e to y and y to w. Combine these diagrams to determine the overall block-diagram representation for the system.

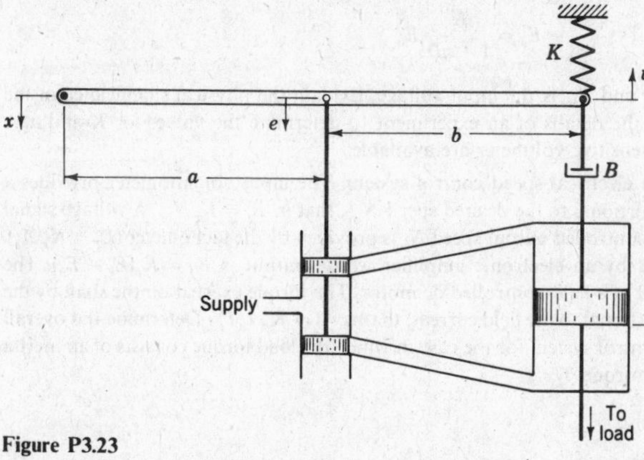

Figure P3.23

3.24 Derive the equation relating p_2 and z for each of the pneumatic control elements shown in Fig. P3.24a and b. Explain the significance of each partial derivative which occurs in these equations.

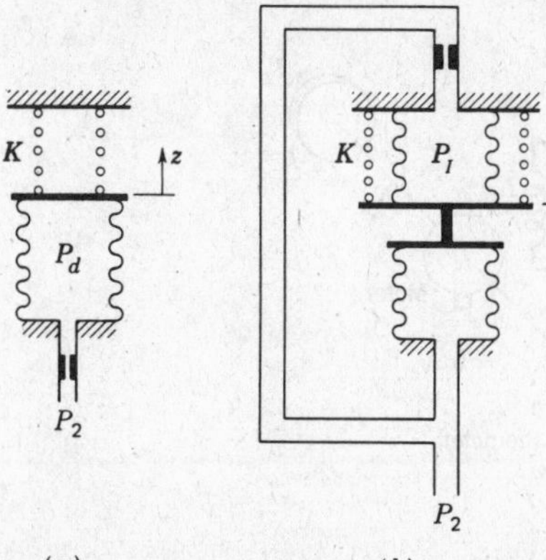

Figure P3.24

3.25 In Fig. P3.25 is shown a flapper amplifier. Determine the overall block diagram which results when the controlled pressure P_2 is connected to each of the pneumatic control elements shown in Fig. P3.24. The position z is fed back to the walking-beam linkage as indicated. Note that for this overall block diagram the input is the error e and the output is the position z. (The time constant for the flapper amplifier may be considered negligible so that $p_2 = -K_1 x$.)

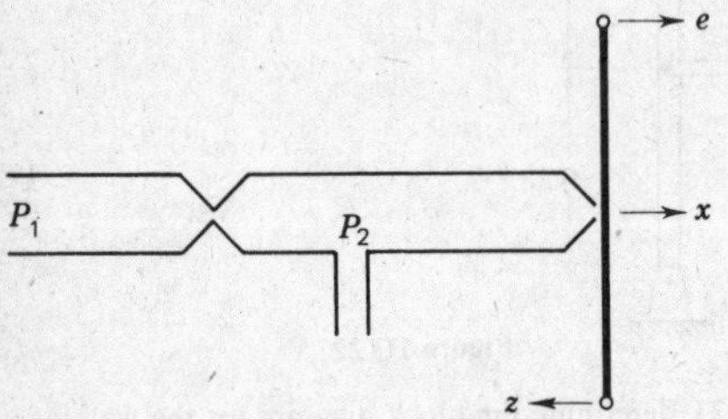

Figure P3.25

3.26 The dynamics of an electronic amplifier can be approximated by the differential equation

$$E_o = \frac{K}{1 + aD} E_{in}$$

where E_o is the output voltage and E_{in} is the input voltage. Explain the physical significance of the parameters K and a. Describe the details of an experiment to determine the values for K and a. A power source, a switch, and a sensitive voltmeter are available.

3.27 In Fig. P3.27 is shown an electrical speed control system. The input potentiometer provides a reference input voltage E_r proportional to the desired speed N_{in}, that is, $E_r = K_r N_{in}$. A voltage signal E_c which is proportional to the controlled output speed N_o is provided by the tachometer ($E_c = K_c N_o$). The error $E_r - E_c$ is amplified by an electronic amplifier whose output is $E_f = K_a(E_r - E_c)$. The voltage E_f is applied to the field of a field-controlled dc motor. The torque exerted on the shaft by the motor (air-gap torque) is proportional to the field current, that is, $T = K_m I_a I_f$. Determine the overall block diagram for this speed control system for the case in which the load torque consists of an inertia $JD^2\theta = JDN_o$ and an external torque T_L.

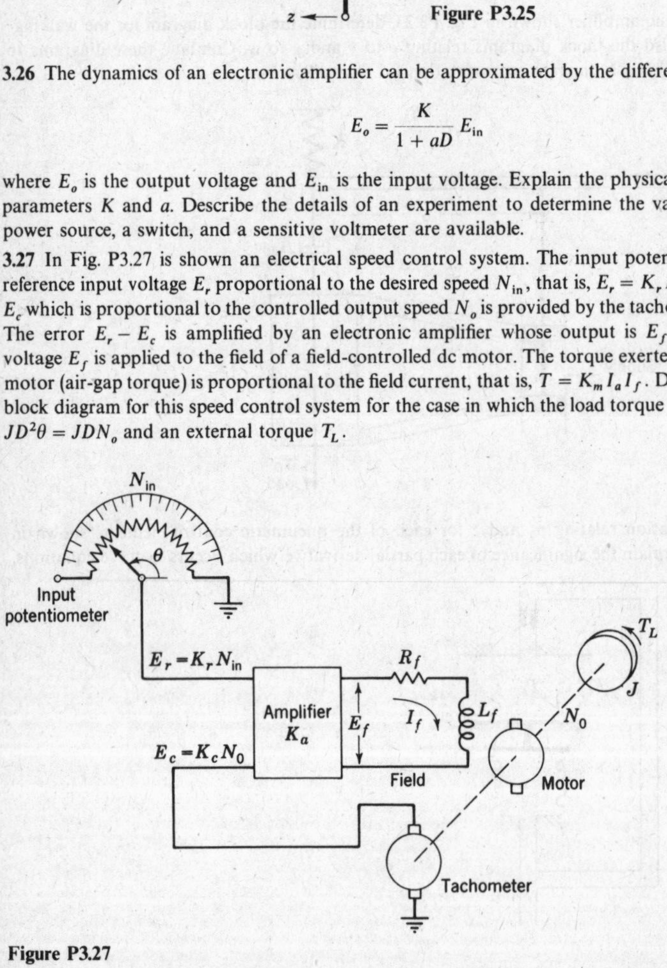

Figure P3.27

3.28 A field-controlled dc motor is shown in Fig. P3.28. The motor drives the load through a gearbox, so that $\omega_c = n\omega$, where n is the gear ratio, ω is the motor speed, and ω_c is the speed of the load (i.e., the controlled speed). The output shaft is connected to a tachometer, which produces a voltage proportional to the controlled speed ($E_c = K_c\omega_c$). An electronic amplifier is used to amplify the error signal by a factor K_a, that is, $E_f = K_a(E_r - E_c)$. Complete the overall block-diagram representation for this system.

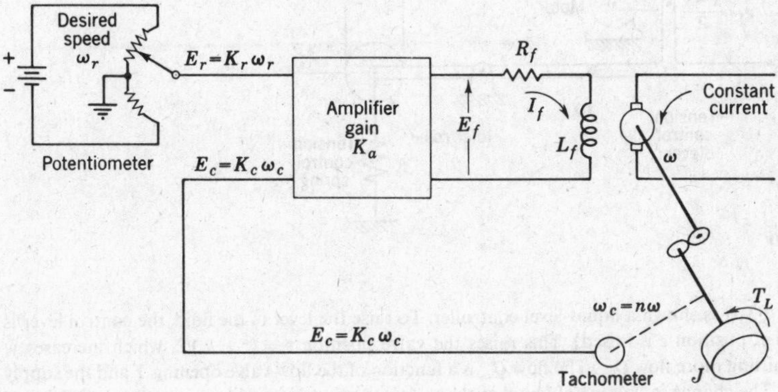

Figure P3.28

3.29 In Fig. P3.29 is shown a generator which is used as a voltage amplifier. The prime mover drives the generator at a constant speed. Determine the equation of operation for the amplification ratio E_2/E_1.

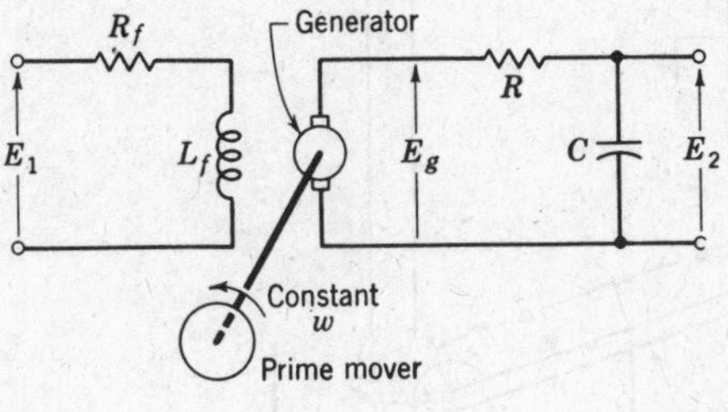

Figure P3.29

3.30 In Fig. P3.30 is shown a tension-regulating apparatus such as is used in the paper industry. To ensure uniform winding, it is necessary to maintain a constant tension F_c as the sheet is being wound on the wind-up roll. To increase the tension in the paper, the tension control lever is raised. This raises the torque control arm of the motor, which increases the torque T_m applied by the motor to the wind-up roll. The change in torque provided by the motor is $t_m = K_m e/(1 + \tau D)$. For the wind-up roll, it follows that $F_c = T_m/R$, where R is the radius of the wheel. Determine the overall block diagram relating a variation f_r of the reference or desired tension to a variation of the controlled tension f_c.

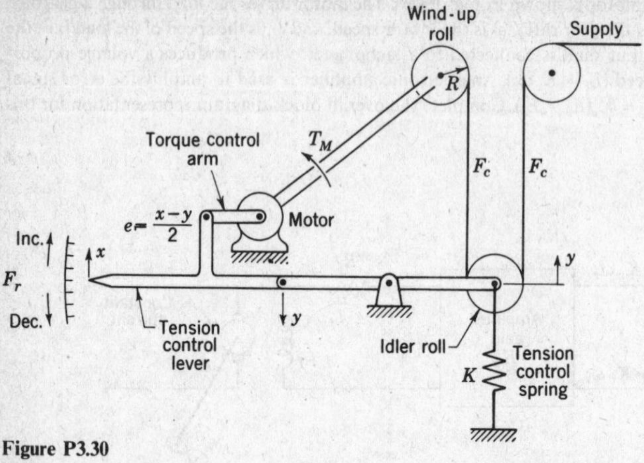

Figure P3.30

3.31 In Fig. P3.31 is shown a liquid-level controller. To raise the level of the fluid, the control lever is moved up (i.e., position z is raised). This raises the valve position $e = (z - h_o)/2$, which increases y, thereby admitting more flow Q_{in}. The flow Q_{in} is a function of the flow valve opening Y and the supply pressure P_s. The change in volume of liquid in the tank is the time integral $(q_{in} - q_o)/D$, which is equal to the cross-sectional area of the tank A_T times the change in level h_o. The flow out Q_o is seen to depend on the pressure head H_o. Determine the overall block diagram for this controller.

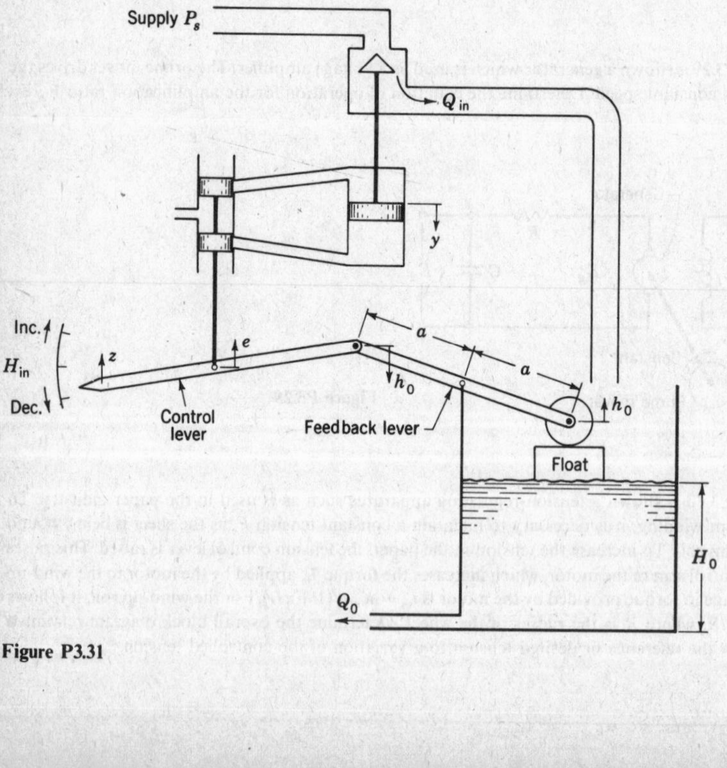

Figure P3.31

3.32 A system for controlling flow is shown in Fig. P3.32. Increasing the desired flow setting increases the compression on spring K_1, which causes x and position e of the balanced valve to move up. This in turn causes the flow valve to move down, which increases the flow. The amount of flow out is measured by a venturi-type flowmeter, so that the pressure drop $P_1 - P_2$ is a function of Q_o. The diaphragm prevents leakage from the high pressure P_1 to the low pressure P_2, but it permits motion, just as a piston would. The effective area of the diaphragm is A_d. The flow Q_o is seen to be a function of the flow-valve opening Y and the supply pressure P_s. Determine the overall block-diagram representation for this system.

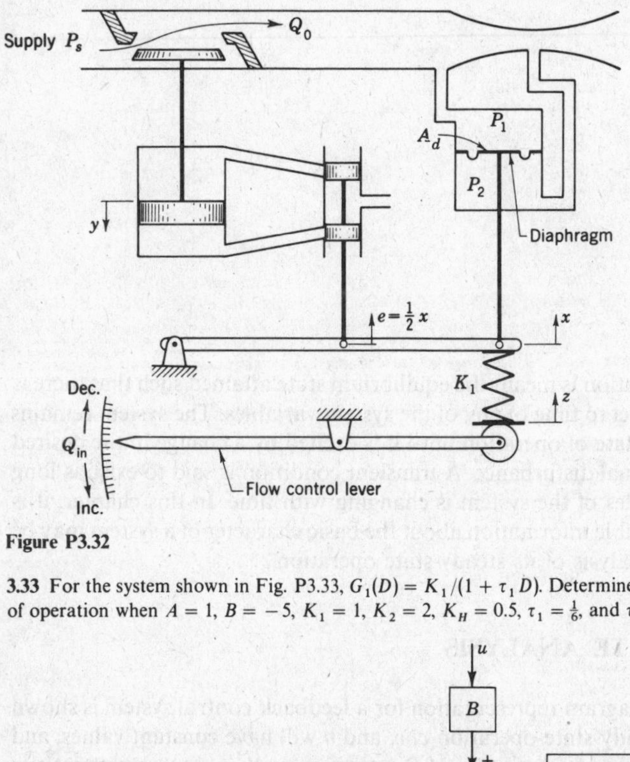

Figure P3.32

3.33 For the system shown in Fig. P3.33, $G_1(D) = K_1/(1 + \tau_1 D)$. Determine the differential equation of operation when $A = 1$, $B = -5$, $K_1 = 1$, $K_2 = 2$, $K_H = 0.5$, $\tau_1 = \frac{1}{6}$, and $\tau_2 = 1$.

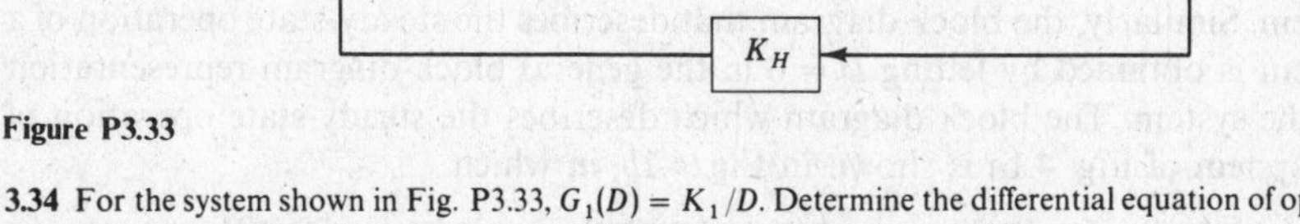

Figure P3.33

3.34 For the system shown in Fig. P3.33, $G_1(D) = K_1/D$. Determine the differential equation of operation when $A = 1$, $B = -1$, $K_1 = 1$, $K_2 = 0.75$, $K_H = 1.0$, and $\tau_2 = 0.25$.

3.35 Same as Prob. 3.34, except $K_2 = 4$.

CHAPTER
FOUR

STEADY-STATE OPERATION

By steady-state operation is meant the equilibrium state attained such that there is no change with respect to time of any of the system variables. The system remains at this equilibrium state of operation until it is excited by a change in the desired input or in the external disturbance. A transient condition is said to exist as long as any of the variables of the system is changing with time. In this chapter, it is shown that considerable information about the basic character of a system may be obtained from an analysis of its steady-state operation.

4.1 STEADY-STATE ANALYSIS

The general block-diagram representation for a feedback control system is shown in Fig. 4.1*a*. For steady-state operation c, v, and u will have constant values, and therefore terms resulting from powers of D operating on these constant quantities will be zero. The equation describing the steady-state operation of a control system is obtained by letting $D = 0$ in the differential equation of operation for the system. Similarly, the block diagram that describes the steady-state operation of a system is obtained by letting $D = 0$ in the general block-diagram representation for the system. The block diagram which describes the steady-state operation of the system of Fig. 4.1*a* is shown in Fig. 4.1*b*, in which

$$K_{G_1} = [G_1(D)]_{D=0} \qquad K_{G_2} = [G_2(D)]_{D=0} \qquad K_H = [H(D)]_{D=0}$$

where K_{G_1} is obtained by letting $D = 0$ in the differential operator $G_1(D)$, etc. From Fig. 4.1*b*, the equation for steady-state operation is found to be

$$[(Av - K_H c)K_{G_1} + Bu]K_{G_2} = c$$

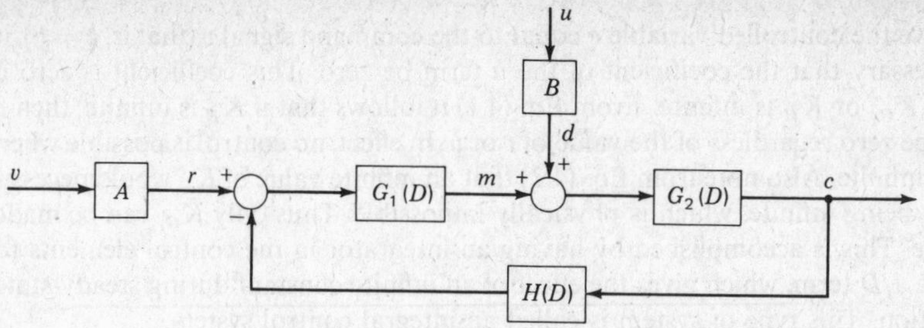

(a)

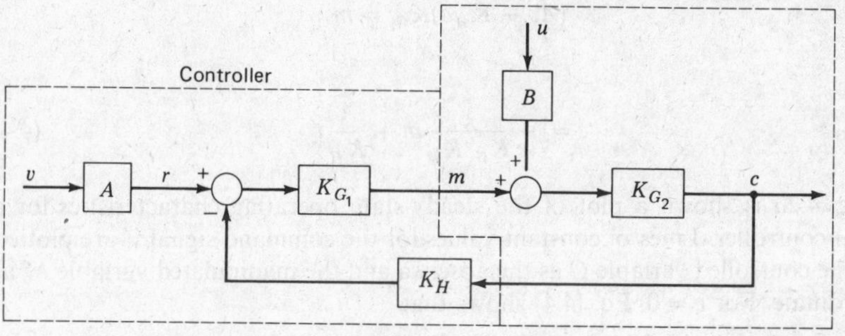

(b)

Figure 4.1 General block-diagram representation for a control system.

or

$$c = \frac{AK_{G_1}K_{G_2}}{1 + K_{G_1}K_{G_2}K_H}\,v + \frac{BK_{G_2}}{1 + K_{G_1}K_{G_2}K_H}\,u \tag{4.1}$$

The constant A which appears in Eq. (4.1) is, in effect, the scale factor for the input dial. To have the coefficient of the v term equal to unity, A must be selected such that

$$\frac{AK_{G_1}K_{G_2}}{1 + K_{G_1}K_{G_2}K_H} = 1$$

or

$$A = \frac{1 + K_{G_1}K_{G_2}K_H}{K_{G_1}K_{G_2}} = \frac{1}{K_{G_1}K_{G_2}} + K_H \tag{4.2}$$

When A is chosen in accordance with Eq. (4.2), the coefficient of the v term is unity, in which case Eq. (4.1) becomes

$$c = v + \frac{BK_{G_2}}{1 + K_{G_1}K_{G_2}K_H}\,u = v + \frac{B}{1/K_{G_2} + K_{G_1}K_H}\,u \tag{4.3}$$

To have the controlled variable c equal to the command signal v (that is, $c = v$), it is necessary that the coefficient of the u term be zero. This coefficient is zero if either K_{G_1} or K_H is infinite. From Eq. (4.1) it follows that if K_H is infinite, then c must be zero regardless of the value of v or u. In effect, no control is possible when K_H is infinite. Also note from Eq. (4.2) that an infinite value of K_H would necessitate A being infinite, which is physically impossible. Thus only K_{G_1} can be made infinite. This is accomplished by having an integrator in the control elements to yield a $1/D$ term, which gives the effect of an infinite constant during steady-state operation. This type of system is called an integral control system.

The left portion of the control system enclosed by the dotted lines in Fig. 4.1*b* is the controller. For the controller it follows that

$$(Av - K_H c)K_{G_1} = m$$

or

$$c = -\frac{1}{K_{G_1}K_H}m + \frac{A}{K_H}v \tag{4.4}$$

In Fig. 4.2*a* is shown a plot of the steady-state operating characteristics for a typical controller. Lines of constant values for the command signal V are plotted with the controlled variable C as the abscissa and the manipulated variable M as the ordinate. For $v = 0$, Eq. (4.4) shows that

$$-K_{G_1}K_H = \frac{m}{c}\bigg|_{v=0} = \frac{\Delta M}{\Delta C}\bigg|_{\Delta V=0} = \frac{\partial M}{\partial C}\bigg|_V \tag{4.5}$$

where $v = \Delta V$ is the change in V from the reference value, $m = \Delta M$ is the change in M from the reference value, and $c = \Delta C$ is the change in C from the reference value. For $v = 0$, then V must be constant. The term $\partial M/\partial C\,|_V$ is the slope of the controller curves shown in Fig. 4.2*a*.

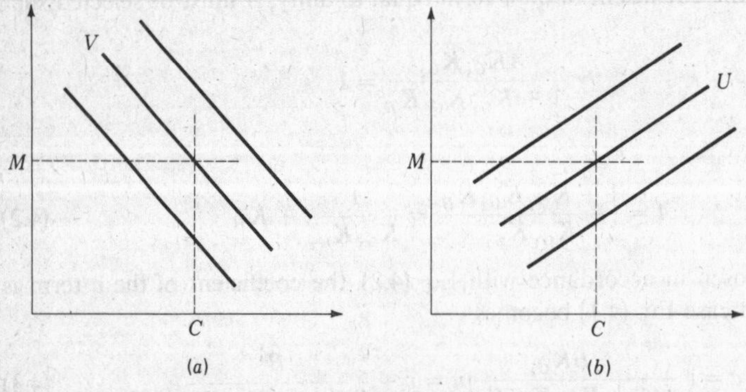

Figure 4.2 Steady-state operating characteristics for (*a*) controller and (*b*) system to be controlled.

For the case in which $c = 0$, Eq. (4.4) becomes

$$AK_{G_1} = \frac{m}{v}\bigg|_{c=0} = \frac{\Delta M}{\Delta V}\bigg|_{\Delta C=0} = \frac{\partial M}{\partial V}\bigg|_{C} \tag{4.6}$$

For $c = 0$, then C must be constant. A line of constant C is a vertical line in Fig. 4.2*a*. The term $\partial M/\partial V|_C$ determines the vertical spacing between lines of constant V.

Finally, for the case in which $m = 0$, Eq. (4.4) shows that

$$\frac{K_H}{A} = \frac{v}{c}\bigg|_{m=0} = \frac{\Delta V}{\Delta C}\bigg|_{\Delta M=0} = \frac{\partial V}{\partial C}\bigg|_{M} \tag{4.7}$$

For $m = 0$, then M must be constant. A line of constant M is a horizontal line. The term $\partial V/\partial C|_M$ determines the horizontal spacing between lines of constant V.

The right portion of Fig. 4.1*b* enclosed by the dotted lines represents the system to be controlled. The equation for the steady-state operation of the system to be controlled is

$$(m + Bu)K_{G_2} = c$$

or

$$c = K_{G_2}m + BK_{G_2}u \tag{4.8}$$

From an analysis similar to that for the controller, it follows that

$$\frac{\partial M}{\partial C}\bigg|_{U} = \frac{1}{K_{G_2}} \qquad \frac{\partial M}{\partial U}\bigg|_{C} = -B \qquad \frac{\partial C}{\partial U}\bigg|_{M} = BK_{G_2} \tag{4.9}$$

Typical steady-state operating curves for the system to be controlled are shown in Fig. 4.2*b*. The first partial $\partial M/\partial C|_U$ is the slope, the second partial $\partial M/\partial U|_C$ determines the vertical spacing, and the last partial $\partial C/\partial U|_M$ determines the horizontal spacing. In summary, the individual constants in the block diagram of Fig. 4.1*b* may be obtained from the steady-state operating curves and vice versa.

Illustrative example The block diagram for a feedback control system is shown in Fig. 4.3. The reference operating point is $V_i = C_i = 100$, $M_i = 50$, and $U_i = 10$. Determine the steady-state constants for this system and then sketch the steady-state operating curves. Select A in accordance with Eq. (4.2).

SOLUTION The steady-state constants are $B = -5$, $K_H = 0.5$, and

$$K_{G_1} = \frac{1}{1 + \tau_1 D}\bigg|_{D=0} = 1 \qquad K_{G_2} = \frac{2}{1 + \tau_2 D}\bigg|_{D=0} = 2$$

The value of A is

$$A = \frac{1}{K_{G_1}K_{G_2}} + K_H = \frac{1}{(1)(2)} + 0.5 = 1.0$$

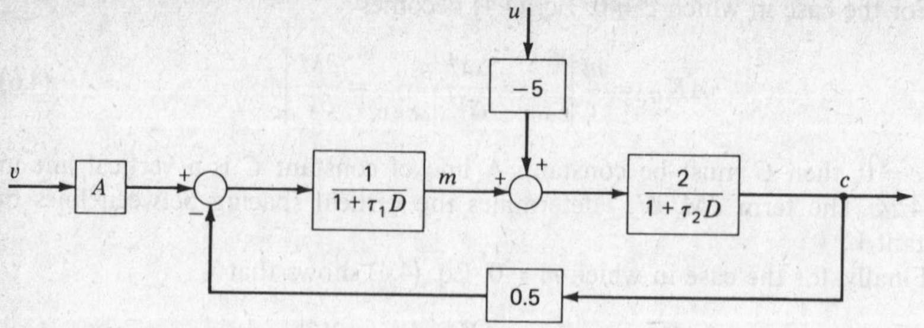

Figure 4.3 A feedback control system.

The slope of the operating curves for the controller is

$$\left.\frac{\partial M}{\partial C}\right|_V = -K_{G_1}K_H = -(1.0)(0.5) = -0.5$$

The line of $V_i = 100$ may now be drawn through the reference point ($M_i = 50$, $C_i = 100$) with a slope of (-0.5), as shown in Fig. 4.4*a*. The horizontal spacing is

$$\left.\frac{\Delta V}{\Delta C}\right|_M = \frac{K_H}{A} = 0.5$$

For $\Delta C = 20$, then $\Delta V = 0.5\Delta C = (0.5)(20) = 10$. Note in Fig. 4.4*a* that when M is constant (a horizontal line), the horizontal spacing is such that as V changes by 10 units, then C changes by 20 units. The vertical spacing is

$$\left.\frac{\Delta M}{\Delta V}\right|_C = AK_{G_1} = (1.0)(1.0) = 1.0$$

For $\Delta V = 10$, then $\Delta M = (1.0)\,\Delta V = (1.0)(10) = 10.0$. Note in Fig. 4.4*a* that when C is constant (a vertical line), the vertical spacing is such that as V changes by 10 units, then M changes by 10 units.

If any two of the three quantities (slope, horizontal spacing, and vertical spacing) are known, then the third quantity is determined. Thus, only two of these three quantities are independent. This fact is proved by noting that for the controller enclosed by the dashed box in Fig. 4.1*b*, the output is the manipulated variable M and the inputs are the command signal V and the controlled variable C. For a given controller the manipulated variable M is a function of V and C. That is,

$$M = M(V, C)$$

The implicit form for this relationship is

$$G(M, V, C) = 0$$

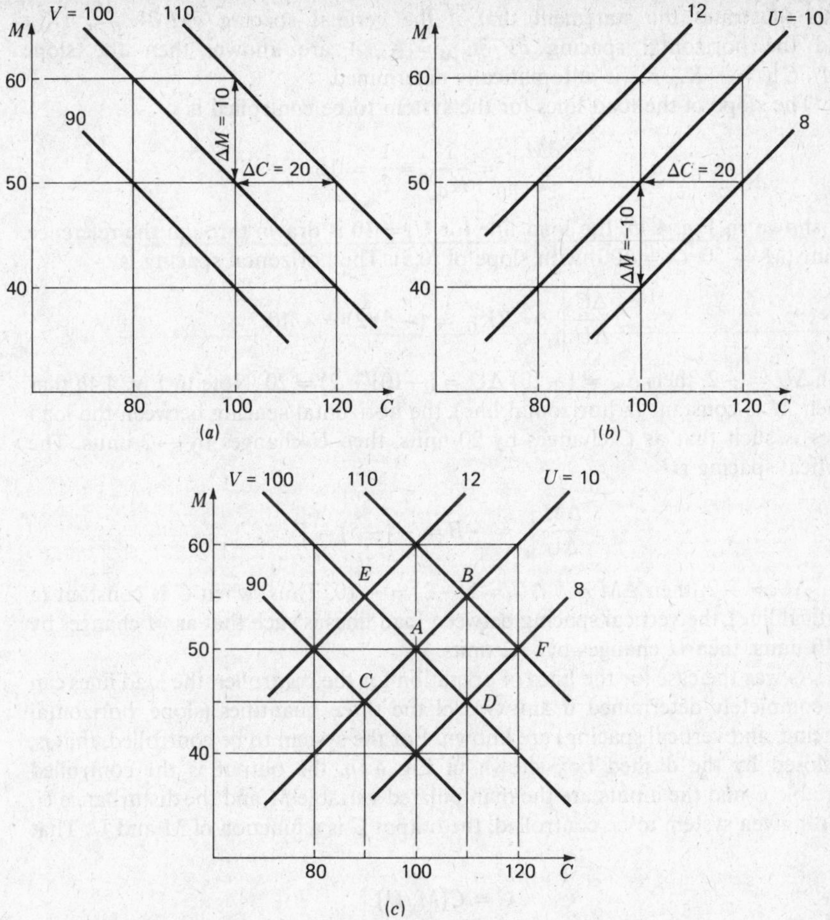

Figure 4.4 Steady-state characteristics for system of Fig. 4.3.

For an implicit function of n variables, the product of the n partial derivatives is $(-1)^n$. For the implicit function G of the three variables M, V, and C, it follows that

$$\left.\frac{\partial M}{\partial V}\right|_C \left.\frac{\partial V}{\partial C}\right|_M \left.\frac{\partial C}{\partial M}\right|_V = -1 \tag{4.10}$$

Solving for the slope $\partial M/\partial C\,|_V$ gives

$$\left.\frac{\partial M}{\partial C}\right|_V = -\left.\frac{\partial M}{\partial V}\right|_C \left.\frac{\partial V}{\partial C}\right|_M = -(AK_{G_1})\left(\frac{K_H}{A}\right) = -K_{G_1}K_H$$

This illustrates the statement that if the vertical spacing $\partial M/\partial V|_C = AK_{G_1}$ and the horizontal spacing $\partial V/\partial C|_M = K_H/A$ are known, then the slope $\partial M/\partial C|_V = -K_{G_1}K_H$ is automatically determined.

The slope of the load lines for the system to be controlled is

$$\left.\frac{\partial M}{\partial C}\right|_U = \frac{1}{K_{G_2}} = \frac{1}{2} = 0.5$$

As shown in Fig. 4.4*b*, the load line for $U_i = 10$ is drawn through the reference point ($M_i = 50$, $C_i = 100$) with slope of (0.5). The horizontal spacing is

$$\left.\frac{\Delta C}{\Delta U}\right|_M = BK_{G_2} = (-5)(2) = -10$$

For $\Delta U = -2$, then $\Delta C = (-10)\,\Delta U = (-10)(-2) = 20$. Note in Fig. 4.4*b* that when M is constant (a horizontal line), the horizontal spacing between the load lines is such that as C changes by 20 units, then U changes by -2 units. The vertical spacing is

$$\left.\frac{\Delta M}{\Delta U}\right|_C = -B = -(-5) = 5$$

For $\Delta U = -2$, then $\Delta M = 5\,\Delta U = 5(-2) = -10$. Thus, when C is constant (a vertical line), the vertical spacing between load lines is such that as M changes by -10 units, then U changes by -2 units.

As was the case for the lines of operation for the controller, the load lines can be completely determined if any two of the three quantities (slope, horizontal spacing, and vertical spacing) are known. For the system to be controlled, that is, enclosed by the dashed box shown in Fig. 4.1*b*, the output is the controlled variable C and the inputs are the manipulated variable M and the disturbance U. For a given system to be controlled, the output C is a function of M and U. That is,

$$C = C(M, U)$$

The implicit form for this relationship is

$$G(C, M, U) = 0$$

The product of the partial derivatives is

$$\left.\frac{\partial C}{\partial M}\right|_U \left.\frac{\partial M}{\partial U}\right|_C \left.\frac{\partial U}{\partial C}\right|_M = -1 \tag{4.11}$$

Solving for the slope $\partial M/\partial C|_U$ gives

$$\left.\frac{\partial M}{\partial C}\right|_U = -\left.\frac{\partial M}{\partial U}\right|_C \left.\frac{\partial U}{\partial C}\right|_M = -(-B)\frac{1}{BK_{G_2}} = \frac{1}{K_{G_2}}$$

Thus, by knowing the vertical spacing $\partial M/\partial U|_C = -B$ and the horizontal spacing $\partial U/\partial C|_M = 1/BK_{G_2}$, the slope $\partial M/\partial C|_U = 1/K_{G_2}$ can be determined.

Because Figs. 4.4*a* and 4.4*b* have the same coordinates (*C*, *M*), they may be superimposed upon each other as shown in Fig. 4.4*c*. Substitution of the values of the constants into Eq. (4.1) yields for the overall equation for steady-state operation

$$c = \frac{AK_{G_1}K_{G_2}}{1 + K_{G_1}K_{G_2}K_H}v + \frac{BK_{G_2}}{1 + K_{G_1}K_{G_2}K_H}u$$

$$= \frac{(1)(1)(2)}{1 + (1)(2)(0.5)}v + \frac{(-5)(2)}{1 + (1)(2)(0.5)}u = v - 5u \tag{4.12}$$

The coefficient of the *v* term and the coefficient of the *u* term may be obtained directly from Fig. 4.4*c* without the need to evaluate all the steady-state constants. For the overall system shown in Fig. 4.1*b*, the output is the controlled variable *C* and the inputs are the command signal *V* and the disturbance *U*. Thus, for any given system, *C* is a function of *V* and *U*. That is,

$$C = C(V, U)$$

Linearization gives

$$c = \left.\frac{\partial C}{\partial V}\right|_U v + \left.\frac{\partial C}{\partial U}\right|_V u \tag{4.13}$$

Comparison of this result with Eq. (4.1) shows that

$$\left.\frac{\partial C}{\partial V}\right|_U = \frac{AK_{G_1}K_{G_2}}{1 + K_{G_1}K_{G_2}K_H} \tag{4.14}$$

and

$$\left.\frac{\partial C}{\partial U}\right|_V = \frac{BK_{G_2}}{1 + K_{G_1}K_{G_2}K_H} \tag{4.15}$$

The term $\partial C/\partial V|_U$ is evaluated by dividing changes in *C* by corresponding changes in *V* with *U* fixed. In Fig. 4.4*c*, with $U = 10$, at point *B* the value of *C* is 110 and the value of *V* is 110. At point *C*, the value of *C* is 90 and the value of *V* is 90. Thus

$$\left.\frac{\Delta C}{\Delta V}\right|_U = \frac{C_B - C_C}{V_B - V_C} = \frac{110 - 90}{110 - 90} = 1$$

where C_B is the value of *C* at point *B*, V_B is the value of *V* at point *B*, etc. The term $\partial C/\partial U|_V$ is evaluated by dividing changes in *C* by corresponding changes in *U* with *V* fixed. In Fig. 4.4*c*, with $V = 100$, at point *D* the value of *C* is 110 and the value of *U* is 8. At point *E*, the value of *C* is 90 and the value of *U* is 12. Thus

$$\left.\frac{\Delta C}{\Delta U}\right|_V = \frac{110 - 90}{8 - 12} = \frac{20}{-4} = -5$$

The point A shown in Fig. 4.4c is the reference point of operation. In going from A to B the command signal changes from 100 to 110, so that $v = 10$. There is no change in the load, so that $u = 0$. Application of Eq. (4.12) gives $c = v - 5u = 10$. Note that in going from point A to point B, the controlled variable changes from 100 to 110, so that $c = 10$. In going from point A to point F, the command signal changes from 100 to 110, so that $v = 10$. The load U changes from 10 to 8, so that $u = -2$. Application of Eq. (4.12) gives $c = v - 5u = 10 - 5(-2) = 20$. In going from A to F the controlled variable changes from 100 to 120, so that $c = 20$.

Because the input scale factor A has been selected in accordance with Eq. (4.2), at the reference load $U_i = 10$ ($u = 0$) the controlled variable is equal to the command signal ($c = v$). Note in Fig. 4.4c that at point A, $V = C = 100$; at point B, $V = C = 110$; and at point C, $V = C = 90$.

4.2 EQUILIBRIUM

In Fig. 4.5a is shown a typical operating line for a controller in which V is the value of the command signal. When the value of the controlled variable is C_1, the value of the manipulated variable being supplied by the controller is M_1. In Fig. 4.5b is shown a typical load line for a system to be controlled in which U is the load. When the value of the manipulated variable being supplied to the system is M_1, the output from the system is C_1. As indicated in Fig. 4.5c by point A, the intersection of the line of operation of the command signal V for the controller and the load line U for the system determines the equilibrium point of operation for the system. That is, at point A the amount of the manipulated variable M_1 being supplied by the controller is the same as that required to maintain the system output at C_1. If the system output were C_2, then point B would be the point of operation for the controller and point C would be the point of operation for the system to be controlled. The amount of the manipulated variable required to maintain the system at point C is M_C. Because the controller is only supplying

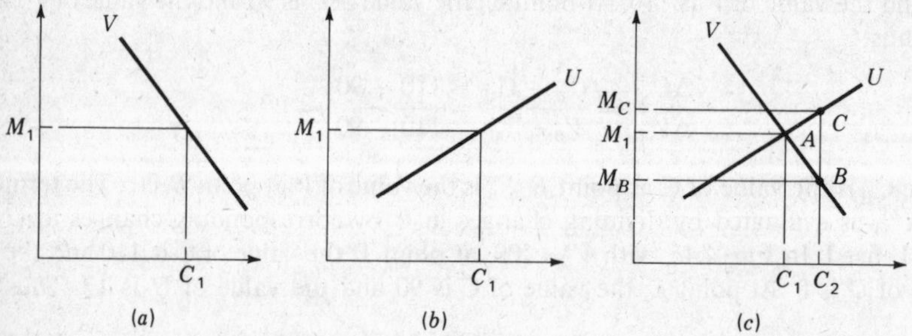

Figure 4.5 (a) Typical operating line for a controller; (b) typical load line for system to be controlled; and (c) superposition of Figs. 4.5a and b.

the amount M_B, the system output C decreases until equilibrium is attained at point A.

The characteristics shown in Fig. 4.6*a* illustrate the effect of changing the command signal from V_1 to V_2 with the load U maintained constant. Initially the system is at equilibrium at point A, the intersection of the V_1 controller curve and the U load curve. When the command signal is changed from V_1 to V_2, the new operating point for the controller is at point B, the intersection of the value of the output C_1 and the V_2 controller curve. The point of operation for the system to be controlled remains at point A, the intersection of the output C_1 and the U load curve. Because the controller is supplying more of the manipulated variable than is required to maintain the system to be controlled at point A ($M_B > M_1$), the output C increases. The new equilibrium point of operation will be at point C, where the value of the manipulated variable supplied by the controller M_2 is the value required to maintain the system output at C_2. If the input dial is calibrated in such a way that the value of the command signal V_1 is equal to the output C_1, the value of the command signal V_2 is equal to the output C_2, etc., then the system is calibrated so that the output will always equal the input for a given loading condition. When this is so, Eq. (4.2) is automatically satisfied.

The characteristics shown in Fig. 4.6*b* illustrate the effect of changing the load from U_1 to U_2 with the command signal V maintained fixed. Initially the system is at equilibrium at point A, the intersection for the controller curve V and the load line U_1. When the load is changed to U_2, the new point of operation for the system to be controlled is at point B, which is the intersection of the value of the output C_1 and the load line U_2. The point of operation of the controller remains at point A, which is the intersection of the value of the output C_1 and the controller line V. Because the amount of manipulated variable M_1 being supplied by the controller is less than the amount M_B required to maintain the system to be controlled at point B, the output C decreases. The new equilibrium point of operation will be at point C, which is the intersection of the new load line U_2 and the controller line V. Note that with the command signal V maintained fixed, the output has changed from C_1 to C_2 due to the change in load.

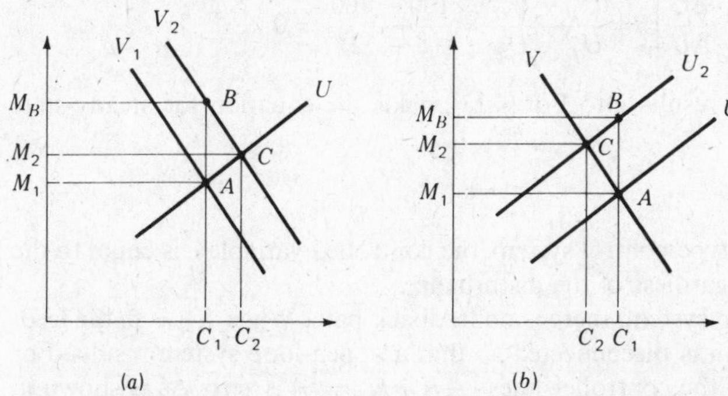

Figure 4.6 Effect of changing (*a*) the command signal and (*b*) the load.

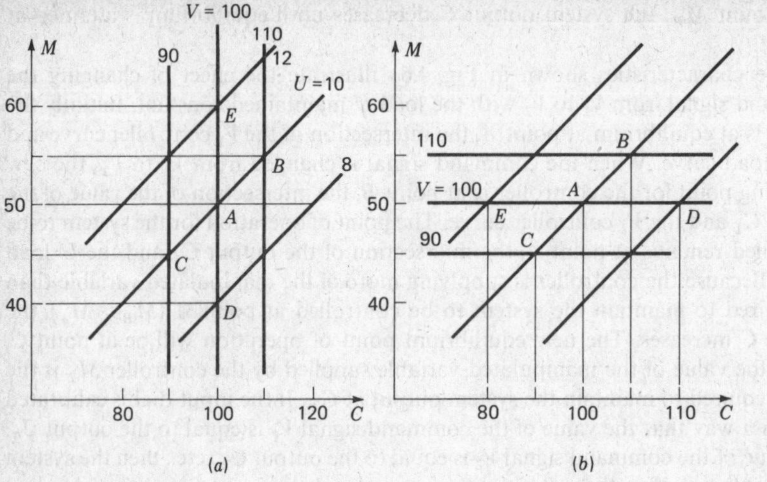

Figure 4.7 Steady-state characteristics for (*a*) an integral control system and (*b*) an open-loop system.

The slope of the controller lines V is $-K_{G_1}K_H$. For an integral-type controller, K_{G_1} is infinite. The resulting controller lines are vertical. For this case there is no change in the output due to a change in the load. Replacing the control element $G_1(D) = 1/(1 + \tau_1 D)$ by the element $G_1(D) = 1/D$ would yield such a system. The resulting steady-state characteristics are shown in Fig. 4.7*a*. Note that for steady-state operation, the value of the controlled variable C is always equal to the command signal V regardless of the value of the disturbance U. Using the points B and C in Fig. 4.7*a* to evaluate the coefficient $\partial C/\partial V|_U$ and using the points D and E to evaluate the coefficient $(\partial C/\partial U)_V$ gives

$$\left.\frac{\Delta C}{\Delta V}\right|_U = \frac{C_B - C_C}{V_B - V_C} = \frac{110 - 90}{110 - 90} = 1$$

$$\left.\frac{\Delta C}{\Delta U}\right|_V = \frac{C_D - C_E}{U_D - U_E} = \frac{100 - 100}{8 - 12} = 0$$

Substitution of these results into Eq. (4.13) yields the equation for steady-state operation

$$c = v$$

Thus for an integral-type control system, the controlled variable c is equal to the command signal v regardless of the disturbance.

For an open-loop system, there is no feedback path. When $K_H = 0$, the feedback path of Fig. 4.1*b* is disconnected so that an open-loop system results. For this case the slope of the controller lines $(-K_{G_1}K_H = 0)$ is zero. As is shown in Fig. 4.7*b*, for an open-loop system the lines of operation for the controller are horizontal. Using the points B and C in Fig. 4.7b to evaluate the coefficient $\partial C/\partial V|_U$ and the points D and E to evaluate the coefficient $\partial C/\partial U|_V$ gives

$$\left.\frac{\Delta C}{\Delta V}\right|_U = \frac{110-90}{110-90} = 1 \qquad \left.\frac{\Delta C}{\Delta U}\right|_V = \frac{120-80}{8-12} = \frac{40}{-4} = -10$$

Substitution of these results into Eq. (4.13) yields the equation for steady-state operation

$$c = v - 10u$$

The slope of the controller lines $\partial M/\partial C|_V = -K_{G_1}K_H$ varies from zero for an open-loop system ($K_H = 0$) to infinity for an integral control system ($K_{G_1} = \infty$). A proportional control system is one for which the controller lines have a finite slope, as shown in Fig. 4.4c. Usually the slope of the control lines for a proportional controller is very steep, so that they are almost vertical. The steeper the slope, the less the variation in the controlled variable C due to a change in the disturbance U. An open-loop system has the greatest change in the controlled variable due to a disturbance, whereas an integral controller has no change in the controlled variable due to a disturbance.

Proportional control systems usually exhibit better transient characteristics than integral control systems. In addition, proportional control systems provide the operator with a "feel" as to what is going on. For example, a power steering system feeds back some of the torque applied to the steering wheel so that the driver has a measure or feel for the turning effort being applied to the wheels. Satisfactory performance may usually be achieved by making the control lines sufficiently steep; this makes the coefficient of the u term sufficiently small so that variations in the external disturbance cause only slight errors. For integral control systems, the coefficient of the u term is zero. For proportional control systems, the coefficient of the u term is finite. The coefficient attains its maximum value for an open-loop system.

4.3 PROPORTIONAL CONTROL SYSTEMS

The differential equation relating the output n_o to the input n_{in} and external disturbance t_L for the speed control system represented by the block diagram of Fig. 3.25 is given by Eq. (3.67). Letting $D = 0$ in Eq. (3.67) yields for the equation describing the steady-state operation of the speed control system

$$n_o = \frac{C_2C_6K_1K_sn_{\text{in}} - C_6C_8t_L}{1 + C_4C_6K_1} \tag{4.16}$$

Letting $D = 0$ in the overall block diagram of Fig. 3.25 yields the block diagram for steady-state operation shown in Fig. 4.8a. Comparison with the general block diagram of Fig. 4.8b shows that $c = n_o$, $v = n_{\text{in}}$, $u = t_L$, $A = C_2K_s$, $B = C_8$, $K_{G_1} = K_1$, $K_{G_2} = C_6$, and $K_H = C_4$. Substitution of these results into Eq. (4.1) verifies Eq. (4.16).

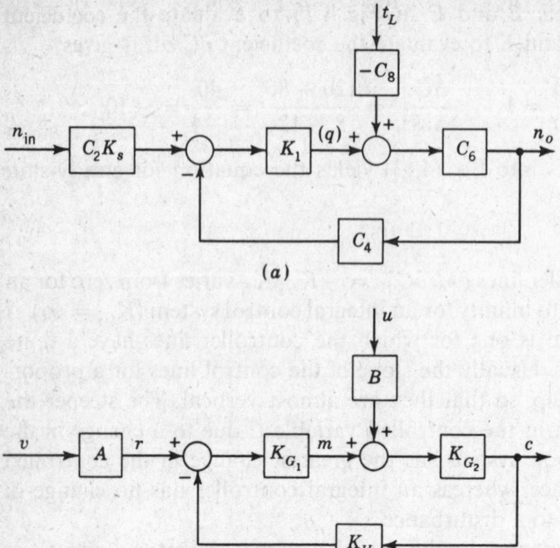

Figure 4.8 Block diagram for steady-state operation.

The speed control system shown in Fig. 3.25 is a proportional control system. Substitution of the corresponding values for this speed control system into Eq. (4.2) gives

$$A = C_2 K_s = \frac{1}{C_6 K_1} + C_4$$

or

$$C_2 = \frac{1}{K_s}\left(\frac{1}{C_6 K_1} + C_4\right) \tag{4.17}$$

The term $C_2 = \partial Z/\partial N_{\text{in}}|_i$ is the scale factor for the speed-setting dial.

Because some of the terms in Eq. (4.17) are partial derivatives evaluated at the reference operating condition, the value of the scale factor C_2 is seen to vary for different reference points. This would result in a nonlinear scale for the input speed dial. The use of a nonlinear scale may be avoided by having the input speed-setting position a cam which in turn sets the desired input position of the top of the spring, as is shown in Fig. 4.9. It is then a relatively easy matter to set up the speed control system so that Eq. (4.17) is satisfied for any reference condition. When this is so, Eq. (4.16) becomes

$$n_o = n_{\text{in}} - \frac{C_6 C_8}{1 + C_4 C_6 K_1} t_L \tag{4.18}$$

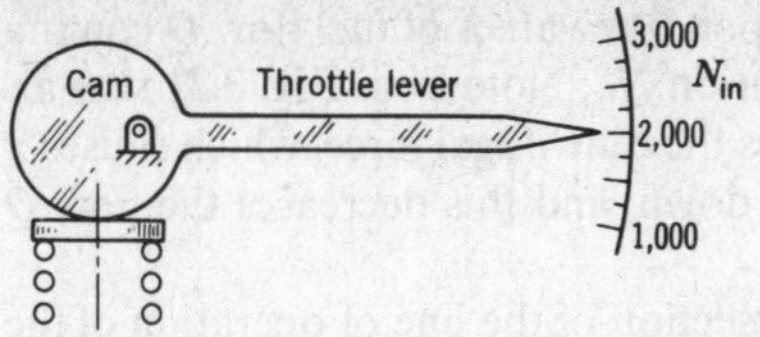

Figure 4.9 Cam to avoid nonlinear input scale.

Equation (4.18) is the typical form of the steady-state relationship that exists between the input, output, and external disturbance for a proportional control system. When the load torque T_L is not equal to the reference value (that is, $t_L \neq 0$), then n_o is not equal to n_{in}. For example, suppose that this is the speed control system for the gas turbine of a jet airplane and that T_{L_i} is the torque required for the airplane in level flight. When the airplane is inclined to gain altitude, a greater load torque T_L is required than that for level flight (that is, $t_L > 0$). Thus, Eq. (4.18) shows that the output speed is slightly less than the desired value for this flight condition.

The physical reason for this can be seen by looking at the schematic diagram Fig. 3.21 for the speed control system. For level flight, the system is set up so that $N_o = N_{in}$. When the airplane is gaining altitude, the load torque is increased. This increased torque results in a decreased speed, which in turn causes a lower position for x. Because of the lower position for x, there is a greater flow of fuel. To have the airplane continue to gain altitude, more flow is required than for level flight. To maintain this increased flow, the engine speed must be slightly less than for level flight.

The steady-state operating curves for this speed control system are shown in Fig. 4.10. For an airplane in level flight, the curve of fuel flow Q required to maintain various speeds N_o is indicated by $T_{L_i} = T_2$. The curve marked T_3 would correspond to operation of the airplane at a certain angle of inclination. Similarly, the curve T_1 would correspond to the airplane losing altitude at a certain angle of declination.

The operating line AB for the controller is obtained by fixing the speed setting

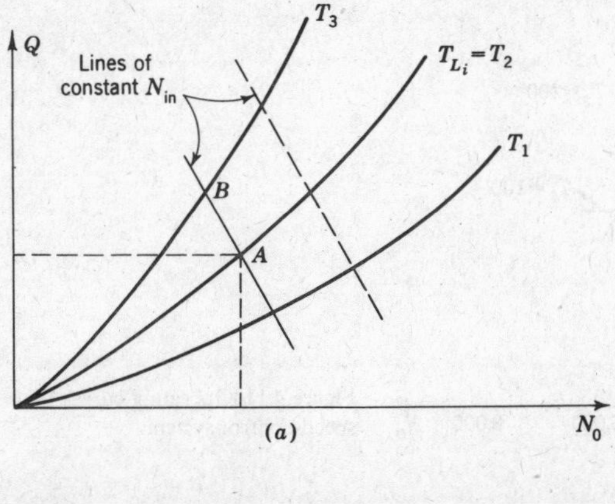

Figure 4.10 Steady-state characteristics for engine and controller.

at some value N_{in}, and then plotting corresponding values of fuel flow Q coming from the controller, for various speeds of rotation N_o. Note from Fig. 3.21 that an increased speed N_o of the flyweights increases the centrifugal force, which causes x to move up. This in turn causes y to move down, and this decreases the flow Q supplied by the controller.

Steady-state operation exists at the intersection of the line of operation of the controller and the torque line for the given flight condition because at this intersection just enough flow is being supplied to maintain the flight condition. For example, if the airplane is in level flight and the operating line for the desired speed setting is AB, then the intersection at point A of the line T_2 and the operating line AB is the steady-state operating point for the system. The speed-setting dial is calibrated by setting the value of speed N_{in} on the dial equal to the steady-state value of the output speed at the reference load T_2. For a given speed setting, such as that indicated by the line AB, if the load is increased to T_3 while the desired speed is unchanged, then the new operating point must be on the line of T_3 at point B. Because AB is not a vertical line, variations in the load are seen to cause variations in the output speed. A proportional controller is sometimes called a droop controller, and the line AB is referred to as the droop line.

Illustrative example A typical family of steady-state operating curves for a speed control system for a diesel or turbine is shown in Fig. 4.11. Determine the steady-state equation for operation in the vicinity of point A. If this were an open-loop rather than a closed-loop system, what would be the equation for steady-state operation about point A?

SOLUTION From Eq. (4.14) it follows that

$$\frac{AK_{G_1}K_{G_2}}{1+K_{G_1}K_{G_2}K_H} = \left.\frac{\Delta C}{\Delta V}\right|_U = \left.\frac{\Delta N_o}{\Delta N_{in}}\right|_{T_2} = \frac{5000-3000}{5000-3000} = 1$$

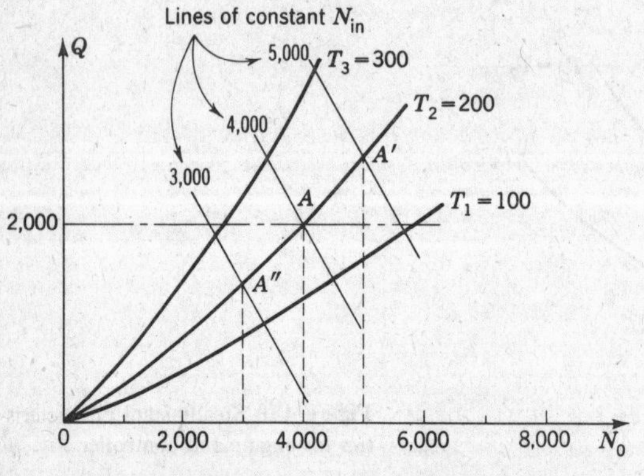

Figure 4.11 Operating curves for a speed-control system.

Similarly from Eq. (4.15)

$$\frac{BK_{G_2}}{1+K_{G_1}K_{G_2}K_H}=\left.\frac{\Delta C}{\Delta U}\right|_V=\left.\frac{\Delta N_o}{\Delta T_L}\right|_{N_{\text{in}}=4000}=\frac{4500-3400}{100-300}=-5.5$$

Thus the equation for steady-state operation in the vicinity of point A is

$$n_o = n_{\text{in}} - 5.5t_L$$

For an open-loop control system there is but one set value of the flow Q for each desired speed. This value of Q must be the flow required to make N_o equal to N_{in} at the reference load torque $T_{L_i} = T_2$. For a desired speed of 4000 r/min, it is to be noted from Fig. 4.11 that the value of Q is 2000 lb/h. Thus the horizontal line of Q equal to 2000 is the open-loop operating line of the controller when $N_{\text{in}} = 4000$. Similarly, when N_{in} is 5000 the operating line is a horizontal line through A', and when N_{in} is 3000 the operating line is a horizontal line through A''. Thus

$$\frac{AK_{G_1}K_{G_2}}{1+K_{G_1}K_{G_2}K_H}=\left.\frac{\Delta N_o}{\Delta N_{\text{in}}}\right|_{T_2}=\frac{5000-3000}{5000-3000}=1$$

and

$$\frac{BK_{G_2}}{1+K_{G_1}K_{G_2}K_H}=\left.\frac{\Delta N_o}{\Delta T_L}\right|_{N_{\text{in}}=4000}=\frac{5800-2700}{100-300}=-15.5$$

The resulting steady-state equation is

$$n_o = n_{\text{in}} - 15.5t_L$$

In effect, an open-loop system may be regarded as a proportional controller in which the droop lines are horizontal.

4.4 INTEGRAL CONTROL SYSTEMS

By eliminating the linkage between x and y of Fig. 3.21 and using the hydraulic integrator shown in Fig. 4.12, the proportional control system is converted to an integral control system. The block-diagram representation for the integrator is also shown in Fig. 4.12. The substitution of this diagram for that of the servomotor which it replaces in Fig. 3.24 yields the block-diagram representation shown in Fig. 4.13*a*.

The value of K_{G_1} is computed as follows:

$$K_{G_1}=\left[\frac{C_1C_5}{(K_s-C_rC_3)A_1D}\right]_{D=0}=\left(\frac{K_I}{D}\right)_{D=0}=\infty \tag{4.19}$$

where $K_I = C_1C_5/(K_s - C_rC_3)A_1$ is the constant associated with the integrating portion of the system, as is shown in Fig. 4.13*b*.

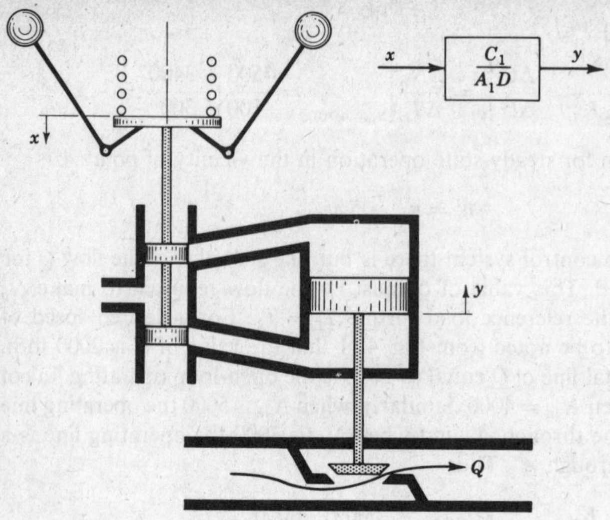

Figure 4.12 Integral controller.

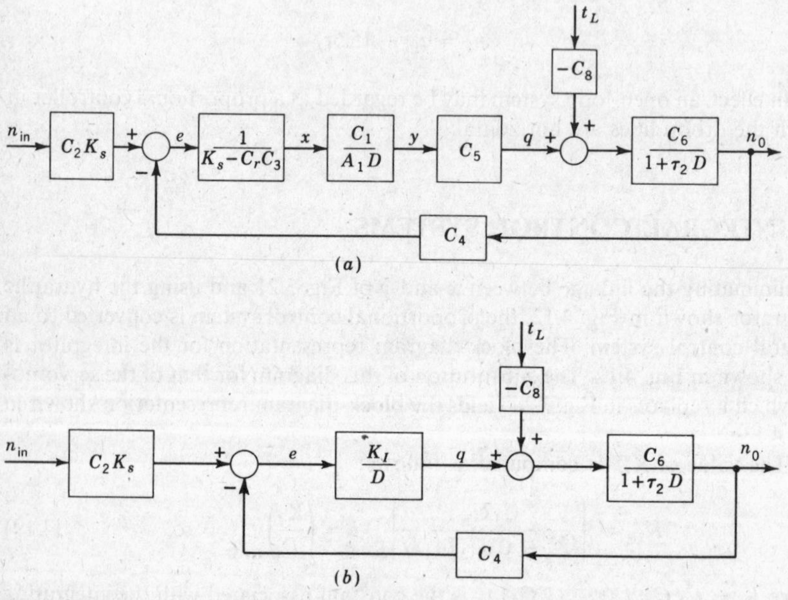

Figure 4.13 Block diagram for integral control system.

Because K_{G_1} is infinite, e must be zero for steady-state operation. Thus, subtracting the feedback signal from the reference input in Fig. 4.13*b* gives

$$C_2 K_s n_{in} - C_4 n_o = e = 0$$

or
$$n_o = \frac{C_2 K_s}{C_4} n_{in} \tag{4.20}$$

The preceding expression shows that the speed is independent of the load torque for an integral control system. It is an easy matter to adjust the scale factor C_2 for the input speed dial so that $C_2 K_s/C_4 = 1$, in which case

$$n_o = n_{in} \tag{4.21}$$

The operation of an integral control system may be visualized as follows: From Fig. 4.12, it can be seen that if x momentarily changes and then returns to its line-on-line position, the position of y has been changed permanently and so has the amount of flow going to the engine. Therefore, changing the amount of flow to account for a new operating torque does not change the steady-state position of x, which must be line on line. Because neither x nor the spring compression changes, the output speed must always be equal to the desired value in order that the flyweight force balances the spring force. (Note that, for the proportional control system, changing the fuel flow requires a permanent change in the position x.)

An integral control is easily recognized because *there must be an integrating component yielding a 1/D term in the block diagram between the comparator and the point where the external disturbance enters the system.* The line of operation of an integral controller is a vertical line. The operating characteristics of an integral control system are shown in Fig. 4.14.

An integral controller is also called a floating controller because of the floating action of the position y of the flow setting valve. Two other terms used for an integral controller are reset controller and isochronous controller.

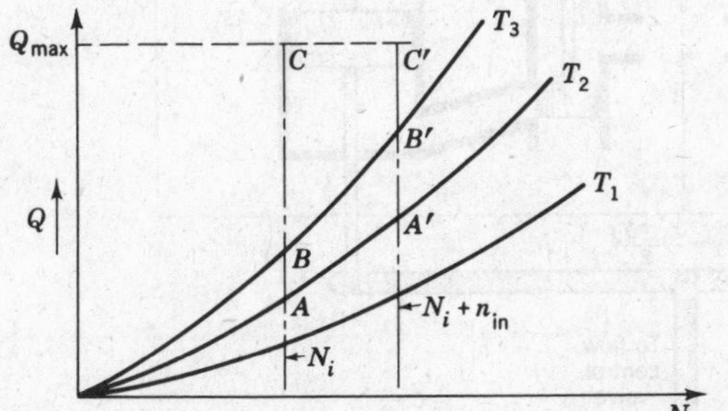

Figure 4.14 Operating characteristics for integral control system.

4.5 PROPORTIONAL PLUS INTEGRAL CONTROL SYSTEMS

From a consideration of steady-state operation only, integral control systems seem preferable to proportional systems. However, it is generally easier to achieve good transient behavior with a proportional system than with an integral system (techniques for determining the transient behavior of systems are presented in Chaps. 5 through 12). It is possible to combine the basic features of a proportional controller and an integral controller to form a proportional plus integral controller.

The action of a proportional plus integral controller in response to a change in the input or external disturbance is initially similar to that of a proportional controller, but as the new equilibrium point is reached, the control action becomes the same as that of an integral controller. (In effect, the slope of the droop line continually increases.)

A proportional plus integral controller combines the desirable transient characteristics of a proportional controller and the feature of no steady-state error of the integral controller.

A proportional plus integral controller is shown in Fig. 4.15. The proportional action is provided by unit 1, which is the same as that for the proportional controller shown in Fig. 3.21. The equation for the proportional action is

$$y_1 = \frac{1}{1 + \tau_1 D} x \tag{4.22}$$

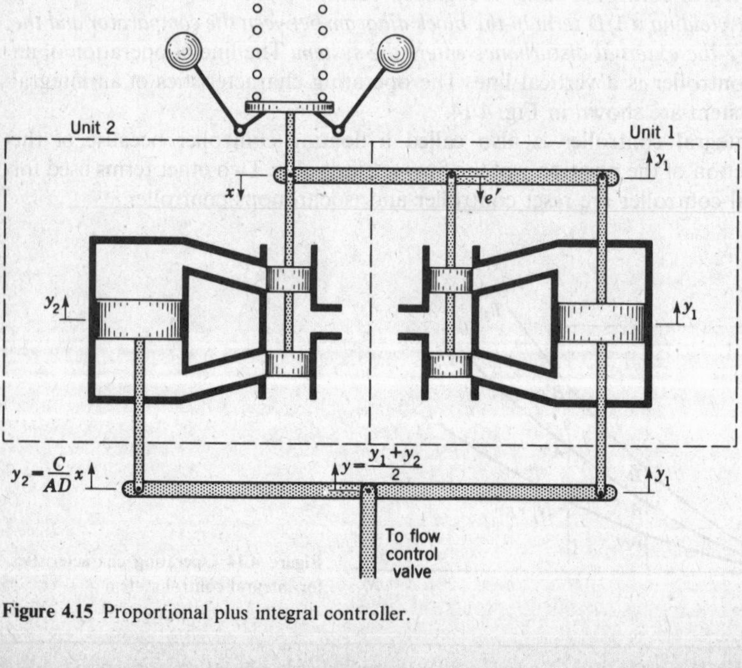

Figure 4.15 Proportional plus integral controller.

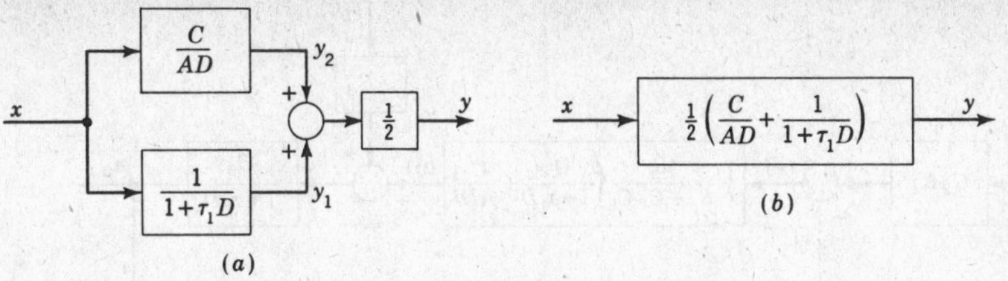

Figure 4.16 Block diagram for proportional plus integral action.

The integral action is provided by unit 2, which is the same as that for the integral controller shown in Fig. 4.13. The equation for this integral action is

$$y_2 = \frac{C}{AD} x \tag{4.23}$$

The proportional and integral actions are added by a walking-beam linkage such that

$$y = \frac{y_1 + y_2}{2} \tag{4.24}$$

The substitution of y_1 and y_2 into the preceding expression gives

$$y = \frac{1}{2}\left(\frac{1}{1+\tau_1 D} + \frac{C}{AD}\right)x \tag{4.25}$$

The individual block diagrams for Eqs. (4.22) to (4.24) are shown in Fig. 4.16*a*. The combined diagram is shown in Fig. 4.16*b*. The substitution of this combined diagram into its corresponding position between x and y of Fig. 4.13*a* yields the resulting representation for this proportional plus integral control system, as is shown in Fig. 4.17.

The value of K_{G_1} for this proportional plus integral control system is

$$K_{G_1} = \frac{C_5}{2(K_s - C_r C_3)}\left(\frac{1}{1+\tau_1 D} + \frac{C}{AD}\right)_{D=0} = \infty \tag{4.26}$$

The proportional plus integral actions are clearly evidenced by Eq. (4.26). Because K_{G_1} is infinite for steady-state operation, it follows that e is zero during steady-state operation. Thus, from Fig. 4.17,

$$C_2 K_s n_{in} - C_4 n_o = e = 0$$

or

$$n_o = \frac{C_2 K_s}{C_4} n_{in} \tag{4.27}$$

Comparison of Eqs. (4.27) and (4.20) shows that the steady-state operation of a proportional plus integral control system is the same as that of an integral control system alone. A proportional plus integral control is sometimes referred to as a compensated isochronous control. To better understand the action of this

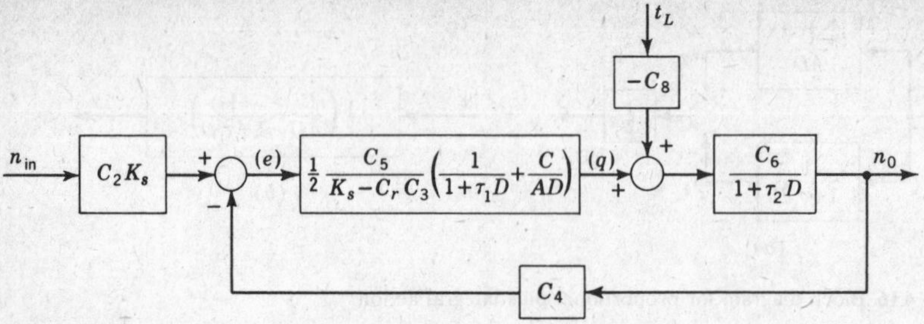

Figure 4.17 Overall block diagram for proportional plus integral control system.

control, suppose that the throttle lever is moved to increase the speed. This causes the position x to move down, as does e'. The time constant τ_1 of the proportional unit is small, so that y_1 changes rapidly to increase the flow setting. The resulting motion of y_1 returns e' to its line-on-line position.

For the integrating unit, the quantity C/A is small, so that y_2 continues to move at a slower rate to provide corrective action. As the speed increases, the position x moves up. The integrating unit continues to provide corrective action until x is returned to its line-on-line position (that is, $x = 0$). In summary, for proportional plus integral control, the initial effect is provided primarily by the proportional action, and the final effect is provided by the integrator.

4.6 MODES OF CONTROL

In addition to proportional, integral, and proportional plus integral control, another mode of control is derivative, or rate, action. For a derivative controller, the steady-state expression for the control elements is

$$K_{G_1} = (KD)_{D=0} = 0 \tag{4.28}$$

The output of a derivative controller is proportional to the rate of change of error. For any constant value of the actuating signal e, the output of the control elements is zero. Thus, steady state may exist in a derivative control system with any constant value of error signal. Because a derivative controller operates on the rate of change of error and not the error itself, the derivative mode of control is never used alone, but rather in combinination with a proportional, or integral, or proportional plus integral controller. The advantage of using derivative action is that the derivative is a measure of how fast the signal is changing and thus tends to give the effect of anticipation. The addition of derivative action is limited primarily to systems which respond very slowly, such as large industrial processes.

The selection of the control elements $G_1(D)$ is seen to have a predominant effect upon the steady-state operation of a system. For more complex control systems, it becomes increasingly difficult, if not impossible, to distinguish the individual modes of control. However, regardless of the various modes that may be present, it is a relatively simple matter to determine whether K_{G_1} is finite or infinite. For an infinite value, the integral action predominates and there is no steady-state error due to variations in the external disturbance. For a finite value, the system behaves as a proportional control system.

A major problem in the design of control systems is the determination of the system parameters to obtain satisfactory transient performance. The transient behavior of a system is prescribed by the differential equation of operation for the system. In the next chapter, it is shown how such differential equations may be solved algebraically by the use of Laplace transforms. In Chap. 6, it is shown that the transient behavior is governed primarily by the roots of the characteristic equation for the system. Thus, the transient characteristics of a system may be ascertained directly from a knowledge of the roots of the characteristic equation.

PROBLEMS

4.1 For the control system shown in Fig. P3.33, determine the steady-state equation relating v, u, and c for each of the following cases:

(a) $G_1(D) = \dfrac{K_1}{1 + \tau_1 D}$ (b) $G_1(D) = \dfrac{K_1}{D}$

(c) $G_1(D) = \dfrac{K_1}{D} + \dfrac{K_1}{1 + \tau_1 D}$

4.2 The steady-state operating curves for a proportional temperature control system are shown in Fig. P4.2.

(a) Determine the equation for steady-state operation about point A.

(b) If this were an open-loop rather than a closed-loop system, what would be the steady-state equation of operation?

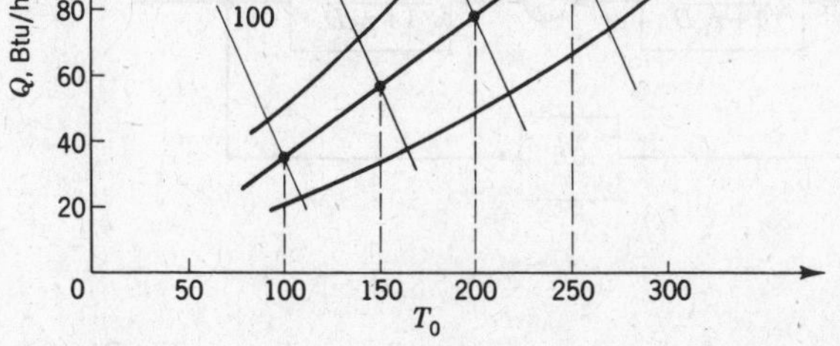

Figure P4.2

4.3 For the illustrative example discussed in Sec. 4.3 (see Fig. 4.11), determine the speed error when $N_{in} = 4000$ and $T_L = 100$. If the slope of the droop line $\partial M/\partial C|_V = -K_H K_{G_1}$ is increased by a factor of 5, what is the new error?

4.4 The block diagram of a feedback control system for operation about a reference operating point is shown in Fig. P4.4. The steady-state equation of operation is

$$c = \frac{\partial C}{\partial V}\bigg|_U v + \frac{\partial C}{\partial U}\bigg|_V u$$

(*a*) Determine the value of K_{G_1} such that $\partial C/\partial U|_V = 0.05$.
(*b*) Determine the value of A such that $\partial C/\partial V|_U = 1$.
(*c*) For the system to be controlled, what is the slope of the lines of constant U?
(*d*) For the system to be controlled, determine the horizontal spacing ΔC between lines of constant U when $\Delta U = 10$ units.

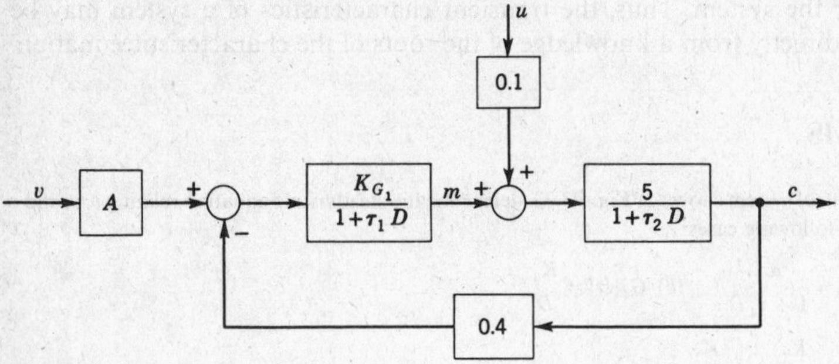

Figure P4.4

4.5 For the system shown in Fig. P4.5,
(*a*) Determine K_{G_1} such that $\partial C/\partial U|_V = 0.1$.
(*b*) Determine A such that $\partial C/\partial V|_U = 1$.

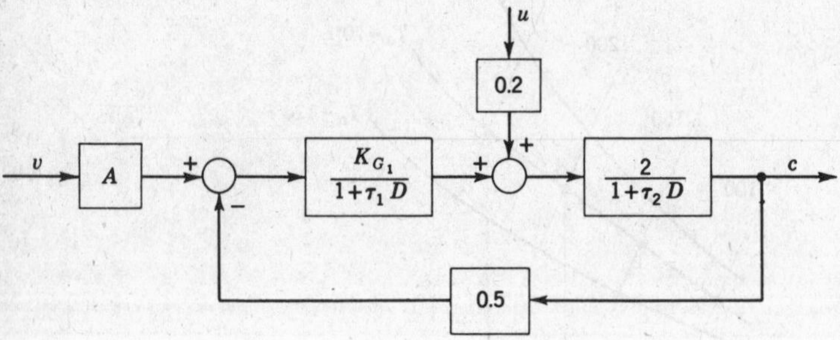

Figure P4.5

4.6 The steady-state operating curves for a system to be controlled are shown in Fig. P4.6.
(*a*) Determine B and K_{G_2} at the reference operating point P.
(*b*) Determine the required slope of the droop lines $(-K_{G_1}K_H)$ such that the variation in C will not exceed 2 percent of its reference value $[c = 0.02(200) = 4$ units$]$ when the external disturbance varies from its reference value to its maximum value ($u = U_{\max} - U_i = 20$ units).

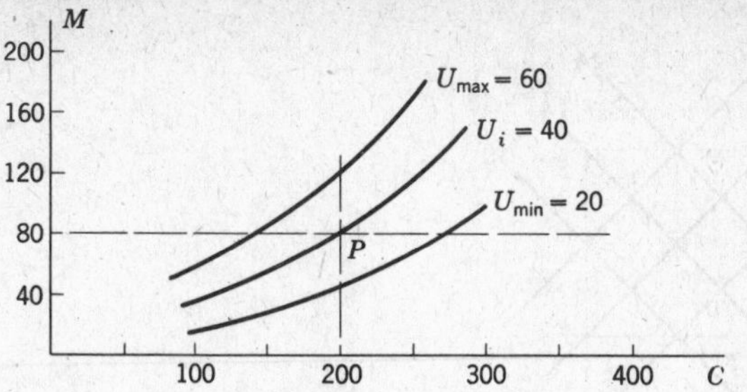

Figure P4.6

4.7 At the reference operating point $C_i = 100$, $M_i = 5$, and $U_i = 10$, the characteristics of a system to be controlled are $B = 0.5$ and $K_{G_2} = 25$. Determine the slope of the load lines U, and then:

(*a*) Draw the nominal load line $U = 10$ for the system to be controlled, and also draw the $U = 6$ and the $U = 14$ load lines. NOTE: Straight lines will suffice because we are working with linearized information about the reference operating point.

(*b*) Calculate the required slope of the droop line such that the output C will not change by more than 1 unit when the load is changed from the nominal value $U = 10$ to $U = 14$.

4.8 Same as Prob. 4.7 except $B = -0.5$.

4.9 The linearized equation of operation for an engine, $N = N(Q, T)$, about the reference point $N_i = 2000$ r/min, $T_i = 400$ ft·lb, and $Q_i = 40$ lb/min is

$$n = 50q - 10t$$

Determine $\Delta N/\Delta Q|_i$, $\Delta N/\Delta T|_i$, and $\Delta T/\Delta Q|_i$. Sketch the operating curve of the engine for $T_1 = 400$ ft·lb and the curve for $T_2 = 500$ ft·lb.

4.10 The block diagram for a feedback control system is shown in Fig. P4.10. At the reference operating condition, $c = u = v = 0$.

(*a*) Determine the value of A such that $c = v$ for steady-state operation.

(*b*) For $u = \Delta U = 10$ units, what is the vertical distance ΔM between lines of constant U?

(*c*) For $v = \Delta V = 10$ units, what is the horizontal distance ΔC between lines of constant V?

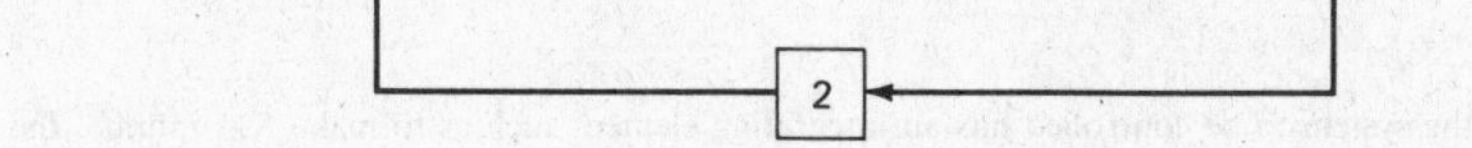

Figure P4.10

4.11 The steady-state operating curves for a unity-feedback system are shown in Fig. P4.11.

(*a*) Evaluate B, K_{G_2}, K_{G_1}, K_H, AK_{G_1}, $\partial C/\partial V|_U$, and $\partial C/\partial U|_V$.

(*b*) If the slope of the droop lines is increased by a factor of 10, what steady-state error results for $V = 400$ ($v = 0$) when U changes from 12 to 10 ($u = -2$)?

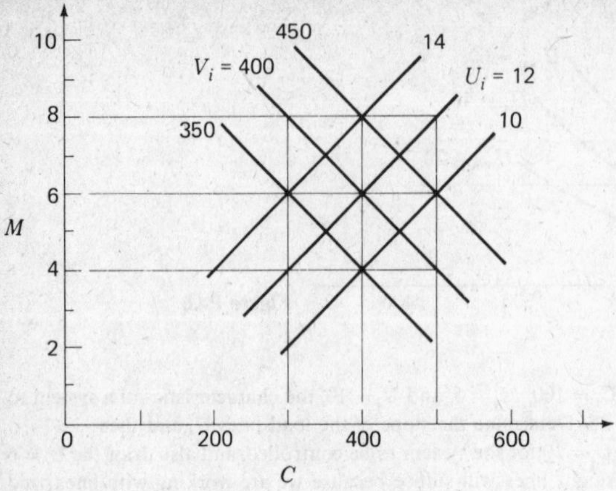

Figure P4.11

4.12 For the control system shown in Fig. P4.12, the reference operating point is $C_i = V_i =$ 4000 r/min, $M_i = 2000$ lb/h, and $U_i = 200$ ft·lb.

(*a*) Determine A such that $c = v$ when $u = 0$.

(*b*) For $V = V_i = 4000$ r/min ($v = \Delta V = 0$), determine the speed error $c = \Delta C$ when $U = 150$ ft·lb ($u = \Delta U = U - U_i = -50$).

(*c*) Determine the required slope of the droop line such that this speed error is reduced to 25 r/min.

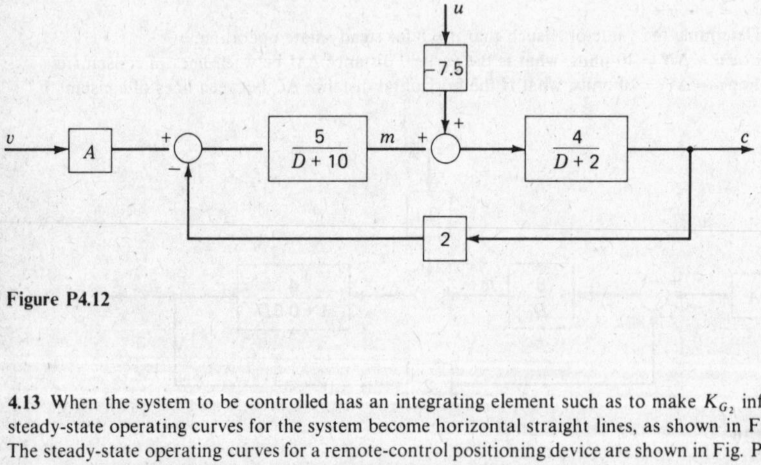

Figure P4.12

4.13 When the system to be controlled has an integrating element such as to make K_{G_2} infinite, the steady-state operating curves for the system become horizontal straight lines, as shown in Fig. P4.13. The steady-state operating curves for a remote-control positioning device are shown in Fig. P4.13. The controlled shaft position is designated by θ_o and the set position by θ_{in}. Variations are to be indicated by $\Delta\theta$. For this remote-control positioning system, the external disturbance is a load torque T_L, and the manipulated variable is a motor torque T_m.

(*a*) Determine the steady-state equation of operation relating $\Delta\theta_o$, $\Delta\theta_{in}$, and t_L for operation about point A.

(*b*) To decrease the error caused by variations in the external disturbance by a factor of 5, what should be the new slope of the droop line?

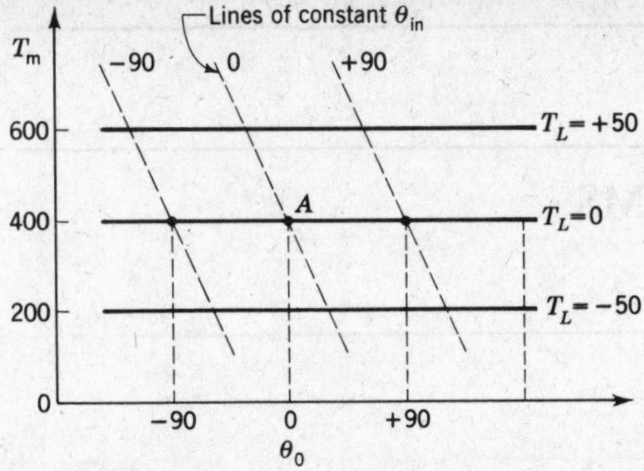

Figure P4.13

4.14 A controller is to be designed for a system such that the output C will not change by more than one unit when the load U increases by 40 units. The steady-state operating curves for the system to be controlled have a slope of 2 units. What is the required slope of the droop lines (*a*) when $B = 0.3$ and (*b*) when $B = -0.3$?

4.15 In Fig. P4.15 is shown the steady-state block diagram for a system which is subjected to two external disturbances. Determine the steady-state equation relating c, v, u_1, and u_2. For which of the following cases will the steady-state operation be independent of variations in u_1? For which cases is it independent of variations in u_2? NOTE: Steady-state operation is independent of K_{G_3}

(*a*) $K_{G_1} = \infty$ $\quad K_{G_2}$ and K_H are finite
(*b*) $K_{G_2} = \infty$ $\quad K_{G_1}$ and K_H are finite

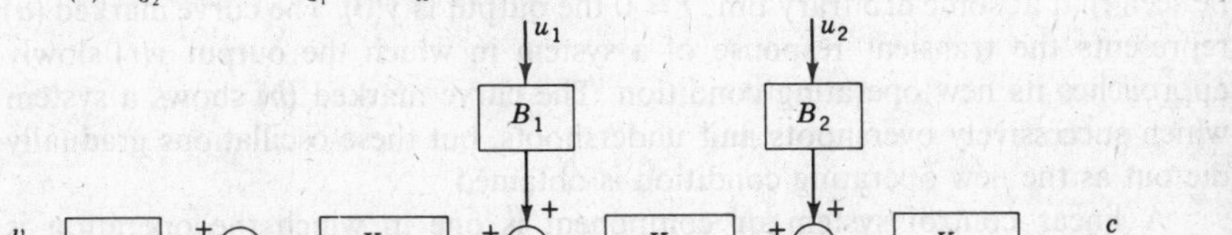

Figure P4.15

4.16 A reproducing shaper is shown in Fig. P4.16. The position y of the duplicating cutter is seen to follow the position x of the master cutter. Determine the mode of operation of the shaper. What modifications would be necessary to convert this to a proportional plus integral controller?

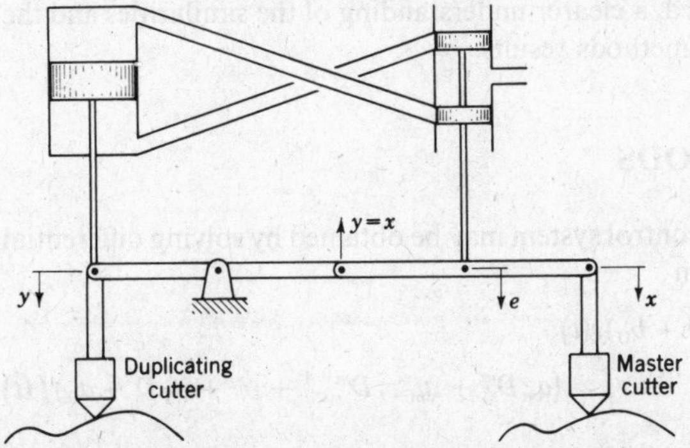

Figure P4.16

CHAPTER

FIVE

LAPLACE TRANSFORMS

By transient response is meant the manner in which a system changes from some initial operating condition to some final condition. For example, in Fig. 5.1 it is to be seen that at some arbitrary time $t = 0$ the output is $y(0)$. The curve marked (a) represents the transient response of a system in which the output $y(t)$ slowly approaches its new operating condition. The curve marked (b) shows a system which successively overshoots and undershoots, but these oscillations gradually die out as the new operating condition is obtained.

A linear control system or component is one in which the operation is described by a linear differential equation, usually with constant coefficients. For a known input, classical methods could be used for determining the output. However, considerable time is saved by using the Laplace transform method of solving linear differential equations. In addition, Laplace transform analysis is closely related to other methods for evaluating system performance, as is explained in later chapters.

A brief review of classical methods for solving differential equations with constant coefficients is first presented. This is done so that, when the Laplace transform method is explained, a clearer understanding of the similarities and the differences between the two methods results.

5.1 CLASSICAL METHODS

The transient response of a control system may be obtained by solving differential equations of the general form

$$(D^n + b_{n-1}D^{n-1} + \cdots + b_1 D + b_0)y(t) = (a_m D^m + a_{m-1}D^{m-1} + \cdots + a_1 D + a_0)f(t)$$

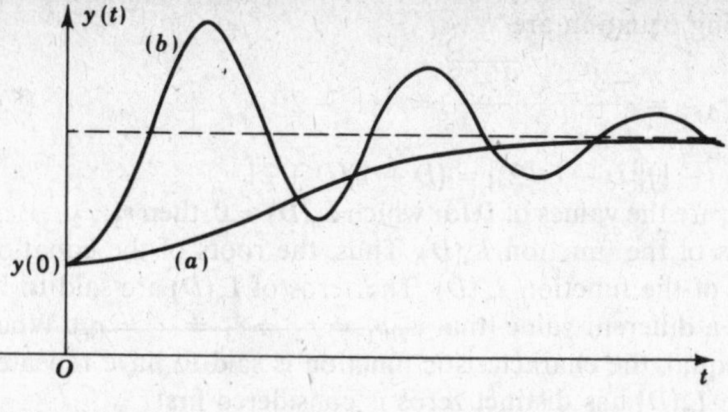

Figure 5.1 Transient response.

If the coefficient b_n of the $D^n y(t)$ term is not unity, it is an easy matter to divide each term by b_n to yield the preceding form. Solving for $y(t)$ gives

$$y(t) = \frac{a_m D^m + a_{m-1} D^{m-1} + \cdots + a_1 D + a_0}{D^n + b_{n-1} D^{n-1} + \cdots + b_1 D + b_0} f(t) \tag{5.1}$$

where $a_0, a_1, \ldots, a_m$ and $b_0, b_1, \ldots, b_{n-1}$ are constants. The term $f(t)$ represents the excitation to the system. This is called the forcing function because it forces or excites the system. The output $y(t)$ is called the response function because it responds to the forcing function $f(t)$. The denominator of Eq. (5.1) is the *characteristic function* of the differential equation. The equation which results from setting the characteristic function equal to zero is called the *characteristic equation*. The value of the exponent n, the highest power of D in the characteristic function, is the order of the differential equation. It is now shown how Eq. (5.1) may be written as the sum of first-order differential equations. First rewrite Eq. (5.1) in the form

$$y(t) = \frac{L_m(D)}{L_n(D)} f(t) \tag{5.2}$$

where
$$L_n(D) = D^n + b_{n-1} D^{n-1} + \cdots + b_1 D + b_0$$
$$L_m(D) = a_m D^m + a_{m-1} D^{m-1} + \cdots + a_1 D + a_0$$

The polynomial $L_n(D)$ may be factored into the form

$$L_n(D) = (D - r_1)(D - r_2) \cdots (D - r_n) \tag{5.3}$$

where $r_1, r_2, \ldots, r_n$ are the roots of the equation $L_n(D) = 0$. In factoring the polynomial $L_n(D)$ as shown in Eq. (5.3), it is to be noted that D may be treated as an algebraic quantity. For example, consider the function

$$L_n(D) = D^2 + 3D + 2 = (D - r_1)(D - r_2) \tag{5.4}$$

Setting $L_n(D)$ equal to zero yields

$$D^2 + 3D + 2 = 0 \tag{5.5}$$

The roots of the preceding equation are

$$r_{1,2} = \frac{-3 \pm \sqrt{9-8}}{2} = -1, -2 \tag{5.6}$$

Therefore, $L_n(D) = [D - (-1)][D - (-2)] = (D + 1)(D + 2)$.

Because $r_1, r_2, \ldots, r_n$ are the values of D for which $L_n(D) = 0$, then $r_1, r_2, \ldots, r_n$ are also called the zeros of the function $L_n(D)$. Thus, the roots of the equation $L_n(D) = 0$ are the zeros of the function $L_n(D)$. The zeros of $L_n(D)$ are said to be distinct if each zero has a different value (that is, $r_1 \neq r_2 \neq r_3 \neq \cdots \neq r_n$). When two or more zeros are equal, the characteristic function is said to have repeated zeros. The case in which $L_n(D)$ has distinct zeros is considered first.

For distinct zeros, $L_m(D)/L_n(D)$ in Eq. (5.2) may be written in the form

$$\frac{L_m(D)}{L_n(D)} = \frac{K_1}{D - r_1} + \frac{K_2}{D - r_2} + \cdots + \frac{K_i}{D - r_i} + \cdots + \frac{K_n}{D - r_n} \tag{5.7}$$

The procedure for obtaining any constant K_i is as follows: First multiply both sides of Eq. (5.7) by $D - r_i$, that is,

$$(D - r_i)\frac{L_m(D)}{L_n(D)} = \frac{D - r_i}{D - r_1}K_1 + \frac{D - r_i}{D - r_2}K_2 + \cdots + K_i + \cdots + \frac{D - r_i}{D - r_n}K_n \tag{5.8}$$

The multiplication of the K_i term in Eq. (5.7) by $D - r_i$ is seen to cancel the denominator, thus leaving K_i alone as shown in Eq. (5.8). Letting $D = r_i$ in Eq. (5.8), each term of the right side of Eq. (5.8) becomes zero except for K_i, which remains. Thus

$$K_i = \lim_{D \to r_i} \left[(D - r_i)\frac{L_m(D)}{L_n(D)}\right] \tag{5.9}$$

Successive application of Eq. (5.9), in which $i = 1, 2, \ldots, n$, yields each of the constants $K_1, K_2, \ldots, K_n$, respectively, in Eq. (5.7). As an example of the use of this partial-fraction-expansion technique, let it be desired to expand $L_m(D)/L_n(D)$, where

$$\frac{L_m(D)}{L_n(D)} = \frac{5D + 8}{D^2 + 3D + 2} = \frac{K_1}{D + 2} + \frac{K_2}{D + 1} \tag{5.10}$$

Application of Eq. (5.9) yields

$$K_1 = \lim_{D \to -2} \left[(D + 2)\frac{5D + 8}{(D + 2)(D + 1)}\right]$$

$$= \lim_{D \to -2} \frac{5D + 8}{D + 1} = \frac{-10 + 8}{-2 + 1} = 2$$

and $$K_2 = \lim_{D \to -1} \frac{5D + 8}{D + 2} = \frac{-5 + 8}{-1 + 2} = 3$$

Thus $$\frac{L_m(D)}{L_n(D)} = \frac{2}{D + 2} + \frac{3}{D + 1} \tag{5.11}$$

The general form for expressing a differential equation as a sum of first-order equations is obtained by substitution of $L_m(D)/L_n(D)$ from Eq. (5.7) into Eq. (5.2). That is,

$$y(t) = \frac{K_1}{D - r_1} f(t) + \cdots + \frac{K_i}{D - r_i} f(t) + \cdots + \frac{K_n}{D - r_n} f(t)$$

$$= \sum_{i=1}^{n} \frac{K_i}{D - r_i} f(t) = \sum_{i=1}^{n} K_i y_i(t) \qquad (5.12)$$

where

$$y_i(t) = \frac{1}{D - r_i} f(t) \qquad (5.13)$$

This differential equation has the same form as Eq. (2.2). The solution corresponding to Eq. (2.3) is

$$y_i(t) = e^{r_i t}\left[\int f(t)e^{-r_i t}\, dt + c_i\right]$$

or

$$y_i(t) = c_i e^{r_i t} + e^{r_i t} \int f(t)e^{-r_i t}\, dt \qquad (5.14)$$

where c_i is the constant of integration. Because the constant of integration is displayed separately in Eq. (5.14), it suffices to evaluate the integral at time t only. Substitution of Eq. (5.14) into Eq. (5.12) yields the following general solution:

$$y(t) = \sum_{i=1}^{n} k_i e^{r_i t} + \sum_{i=1}^{n} K_i e^{r_i t} \int f(t)e^{-r_i t}\, dt \qquad (5.15)$$

where $k_i = c_i K_i$ is a constant. The terms in the first summation of the right side of Eq. (5.15) compose the complementary solution, and the terms in the second summation compose the particular solution. That is,

$$y_c(t) = \sum_{i=1}^{n} k_i e^{r_i t} \qquad (5.16)$$

and

$$y_p(t) = \sum_{i=1}^{n} K_i e^{r_i t} \int f(t)e^{-r_i t}\, dt \qquad (5.17)$$

where $y_c(t)$ is the complementary solution and $y_p(t)$ is the particular solution.

Illustrative example 1 Determine the solution of the following differential equation when all the initial conditions are zero and $f(t) = 4t$.

$$(D^2 + 3D + 2)y(t) = f(t)$$

or

$$y(t) = \frac{1}{(D + 1)(D + 2)} f(t) = \left(\frac{1}{D + 1} - \frac{1}{D + 2}\right) f(t) \qquad (5.18)$$

SOLUTION The substitution of $r_1 = -1$ and $r_2 = -2$ into Eq. (5.16) yields for the complementary solution

$$y_c = k_1 e^{r_1 t} + k_2 e^{r_2 t} = k_1 e^{-t} + k_2 e^{-2t} \qquad (5.19)$$

For $K_1 = 1$ and $K_2 = -1$, the particular solution is evaluated from Eq. (5.17) as follows:

$$y_p = K_1 e^{-t} \int (4t)e^t \, dt + K_2 e^{-2t} \int (4t)e^{2t} \, dt$$
$$= e^{-t}[4e^t(t-1)] - e^{-2t}[e^{2t}(2t-1)]$$
$$= 4(t-1) - (2t-1) = 2t - 3 \tag{5.20}$$

The general solution is the sum of the complementary and the particular solutions. That is,

$$y(t) = k_1 e^{-t} + k_2 e^{-2t} + 2t - 3$$

The derivative $dy/dt = y'(t)$ is

$$y'(t) = -k_1 e^{-t} - 2k_2 e^{-2t} + 2$$

Because the initial conditions are zero, $y(0) = y'(0) = 0$. Evaluation of $y(t)$ and $y'(t)$ at time $t = 0$ gives

$$y(0) = k_1 + k_2 - 3 = 0$$
$$y'(0) = -k_1 - 2k_2 + 2 = 0$$

Solving these two equations simultaneously for k_1 and k_2 yields $k_1 = 4$ and $k_2 = -1$. Thus, the desired result is

$$y(t) = 4e^{-t} - e^{-2t} + 2t - 3 \tag{5.21}$$

Different initial conditions would yield different values for the constants k_1 and k_2.

Repeated Zeros

Suppose that the characteristic function $L_n(D)$ has a multiple or repeated zero r which occurs q times, i.e.,

$$L_n(D) = (D-r)^q(D-r_1)(D-r_2)\cdots(D-r_{n-q}) \tag{5.22}$$

For repeated zeros the partial-fraction expansion has the general form

$$y(t) = \frac{L_m(D)}{L_n(D)} f(t) = \frac{C_q f(t)}{(D-r)^q} + \frac{C_{q-1} f(t)}{(D-r)^{q-1}} + \cdots + \frac{C_1 f(t)}{D-r}$$
$$+ \frac{K_1 f(t)}{D-r_1} + \frac{K_2 f(t)}{D-r_2} + \cdots + \frac{K_{n-q} f(t)}{D-r_{n-q}} \tag{5.23}$$

The constants K_1, K_2, ..., K_{n-q} are evaluated as before by application of Eq. (5.9); however, the constants C_q, C_{q-1}, ..., C_1, which arise from the partial-fraction expansion of the repeated zero, are evaluated as follows:

$$C_q = \lim_{D\to r}\left[(D-r)^q \frac{L_m(D)}{L_n(D)}\right]$$

$$C_{q-1} = \lim_{D\to r}\left\{\frac{1}{1!}\frac{d}{dD}\left[(D-r)^q \frac{L_m(D)}{L_n(D)}\right]\right\} \tag{5.24}$$

$$C_{q-k} = \lim_{D\to r}\left\{\frac{1}{k!}\frac{d^k}{dD^k}\left[(D-r)^q \frac{L_m(D)}{L_n(D)}\right]\right\}$$

The portion of the response due to the term $C_i f(t)/(D-r)^i$ in Eq. (5.23) is

$$y_i(t) = \frac{C_i f(t)}{(D-r)^i} = (c_0 + c_1 t + \cdots + c_{i-1}t^{i-1})e^{rt} + C_i e^{rt}\int\cdots\int f(t)e^{-rt}(dt)^i \qquad i = 2, 3, \ldots, q \tag{5.25}$$

where c_0, c_1, ..., c_{i-1} are constants which must be evaluated from the initial conditions. The first term containing the c constants is the complementary solution, whereas the second term on the right side of the preceding expression is the particular solution. The response due to the distinct zeros in Eq. (5.23) may be evaluated by application of Eq. (5.15).

Illustrative example 2 Determine the solution of the following differential equation when all the initial conditions are zero and $f(t) = e^{-t}$

$$(D+1)^2(D+2)y(t) = f(t)$$

or

$$y(t) = \frac{1}{(D+1)^2(D+2)} f(t) = \left[\frac{C_2}{(D+1)^2} + \frac{C_1}{(D+1)} + \frac{K_1}{(D+2)}\right] f(t) \tag{5.26}$$

SOLUTION For this example q is 2, so that

$$C_2 = \lim_{D\to -1}\left[(D+1)^2\frac{1}{(D+1)^2(D+2)}\right] = \left[\frac{1}{D+2}\right]_{D=-1} = 1$$

$$C_1 = \lim_{D\to -1}\left[\frac{d}{dD}\frac{1}{D+2}\right] = \left[\frac{-1}{(D+2)^2}\right]_{D=-1} = -1 \tag{5.27}$$

$$K_1 = \lim_{D\to -2}\left[(D+2)\frac{1}{(D+1)^2(D+2)}\right] = \left[\frac{1}{(D+1)^2}\right]_{D=-2} = 1$$

Application of Eq. (5.25) yields for the response due to the first term on the right side of Eq. (5.26)

$$y = (c_0 + c_1 t)e^{-t} + C_2 e^{-t} \iint e^{-t}e^{t}\,dt\,dt$$

$$= (c_0 + c_1 t)e^{-t} + 0.5t^2 e^{-t}$$

The response due to the second term is

$$y = c_2 e^{-t} + C_1 e^{-t} \int e^{-t}e^{t}\,dt = c_2 e^{-t} - te^{-t}$$

Application of Eq. (5.15) yields for the response due to the last term

$$y = k_3 e^{-2t} + K_1 e^{-2t} \int e^{-t}e^{2t}\,dt = k_3 e^{-2t} + e^{-t}$$

The general solution is the sum of the responses due to each of these three terms. That is,

$$y(t) = [(c_0 + c_2) + c_1 t]e^{-t} + k_3 e^{-2t} + (1 - t + 0.5t^2)e^{-t}$$

$$= (k_1 + k_2 t)e^{-t} + k_3 e^{-2t} + 0.5t^2 e^{-t} \tag{5.28}$$

where $k_1 = c_0 + c_2 + 1$ and $k_2 = c_1 - 1$. Successive differentiation yields

$$y'(t) = [-k_1 + k_2(1 - t)]e^{-t} - 2k_3 e^{-2t} + (t - 0.5t^2)e^{-t}$$

$$y''(t) = [k_1 - k_2(2 - t)]e^{-t} + 4k_3 e^{-2t} + (1 - 2t + 0.5t^2)e^{-t}$$

Because the initial conditions are zero, $y(0) = y'(0) = y''(0) = 0$. Thus, evaluation of $y(t)$, $y'(t)$, and $y''(t)$ at $t = 0$ gives

$$y(0) = k_1 + k_3 = 0$$

$$y'(0) = -k_1 + k_2 - 2k_3 = 0$$

$$y''(0) = k_1 - 2k_2 + 4k_3 + 1 = 0$$

Solving these three equations simultaneously yields $k_1 = 1$, $k_2 = -1$, and $k_3 = -1$. Thus the desired result is

$$y(t) = (1 - t + 0.5t^2)e^{-t} - e^{-2t} \tag{5.29}$$

Numerous techniques such as the method of undetermined coefficients, variation of parameters, etc., have been developed for solving linear differential equations with constant coefficients. However, the method of Laplace transforms, which is next described, is best suited for solving the type of problems which are of interest to control engineers. In many ways, the Laplace transform method is similar to the preceding method of using the partial-fraction expansion to reduce an nth order equation to the sum of n lower-order equations. A major difference is that, in the Laplace transform method, the response due to each term in the partial-fraction expansion is determined directly from the transform table. Thus, there is no need to perform the integrations indicated by either Eq. (5.15) or Eq. (5.25). Because initial conditions are automatically incorporated into the Laplace transforms, the resulting response expression yields directly the total solution (i.e., complementary plus particular solution). Thus, the constants arising from the initial conditions are automatically evaluated, so that the final desired result is obtained directly.

5.2 LAPLACE TRANSFORMATION METHOD

This method of solving differential equations is somewhat analogous to the process of multiplying or dividing using logarithms. In the well-known transformation of logarithms, numbers are transformed into powers of the base 10 or some other base. This process in effect makes it possible to multiply and divide by using the simpler operations of addition and subtraction. After obtaining the desired answer in logarithms, the transformation back to the real-number system is accomplished by finding antilogarithms.

In the method of Laplace transforms, transformation of the terms of the differential equation yields an algebraic equation in another variable s. Thereafter, the solution of the differential equation is effected by simple algebraic manipulations in the s domain (the new variable is s rather than time t). To obtain the desired time solution, it is necessary to invert the transform of the solution from the s domain back to the time domain. Actually, for much control work, information obtained in the s domain suffices, so that it may be unnecessary to invert back to the time domain.

The Laplace transformation $F(s)$ of a function of time $f(t)$ is[1]

$$F(s) = \mathscr{L}[f(t)] = \int_0^\infty f(t)e^{-st}\,dt \tag{5.30}$$

where $\mathscr{L}$ is the symbol for taking the Laplace transform. The symbol $\mathscr{L}$ is read "transform of," so that $\mathscr{L}[f(t)]$ means "transform of $f(t)$." For the integral on the right side of Eq. (5.30) the variable t vanishes after evaluation between the limits of integration. Thus, the resulting expression is a function of s only [that is, $F(s)$].

Transforming Functions from the Time Domain to the s Domain

Some input functions which are frequently used for investigating the characteristics of a control system are the step function, pulse function, impulse function, exponentially decaying function, and sinusoid.

[1] F. H. Raven, "Mathematics of Engineering Systems," McGraw-Hill Book Co., New York, 1966.

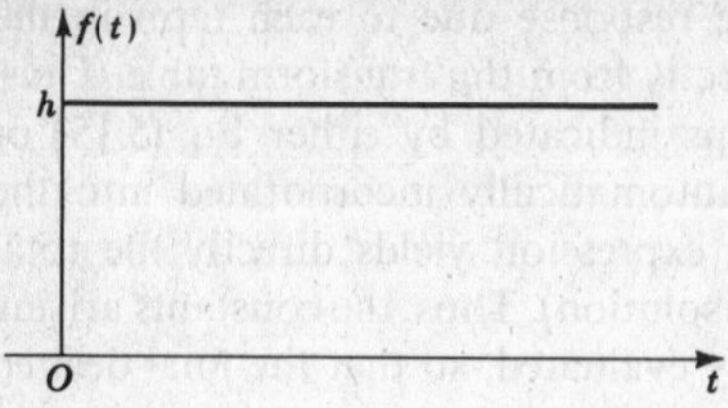

Figure 5.2 Step function.

Step Function

A graphical representation of a step function is shown in Fig. 5.2. A step function is designated by the symbol $hu(t)$, where h is the height and $u(t)$ is the symbol for a unit step function whose height is 1. Application of Eq. (5.30) gives

$$F(s) = \mathscr{L}[hu(t)] = \int_0^\infty he^{-st}\,dt = -\frac{he^{-st}}{s}\bigg|_0^\infty = \frac{h(-e^{-s(\infty)} + e^{-s(0)})}{s} = \frac{h}{s} \tag{5.31}$$

In evaluating a transform, the term s is regarded as any constant which makes $F(s)$ convergent. As illustrated by Eq. (5.31), if s is any positive constant $(s > 0)$, then $e^{-s\infty} = 0$ and $e^{-s0} = e^{-0} = 1$, so that the result follows. However, it should be noted, for negative values of s, that $e^{-s\infty} = e^{\infty} = \infty$, in which case $F(s)$ would be divergent. The operator s must be taken as any constant such that $F(s)$ is convergent. Although there is a range of values of s over which $F(s)$ is convergent, there is but one transform $F(s)$ corresponding to each time function $f(t)$. In Table 5.1 is shown a list of time functions $f(t)$ and their corresponding transforms $F(s)$. In solving problems by Laplace transforms, the term s acts as a dummy operator, and thus there is no need to know the range of values over which $F(s)$ exists.

The listing of transform pairs [i.e., corresponding values of $F(s)$ and $f(t)$] given in Table 5.1 is adequate for the solution of most problems which arise in control engineering. The derivation of most of these transform pairs is now explained.

Pulse Function

A pulse function is shown in Fig. 5.3. The height of the function is h and the width t_0, so that its area is ht_0. The Laplace transform is obtained by applying Eq. (5.30), in which $f(t) = h$ for $0 < t < t_0$ and $f(t) = 0$ for $t > t_0$.

$$F(s) = \int_0^{t_0} he^{-st}\,dt = h\left[\frac{-e^{-st}}{s}\right]_0^{t_0} = \frac{h}{s}(1 - e^{-t_0 s}) \tag{5.32}$$

A special case of a pulse function is an impulse function. If the height is designated as $h = k/t_0$, it follows that the area is always equal to k. Now, as the width t_0

Table 5.1 Laplace transform pairs

$f(t)$	$F(s)$
$u(t)$	$\frac{1}{s}$
$u_1(t)$	1
e^{at}	$\frac{1}{s-a}$
t^n	$\frac{n!}{s^{n-1}}$
$t^n e^{at}$	$\frac{n!}{(s-a)^{n-1}}$
$\sin \omega t$	$\frac{\omega}{s^2+\omega^2}$
$\cos \omega t$	$\frac{s}{s^2+\omega^2}$
$e^{at} \sin \omega t$	$\frac{\omega}{(s-a)^2+\omega^2}$
$e^{at} \cos \omega t$	$\frac{(s-a)}{(s-a)^2+\omega^2}$

approaches zero, the height becomes infinite but the area remains equal to k. This limiting case of a pulse function is called an impulse. The symbol $ku_1(t)$ represents an impulse function whose area is k. Substitution of $h = k/t_0$ into Eq. (5.32) and taking the limit as t_0 approaches zero gives the following transform for an impulse:

$$F(s) = \mathscr{L}[ku_1(t)] = \lim_{t_0 \to 0} \left[\frac{k}{t_0 s} (1 - e^{-t_0 s}) \right] = \frac{0}{0}$$

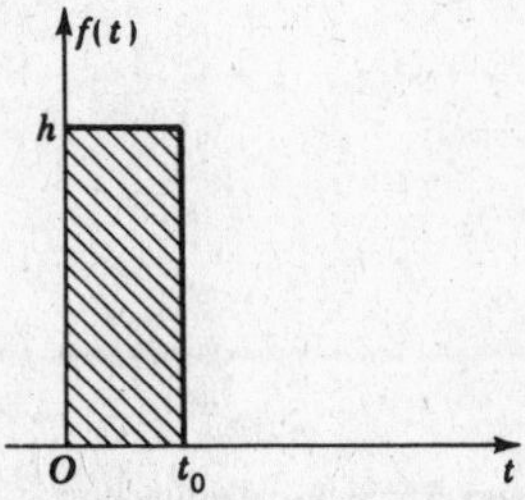

Figure 5.3 Pulse function.

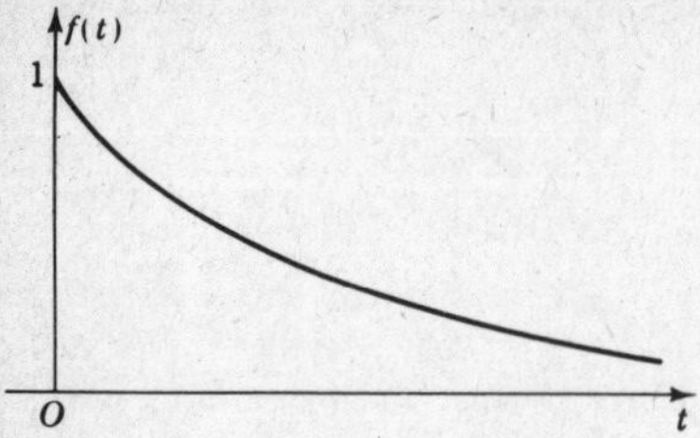

Figure 5.4 Exponentially decaying function.

Application of Lhopital's rule for evaluating the preceding indeterminant gives

$$F(s) = \lim_{t_0 \to 0} \frac{d[k(1 - e^{-t_0 s})]/dt_0}{d(t_0 s)/dt_0} = \lim_{t_0 \to 0} \frac{kse^{-t_0 s}}{s} = k \tag{5.33}$$

The transform of an impulse function is thus seen to be equal to the area of the function. The impulse function whose area is unity, $u_1(t)$, is called a unit impulse. Much information about the transient behavior of a system may be obtained by determining the manner in which a system returns to its equilibrium state after the system has been excited by a momentary disturbance such as a pulse or an impulse.

Exponentially Decaying Function

The function $f(t) = e^{-at}$ is shown in Fig. 5.4. Applying Eq. (5.30) gives the transform of this exponentially decaying function.

$$F(s) = \mathscr{L}(e^{-at}) = \int_0^\infty e^{-(a+s)t}\, dt = -\left.\frac{e^{-(a+s)t}}{s+a}\right|_0^\infty = \frac{1}{s+a} \tag{5.34}$$

Sinusoidal Function

A sinusoidal time function is shown in Fig. 5.5. The equation for this sinusoidal is $f(t) = \sin \omega t$. Thus

$$F(s) = \mathscr{L}(\sin \omega t) = \int_0^\infty e^{-st} \sin \omega t\, dt \tag{5.35}$$

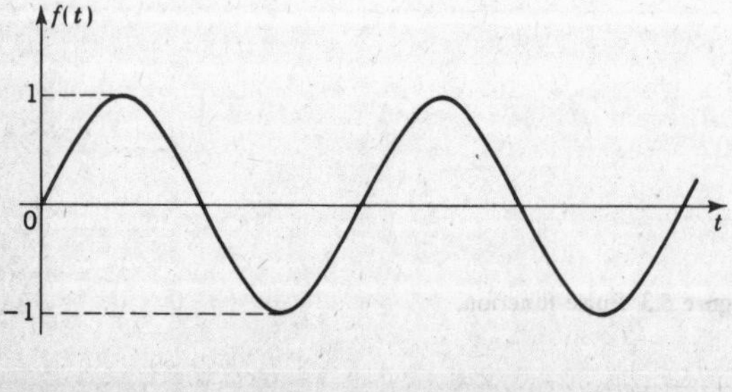

Figure 5.5 Sinusoidal function.

The preceding integration is simplified by making use of Euler's equations.

$$e^{j\theta} = \cos\theta + j\sin\theta$$
$$e^{-j\theta} = \cos\theta - j\sin\theta \tag{5.36}$$

Adding Euler's equations and dividing by 2 yields

$$\cos\theta = \frac{e^{j\theta} + e^{-j\theta}}{2} \tag{5.37}$$

Subtracting the second of Euler's equations from the first and dividing by $2j$ yields

$$\sin\theta = \frac{e^{j\theta} - e^{-j\theta}}{2j} \tag{5.38}$$

Substitution of the exponential form for $\sin\theta$ as given by Eq. (5.38) into Eq. (5.35) gives

$$F(s) = \int_0^\infty \frac{e^{j\omega t} - e^{-j\omega t}}{2j} e^{-st}\,dt$$
$$= \frac{1}{2j}\left(\frac{1}{s - j\omega} - \frac{1}{s + j\omega}\right) = \frac{\omega}{s^2 + \omega^2} \tag{5.39}$$

The response of a system to a sinusoidal forcing function forms the basis for appraising the performance of systems by frequency-response techniques, as discussed in Chaps. 11 and 12.

The validity of Euler's equations is proved by expanding $e^{j\theta}$, $\cos\theta$, and $\sin\theta$ by use of Maclaurin's series. Thus,

$$e^{j\theta} = 1 + j\theta + \frac{(j\theta)^2}{2!} + \frac{(j\theta)^3}{3!} + \frac{(j\theta)^4}{4!} + \frac{(j\theta)^5}{5!} + \cdots$$
$$= \left(1 - \frac{\theta^2}{2!} + \frac{\theta^4}{4!} - \cdots\right) + j\left(\theta - \frac{\theta^3}{3!} + \frac{\theta^5}{5!} - \cdots\right)$$
$$\cos\theta = 1 - \frac{\theta^2}{2!} + \frac{\theta^4}{4!} - \cdots$$
$$\sin\theta = \theta - \frac{\theta^3}{3!} + \frac{\theta^5}{5!} - \cdots$$

The results of Eq. (5.36) follow directly from the preceding expansions.

Because the vector $e^{j\theta}$ is the vector sum of $\cos\theta + j\sin\theta$, the magnitude of $e^{j\theta}$ is always $\cos^2\theta + \sin^2\theta = 1$. The physical significance of the unit vector $e^{j\theta}$ is shown in Fig. 5.6. Here it is to be noticed that $e^{j\theta}$ is a unit vector which is rotated counterclockwise an angle θ from the real axis. For θ equal to 90°, it is seen from the unit circle that $e^{j90^\circ} = j$. Squaring the preceding unit vector yields $j^2 = e^{j90^\circ}e^{j90^\circ} = e^{j180^\circ}$. From the unit circle, this vector is seen to be equal to -1. Thus, $j^2 = -1$, and $j = \sqrt{-1}$.

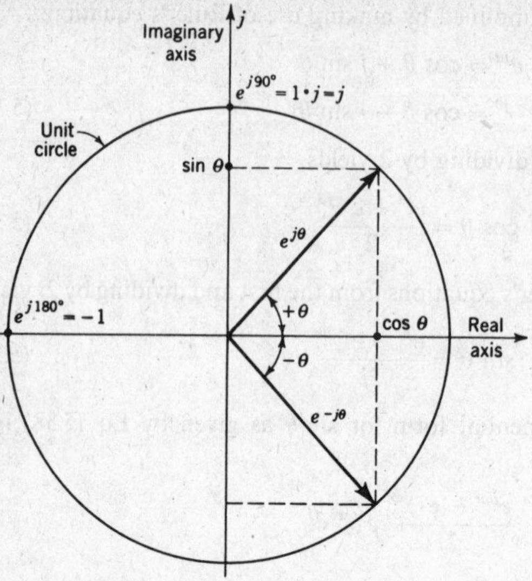

Figure 5.6 Physical significance of unit vector, $e^{j\theta}$

5.3 TRANSFORM PROPERTIES

Significant characteristics and theorems pertaining to Laplace transformations are developed in this section. A list of Laplace transform properties is given in Table 5.2. With the aid of these properties, the usefulness of the Laplace transformation method is greatly extended. In addition these theorems help us to obtain a much better understanding of the method.

Real Translation

The Laplace transform of a function $f(\tau) = f(t - t_0)$ which begins at some time $t = t_0$, as shown in Fig. 5.7, rather than at $t = 0$, may be obtained directly by application of the real-translation theorem. From Eq. (5.30), the Laplace transform for $f(\tau)$ is

$$\mathscr{L}[f(\tau)] = \int_0^\infty f(\tau)e^{-st}\,dt = \int_{t_0}^\infty f(\tau)e^{-st}\,dt \tag{5.40}$$

where $f(\tau) = f(t - t_0)$ is zero for $t < t_0$. By noting that $t = t_0 + \tau$, $dt = d\tau$, and the lower limit of integration $t = t_0$ corresponds to $\tau = 0$, the preceding integral becomes

$$\mathscr{L}[f(\tau)] = \int_0^\infty f(\tau)e^{-s(t_0+\tau)}\,d\tau = e^{-t_0 s}\int_0^\infty f(\tau)e^{-s\tau}\,d\tau \tag{5.41}$$

Table 5.2 Laplace transform properties

Time function	Laplace transform
$kf(t)$	$kF(s)$
$f_1(t) \pm f_2(t)$	$F_1(s) \pm F_2(s)$
$f'(t)$	$sF(s) - f(0)$
$f''(t)$	$s^2F(s) - sf(0) - f'(0)$
$f^n(t)$	$s^nF(s) - s^{n-1}f(0) - \cdots - f^{n-1}(0)$
$f^{(-1)}(t)$	$\dfrac{F(s)}{s} + \dfrac{f^{(-1)}(0)}{s}$
$f^{(-n)}(t)$	$\dfrac{F(s)}{s^n} + \dfrac{f^{(-1)}(0)}{s^n} + \cdots + \dfrac{f^{(-n)}(0)}{s}$
$f(at)$	$\dfrac{1}{a}F\left(\dfrac{s}{a}\right)$
$e^{at}f(t)$	$F(s-a)$
$t^nf(t)$	$(-1)^n \dfrac{d^n}{ds^n} F(s)$
$f(\tau) = f(t - t_0)$	$e^{-t_0 s}F(s)$
$\int_0^t f(\lambda)g(t-\lambda)\,d\lambda$	$F(s)G(s)$

It is to be noted that

$$\int_0^\infty f(\tau)e^{-s\tau}\,d\tau = \int_0^\infty f(t)e^{-st}\,dt = F(s)$$

where $F(s)$ is the transform of the function if it is not delayed. Substitution of the preceding result into Eq. (5.41) gives

$$\mathscr{L}[f(\tau)] = \mathscr{L}[f(t - t_0)] = e^{-t_0 s}F(s) \qquad (5.42)$$

An application of Eq. (5.42) is immediately evident by noting that the pulse function shown in Fig. 5.3 may be regarded as a step function of height h which

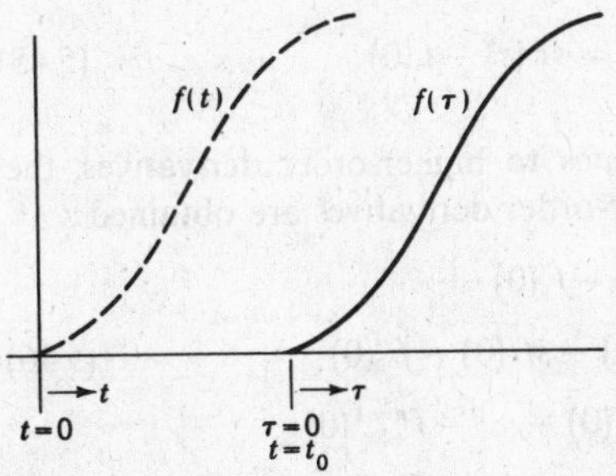

Figure 5.7 Delayed time function.

begins at $t = 0$ minus a step function of height h which begins at $t = t_0$. The transform for the first step function is h/s, while that for the delayed step function is $(h/s)e^{-t_0 s}$. Subtracting the delayed step function from the first yields the following transform for the pulse:

$$\frac{h}{s}(1 - e^{-t_0 s})$$

This is the result given by Eq. (5.32).

Transform of a Derivative

Any linear differential equation will of course have derivatives of various orders. The order of each derivative is the same as the exponent of the operator D in the operational representation of the term. The general expression for transforming derivatives is obtained as follows:

The form for integration by parts is

$$\int u\,dv = uv - \int v\,du$$

Let $u = f(t)$, and $v = -e^{-st}/s$; then $du = (d/dt)[f(t)]\,dt$ and $dv = e^{-st}\,dt$. Integration between the limits of zero and infinity gives

$$\int_0^\infty f(t)e^{-st}\,dt = -f(t)\frac{e^{-st}}{s}\bigg|_0^\infty + \frac{1}{s}\int_0^\infty \frac{d}{dt}f(t)e^{-st}\,dt \qquad (5.43)$$

The left side is $F(s)$. The upper limit of the first term on the right side is zero. Thus

$$F(s) = \frac{f(0)}{s} + \frac{1}{s}\int_0^\infty \frac{d[f(t)]}{dt}e^{-st}\,dt$$

$$= \frac{f(0)}{s} + \frac{1}{s}\mathscr{L}\left[\frac{df(t)}{dt}\right] \qquad (5.44)$$

where $f(0)$ is the initial value of $f(t)$. Solving Eq. (5.44) for the transform of the derivative gives

$$\mathscr{L}\left[\frac{df(t)}{dt}\right] = \mathscr{L}[f'(t)] = sF(s) - f(0) \qquad (5.45)$$

By the extension of the preceding techniques to higher-order derivatives, the following equations for transforms of higher-order derivatives are obtained:

$$\begin{aligned}\mathscr{L}[f''(t)] &= s^2F(s) - sf(0) - f'(0)\\ \mathscr{L}[f'''(t)] &= s^3F(s) - s^2f(0) - sf'(0) - f''(0)\\ \mathscr{L}[f^n(t)] &= s^nF(s) - s^{n-1}f(0) - \cdots - f^{n-1}(0)\end{aligned} \qquad (5.46)$$

where $f'(t) = df(t)/dt$, $f''(t) = d^2f(t)/dt^2, \ldots, f^n(t) = d^nf(t)/dt^n$, and $f'(0)$ is the initial value of $f'(t)$, etc. The initial conditions $f(0), f'(0), f''(0), \ldots$ associated with a particular differential equation must, of course, be given.

An interesting result is obtained when Eq. (5.45) is applied to the function shown in Fig. 5.8*a*. The initial value of this function is $f(0)$. Because of the step change of height h_c, the value of the function for $t > 0$ is $h = h_c + f(0)$. The transform of this function is

$$F(s) = \mathscr{L}[f(t)] = \mathscr{L}\{[h_c + f(0)]u(t)\} = \frac{h_c + f(0)}{s}$$

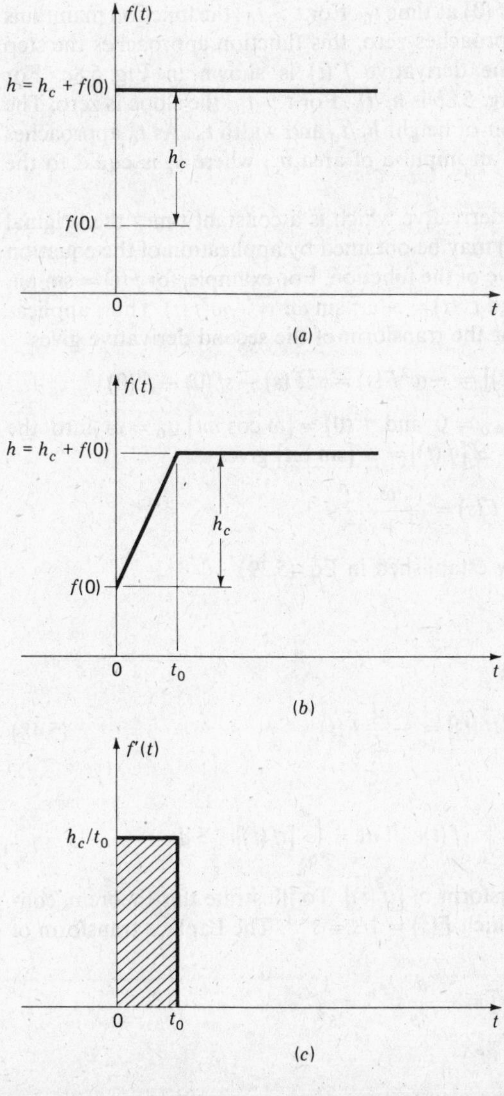

Figure 5.8 Derivative of step change h_c is impulse of area h_c

Application of Eq. (5.45) to obtain the transform of the derivative of this function gives

$$\mathscr{L}\left[\frac{d}{dt}f(t)\right] = sF(s) - f(0) = \frac{s(h_c + f(0))}{s} - f(0) = h_c \tag{5.47}$$

The preceding transform is the same as that obtained for an impulse function. Thus, the derivative of a step change is an impulse function whose area is equal to the change in height h_c of the step.

This result may also be verified geometrically. In Fig. 5.8*b* is shown the function $f(t)$ whose initial value is $f(0)$. The function increases linearly from its initial value $f(0)$ to the value $h = h_c + f(0)$ at time t_0. For $t > t_0$, the function maintains the value h. Note that as t_0 approaches zero, this function approaches the step change shown in Fig. 5.8*a*. The derivative $f'(t)$ is shown in Fig. 5.8*c*. For $0 < t < t_0$, the slope of $f(t)$ in Fig. 5.8*b* is h_c/t_0. For $t > t_0$, the slope is zero. The derivative $f'(t)$ is a pulse function of height h_c/t_0 and width t_0. As t_0 approaches zero, the derivative approaches an impulse of area h_c, where h_c is equal to the change in height of the step.

When a function $f(t)$ has a derivative which is a constant times the original function, then the transform $F(s)$ may be obtained by application of the equation for the transform of the derivative of the function. For example, for $f(t) = \sin \omega t$, it follows that $f'(t) = \omega \cos \omega t$ and $f''(t) = -\omega^2 \sin \omega t = -\omega^2 f(t)$. Thus, application of the general expression for the transform of the second derivative gives

$$\mathscr{L}[f''(t)] = \mathscr{L}[-\omega^2 f(t)] = -\omega^2 F(s) = s^2 F(s) - sf(0) - f'(0)$$

Substitution of $f(0) = [\sin \omega t]_{t=0} = 0$ and $f'(0) = [\omega \cos \omega t]_{t=0} = \omega$ into the preceding and solving for $F(s) = \mathscr{L}[f(t)] = \mathscr{L}[\sin \omega t]$ gives

$$F(s) = \frac{\omega}{s^2 + \omega^2}$$

This verifies the result previously established in Eq. (5.39)

Multiplication by *t*

The Laplace transform of $tf(t)$ is

$$\mathscr{L}[tf(t)] = -\frac{d}{ds}F(s) \tag{5.48}$$

To verify this theorem, note that

$$-\frac{d}{ds}F(s) = -\frac{d}{ds}\int_0^\infty f(t)e^{-st}\,dt = \int_0^\infty [tf(t)]e^{-st}\,dt$$

The last term is the Laplace transform of $[tf(t)]$. To illustrate this theorem, consider the function $f(t) = 1$, for which $F(s) = 1/s = s^{-1}$. The Laplace transform of $tf(t) = t$ is

$$\mathscr{L}[t] = -\frac{d}{ds}s^{-1} = \frac{1}{s^2}$$

For $f(t) = t$ and $F(s) = 1/s^2$, the Laplace transform of $tf(t) = t^2$ is

$$\mathscr{L}[t^2] = -\frac{d}{ds}(s^{-2}) = \frac{2}{s^3}$$

In general, it follows that

$$\mathscr{L}[t^n] = \frac{n!}{s^{n+1}}$$

Multiplication by e^{at}

The Laplace transform of $e^{at}f(t)$ is

$$\mathscr{L}[e^{at}f(t)] = F(s-a) \tag{5.49}$$

This theorem is verified directly by replacing s by $(s-a)$ in the general expression for $F(s)$. That is,

$$F(s-a) = \int_0^\infty f(t)e^{-(s-a)t}\,dt = \int_0^\infty [e^{at}f(t)]e^{-st}\,dt$$

Thus, $F(s-a)$ is the Laplace transform of the term in brackets, $[e^{at}f(t)]$. To illustrate the application of this theorem, let $f(t) = t^n$. For $F(s) = n!/s^{n+1}$, it follows that

$$\mathscr{L}[e^{at}t^n] = \frac{n!}{(s-a)^{n+1}}$$

As another application, consider the function $f(t) = \sin \omega t$. For $F(s) = \omega/(s^2 + \omega^2)$, it follows that

$$\mathscr{L}[e^{at}\sin \omega t] = \frac{\omega}{(s-a)^2 + \omega^2}$$

Change of Scale

The Laplace transform of $f(at)$ is

$$\mathscr{L}[f(at)] = \frac{1}{a}F\left(\frac{s}{a}\right) \tag{5.50}$$

To verify this theorem, first note that

$$\frac{1}{a}F\left(\frac{s}{a}\right) = \frac{1}{a}\int_0^\infty f(t)e^{-(s/a)t}\,dt$$

Next, replacing t by at, in which case dt is replaced by $a\,dt$, gives

$$\frac{1}{a}F\left(\frac{s}{a}\right) = \int_0^\infty [f(at)]e^{-st}\,dt$$

The right side is the transform of $f(at)$. To illustrate the application of this theorem, consider the function $f(t) = \sin t$, for which $F(s) = 1/(s^2 + 1)$. Thus

$$\mathscr{L}[\sin \omega t] = \frac{1}{\omega} F\left(\frac{s}{\omega}\right) = \frac{1}{\omega} \frac{1}{(s/\omega)^2 + 1} = \frac{\omega}{s^2 + \omega^2}$$

Transform of an Integral

In using the Laplace transform method to solve integrodifferential equations, it is necessary to obtain the transform of an integral. The procedure for obtaining the equation for the transform of an integral is similar to that for a differential. In the general expression for integration by parts let $u = \int f(t)\, dt = f^{-1}(t)$ and $dv = e^{-st}\, dt$. Then application of the equation for integration by parts yields

$$\mathscr{L}[f^{(-1)}(t)] = \frac{F(s)}{s} + \frac{f^{(-1)}(0)}{s} \tag{5.51}$$

where $f^{(-1)}(t) = \int f(t)\, dt$ and $f^{(-1)}(0) = \int f(t)\, dt \,|_{t=0}$ is the initial value of the integral.

By the repeated application of this procedure, it is found that

$$\mathscr{L}[f^{(-2)}(t)] = \frac{F(s)}{s^2} + \frac{f^{(-1)}(0)}{s^2} + \frac{f^{(-2)}(0)}{s}$$

$$\mathscr{L}[f^{(-n)}(t)] = \frac{F(s)}{s^n} + \frac{f^{(-1)}(0)}{s^n} + \frac{f^{(-2)}(0)}{s^{n-1}} + \cdots + \frac{f^{(-n)}(0)}{s}$$

where $f^{(-n)}(t) = \int \cdots \int f(t)\, dt^n$.

Linearity Theorem

The linearity characteristic of Laplace transformations is a very useful property. If k is a constant or a variable which is independent of both t and s, then it follows from Eq. (5.30) that

$$\mathscr{L}[kf(t)] = k\mathscr{L}[f(t)] = kF(s) \tag{5.52}$$

Another important linearity property is

$$\mathscr{L}[f_1(t) \pm f_2(t)] = F_1(s) \pm F_2(s) \tag{5.53}$$

Final-value Theorem

This theorem enables one to obtain the value $f(t)$ of a time function at $t = \infty$ directly from the Laplace transform $F(s)$. This is in effect the same type of information which is obtained from a steady-state analysis.

To develop the final-value theorem, first write the equation for the transform of a derivative in the form

$$\int_0^\infty f'(t)e^{-st}\,dt = sF(s) - f(0)$$

For s equal to zero, $e^{-st} = 1$. Thus

$$\int_0^\infty f'(t)\,dt = [sF(s)]_{s=0} - f(0)$$

The left side may be written in the form

$$\int_0^\infty f'(t)\,dt = f(t)\Big|_0^\infty = \lim_{t\to\infty}[f(t)] - f(0)$$

The desired final-value theorem is obtained by equating the right sides of the preceding expressions. That is,

$$\lim_{t\to\infty}[f(t)] = [sF(s)]_{s=0} \tag{5.54}$$

For functions such as $\sin t$, t^n, or e^{at} where $a > 0$, $\int_0^\infty f'(t)\,dt$ does not exist. When the poles of $sF(s)$ are located on or to the right of the imaginary axis, this integral does not exist. The final-value theorem is not applicable in such cases.

Initial-value Theorem

With the aid of the initial-value theorem, the value $f(t)$ of a time function at $t = (0+)$ may be computed directly from the transform $F(s)$ for the function. It is to be noted that $f(0+)$ is not the initial value $f(0)$, but rather the value of the function at a time slightly greater than zero.

The derivation of the initial-value theorem follows: For $t \approx 0$, then $e^{-st} \approx 1$; thus the equation for the transform of a derivative can be written as

$$\mathcal{L}[f'(t)] = \int_0^{0+} f'(t)(1)\,dt + \int_{0+}^\infty f'(t)e^{-st}\,dt = sF(s) - f(0) \tag{5.55}$$

As s approaches infinity, $e^{-st} \approx 0$. Thus, as $s \to \infty$ in Eq. (5.55), the second integral vanishes. Hence,

$$f(0+) - f(0) = \lim_{s\to\infty} sF(s) - f(0)$$

or

$$f(0+) = \lim_{s\to\infty} sF(s) \tag{5.56}$$

This is the mathematical formulation of the initial-value theorem. Application of the initial-value theorem to the step function shown in Fig. 5.8a gives

$$f(0+) = [sF(s)]_{s=\infty} = \frac{s[h_c + f(0)]}{s}\Bigg|_{s=\infty} = h_c + f(0) \tag{5.57}$$

Thus, a step change of height h_c is seen to occur at $t = 0$.

Illustrative example 1 Use the method of Laplace transforms to verify the solution of Illustrative Example 1 in Sec. 5.1. That is,

$$(D^2 + 3D + 2)y(t) = f(t) \tag{5.18}$$

where $f(t) = 4t$ and all initial conditions are zero.

SOLUTION Transforming each term yields for the transformed equation

$$[s^2Y(s) - sy(0) - y'(0)] + 3[sY(s) - y(0)] + 2Y(s) = F(s)$$

For $y(0) = y'(0) = 0$, the transformed equation becomes

$$(s^2 + 3s + 2)Y(s) = F(s)$$

Comparison of this transformed equation with the differential equation shows that when all the initial conditions are zero, the transformed equation is obtained by replacing D, $y(t)$, and $f(t)$ in the differential equation by s, $Y(s)$, and $F(s)$, respectively. The transformed equation is now written in the form

$$Y(s) = \frac{F(s)}{(s+1)(s+2)} = \frac{4}{s^2(s+1)(s+2)}$$

$$= \frac{C_2}{s^2} + \frac{C_1}{s} + \frac{K_1}{s+1} + \frac{K_2}{s+2}$$

where $F(s) = \mathscr{L}[f(t)] = \mathscr{L}[4t] = 4/s^2$. The partial-fraction-expansion constants are evaluated as follows:

$$C_2 = \lim_{s\to 0}\left[s^2\frac{4}{s^2(s+1)(s+2)}\right] = \left[\frac{4}{(s+1)(s+2)}\right]_{s=0} = 2$$

$$C_1 = \lim_{s\to 0}\left[\frac{d}{ds}\frac{4}{s^2+3s+2}\right] = \left[\frac{-4(2s+3)}{(s^2+3s+2)^2}\right]_{s=0} = -3$$

$$K_1 = \lim_{s\to -1}\left[(s+1)\frac{4}{s^2(s+1)(s+2)}\right] = \left[\frac{4}{s^2(s+2)}\right]_{s=-1} = 4$$

$$K_2 = \lim_{s\to -2}\left[(s+2)\frac{4}{s^2(s+1)(s+2)}\right] = \left[\frac{4}{s^2(s+1)}\right]_{s=-2} = -1$$

The resulting transformed equation is

$$Y(s) = \frac{2}{s^2} - \frac{3}{s} + \frac{4}{s+1} - \frac{1}{s+2}.$$

Inverting yields

$$y(t) = 4e^{-t} - e^{-2t} + 2t - 3 \tag{5.21}$$

This verifies the result obtained by classical methods, Eq. (5.21). Differentiation was involved in the evaluation of C_1. An alternative technique which eliminates the need for differentiation is to evaluate all constants which do not require differentiation (e.g., C_2, K_1, and K_2) and then write $Y(s)$ in terms of the unknown constant. Thus

$$Y(s) = \frac{4}{s^2(s+1)(s+2)} = \frac{2}{s^2} + \frac{C_1}{s} + \frac{4}{s+1} - \frac{1}{s+2}$$

This result must hold for any value of s. For $s = 1$, it becomes

$$Y(1) = \frac{4}{(1)^2(2)(3)} = \frac{2}{1^2} + \frac{C_1}{1} + \frac{4}{2} - \frac{1}{3}$$

Hence $\quad C_1 = \frac{2}{3} - 2 - 2 + \frac{1}{3} = -3$

Illustrative example 2 Use the method of Laplace transforms to verify the solution of Illustrative Example 2 in Sec. 5.1. That is,

$$(D+1)^2(D+2)y(t) = (D^3 + 4D^2 + 5D + 2)y(t) = f(t) \qquad (5.26)$$

where $f(t) = e^{-t}$ and all the initial conditions are zero.

SOLUTION Transforming each term in the differential equation yields for the transformed equation

$$[s^3Y(s) - s^2y(0) - sy'(0) - y''(0)] + 4[s^2Y(s) - sy(0) - y'(0)] + 5[sY(s) - y(0)] + 2Y(s) = F(s)$$

For $y(0) = y'(0) = y''(0) = 0$, it follows that

$$(s^3 + 4s^2 + 5s + 2)Y(s) = F(s)$$

The transformed equation may now be written in the form

$$Y(s) = \frac{F(s)}{(s+1)^2(s+2)} = \frac{1}{(s+1)^3(s+2)}$$

$$= \frac{C_3}{(s+1)^3} + \frac{C_2}{(s+1)^2} + \frac{C_1}{s+1} + \frac{K_1}{s+2}$$

where $F(s) = \mathscr{L}[f(t)] = \mathscr{L}[e^{-t}] = 1/(s+1)$. The partial-fraction constants are

$$C_3 = \lim_{s \to -1} \left[(s+1)^3 \frac{1}{(s+1)^3(s+2)}\right] = \left[\frac{1}{(s+2)}\right]_{s=-1} = 1$$

$$C_2 = \lim_{s \to -1} \left[\frac{d}{ds}\left(\frac{1}{s+2}\right)\right] = \left[\frac{-1}{(s+2)^2}\right]_{s=-1} = -1$$

$$C_1 = \lim_{s \to -1} \left[\frac{1}{2!}\frac{d^2}{ds^2}\left(\frac{1}{s+2}\right)\right] = \left[\frac{1}{(s+2)^3}\right]_{s=-1} = 1$$

$$K_1 = \lim_{s \to -2} \left[(s+2)\frac{1}{(s+1)^3(s+2)}\right] = \left.\frac{1}{(s+1)^3}\right|_{s=-2} = -1$$

The resulting partial-fraction expansion is

$$Y(s) = \frac{1}{(s+1)^3} - \frac{1}{(s+1)^2} + \frac{1}{s+1} - \frac{1}{s+2}$$

Inverting yields

$$y(t) = 0.5t^2e^{-t} - te^{-t} + e^{-t} - e^{-2t} = (1 - t + 0.5t^2)e^{-t} - e^{-2t} \tag{5.29}$$

This checks the result obtained by classical methods, Eq. (5.29).

The alternative technique for evaluating C_1 and C_2 without the need for differentiation is to substitute the constants $C_1 = 1$ and $K_1 = -1$, which do not require differentiation, into the expression for $Y(s)$. Thus

$$Y(s) = \frac{1}{(s+1)^3(s+2)} = \frac{1}{(s+1)^3} + \frac{C_2}{(s+1)^2} + \frac{C_1}{s+1} - \frac{1}{s+2}$$

This expression is valid for any value of s. For $s = 0$ and for $s = 1$, we obtain

$$Y(0) = \frac{1}{2} = 1 + C_2 + C_1 - \frac{1}{2} \qquad \text{or} \qquad C_1 + C_2 = 0$$

$$Y(1) = \frac{1}{2^3(3)} = \frac{1}{24} = \frac{1}{8} + \frac{C_2}{4} + \frac{C_1}{2} - \frac{1}{3} \qquad \text{or} \qquad 2C_1 + C_2 = 1$$

Solving these equations simultaneously verifies that $C_1 = 1$ and $C_2 = -1$.

Illustrative example 3 The block-diagram representation for a proportional control system is shown in Fig. 5.9. For $A = 1$, $K_1 = 1$, $K_2 = 2$, $K_H = 0.5$, $B = -5$, $\tau_1 = 1/6$, and $\tau_2 = 1.0$, this system is the same as that discussed in Illustrative Example 1 of Sec. 4.1. Determine the response of this system for each of the following cases:

(*a*) v is a step function of constant value v, and $u = 0$.
(*b*) u is a step function of constant value u, and $v = 0$.

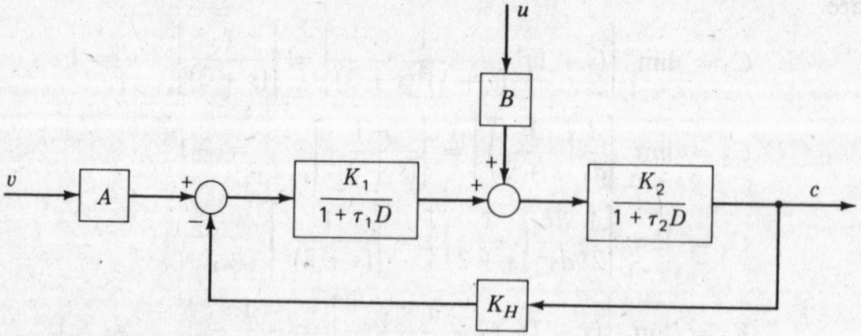

Figure 5.9 Proportional control system.

SOLUTION The differential equation of operation is

$$c(t) = \frac{K_1 K_2 v + BK_2(1 + \tau_1 D)u}{(1 + \tau_1 D)(1 + \tau_2 D) + K_1 K_2 K_H} \tag{5.58}$$

Because the initial conditions are zero, the transformed equation is obtained by replacing D by s, $c(t)$ by $C(s)$, u by $U(s)$, and v by $V(s)$. Thus

$$C(s) = \frac{K_1 K_2 V(s) + BK_2(1 + \tau_1 s)U(s)}{(1 + \tau_1 s)(1 + \tau_2 s) + K_1 K_2 K_H}$$

$$= \frac{(K_1 K_2/\tau_1 \tau_2)V(s) + (BK_2/\tau_1 \tau_2)(1 + \tau_1 s)U(s)}{s^2 + (1/\tau_1 + 1/\tau_2)s + (K_1 K_2 K_H + 1)/\tau_1 \tau_2}$$

Substitution of numerical values into this transformed equation gives

$$C(s) = \frac{12V(s) - 10(6 + s)U(s)}{s^2 + 7s + 12} \tag{5.59}$$

(*a*) For $V(s) = v/s$ and $U(s) = 0$, the preceding becomes

$$C(s) = \frac{12v}{s(s + 3)(s + 4)} = \left(\frac{1}{s} - \frac{4}{s + 3} + \frac{3}{s + 4}\right)v$$

Inverting yields for the response

$$c(t) = (1 - 4e^{-3t} + 3e^{-4t})v$$

Note that as time approaches infinity, $c = v$. Because $c = v$ for steady-state operation, the coefficient of the v term in Eq. (4.1) must be unity. This fact is substantiated by Eq. (4.12), which describes the steady-state behavior of this system.

(*b*) For $V(s) = 0$ and $U(s) = u/s$, the transformed equation is

$$C(s) = \frac{-10(6 + s)u}{s(s + 3)(s + 4)} = \left(-\frac{5}{s} + \frac{10}{s + 3} - \frac{5}{s + 4}\right)u$$

Inverting yields

$$c(t) = (-5 + 10e^{-3t} - 5e^{-4t})u$$

For steady-state operation, $c = -5u$. As is verified by Eq. (4.12), the coefficient of the u term is -5.

The steady-state behavior does not depend on the values of τ_1 and τ_2, but the transient behavior does. For example, if $\tau_1 = 1/15$ and $\tau_2 = 1/2$, the transformed equation becomes

$$C(s) = \frac{60V(s) - 20(15 + s)U(s)}{(s + 5)(s + 12)} \tag{5.60}$$

For $V(s) = v/s$ and $U(s) = 0$, the response is

$$c(t) = [1 - (12/7)e^{-5t} + (5/7)e^{-12t}]v$$

For $V(s) = 0$ and $U(s) = 1/s$, the response is

$$c(t) = [-5 + (40/7)e^{-5t} - (5/7)e^{-12t}]u$$

Illustrative example 4 The block-diagram representation for an integral-type speed control system such as that discussed in Sec. 4.4 is shown in Fig. 5.10. The output speed is n_o, the desired (input) speed is n_{in}, and the load torque is u. For $\tau = 0.25$, $K_1 = 1.0$, $K_2 = 0.75$, and all initial conditions zero, determine the response of the system for each of the following cases:
(*a*) n_{in} is a step function of constant value n_{in}, and $u = 0$.
(*b*) u is a step function of constant value u, and $n_{in} = 0$.

SOLUTION The differential equation of operation is

$$n_o = \frac{K_1 K_2 n_{in} - K_2 Du}{D(1 + \tau D) + K_1 K_2} = \frac{(K_1 K_2/\tau)n_{in} - (K_2 D/\tau)u}{D^2 + (1/\tau)D + (K_1 K_2/\tau)} \tag{5.61}$$

Because the initial conditions are zero, the transformed equation is obtained by replacing D by s, n_o by $N_o(s)$, n_{in} by $N_{in}(s)$, and u by $U(s)$. Thus

$$N_o(s) = \frac{(K_1 K_2/\tau)N_{in}(s) + (K_2 s/\tau)U(s)}{s^2 + (1/\tau)s + K_1 K_2/\tau}$$

Substitution of $\tau = 0.25$, $K_1 = 1.0$, and $K_2 = 0.75$ gives

$$N_o(s) = \frac{3N_{in}(s) - 3sU(s)}{s^2 + 4s + 3} \tag{5.62}$$

(*a*) For $N_{in}(s) = n_{in}/s$ and $U(s) = 0$, the preceding becomes

$$N_o(s) = \frac{3n_{in}}{s(s + 1)(s + 3)} = \left(\frac{1.0}{s} - \frac{1.5}{s - 1} + \frac{0.5}{s + 3}\right)n_{in}$$

Inverting yields for the response

$$n_o(t) = (1.0 - 1.5e^{-t} + 0.5e^{-3t})n_{in}$$

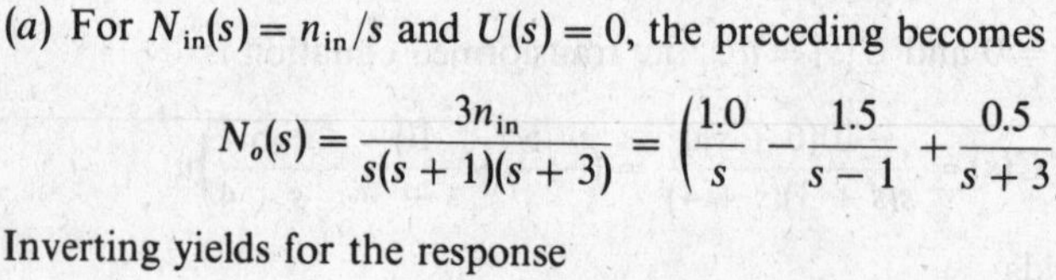

Figure 5.10 Integral control system.

Note that as time approaches infinity, $n_o = n_{in}$. Because $n_o = n_{in}$ for steady-state operation, the coefficient of the v term in Eq. (4.1) must be unity. Checking shows that

$$\frac{AK_{G_1}K_{G_2}}{1 + K_{G_1}K_{G_2}K_H} = \frac{AK_{G_2}}{1/K_{G_1} + K_{G_2}K_H} = \frac{A}{K_H} = 1$$

where $K_{G_1} = K_1/D|_{D=0} = \infty$, $A = 1$, and $K_H = 1$.
(*b*) For $N_{in}(s) = 0$ and $U(s) = u/s$, the transformed equation is

$$N_o(s) = \frac{-3u}{(s+1)(s+3)} = \left(\frac{1.5}{s+3} - \frac{1.5}{s+1}\right)u$$

Inverting yields

$$n_o(t) = (1.5e^{-3t} - 1.5e^{-t})u$$

Note that as time approaches infinity, $n_o = 0$. Because this is an integral-type control system, there is no steady-state error due to the disturbance u. For this case the coefficient of the u term in Eq. (4.1) must be zero. Checking shows that

$$\frac{BK_{G_2}}{1 + K_{G_1}K_{G_2}K_H} = \frac{(-1)(0.75)}{1 + (\infty)(0.75)(1)} = 0$$

where $B = -1$, $K_H = 1$, $K_{G_2} = [K_2/(1 + \tau D)]_{D=0} = K_2 = 0.75$, and $K_{G_1} = (K_1/D)_{D=0} = \infty$.

5.4 INITIAL CONDITIONS

The initial state of the system is specified by the initial conditions. Because initial conditions are the state of the system as t approaches zero from a negative direction, to be more precise these initial condition terms should be designated $f(0-)$, $f'(0-)$, $f''(0-)$, etc. However, for the sake of simplicity, initial conditions are designated as $f(0)$, $f'(0)$, $f''(0)$, etc., throughout this text.

The initial value at time $t = 0-$ for the function shown in Fig. 5.11*a* is indicated by $f(0)$. For $t > 0$, the excitation is he^{-t}. For $t = 0+$, the value of the function is h. Thus, a discontinuity or step change $h - f(0)$ occurs at the origin. The Laplace transform for $f(t)$ is

$$F(s) = \mathscr{L}[f(t)] = \int_0^\infty he^{-t}e^{-st}\,dt = h\int_0^\infty e^{-(s+1)t}\,dt = \frac{h}{s+1}$$

The inverse is

$$f(t) = \mathscr{L}^{-1}[F(s)] = he^{-t} \qquad t > 0$$

Note that the inverse Laplace transform contains no information about the initial condition. Because the inverse yields the response for $t > 0$, the Laplace transform

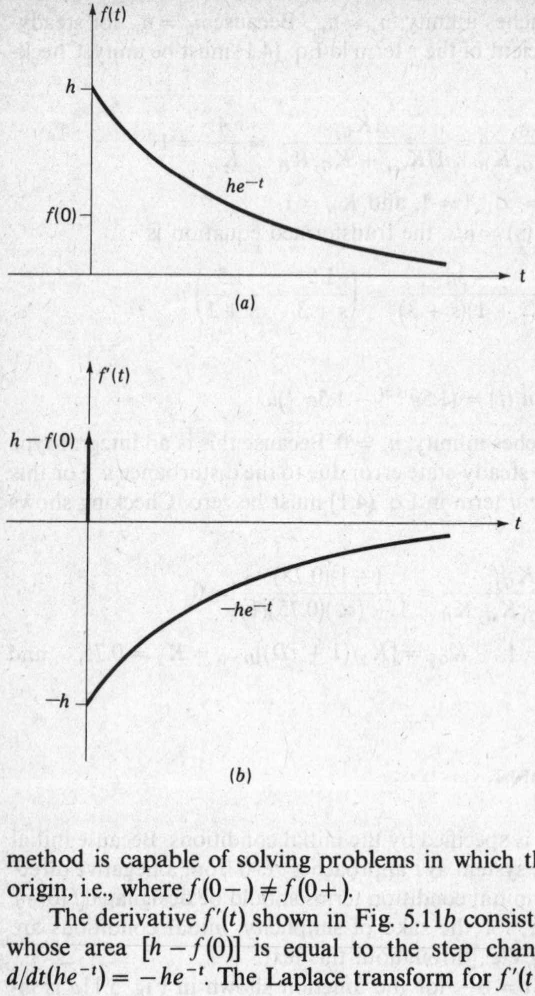

Figure 5.11 Function with a discontinuity at the origin and its derivative.

method is capable of solving problems in which there is a discontinuity at the origin, i.e., where $f(0-) \neq f(0+)$.

The derivative $f'(t)$ shown in Fig. 5.11*b* consists of the impulse at the origin whose area $[h - f(0)]$ is equal to the step change in $f(t)$ and the function $d/dt(he^{-t}) = -he^{-t}$. The Laplace transform for $f'(t)$ is

$$\mathscr{L}[f'(t)] = [h - f(0)] - \frac{h}{s+1}$$

This result may be verified by application of the formula for the transform of a derivative. That is,

$$\mathscr{L}[f'(t)] = sF(s) - f(0) = s\frac{h}{s+1} - f(0) = \left[\frac{sh}{s+1} - h\right] + [h - f(0)]$$

$$= [h - f(0)] - \frac{h}{s+1}$$

Note that the initial condition at time $t = 0-$ must be substituted into the equation for the transform of a derivative.

In taking the Laplace transform of a differential equation, initial condition terms arise in transforming derivative terms. The initial conditions at time $t = 0-$ are substituted into the resulting transformed equation. Inverting this transformed equation yields the response for $t > 0$. Values at time $t = 0+$ are obtained by letting $t = 0+$ in the response equations. Because it is not necessary that the $0-$ values equal the $0+$ values, the transform method can be used for solving differential equations in which there are discontinuities at the origin. Classical methods are not applicable for such discontinuities. The following examples will help clarify this situation. For a more rigorous presentation of this distinction, see Raven.[1]

Illustrative example 1 Use the Laplace transform method to determine the solution of the following differential equation:

$$\frac{dy}{dt} + y = u_1(t) \tag{5.63}$$

The initial condition is $y(0) = 0$.

SOLUTION The transform of the differential equation is

$$[sY(s) - y(0)] + Y(s) = 1$$

For $y(0) = 0$, the transformed equation becomes

$$Y(s) = \frac{1}{s+1}$$

Inverting yields the response

$$y(t) = e^{-t} \qquad t > 0 \tag{5.64}$$

The value at time $t = 0+$ is

$$y(0+) = e^{-(0+)} = 1$$

This result may also be obtained by application of the initial-value theorem,

$$y(0+) = \lim_{s\to\infty} sY(s) = \left.\frac{s}{s+1}\right|_{s=\infty} = \left.\frac{1}{1+1/s}\right|_{s=\infty} = 1$$

As illustrated in Fig. 5.12, the response function $y(t)$ has a discontinuity at the origin $[y(0-) = 0,\ y(0+) = 1]$. To solve such problems by classical methods, it is necessary to use independent methods to determine the state of the system at time $t = 0+$. Because the system is continuous for $t > 0$, the solution may

[1] F. H. Raven, "Mathematics of Engineering Systems," Chap. 2, McGraw-Hill Book Company, New York, 1966.

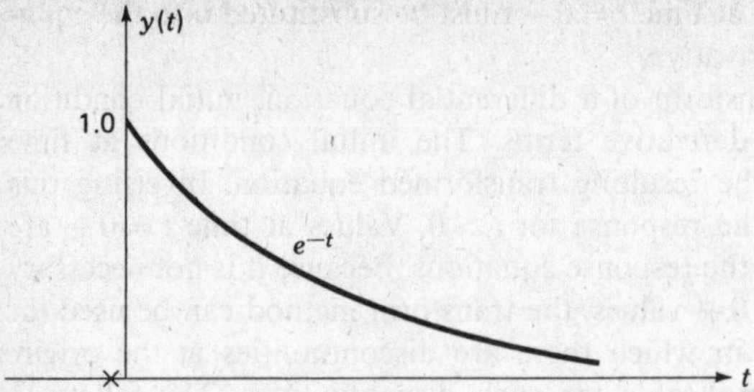

Figure 5.12 Response function.

then be found by classical procedures. To determine the state of the system at $t = 0+$, each term of the differential equation is integrated from $t = 0-$ to $t = 0+$. Thus

$$\int_{0-}^{0+} \frac{dy}{dt}\,dt + \int_{0-}^{0+} y\,dt = \int_{0-}^{0+} u_1(t)\,dt$$

The value of the first term is $y(0+) - y(0-)$. Because y is a bounded function, the integral from $0-$ to $0+$ vanishes. The right side is the area of the impulse at the origin which is unity. Thus

$$y(0+) - y(0-) = 1 \qquad \text{or} \qquad y(0+) = y(0-) + 1 = 1$$

For $t > 0$, the excitation $u_1(t)$ is zero. Thus, for $t > 0$ the differential equation is

$$\frac{dy}{dt} + y = 0 \qquad y(0+) = 1$$

Because $f(t) = 0$, the particular solution is zero. The general solution consists of the complementary solution only,

$$y(t) = k_1 e^{-t}$$

The constant k_1 is evaluated from the boundary condition that $y(0+) = 1$ when $t = 0+$. Thus

$$1 = k_1 e^{-(0+)} = k_1$$

The resulting response is

$$y(t) = e^{-t} \qquad t > 0$$

This verifies the solution obtained by transform methods, Eq. (5.64).

Illustrative example 2 Determine the solution of the differential equation:

$$y(t) = \frac{D+4}{(D+2)(D+3)} f(t) \tag{5.65}$$

The forcing function is $f(t) = 2e^{-t}$, and all initial conditions are zero.

SOLUTION Because all initial conditions are zero, the substitution of s for D, $Y(s)$ for $y(t)$, and $F(s)$ for $f(t)$ yields for the transformed equation

$$Y(s) = \frac{s+4}{(s+2)(s+3)}F(s) = \frac{2(s+4)}{(s+1)(s+2)(s+3)}$$

$$= \frac{K_1}{s+1} + \frac{K_2}{s+2} + \frac{K_3}{s+3}$$

where $F(s) = \mathscr{L}[2e^{-t}] = 2/(s+1)$. The partial-fraction-expansion constants are $K_1 = 3$, $K_2 = -4$, and $K_3 = 1$. Thus,

$$Y(s) = \frac{3}{s+1} - \frac{4}{s+2} + \frac{1}{s+3}$$

Inverting yields for the response

$$y(t) = 3e^{-t} - 4e^{-2t} + e^{-3t} \tag{5.66}$$

The derivative is

$$y'(t) = -3e^{-t} + 8e^{-2t} - 3e^{-3t}$$

The substitution of $t = 0+$ into the preceding expressions shows that $y(0+) = 0$ and $y'(0+) = 2$. These values may also be verified by application of the initial-value theorem.

$$y(0+) = \lim_{s\to\infty} s\mathscr{L}[y(t)] = sY(s)\Big|_{s=\infty} = \frac{2s(s+4)}{(s+1)(s+2)(s+3)}\Big|_{s=\infty}$$

$$= \frac{2(1/s + 4/s^2)}{(1+1/s)(1+2/s)(1+3/s)}\Big|_{s=\infty} = 0$$

$$y'(0+) = \lim_{s\to\infty} s\mathscr{L}[y'(t)] = s[sY(s) - y(0)]_{s=\infty} = s^2Y(s)\Big|_{s=\infty} = 2$$

To effect a classical solution, it is first necessary to use independent means to determine the state of the system at $t = 0+$. The differential equation is written in the form

$$y''(t) + 5y'(t) + 6y(t) = f'(t) + 4f(t)$$

Integrating each term twice and then evaluating between the limits $(0-)$ to $(0+)$ shows that $y(0+) = y(0-) = 0$. Next, integrating each term once and then evaluating between the limits $(0-)$ to $(0+)$ shows that $y'(0+) = y'(0-) + f(0+) - f(0-) = f(0+) = 2$. This second-order differential equation is now expressed as the sum of two first-order differential equations. That is,

$$y(t) = \frac{D+4}{(D+2)(D+3)}f(t) = \left(\frac{2}{D+2} - \frac{1}{D+3}\right)f(t)$$

For $r_1 = -2$ and $r_2 = -3$, the complementary solution is

$$y_c = k_1 e^{-2t} + k_2 e^{-3t}$$

For $K_1 = 2$ and $K_2 = -1$, the particular solution is

$$y_p = 2e^{-2t} \int e^{2t}(2e^{-t})\,dt - e^{-3t} \int e^{3t}(2e^{-t})\,dt$$

$$= 2e^{-2t}(2e^{t}) - e^{-3t}(e^{2t}) = 4e^{-t} - e^{-t} = 3e^{-t}$$

Adding the complementary and the particular solutions yields for the general solution

$$y(t) = 3e^{-t} + k_1 e^{-2t} + k_2 e^{-3t}$$

Differentiation gives

$$y'(t) = -3e^{-t} - 2k_1 e^{-2t} - 3k_2 e^{-3t}$$

Evaluation of $y(t)$ and $y'(t)$ at $t = 0+$, in which case $y(0+) = 0$ and $y'(0+) = 2$, gives $k_1 = -4$ and $k_2 = 1$. This checks the result given by Eq. (5.66).

Illustrative example 3 Determine the response of the following system to a unit impulse $[f(t) = u_1(t)]$ when all the initial conditions are zero.

$$(D^2 + 5D + 6)y(t) = 3(D + 4)f(t) \tag{5.67}$$

SOLUTION Because the initial conditions are zero, substitution of s for D, $Y(s)$ for $y(t)$, and $F(s)$ for $f(t)$ gives

$$Y(s) = \frac{3(s+4)F(s)}{(s+2)(s+3)} = \frac{3(s+4)}{(s+2)(s+3)}$$

where $F(s) = 1$ for a unit impulse. Performing a partial-fraction expansion gives

$$Y(s) = \frac{K_1}{s+2} + \frac{K_2}{s+3} = \frac{6}{s+2} - \frac{3}{s+3}$$

Inverting yields for the desired response

$$y(t) = 6e^{-2t} - 3e^{-3t}$$

The derivative is

$$\frac{dy}{dt} = -12e^{-2t} + 9e^{-3t}$$

Evaluation of $y(t)$ and $y'(t)$ at $t = 0+$ shows that $y(0+) = 3$ and $y'(0+) = -3$.

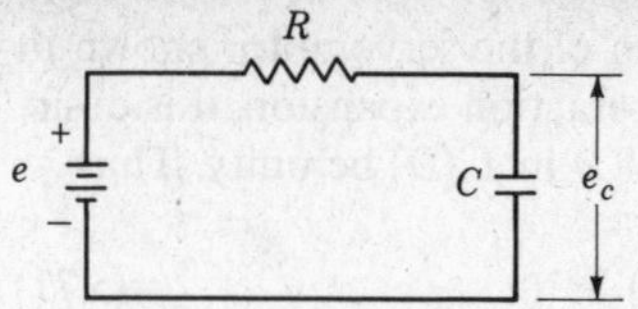

Figure 5.13 Series *RC* circuit.

Integrodifferential Equations

A resistor R and a capacitor C in series are shown in Fig. 5.13. The total voltage drop is the sum of the voltage drop Ri across the resistor and the voltage drop $e_c = \int i\,dt/C$ across the capacitor.

$$e = Ri + \frac{1}{C}\int i\,dt \tag{5.68}$$

The Laplace transform for this integrodifferential equation is

$$E(s) = RI(s) + \frac{1}{sC}\left[I(s) + \left(\int i\,dt\right)_{t=0}\right] = \frac{1}{sC}[1 + RCs]I(s) + \frac{e_c(0)}{s}$$

Solving for $I(s)$ gives

$$I(s) = \frac{C[sE(s) + e_c(0)]}{1 + RCs} \tag{5.69}$$

where $e_c(0) = \int i\,dt/C\,|_{t=0}$ is the initial voltage across the capacitor. The process of obtaining the transform of the integral term may be avoided by first differentiating Eq. (5.68) and then transforming this result. Thus

$$\frac{de}{dt} = R\frac{di}{dt} + \frac{1}{C}i$$

The corresponding transform is

$$sE(s) - e(0) = R[sI(s) - i(0)] + \frac{I(s)}{C}$$

or $$\frac{1}{C}[1 + RCs]I(s) = sE(s) - [e(0) - Ri(0)] = sE(s) - e_c(0)$$

The voltage drop e_c across the capacitor is the applied voltage e minus the voltage drop Ri across the resistor. Solving for $I(s)$ yields the same result given by Eq. (5.69).

5.5 GENERAL PROCEDURES

Let it be desired to determine the solution of the following differential equation:

$$(\tau D + 1)y(t) = Kf(t) \tag{5.70}$$

When $K = 1$, this equation describes the operation of the servomotor shown in Fig. 3.7. For convenience in performing the partial-fraction expansion, it is desirable to have the coefficient of the highest power of D in $L_n(D)$ be unity. Thus

$$\left(D + \frac{1}{\tau}\right)y(t) = \frac{K}{\tau}f(t) \tag{5.71}$$

Transforming each term of this differential equation and solving for $Y(s)$ gives

$$Y(s) = \frac{(K/\tau)F(s) + y(0)}{s + 1/\tau} \tag{5.72}$$

The symbol $F(s)$ is the transform of the input. The nature of the expression $F(s)$ depends upon the particular input to the system, such as a step function, exponential, sinusoidal, etc.

All Initial Conditions Zero

Let it be desired to determine the response of this system to a step-function input $f(t)$ when all the initial conditions are zero. A plot of the input $f(t)$ is shown in Fig. 5.14*a*. The initial value is $f(0) = 0$, and then a step change h_c occurs so that the height of this function is $h = h_c$. The substitution of $F(s) = h_c/s$ and $y(0) = 0$ into Eq. (5.72) gives

$$Y(s) = \frac{Kh_c/\tau}{s(s + 1/\tau)}$$

The partial-fraction expansion is

$$Y(s) = Kh_c\left(\frac{1}{s} - \frac{1}{s + 1/\tau}\right)$$

Inverting yields for the response

$$y(t) = Kh_c(1 - e^{-t/\tau}) \qquad t > 0 \tag{5.73}$$

A graph of this response is also shown in Fig. 5.14*a*.

Initially at a Steady-state Operating Condition

A system is initially at a steady-state operating condition if the initial value of all the time derivatives is zero (that is, $D^n y = D^m f = 0$, $n = 1, 2, 3, \ldots$, and $m = 1, 2, 3, \ldots$). When this system is initially at a steady-state operating condition, then from Eq. (5.71) it follows that $y(0) = Kf(0)$.

Let us now determine the response for the case in which the initial value of the input is $f(0)$, as shown in Fig. 5.14*b*. The height h of the step input is the initial value $f(0)$ plus the change h_c. Thus

$$F(s) = \frac{h}{s} = \frac{h_c + f(0)}{s} = \frac{h_c + y(0)/K}{s}$$

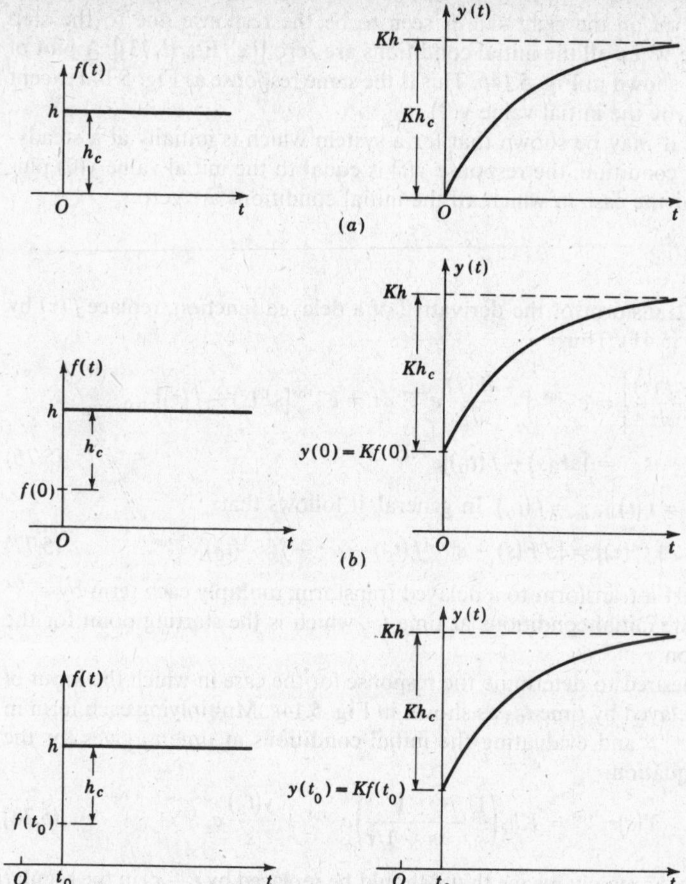

Figure 5.14 Response of first-order system to a step input.

The substitution of this value of $F(s)$ into Eq. (5.72) gives

$$Y(s) = \frac{Kh_c/\tau}{s(s + 1/\tau)} + \frac{y(0)}{s}$$

The partial-fraction expansion is

$$Y(s) = Kh_c\left(\frac{1}{s} - \frac{1}{s + 1/\tau}\right) + \frac{y(0)}{s} \tag{5.74}$$

Inverting yields

$$y(t) = Kh_c(1 - e^{-t/\tau}) + y(0) \qquad t > 0 \tag{5.75}$$

The first term on the right side is seen to be the response due to the step change h_c alone when all the initial conditions are zero [i.e., Eq. (5.73)]. A plot of this response is shown in Fig. 5.14*b*. This is the same response as Fig. 5.14*a* except that it is raised by the initial value $y(0)$.

In general, it may be shown that for a system which is initially at a steady-state operating condition, the response $y(t)$ is equal to the initial value $y(0)$ plus the response for the case in which all the initial conditions are zero.

Time Delay

To obtain the transform of the derivative of a delayed function, replace $f(\tau)$ by $df(\tau)/d\tau$ in Eq. (5.41). Thus

$$\mathscr{L}\left[\frac{df(\tau)}{d\tau}\right] = e^{-t_0 s} \int_0^\infty \frac{df(\tau)}{d\tau} e^{-s\tau}\, d\tau = e^{-t_0 s}[sF(s) - f(\tau)]_{\tau=0}$$

$$= [sF(s) - f(t_0)]e^{-t_0 s} \tag{5.76}$$

where $f(\tau)|_{\tau=0} = f(t)|_{t=t_0} = f(t_0)$. In general, it follows that

$$\mathscr{L}[f^n(\tau)] = [s^n F(s) - s^{n-1} f(t_0) - \cdots - f^{n-1}(t_0)]e^{-t_0 s} \tag{5.77}$$

Thus, to convert a transform to a delayed transform, multiply each term by $e^{-t_0 s}$ and evaluate the initial conditions at time t_0, which is the starting point for the delayed function.

Let it be desired to determine the response for the case in which the input of Fig. 5.14*b* is delayed by time t_0, as shown in Fig. 5.14*c*. Multiplying each term in Eq. (5.74) by $e^{-t_0 s}$ and evaluating the initial conditions at time t_0 gives for the transformed equation

$$Y(s)e^{-t_0 s} = Kh_c\left(\frac{1}{s} - \frac{1}{s + 1/\tau}\right)e^{-t_0 s} + \frac{y(t_0)}{s}e^{-t_0 s} \tag{5.78}$$

The operator $e^{-t_0 s}$ merely means that t should be replaced by $t - t_0$ in the regular transform. Thus, the inverse of Eq. (5.78) is

$$y(t - t_0) = Kh_c(1 - e^{-(t-t_0)/\tau}) + y(t_0) \qquad t > t_0 \tag{5.79}$$

This is the same as Eq. (5.77) except that t has been replaced by $t - t_0$, and the starting point is at time t_0 rather than at $t = 0$. The response shown in Fig. 5.14*c* is the same as that shown in Fig. 5.14*b* except that it is delayed a time t_0. It is not necessary that a system be initially at a steady-state operating condition to effect a time shift. For most problems in which a time shift occurs, it is more convenient to work the problem initially as though there were no time shift, and then replace t by $(t - t_0)$ to obtain the desired result.

The general procedure used to solve differential equations by Laplace transforms may be summarized as follows:

1. Transform each term of the differential equation from the time domain to the s domain, and then solve for $Y(s)$.

2. Substitute the value of the initial conditions and the transform of the input into the expression obtained in step 1.
3. Perform a partial-fraction expansion.
4. Invert each term back to the time domain to obtain the desired time response.

Much simplification in carrying out the algebraic manipulations of a Laplace transform solution is afforded for the following special cases:

1. *All initial conditions zero.* When all the initial conditions are zero, then the transform of a derivative is $\mathscr{L}[D^n f(t)] = s^n F(s)$. Thus, it follows that the transformed equation is obtained by substituting s for D, $Y(s)$ for $y(t)$, and $F(s)$ for $f(t)$ in the original differential equation.
2. *System initially at a steady-state operating condition.* When all the initial derivatives are zero, then evaluating Eq. (5.1) at $t = 0$ shows that $ay(0) = bf(0)$ or $y(0) = (b/a)f(0)$. For this case, the response $y(t)$ is obtained by adding the initial value $y(0)$ to the response for the case in which all the initial conditions are zero (i.e., case 1).
3. *Time shift.* A time shift is effected by substituting $t - t_0$ for t. It is not necessary that all the initial conditions be zero nor that the system be initially at a steady-state operating condition in order to effect a time shift.

Illustrative example 1 Determine the response of the system described by the following differential equation:

$$(D^2 + 7D + 12)y(t) = 6(D + 2)f(t) \tag{5.80}$$

The forcing function $f(t)$ is a unit step function, and all initial conditions are zero.

SOLUTION Because the initial conditions are zero, substitution of s for D, $Y(s)$ for $y(t)$, and $F(s)$ for $f(t)$ yields

$$Y(s) = \frac{6(s+2)F(s)}{s^2 + 7s + 12} = \frac{6(s+2)}{s(s+3)(s+4)}$$

where $F(s) = 1/s$ for a unit step function. Performing a partial-fraction expansion gives

$$Y(s) = \frac{1}{s} + \frac{2}{s+3} - \frac{3}{s+4}$$

Inverting yields for the time response

$$y(t) = 1 + 2e^{-3t} - 3e^{-4t} \tag{5.81}$$

Let it now be desired to determine the response of this system for the case in which the system is initially at a steady-state operating condition (i.e., initially all derivative terms are zero). The initial value of $f(t)$ is $f(0) = 5$. The unit step function is superimposed upon the constant value $f(0) = 5$, so that for $t > 0$, the input is $f(0) + 1 = 5 + 1 = 6$. The initial steady-state value of y is obtained by letting all derivative terms be zero in the differential equation. Thus, $12y(0) = 6(2)f(0)$ or $y(0) = f(0) = 5$. Adding the initial value of y to the response for the case in which all initial conditions are zero yields for the response

$$y(t) = (1 + 2e^{-3t} - 3e^{-4t}) + y(0) = (1 + 2e^{-3t} - 3e^{-4t}) + 5 \qquad (5.82)$$

This response may also be verified by transforming the differential equation termwise.

$$[s^2Y(s) - sy(0) - y'(0)] + 7[sY(s) - y(0)] + 12Y(s)$$
$$= 6[sF(s) - f(0)] + 12F(s)$$

Substituting $f(0) = y(0)$, $y'(0) = 0$, and $F(s) = [f(0) + 1]/s$ gives

$$(s^2 + 7s + 12)Y(s) = (s + 7)y(0) + 6 + \frac{12[y(0) + 1]}{s}$$

Thus,

$$Y(s) = \frac{6(s + 2) + (s^2 + 7s + 12)y(0)}{s(s^2 + 7s + 12)} = \frac{6(s + 2)}{s(s^2 + 7s + 12)} + \frac{y(0)}{s}$$

Inverting verifies the response obtained directly by application of the vertical shifting theorem, Eq. (5.82).

Illustrative example 2 The system shown in Fig. 5.15 is in a state of equilibrium, with $r = 1$ and $d = 0$. A step-function disturbance $d(t) = u(t)$ is then initiated at time $t = 0$. Determine the response $c(t)$ for $t > 0$.

SOLUTION The differential equation of operation for this system is

$$(D^2 + 5D + 6)c(t) = 6r(t) + 3Dd(t) \qquad (5.83)$$

The expression for steady-state operation at $t = 0$ is obtained by letting $D = 0$ in the differential equation of operation. Thus $6c(0) = 6r(0)$ or $c(0) = r(0) = 1$. Transforming each term in the differential equation gives

$$[s^2C(s) - sc(0) - c'(0)] + 5[sC(s) - c(0)] + 6C(s) = 6R(s) + 3[sD(s) - d(0)]$$

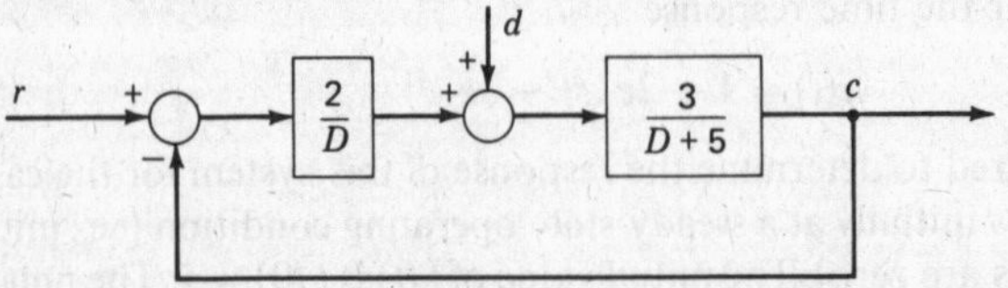

Figure 5.15 Feedback control system.

For $c(0) = r(0) = 1, c'(0) = 0, d(0) = 0, R(s) = 1/s$, and $D(s) = 1/s$, the resulting transformed equation becomes

$$(s^2 + 5s + 6)C(s) = \frac{6}{s} + \frac{3}{s}s + s + 5 = \frac{s^2 + 8s + 6}{s}$$

Hence

$$C(s) = \frac{s^2 + 8s + 6}{s(s+2)(s+3)} = \frac{1}{s} + \frac{3}{s+2} - \frac{3}{s+3}$$

Inverting yields for the response

$$c(t) = 1 + 3e^{-2t} - 3e^{-3t} \tag{5.84}$$

Because the system is initially at a steady-state operating condition, this result may be obtained directly by adding the initial value $c(0) = 1$ to the response of the system to the step change $d(t) = 1$ for the case in which all initial conditions are zero. The transformed equation when all initial conditions are zero is

$$C(s) = \frac{3sD(s)}{s^2 + 5s + 6} = \frac{3}{s^2 + 5s + 6} = \frac{3}{s+2} - \frac{3}{s+3}$$

where $D(s) = 1/s$.

Inverting yields for the response due to the step change only

$$c(t) = 3e^{-2t} - 3e^{-3t}$$

Thus, adding the initial value $c(0) = 1$ verifies the response previously obtained.

5.6 PIECEWISE CONTINUOUS FUNCTIONS

As is illustrated in Fig. 5.16, a piecewise continuous function is characterized by the fact that the equation for the function changes from interval to interval. For example, in Fig. 5.16*a*, for $0 < t \le t_0, f(t) = at$; and for $t > t_0, f(t) = at_0$. For the first interval $0 < t \le t_0$, the input function is inclined at the slope a. Such an inclined straight line is called a ramp function. For $t > t_0$, the input is seen to be a step function. The solution of such problems is effected by starting with the first interval and successively solving for the response in each interval.

Illustrative example Determine the solution of the following differential equation:

$$\frac{dy}{dt} + y = f(t) \tag{5.85}$$

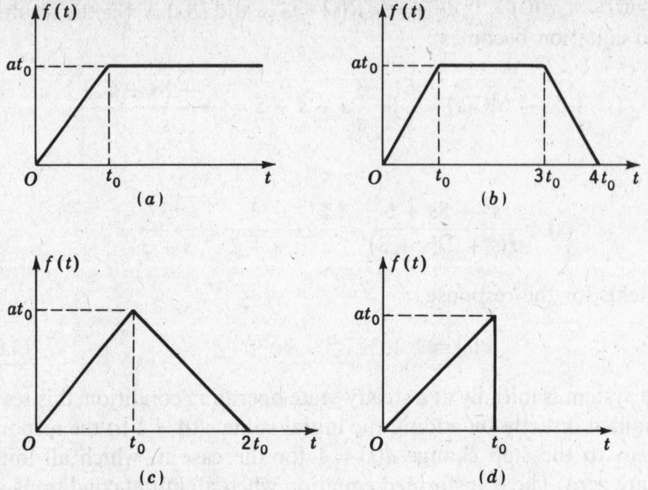

Figure 5.16 Piecewise continuous functions.

where $f(t)$ is the function shown in Fig. 5.17*a* and all the initial conditions are zero. For $a = 1$ and $t_0 = 1$, the function shown in Fig. 5.16*a* becomes identical to that shown in Fig. 5.17*a*.

SOLUTION The transform of the differential equation is

$$sY(s) - y(0) + Y(s) = F(s)$$

Solving for $Y(s)$ gives

$$Y(s) = \frac{F(s) + y(0)}{s + 1} \tag{5.86}$$

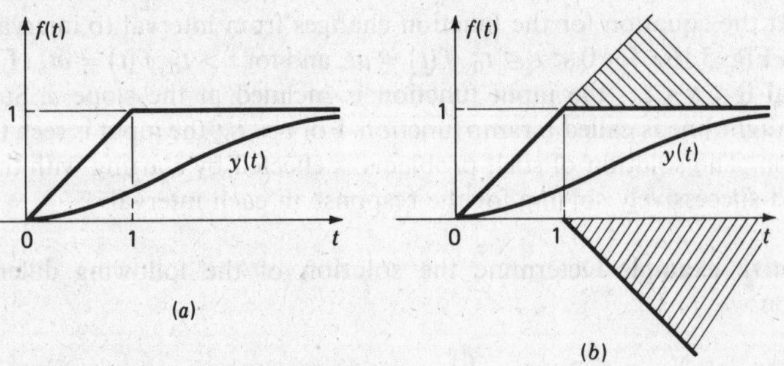

Figure 5.17 A piecewise continuous function.

For the interval $0 < t \leq 1$, the input is the ramp function $f(t) = t$, for which $F(s) = 1/s^2$. Thus, the transformed equation becomes

$$Y(s) = \frac{1/s^2 + y(0)}{s + 1} \tag{5.87}$$

For $y(0) = 0$, it follows that

$$Y(s) = \frac{1}{s^2(s+1)} = \frac{C_2}{s^2} + \frac{C_1}{s} + \frac{K_1}{s+1} = \frac{1}{s^2} - \frac{1}{s} + \frac{1}{s+1}$$

Inverting yields for the response for the first interval

$$y(t) = t - 1 + e^{-t} \qquad 0 < t \leq 1 \tag{5.88}$$

For the second interval ($t > 1$), the input is a unit step function. The initial condition for this second interval is obtained by evaluating the response for the preceding interval at the transition point, $t = 1$. Thus

$$y(1) = [(t - 1) + e^{-t}]_{t=1} = 0.368$$

Because all terms in the differential equation are delayed a time $t_0 = 1$, it is more convenient to determine the response for the second interval as though there were no delay and then replace t by $t - t_0 = t - 1$ in the final answer. The substitution of $y(0) = 0.368$ and $F(s) = 1/s$ into Eq. (5.87), which is the transform of the differential equation, gives

$$Y(s) = \frac{F(s) + y(0)}{s + 1} = \frac{1/s + 0.368}{s + 1} = \frac{1 + 0.368s}{s(s + 1)}$$

$$= \frac{K_1}{s} + \frac{K_2}{s+1} = \frac{1}{s} - \frac{0.632}{s+1}$$

where $$K_1 = \left.\frac{1 + 0.368s}{s + 1}\right|_{s=0} = 1$$

$$K_2 = \left.\frac{1 + 0.368s}{s}\right|_{s=-1} = -0.632$$

Inverting gives

$$y(t) = 1 - 0.632e^{-t}$$

Replacing t by $t - t_0 = t - 1$ yields for the response for $t > 1$

$$y(t - 1) = 1 - 0.632e^{-(t-1)} \qquad t > 1 \tag{5.89}$$

The resulting response is indicated by the $y(t)$ curve in Fig. 5.17*a*.

In this method, the initial conditions for a new interval are obtained by evaluating the equation for the preceding interval at the value of time when the preceding interval ceases and the new one begins.

An alternative method for solving piecewise continuous problems is to regard the input as being the sum of separate functions, as is illustrated in

Fig. 5.17*b*. The sum of the ramp function which begins at $t = 0$ and the equal but opposite ramp function which begins at $t_0 = 1$ is seen to yield the function of Fig. 5.17*a*. Similarly, it is possible to represent any piecewise continuous function as the sum of other functions which are continuous.

The transform for the first ramp function in Fig. 5.17*b* is $1/s^2$, and that for the delayed ramp function is $-(1/s^2)e^{-t_0 s}$. Thus, the transform $F(s)$ of the input is

$$F(s) = \frac{1}{s^2} - \frac{1}{s^2}e^{-t_0 s}$$

Substitution of this result into Eq. (5.86) yields for the transformed equation

$$Y(s) = \frac{1/s^2 + y(0)}{s+1} - \frac{1/s^2}{s+1}e^{-t_0 s} \tag{5.90}$$

Because of the delaying factor $e^{-t_0 s} = e^{-s}$, the second term on the right side should be ignored for $t < t_0 = 1$. Thus for $0 < t \le 1$, the transform is the same as that given by Eq. (5.87). The corresponding response for $0 < t \le 1$ is given by Eq. (5.88). For $t > 1$, the response is the sum of that due to the second term of Eq. (5.90) and that already obtained for the first term [Eq. (5.88)]. The inverse of $(1/s^2)/(s+1)$ is given by Eq. (5.88). To take into account the time shift, replace t by $t - t_0 = t - 1$. Thus, for $t > 1$ the total response is

$$\begin{aligned} y(t) &= [t - 1 + e^{-t}] - [(t-1) - 1 + e^{-(t-1)}] \\ &= 1 + e^{-t} - e^{-(t-1)} = 1 - 0.632e^{-(t-1)} \qquad t > 1 \end{aligned} \tag{5.89}$$

where $e^{-t} = e^{-1}e^{-(t-1)} = 0.368e^{-(t-1)}$

This verifies the result obtained by the first method.

An advantage of this second method of solution is that initial conditions appear only in the transformed expression for the first interval. However, in this latter method, the amount of computational effort increases with the number of separate functions required to make up the overall piecewise continuous function. Thus, the choice of the first or second method depends on the particular problem to be solved. Next, how the convolution integral may be used to determine the response to any arbitrary input function will be shown.

Convolution Integral[1]

This integral may be used to determine the response of a system to any arbitrary input $f(t)$. Consider the transformed equation

$$Y(s) = G(s)F(s)$$

[1] F. H. Raven, "Mathematics of Engineering Systems," chap. 3, McGraw-Hill Book Company, New York, 1966.

The inverse Laplace transform is

$$y(t) = \mathscr{L}^{-1}[G(s)F(s)] = \mathscr{L}^{-1}\left[G(s)\int_0^\infty f(\lambda)e^{-\lambda s}\,d\lambda\right] = \int_0^\infty f(\lambda)\mathscr{L}^{-1}[G(s)e^{-\lambda s}]\,d\lambda$$

where $F(s) = \int_0^\infty f(\lambda)e^{-\lambda s}\,d\lambda$. Application of the real translation theorem, Eq. (5.42), shows that the inverse of $G(s)e^{-\lambda s}$ is $g(t-\lambda)$ for $\lambda < t$ and is zero for $\lambda > t$. Thus,

$$y(t) = \mathscr{L}^{-1}[G(s)F(s)] = \int_0^t f(\lambda)g(t-\lambda)\,d\lambda \tag{5.91}$$

This is the convolution integral.

The function $g(t-\lambda)$ is obtained by designating the inverse of $G(s)$ as $g(\lambda)$ and then replacing λ by $t-\lambda$. Similarly, $f(\lambda)$ is obtained by replacing t by λ in the equation $f(t)$ for the forcing function. Note that the input $f(\lambda)$ is used directly (without transforming) in this integral procedure for determining the response $y(t)$. The physical significance of $g(t)$ is determined by noting that when $f(t)$ is a unit impulse, then $Y(s) = G(s)$. Thus $g(t) = \mathscr{L}^{-1}[G(s)]$ is the unit impulse response of the system.

Interchanging $F(s)$ and $G(s)$ in the preceding development yields the alternative form:

$$y(t) = \mathscr{L}^{-1}[F(s)G(s)] = \int_0^t g(\lambda)f(t-\lambda)\,d\lambda$$

The convolution integral is also used to obtain the inverse of the product of two transforms. For example, for $F(s) = 1/s^2$ and $G(s) = 1/(s+1)$, then $f(\lambda) = \lambda$, $g(\lambda) = e^{-\lambda}$, and $g(t-\lambda) = e^{-(t-\lambda)}$.

Thus,

$$\mathscr{L}^{-1}[G(s)F(s)] = \mathscr{L}^{-1}\left[\frac{1}{s^2}\frac{1}{s+1}\right] = \int_0^t \lambda e^{-(t-\lambda)}\,d\lambda = e^{-t}\int_0^t \lambda e^{\lambda}\,d\lambda$$

$$= e^{-t}[e^{\lambda}(\lambda-1)]_0^t = e^{-t} + t - 1$$

Using the alternative form $f(t-\lambda) = (t-\lambda)$ and $g(\lambda) = e^{-\lambda}$ yields the same result. It is important to note that $\mathscr{L}^{-1}[F(s)G(s)]$ is not equal to the product $\mathscr{L}^{-1}[F(s)]\mathscr{L}^{-1}[G(s)]$. For the preceding, $\mathscr{L}^{-1}[F(s)] = t$ and $\mathscr{L}^{-1}[G(s)] = e^{-t}$ This product te^{-t} is not the correct answer.

As another example, let it be desired to determine the inverse of $[\omega/(s^2+\omega^2)]^2$. By letting

$$F(s) = G(s) = \omega/(s^2+\omega^2)$$

then $f(\lambda) = \sin \omega\lambda$ and $g(t - \lambda) = \sin \omega(t - \lambda)$. Application of the convolution integral gives

$$\mathscr{L}^{-1}\left[\frac{\omega}{s^2 + \omega^2}\right]^2 = \int_0^t [\sin \omega\lambda \sin \omega(t - \lambda)]\, d\lambda$$

$$= \frac{1}{2}\int_0^t [\cos \omega(2\lambda - t) - \cos \omega t]\, d\lambda$$

$$= \frac{1}{2}\left[\frac{\sin \omega t}{\omega} - t \cos \omega t\right]$$

5.7 ERROR COEFFICIENTS

For the system shown in Fig. 5.18, the error signal is $e(t) = r(t) - H(D)c(t) = r(t) - G(D)H(D)e(t)$. When all initial conditions are zero, the transformed equation is

$$E(s) = \frac{R(s)}{1 + G(s)H(s)}$$

Application of the final-value theorem yields for the steady-state error

$$e_{ss} = \lim_{t\to\infty} e(t) = \lim_{s\to 0} sE(s)$$

For a unit step input $[R(s) = 1/s]$, the steady-state error is

$$e_{ss} = \lim_{s\to 0} s\frac{1/s}{1 + G(s)H(s)} = \lim_{s\to 0}\frac{1}{1 + G(s)H(s)} = \frac{1}{1 + K_p} \tag{5.92}$$

where $K_p = \lim_{s\to 0} G(s)H(s)$ is called the positional error constant.

For a unit ramp input $[r(t) = t,\ R(s) = 1/s^2]$, the steady-state error is

$$e_{ss} = \lim_{s\to 0} s\frac{1/s^2}{1 + G(s)H(s)} = \lim_{s\to 0}\frac{1}{s + sG(s)H(s)} = \lim_{s\to 0}\frac{1}{sG(s)H(s)} = \frac{1}{K_v} \tag{5.93}$$

where $K_v = \lim_{s\to 0} sG(s)H(s)$ is called the velocity error constant.

For a unit parabolic input $[r(t) = t^2/2,\ R(s) = 1/s^3]$, the steady-state error is

$$e_{ss} = \lim_{s\to 0}\frac{1}{s^2 + s^2G(s)H(s)} = \lim_{s\to 0}\frac{1}{s^2G(s)H(s)} = \frac{1}{K_a} \tag{5.94}$$

Figure 5.18 Feedback control system.

where $K_a = \lim_{s\to 0} s^2G(s)H(s)$ is called the acceleration error constant. The error constant provides a convenient method for determining the steady-state error to a unit step, unit ramp, or unit parabolic input. Because the response due to initial conditions dies out as time approaches infinity, the preceding results are valid even if the initial conditions are not zero.

Illustrative example 1 The system shown in Fig. 5.9 is discussed in Illustrative Example 3 of Sec. 5.3. For this system, determine the steady-state error to a unit step function input.

SOLUTION From Fig. 5.9, it follows that

$$G(s) = \frac{K_1}{1+\tau_1 s}\frac{K_2}{1+\tau_2 s} \qquad H(s) = K_H$$

The positional error constant is

$$K_p = \lim_{s\to 0} G(s)H(s) = K_1 K_2 K_H = (1.0)(2.0)(0.5) = 1.0$$

Thus, the steady-state error due to a unit step input is

$$e_{ss} = \frac{1}{1+K_p} = 0.5$$

The corresponding steady-state values for c and v may be determined by noting from Fig. 5.9 that $e = r - K_H c = r - 0.5c$ and $r = Av = v$. For a unit step input, $r = 1$, and thus $c = 2(r - e_{ss}) = 2(1 - 0.5) = 1.0$ and $v = r = 1.0$. This agrees with the result of Illustrative Example 3, in which it was found that for a constant input, $c = v$. As demonstrated by this example, the presence of a steady-state error signal does not necessarily imply that the controlled variable is not equal to the command signal.

Illustrative example 2 For the system shown in Fig. 5.19*a*, determine the response to a unit step function, a unit ramp function, and a unit parabolic function when all initial conditions are zero. What is the steady-state error to each of these inputs?

SOLUTION The differential equation of operation is

$$(D^2 + 3D + 2)c(t) = 2r(t)$$

The transformed equation is

$$C(s) = \frac{2R(s)}{(s+1)(s+2)} \tag{5.95}$$

For a unit step function input, $R(s) = 1/s$. Carrying out the partial-fraction expansion and inverting yields for the time response

$$c(t) = 1 - 2e^{-t} + e^{-2t}$$

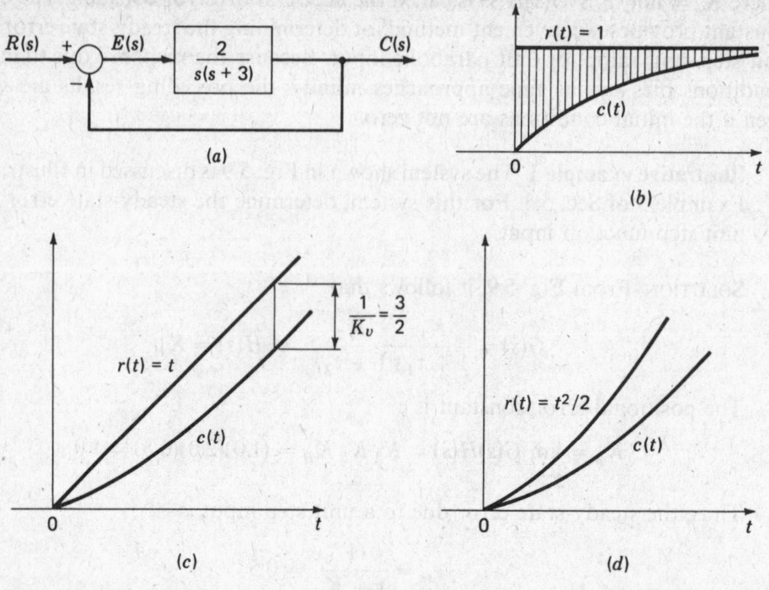

Figure 5.19 Response of system to unit step, unit ramp, and unit parabolic inputs.

The corresponding input $r(t) = u(t)$ and response are shown in Fig. 5.19*b*. The error $e(t) = r(t) - c(t)$ is $e(t) = 1 - (1 - 2e^{-t} + e^{-2t}) = 2e^{-t} - 3^{-2t}$. Taking the limit as t approaches infinity yields for the steady-state error

$$e_{ss} = \lim_{t\to\infty} e(t) = \lim_{t\to\infty} (2e^{-t} - e^{-2t}) = 0$$

The positional error constant is

$$K_p = \lim_{s\to 0} G(s)H(s) = \frac{2}{s(s+3)}\bigg|_{s=0} = \infty$$

Thus, the steady-state error to a unit step function is

$$e_{ss} = \frac{1}{1 + K_p} = \frac{1}{1+\infty} = 0$$

For a unit ramp input, $r(t) = t$. Substitution of $R(s) = 1/s^2$ into Eq. (5.95) gives

$$C(s) = \frac{2}{s^2(s+1)(s+2)} = \frac{1}{s^2} - \frac{3/2}{s} + \frac{2}{s+1} - \frac{1/2}{s+2}$$

Inverting yields for the response

$$c(t) = t - \tfrac{3}{2} + 2e^{-t} - \tfrac{1}{2}e^{-2t}$$

A plot of the input $r(t) = t$ and the response $c(t)$ is shown in Fig. 5.19*c*. The error $e(t) = r(t) - c(t)$ is

$$e(t) = t - (t - \tfrac{3}{2} + 2e^{-t} - \tfrac{1}{2}e^{-2t}) = \tfrac{3}{2} + 2e^{-t} + \tfrac{1}{2}e^{-2t}$$

Taking the limit as t approaches infinity yields for the steady-state error

$$e_{ss} = \lim_{t\to\infty} e(t) = \tfrac{3}{2}$$

The velocity error constant is

$$K_v = \lim_{s\to 0} sG(s)H(s) = \left.\frac{2s}{s(s+3)}\right|_{s=0} = \frac{2}{3}$$

Thus, the steady-state error to a unit ramp function is

$$e_{ss} = \frac{1}{K_v} = \frac{3}{2}$$

For a unit parabolic input, $r(t) = t^2/2$. Substitution of $R(s) = 1/s^3$ into Eq. (5.95) gives

$$C(s) = \frac{2}{s^3(s+1)(s+2)} = \frac{1}{s^3} - \frac{3/2}{s^2} + \frac{7/4}{s} - \frac{2}{s+1} + \frac{1/4}{s+2}$$

Inverting yields for the response

$$c(t) = \frac{t^2}{2} - \frac{3}{2}t + \frac{7}{4} - 2e^{-t} + \frac{1}{4}e^{-2t}$$

The error, $e(t) = r(t) - c(t)$, is

$$e(t) = \tfrac{3}{2}t - \tfrac{7}{4} + 2e^{-t} - \tfrac{1}{4}e^{-2t}$$

In the limit as t approaches infinity, the error is

$$e_{ss} = \lim_{t\to\infty} e(t) = [\tfrac{3}{2}t - \tfrac{7}{4}]_{t=\infty} = \infty$$

A plot of the input $r(t) = t^2/2$ and the response $c(t)$ is shown in Fig. 5.19*d*. Note that the error keeps growing as t increases. The acceleration error constant is

$$K_a = \lim_{s\to 0} s^2G(s)H(s) = \left.\frac{2s^2}{s(s+3)}\right|_{s=0} = \left.\frac{2}{(1+3/s)}\right|_{s=0} = \frac{2}{1+\infty} = 0$$

Thus, the steady-state error to a unit parabolic input is

$$e_{ss} = \frac{1}{K_a} = \frac{1}{0} = \infty$$

Consider now the case in which the input is a unit step function $r(t) = u(t)$. The transform of the error signal is

$$E(s) = \frac{R(s)}{1 + G(s)H(s)} = \frac{1/s}{1 + G(s)H(s)}$$

Taking the limit as s approaches zero shows that

$$\lim_{s \to 0} E(s) = \lim_{s \to 0} \frac{1}{s + sG(s)H(s)} = \lim_{s \to 0} \frac{1}{sG(s)H(s)} = \frac{1}{K_v}$$

From the definition of the Laplace transform, it follows that

$$\lim_{s \to 0} E(s) = \lim_{s \to 0} \int_0^\infty e(t)e^{-st}\,dt = \int_0^\infty e(t)\,dt \tag{5.96}$$

The right side is the time integral of the error to a unit step input. This integral, shown shaded in Fig. 5.19*b*, is

$$\int_0^\infty e(t)\,dt = \frac{1}{K_v} = \frac{3}{2}$$

This result may also be checked by integration. Thus

$$\int_0^\infty e(t)\,dt = \int_0^\infty (2e^{-t} - e^{-2t})\,dt = [-2e^{-t} + \tfrac{1}{2}e^{-2t}]_0^\infty$$

$$= 0 - (-2 + \tfrac{1}{2}) = \tfrac{3}{2}$$

As demonstrated in the preceding, many interesting features and characteristics of systems may be obtained directly from the transformed equation without the need to invert and obtain the time response.

PROBLEMS

5.1 Determine the general solution for the first-order differential equation

$$(D - r)y(t) = f(t)$$

5.2 Expand the following operators by use of partial-fraction expansion techniques:

(*a*) $\dfrac{L_m(D)}{L_n(D)} = \dfrac{6}{(D+1)(D+4)}$ (*b*) $\dfrac{L_m(D)}{L_n(D)} = \dfrac{2D+3}{D(D+3)}$

(*c*) $\dfrac{L_m(D)}{L_n(D)} = \dfrac{D^2 + 6D + 15}{(D+1)(D+3)(D+6)}$ (*d*) $\dfrac{L_m(D)}{L_n(D)} = \dfrac{18D + 30}{D(D+2)(D+5)}$

5.3 Determine the partial-fraction expansion for the following operators:

(*a*) $\dfrac{L_m(D)}{L_n(D)} = \dfrac{D+3}{D(D+1)^2}$ (*b*) $\dfrac{L_m(D)}{L_n(D)} = \dfrac{3}{D^2(D+3)^2}$

(*c*) $\dfrac{L_m(D)}{L_n(D)} = \dfrac{11D + 6}{D^3(D+2)(D+3)}$

5.4 Consider the differential equation

$$\frac{dy}{dt} + y = f(t)$$

Use classical techniques to determine the solution for each of the following cases:

(a) $f(t) = 0$ and $y(0) = 1$
(b) $f(t) = 1$ and $y(0) = 0$
(c) $f(t) = t$ and $y(0) = 0$
(d) $f(t) = e^{-t}$ and $y(0) = 0$

5.5 Using classical techniques, determine the solutions of the following differential equations for the case in which $f(t)$ is a unit step function. All initial conditions are zero.

(a) $$y(t) = \frac{12}{(D+1)(D+3)} f(t)$$

(b) $$y(t) = \frac{12}{(D+1)^2(D+3)} f(t)$$

5.6 Use the Laplace transform method to verify the solution of Prob. 5.4.

5.7 Use the Laplace transform method to verify the solution of Prob. 5.5.

5.8 Determine the Laplace transform for:

(a) $f(t) = at$
(b) $f(t) = at^2$
(c) $f(t) = \cos \omega t$

5.9 The operation of an amplifier is described by the differential equation

$$\frac{dy}{dt} + 0.2y = f(t)$$

Determine the response $y(t)$ to a unit step function $f(t) = u(t)$. All the initial conditions are zero. Identify the time constant and steady-state gain.

5.10 Consider the differential equation

$$\frac{dy}{dt} + y = u(t) + e^{-t} \qquad y(0) = 0$$

where $u(t)$ is a unit step function. Determine the transform of the derivative $\mathscr{L}[y'(t)] = [sY(s) - y(0)]$, and then invert to obtain $y'(t)$.

5.11 The differential equation of operation for a system is

$$y(t) = \frac{12(D+1)}{(D+3)(D+4)} f(t)$$

Determine the response $y(t)$ when $f(t) = u(t)$ is a unit step function and all initial conditions are zero.

5.12 Determine the response $y(t)$ for the system of Prob. 5.11 when $f(t) = 0$, $y(0) = 1$, and $y'(0) = 0$.

5.13 Determine the response $y(t)$ for the system of Prob. 5.11 when $f(t) = 0$, $y(0) = 0$, and $y'(0) = 1$.

5.14 For the feedback control system shown in Fig. P5.14, all the initial conditions are zero and $K = 1.5$. Determine the response for each of the following cases:

(a) $r(t)$ is a unit step function and $d(t) = 0$.
(b) $d(t)$ is a unit step function and $r(t) = 0$.
(c) Both $r(t)$ and $d(t)$ are unit step functions.

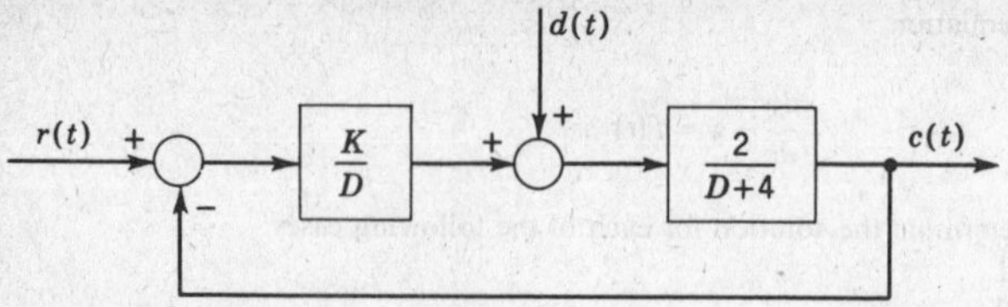

Figure P5.14

5.15 Same as Prob. 5.14 except $K = 2$.

5.16 Using the Laplace transform method, determine the solution of the following differential equations for the case in which $f(t)$ is a step function of height $h = 6$; all initial conditions are zero.

(*a*) $y(t) = \dfrac{D+5}{(D+1)(D+3)} f(t)$

(*b*) $y(t) = \dfrac{D+5}{(D+1)^2(D+3)} f(t)$

5.17 Verify the solution of Prob. 5.16 by using the classical method.

5.18 A switch is inserted in series in the circuit of Fig. 5.13. For $t < 0$, the switch is open and all initial conditions are zero. For $t > 0$, the switch is closed and the voltage source $e = 100$ V is applied to the circuit. For $R = 10^6$ ohms = 1 megohm and $C = 10^{-6}$ F = 1 μF, determine the equation for the resulting current i that flows through the circuit and the voltage e_c across the capacitor.

5.19 Using the Laplace transform method, a student found the solution of the differential equation

$$\ddot{y} + 4\dot{y} + 3y = 4u_1(t) \qquad y(0) = \dot{y}(0) = 0$$

to be

$$y = 2e^{-t} - 2e^{-3t}$$

Being rather thorough, the student decided to check the answer by checking the initial conditions and checking whether the solution satisfied the differential equation. The results were $y(0) = 2 - 2 = 0$, $\dot{y}(0) = -2 + 6 = 4$, and $\ddot{y} + 4\dot{y} + 3y = 0$. Since this solution satisfied neither the differential equation nor the one initial condition, the student concluded there had been an error in determining y. Is the error in the solution or the conclusion? Explain.

5.20 A mass-spring-damper system is shown in Fig. P5.20.

(*a*) Write the differential equation.

(*b*) Use Laplace transforms to solve this equation when $x(0) = 0$, $x'(0) = 1$, $f = 0$, $M = 1$, $B = 3$, and $K = 2$.

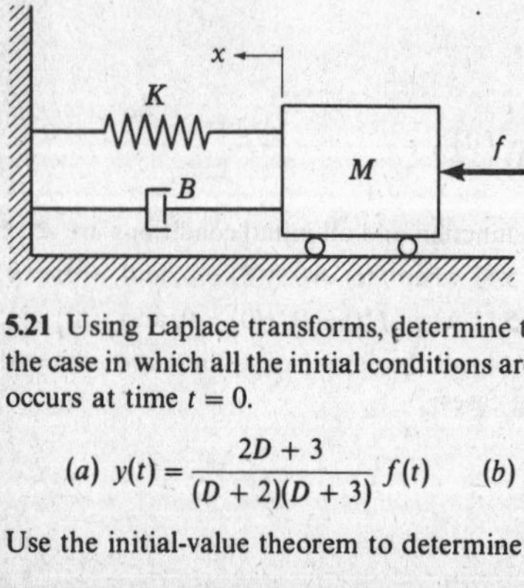

Figure P5.20

5.21 Using Laplace transforms, determine the response $y(t)$ for the following differential equations for the case in which all the initial conditions are zero and the input $f(t)$ is an impulse of area $k = 2$ which occurs at time $t = 0$.

(*a*) $y(t) = \dfrac{2D+3}{(D+2)(D+3)} f(t)$ (*b*) $y(t) = \dfrac{2D+3}{D(D+2)(D+3)} f(t)$

Use the initial-value theorem to determine $y(0+)$ and the final-value theorem to determine $y(\infty)$.

5.22 Same as Prob. 5.21 except that the system is initially at a steady-state operating condition, with $y(0) = 1$.

5.23 The dynamics of a system are described by the differential equation

$$y(t) = \frac{10(2D + 1)}{(D + 2)(D + 5)} f(t)$$

Use the Laplace transform method to determine the response $y(t)$ when all the initial conditions are zero and the forcing function $f(t)$ is

(*a*) a unit impulse $u_1(t)$
(*b*) a unit step function $u(t)$
(*c*) an exponential e^{-t}

5.24 Use the classical method to verify the solution of Prob. 5.23.

5.25 Same as Prob. 5.23 except that the system is initially at a steady-state operating condition with $f(0) = 3$.

5.26 The system shown in Fig. P5.26 is in a state of equilibrium, with $r = 3$ and $d = 0$. A step-function disturbance $d(t) = 6u(t)$ is then initiated at time $t = 0$. Determine the response $c(t)$ for $t > 0$.

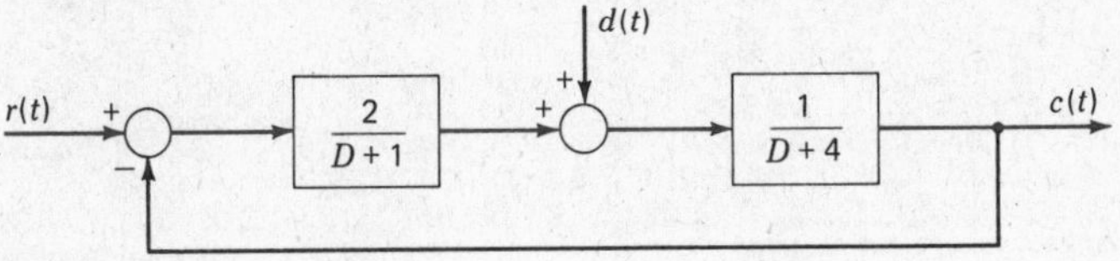

Figure P5.26

5.27 The system shown in Fig. P5.26 is in a state of equilibrium, with $r = 0$ and $d = 6$. A step-function change $r(t) = 3u(t)$ is then initiated at time $t = 0$. Determine the response $c(t)$ for $t > 0$.

5.28 The system shown in Fig. P5.28 is initially at equilibrium, with $r = 1$ and $d = 0$. A step-function disturbance $d(t) = u(t)$ is then initiated at time $t = 0$. Determine the response $c(t)$ for $t > 0$.

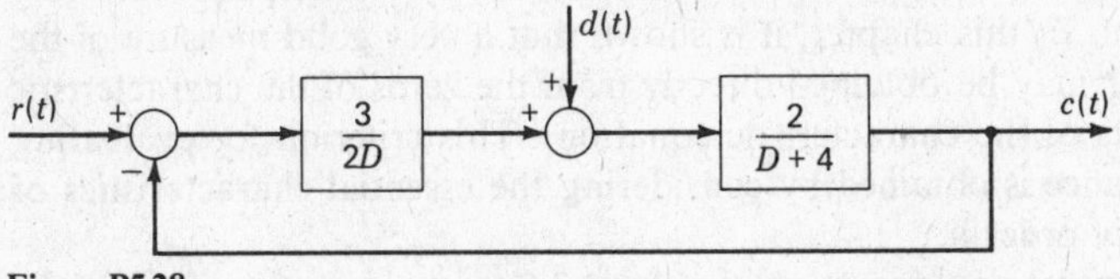

Figure P5.28

5.29 A system is described by the differential equation

$$\frac{dy}{dt} + 0.2y = f(t)$$

All initial conditions are zero, and then a unit step input $f(t) = u(t)$ is applied for 5 s, as shown in Fig. P5.29. Determine the response $y(t)$ for $0 < t \leq 5$ and for $t > 5$.

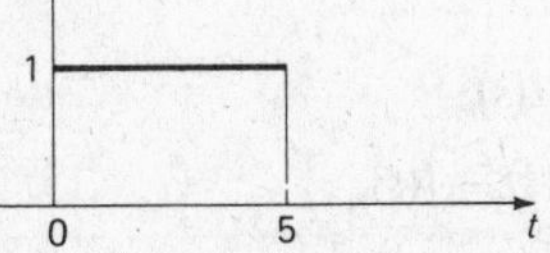

Figure P5.29

5.30 Determine the position, velocity, and acceleration error constants and then determine the steady-state error to a unit step, a unit ramp, and a unit parabolic input for the system shown (*a*) in Fig. P5.26 and (*b*) in Fig. P5.28.

CHAPTER

SIX

TRANSIENT RESPONSE

Because an actual system may be subjected to all types and varieties of input excitations $f(t)$, it becomes impractical to calculate the system response for every possible excitation. In this chapter, it is shown that a very good measure of the transient behavior may be obtained directly from the zeros of the characteristic function (i.e., roots of the characteristic equation). This criterion for evaluating transient performance is obtained by considering the essential characteristics of a general system of order n.

The general operational representation for a differential equation of order n is

$$y(t) = \frac{a_m D^m + a_{m-1} D^{m-1} + \cdots + a_1 D + a_0}{D^n + b_{n-1} D^{n-1} + \cdots + b_1 D + b_0} f(t) \tag{6.1}$$

The transform of each term is

$$\mathscr{L}[D^n y(t)] = s^n Y(s) - I(s)_n$$

$$b_{n-1} \mathscr{L}[D^{n-1} y(t)] = b_{n-1} s^{n-1} Y(s) - I(s)_{n-1}$$

$$\cdots\cdots\cdots\cdots\cdots\cdots\cdots\cdots\cdots\cdots\cdots\cdots$$

$$a_m \mathscr{L}[D^m f(t)] = a_m s^m F(s) - I(s)_m$$

$$a_{m-1} \mathscr{L}[D^{m-1} f(t)] = a_{m-1} s^{m-1} F(s) - I(s)_{m-1}$$

$$\cdots\cdots\cdots\cdots\cdots\cdots\cdots\cdots\cdots\cdots\cdots\cdots$$

where $I_n, I_{n-1}, \ldots$ represent the initial conditions associated with each transform.

Transforming each term of Eq. (6.1) accordingly and collecting terms yields

$$Y(s) = \frac{(a_m s^m + a_{m-1} s^{m-1} + \cdots + a_1 s + a_0)F(s) + I(s)}{s^n + b_{n-1} s^{n-1} + \cdots + b_1 s + b_0}$$

$$= \frac{L_m(s)F(s) + I(s)}{L_n(s)} \tag{6.2}$$

where $I(s) = I(s)_n + I(s)_{n-1} + \cdots - I(s)_m - I(s)_{m-1} - \cdots$ is the sum of all the initial conditions. By comparison of Eqs. (6.1) and (6.2), it is to be noted that the characteristic function in the s domain, $L_n(s)$, is the same as that in the D domain $L_n(D)$. The numerator also has the same form, with the exception that the initial conditions $I(s)$ are added in the s domain. Comparison of Eqs. (6.1) and (6.2) shows that *when all the initial conditions are zero, the transform is obtained by merely substituting s for D, Y(s) for y(t), and F(s) for f(t) in the operational form of the differential equation.*

For this case,

$$Y(s) = \frac{L_m(s)}{L_n(s)} F(s) \tag{6.3}$$

where $L_m(s)/L_n(s)$ is called the *transfer function.* It is to be noted that $L_m(s)$ and $L_n(s)$ are obtained directly from the differential equation of operation for the system. Thus, *the transfer function contains basic information concerning the essential characteristics of a system* without regard to initial conditions or excitation.

The term $F(s)$ in Eq. (6.2) is the general representation for the transform of the input signal or forcing function. This term may be written as

$$F(s) = \frac{N_{F(s)}}{D_{F(s)}}$$

where $N_{F(s)}$ is the numerator of $F(s)$ and $D_{F(s)}$ is the denominator of $F(s)$. For example, for a unit step function, $F(s) = 1/s$, and thus $N_{F(s)} = 1$ and $D_{F(s)} = s$. Substitution of the preceding representation $F(s) = N_{F(s)}/D_{F(s)}$ into Eq. (6.2) yields the following general transformed form for $Y(s)$:

$$Y(s) = \frac{L_m(s)N_{F(s)} + I(s)D_{F(s)}}{L_n(s)D_{F(s)}} = \frac{A(s)}{B(s)} \tag{6.4}$$

where $A(s)$ and $B(s)$ are polynomials in s.

6.1 INVERSE TRANSFORMATIONS

By an inverse transformation is meant the process of inverting a function from the s domain back to the time domain. The inverse transform $\mathscr{L}^{-1}$ of a function $F(s)$ is defined by the equation

$$\mathscr{L}^{-1}[F(s)] = \frac{1}{2\pi j} \int_C F(s)e^{ts}\, ds = f(t) \tag{6.5}$$

where C is a suitably chosen contour in the s domain.[1] This integral method of evaluating the inverse transform is not employed when the much simpler process of entering a transform table with the given $F(s)$ and reading directly the desired $f(t)$ can be utilized, as is the case for ordinary control analysis. A partial listing of commonly used transforms is given in Table 5.1.

The transform table may be used to obtain the Laplace transform $F(s)$ of a given function of time or to obtain the inverse transform $f(t)$ for a given function of s. This process is analogous to using a logarithmic table for obtaining the logarithm of a number or to using the same table for the opposite process of obtaining antilogarithms.

At first it would appear that the listing of transforms given in Table 5.1 would have to be extended considerably so that it would be applicable to the wide range of problems encountered in the design of systems. However, this is not the case. The listing given in Table 5.1 is adequate for the solution of most ordinary problems that arise in control engineering. The reason for this is that relatively few different types of terms appear in the differential equation after it has been expanded by a partial-fraction expansion. In particular, the zeros of $B(s)$ are either distinct or repeated.

Distinct Zeros

The transformed function $B(s)$ is the denominator of Eq. (6.4). When the zeros of $B(s)$ are distinct, the denominator $B(s)$ can be factored in the form

$$B(s) = (s - r_1)(s - r_2) \cdots (s - r_n) \tag{6.6}$$

where $r_1, r_2, \ldots, r_n$ are n distinct zeros of $B(s)$.

The partial-fraction expansion of Eq. (6.4) is of the form

$$Y(s) = \frac{K_1}{s - r_1} + \frac{K_2}{s - r_2} + \cdots + \frac{K_i}{s - r_i} + \cdots + \frac{K_n}{s - r_n} \tag{6.7}$$

where $K_1, K_2, \ldots, K_n$ are n constants. Each constant K_i may be evaluated by the method used to obtain Eq. (5.9). That is, first multiply both sides of Eq. (6.7) by $s - r_i$; then take the limit as s approaches r_i. After performing these operations, the only term remaining on the right side of Eq. (6.7) is K_i. Thus

$$K_i = \lim_{s \to r_i} [(s - r_i)Y(s)] \tag{6.8}$$

The inverse transform of Eq. (6.7) is obtained directly from the transform table and is

$$y(t) = K_1 e^{r_1 t} + K_2 e^{r_2 t} + \cdots + K_n e^{r_n t} \tag{6.9}$$

[1] F. H. Raven, "Mathematics of Engineering Systems," chap. 6, McGraw-Hill Book Company, New York, 1966.

Equation (6.9) shows that *each distinct zero of* $B(s) = L_n(s)D_{F(s)}$ *yields an exponential-type term* $K_i e^{r_i t}$ *in the response function.* The exponent r_i is the corresponding zero of $B(s)$. Each zero $r_1, r_2, \ldots, r_n$ must be negative in order that each term $K_i e^{r_i t}$ in $y(t)$ be a decaying function. If any zero of $B(s)$ is positive, $y(t)$ will increase without bound as t increases to infinity. A constant term results if $r_i = 0$, because $K_i e^{(0)t} = K_i$.

Repeated Zeros

For the case in which $B(s)$ has a multiple or repeated zero r which occurs q times, $B(s)$ may be factored in the form

$$B(s) = (s - r)^q (s - r_1)(s - r_2) \cdots (s - r_{n-q}) \tag{6.10}$$

The corresponding partial-fraction expansion for $Y(s)$ is

$$Y(s) = \frac{C_q}{(s-r)^q} + \frac{C_{q-1}}{(s-r)^{q-1}} + \cdots + \frac{C_1}{s-r} + \frac{K_1}{s-r_1} + \frac{K_2}{s-r_2} + \cdots + \frac{K_{n-q}}{s-r_{n-q}} \tag{6.11}$$

The constant coefficients for the multiple terms are evaluated as follows:

$$\begin{aligned} C_q &= \lim_{s \to r} [(s-r)^q Y(s)] \\ C_{q-1} &= \lim_{s \to r} \left\{ \frac{d}{ds} [(s-r)^q Y(s)] \right\} \\ C_{q-k} &= \lim_{s \to r} \left\{ \frac{1}{k!} \frac{d^k}{ds^k} [(s-r)^q Y(s)] \right\} \end{aligned} \tag{6.12}$$

From the transform table, the inverse transform of Eq. (6.11) is found to be

$$y(t) = \left[\frac{C_q t^{q-1}}{(q-1)!} + \frac{C_{q-1} t^{q-2}}{(q-2)!} + \cdots + \frac{C_2 t}{1!} + C_1 \right] e^{rt} + K_1 e^{r_1 t} + \cdots + K_{n-q} e^{r_{n-q} t} \tag{6.13}$$

Each response term associated with the repeated zero $(s - r)^q$ is seen to be multiplied by the exponential factor e^{rt}. If the value of r is positive, $y(t)$ will become infinite as time increases. For negative values of r, a decreasing exponential results, and thus the response term due to the repeated zero eventually vanishes.

Illustrative example Let it be desired to determine the time response $y(t)$ for the transformed equation

$$Y(s) = \frac{11s + 28}{(s+2)^2(s+5)} = \frac{C_2}{(s+2)^2} + \frac{C_1}{s+2} + \frac{K_1}{s+5} \tag{6.14}$$

The constants are evaluated as follows:

$$C_2 = \lim_{s \to -2} \frac{11s + 28}{s + 5} = 2$$

$$C_1 = \lim_{s \to -2} \left[\frac{d}{ds}\left(\frac{11s + 28}{s + 5}\right)\right] = \lim_{s \to -2} \frac{(s + 5)11 - (11s + 28)}{(s + 5)^2} = 3$$

$$K_1 = \lim_{s \to -5} \frac{11s + 28}{(s + 2)^2} = -3$$

Thus,
$$Y(s) = \frac{2}{(s + 2)^2} + \frac{3}{s + 2} - \frac{3}{s + 5}$$

By use of Table 5.1, the inverse transform of the preceding equation is found to be

$$y(t) = (2t + 3)e^{-2t} - 3e^{-5t} \tag{6.15}$$

6.2 COMPLEX CONJUGATE ZEROS

Complex zeros of $B(s)$ always occur in pairs, and furthermore these zeros are always conjugates of one another. That is, they have the same real part but equal and opposite imaginary parts. Thus, if the polynomial $B(s)$ has a complex zero $a + jb$, the complex conjugate $a - jb$ will also be a zero of $B(s)$. Although the preceding discussion of distinct zeros is also applicable to complex conjugate zeros, the following analysis brings out more clearly the fact that a pair of complex conjugate zeros in $B(s)$ combine to introduce an exponentially damped sinusoidal term in $y(t)$.

A pair of complex conjugate zeros when multiplied together yield the following quadratic:

$$[s - (a + jb)][s - (a - jb)] = s^2 - 2as + (a^2 + b^2) \tag{6.16}$$

For any given quadratic term, the values of a and b may be computed by equating coefficients of like terms as follows: Consider the expression

$$s^2 + 4s + 9$$

The coefficient 4 of the s term is equal to $-2a$, so that $-2a = 4$ or $a = -2$. Similarly equating the constant terms gives $a^2 + b^2 = 9$ or $b = \sqrt{9 - 4} = \sqrt{5}$. Thus, the complex conjugate zeros are $a \pm jb = -2 \pm j\sqrt{5}$. If in the determination of b it is found that b is an imaginary number, the two zeros are real and unequal rather than complex conjugates. For example, consider the quadratic

$$s^2 + 8s + 12$$

The value of a is equal to -4, so that $b = \sqrt{12 - 16} = j\sqrt{4} = j2$. For this case, the zeros are $a \pm jb = -4 \pm (j^2 2) = -4 \mp 2 = -6, -2$. Because the case of real zeros has been previously discussed, it is assumed in the following analysis that b is real, so that the zeros are complex conjugates.

For complex conjugate zeros $B(s)$ may be factored in the form

$$B(s) = (s - a - jb)(s - a + jb)(s - r_1) \cdots (s - r_{n-2}) \tag{6.17}$$

The partial-fraction expansion for $Y(s) = A(s)/B(s)$ is of the form

$$Y(s) = \frac{K_c}{s - a - jb} + \frac{K_{-c}}{s - a + jb} + \frac{K_1}{s - r_1} + \cdots + \frac{K_{n-2}}{s - r_{n-2}} \tag{6.18}$$

The inverse transform of Eq. (6.18) is

$$y(t) = K_c e^{(a+jb)t} + K_{-c} e^{(a-jb)t} + K_1 e^{r_1 t} + \cdots + K_{n-2} e^{r_{n-2} t} \tag{6.19}$$

The constants K_c and K_{-c} associated with the complex conjugate zeros are evaluated as usual for distinct zeros by the application of Eq. (6.8). That is,

$$K_c = \lim_{s \to a+jb} \left[(s - a - jb) \frac{A(s)}{(s - a - jb)(s - a + jb)(s - r_1) \cdots (s - r_{n-2})} \right]$$

$$= \lim_{s \to a+jb} \left[\frac{1}{2jb} \frac{A(s)}{(s - r_1) \cdots (s - r_{n-2})} \right] = \frac{1}{2jb} K(a + jb) \tag{6.20}$$

where $$K(a + jb) = \lim_{s \to a+jb} \frac{A(s)}{(s - r_1) \cdots (s - r_{n-2})}$$

$$= \left[(s^2 - 2as + a^2 + b^2) \frac{A(s)}{B(s)} \right]_{s=a+jb}$$

Similarly, the constant K_{-c} is obtained as follows:

$$K_{-c} = \lim_{s \to a-jb} \left[(s - a + jb) \frac{A(s)}{(s - a - jb)(s - a + jb)(s - r_1) \cdots (s - r_{n-2})} \right]$$

$$= \lim_{s \to a-jb} \frac{1}{(-2jb)} \frac{A(s)}{(s - r_1) \cdots (s - r_{n-2})} = -\frac{1}{2jb} K(a - jb) \tag{6.21}$$

where $$K(a - jb) = \lim_{s \to a-jb} \frac{A(s)}{(s - r_1) \cdots (s - r_{n-2})}$$

$$= \left[(s^2 - 2as + a^2 + b^2) \frac{A(s)}{B(s)} \right]_{s=a+jb}$$

The constants $K(a + jb)$ and $K(a - jb)$ are complex conjugate numbers. These complex numbers may be represented as shown graphically in Fig. 6.1, whence

$$K(a + jb) = |K(a + jb)| e^{j\alpha}$$

$$K(a - jb) = |K(a + jb)| e^{-j\alpha} \tag{6.22}$$

where $|K(a + jb)| = |K(a - jb)|$ is the length of either vector, α is the angle of the vector $K(a + jb)$, and $-\alpha$ is the angle of the vector $K(a - jb)$.

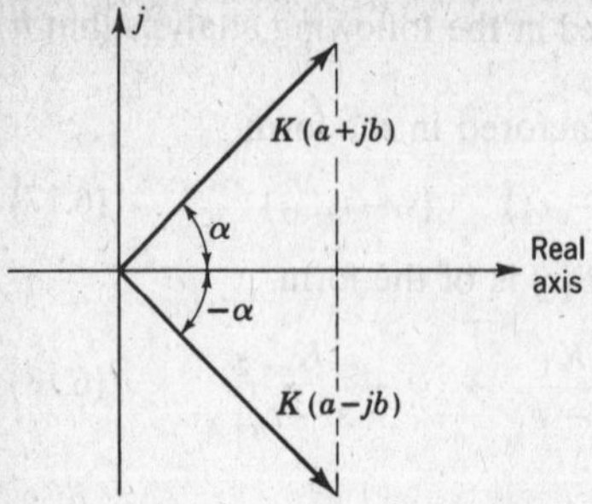

Figure 6.1 Vector representation for $K(a+jb)$ and $K(a-jb)$.

The constants K_c and K_{-c}, which are also complex conjugate numbers, may be written in the form

$$K_c = \frac{1}{2jb}\,|K(a+jb)|\,e^{j\alpha}$$

$$K_{-c} = -\frac{1}{2jb}\,|K(a+jb)|\,e^{-j\alpha} \tag{6.23}$$

Substitution of K_c and K_{-c} from Eq. (6.23) into Eq. (6.19) gives

$$y(t) = \frac{1}{b}\,|K(a+jb)|\,e^{at}\,\frac{e^{j(bt+\alpha)} - e^{-j(bt+\alpha)}}{2j} + K_1 e^{r_1 t} + \cdots + K_{n-2} e^{r_{n-2} t}$$

or

$$y(t) = \frac{1}{b}\,|K(a+jb)|\,e^{at}\sin(bt+\alpha) + K_1 e^{r_1 t} + \cdots + K_{n-2} e^{r_{n-2} t} \tag{6.24}$$

Illustrative example Determine the inverse transformation of the following transformed equation:

$$Y(s) = \frac{75}{(s^2+4s+13)(s+6)}$$

SOLUTION Equating coefficients to obtain the value of a and b for the quadratic yields $-2a = 4$, or $a = -2$, and $a^2 + b^2 = 13$, or $b = \sqrt{13-4} = 3$. Evaluation of $K(a+jb)$ gives

$$K(a+jb) = \left[(s^2 - 2as + a^2 + b^2)\frac{A(s)}{B(s)}\right]_{s=a+jb}$$

$$= \left(\frac{75}{s+6}\right)_{s=-2+j3} = \frac{75}{4+j3} \tag{6.25}$$

As shown in Fig. 6.2, the vector whose real part is 4 and whose imaginary part is 3 may be expressed in the polar form

$$4 + j3 = 5\,\underline{/36.9^\circ}$$

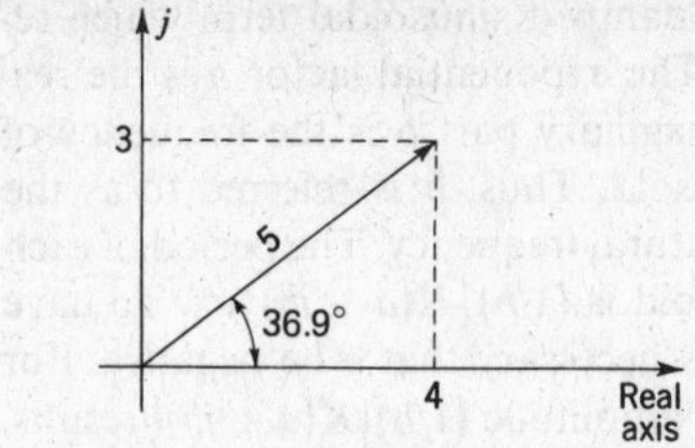

Figure 6.2 Vector representation for $(4 + j3)$.

Hence, Eq. (6.25) becomes

$$K(a + jb) = \frac{75}{5\angle 36.9^\circ} = 15\angle -36.9^\circ$$

Thus $\qquad |K(a + jb)| = 15$

and $\qquad \alpha = \measuredangle K(a + jb) = -36.9^\circ$

The general form of the inverse transformation is

$$y(t) = \frac{1}{b}|K(a + jb)|e^{at} \sin (bt + \alpha) + K_1 e^{r_1 t}$$

Evaluation of K_1 gives

$$K_1 = \lim_{s \to -6} \frac{75}{s^2 + 4s + 13} = \frac{75}{25} = 3$$

Thus the desired result is

$$y(t) = 5e^{-2t} \sin (3t - 36.9^\circ) + 3e^{-6t} \qquad (6.26)$$

Application of the relationship $\sin (\alpha + \beta) = \sin \alpha \cos \beta + \cos \alpha \sin \beta$ in which $\alpha = 3t$ and $\beta = -36.9^\circ$ yields the alternate form

$$y(t) = e^{-2t}(4 \sin 3t - 3 \cos 3t) + 3e^{-6t}$$

This result may also be obtained as follows

$$Y(s) = \frac{75}{(s^2 + 4s + 13)(s + 6)} = \frac{As + B}{(s + 2)^2 + 3^2} + \frac{K_1}{s + 6}$$

Evaluation of the constants yields $A = -3$, $B = 6$, and $K_1 = 3$, whence

$$Y(s) = 4\frac{3}{(s + 2)^2 + 3^2} - 3\frac{(s + 2)}{(s + 2)^2 + 3^2} + \frac{3}{s + 6}$$

Inverting yields directly the preceding form for $y(t)$.

Equation (6.24) shows the exponentially damped sinusoidal term which results from complex conjugate zeros of $B(s)$. The exponential factor a is the real part of the complex conjugate zeros. The imaginary part b is the frequency of oscillation of the exponentially damped sinusoid. Thus, b is referred to as the damped frequency of oscillation or damped natural frequency. The period of each oscillation is $2\pi/b$. The envelope of this sinusoid is $(1/b)|K(a+jb)|e^{at}$. To have the exponential term decreasing with time, it is necessary that a be negative. For the case in which $a = 0$, a sinusoid of constant amplitude $(1/b)|K(a+jb)|$ results. For $a = 0$, Eq. (6.24) becomes

$$y(t) = \frac{1}{b}\,|K(a+jb)|\,\sin(bt+\alpha) + K_1 e^{r_1 t} + \cdots + K_{n-2} e^{r_{n-2} t} \qquad (6.27)$$

In Fig. 6.3 are graphically illustrated the types of time-response terms that result from complex conjugate zeros. When the zeros lie to the left of the imaginary axis ($a < 0$), a decreasing sinusoid results; when the zeros are on the imaginary axis ($a = 0$), a sinusoid of constant amplitude results; and when the zeros are to the right of the imaginary axis ($a > 0$), an increasing sinusoid results.

In Fig. 6.4 is shown a plot of types of response terms that result from real zeros. These results follow directly from Eq. (6.9). Because the exponential factor is the value of the zero, a negative zero ($r_i < 0$) yields an exponentially decreasing term, while a positive zero ($r_i > 0$) yields an exponentially increasing term. A zero at the origin ($r_i = 0$) results in a constant term. Even though a zero may be repeated, the exponential term dominates the response.

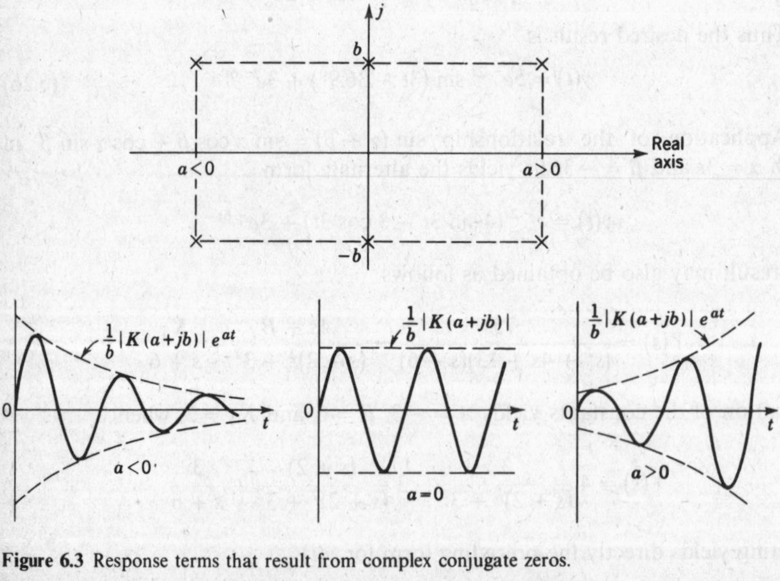

Figure 6.3 Response terms that result from complex conjugate zeros.

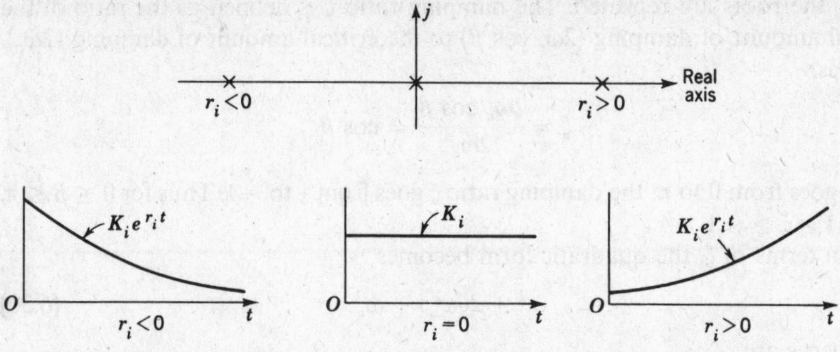

Figure 6.4 Response terms that result from real zeros.

6.3 DAMPING RATIO AND NATURAL FREQUENCY

In Fig. 6.5 is shown a pair of complex conjugate zeros. The distance from the origin to each zero is

$$\omega_n = \sqrt{a^2 + b^2}$$

The angle β is such that

$$\cos(\pi - \beta) = -\cos\beta = \frac{a}{\omega_n}$$

In terms of the polar coordinates β and ω_n, the quadratic form is

$$s^2 - 2as + a^2 + b^2 = s^2 + (2\omega_n \cos\beta)s + \omega_n^2 \qquad 0 < \beta < \pi \tag{6.28}$$

The coefficient of the s term $(2\omega_n \cos\beta)$ is a measure of the amount of damping in the system. The response ceases to be sinusoidal when $\beta = 0$. For this critically damped case, the quadratic form is

$$s^2 + 2\omega_n s + \omega_n^2 = (s + \omega_n)^2 \tag{6.29}$$

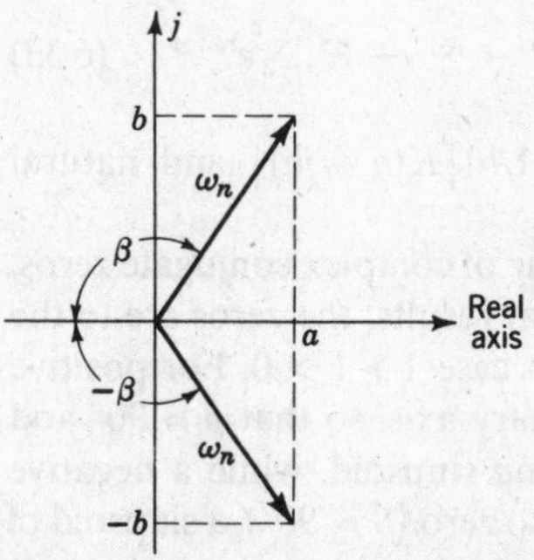

Figure 6.5 Complex conjugate zeros.

Thus, the roots are repeated. The damping ratio ζ is defined as the ratio of the actual amount of damping ($2\omega_n \cos \beta$) to the critical amount of damping ($2\omega_n$). That is,

$$\zeta = \frac{2\omega_n \cos \beta}{2\omega_n} = \cos \beta$$

As β goes from 0 to π, the damping ratio ζ goes from 1 to -1. Thus for $0 \leq \beta \leq \pi$, then $1 \geq \zeta \geq -1$.

In terms of ζ, the quadratic form becomes

$$s^2 + 2\zeta\omega_n s + \omega_n^2 \tag{6.30}$$

The zeros are

$$r_{1,2} = -\zeta\omega_n \pm j\omega_n\sqrt{1-\zeta^2} \tag{6.31}$$

For any given quadratic expression, the numerical values of ζ and ω_n are computed by equating coefficients. For example, consider the expression $s^2 + 4s + 9$. The constant term is $\omega_n^2 = 9$ or $\omega_n = 3$. The reason for using only the positive value when mathematically

$$\omega_n = \sqrt{9} = \pm 3$$

is that ω_n is the distance from the origin to the zero and must be positive. The coefficients for the s term give $2\zeta\omega_n = 4$, or $\zeta = 4/2\omega_n = \frac{2}{3}$. If so desired, the values of a and b are readily computed; that is,

$$a = -\omega_n\zeta = -3(\tfrac{2}{3}) = -2$$

and
$$b = \omega_n\sqrt{1-\zeta^2} = 3\sqrt{1-\tfrac{4}{9}} = 3\sqrt{\tfrac{5}{9}} = \sqrt{5}$$

The time response due to complex conjugate zeros of $B(s)$ [Eq. (6.24)] may be written in terms of the damping ratio and natural frequency as follows:

$$y(t) = \frac{1}{b}\,|K(a+jb)|\,e^{-\zeta\omega_n t} \sin\,[(\omega_n\sqrt{1-\zeta^2})t + \alpha] + K_1 e^{r_1 t} + \cdots + K_{n-2} e^{r_{n-2} t} \qquad -1 < \zeta < 1 \tag{6.32}$$

For the case in which $\zeta = 0$,

$$y(t) = \frac{1}{b}\,|K(a+jb)|\,\sin\,(\omega_n t + \alpha) + K_1 e^{r_1 t} + \cdots + K_{n-2} e^{r_{n-2} t} \tag{6.33}$$

Thus, a sinusoidal term of constant amplitude $(1/b)|K(a+jb)|$ and natural frequency of oscillation ω_n is seen to result.

In Fig. 6.6 is shown a more general plot of a pair of complex conjugate zeros. When a is negative, so that a decreasing exponential results, the zeros are to the left of the imaginary axis, so that $\beta < 90°$, in which case $1 > \zeta > 0$. For positive values of a, the zeros are to the right of the imaginary axis, so that $\beta > 90°$ and $0 > \zeta > -1$. A positive value of ζ yields a decreasing sinusoid, while a negative value results in an increasing sinusoid. For ζ equal to zero ($\beta = 90°$), a sinusoid of

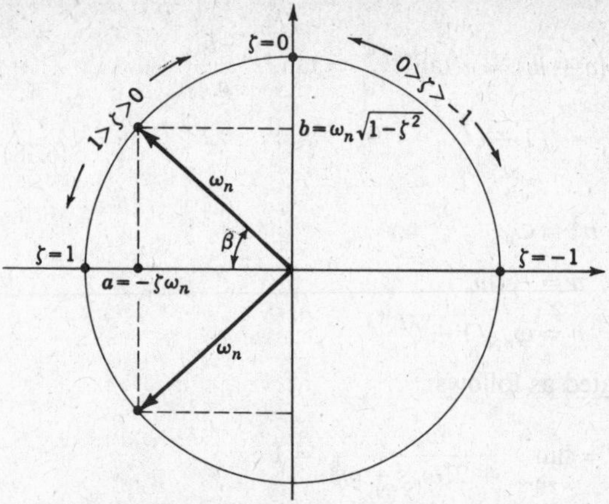

Figure 6.6 General plot of complex conjugate zeros.

constant amplitude is obtained. When the magnitude of ζ is greater than 1, two real zeros result rather than complex conjugate zeros. The case of real zeros has previously been discussed.

Illustrative example Let it be desired to detetermine the general equation for the transient response of a second-order system to a unit-step-function change which occurs at $t = 0$. The operational form of the differential equation is

$$y(t) = \frac{\omega_n^2}{D^2 + 2\zeta\omega_n D + \omega_n^2} f(t) \tag{6.34}$$

Assume that all the initial conditions are zero.

SOLUTION The transform for this differential equation is

$$Y(s) = \frac{\omega_n^2 F(s)}{s^2 + 2\zeta\omega_n s + \omega_n^2} = \frac{\omega_n^2}{(s^2 + 2\zeta\omega_n s + \omega_n^2)s} \tag{6.35}$$

where $F(s) = 1/s$ is the transform for the step input.

For complex conjugate zeros (that is, $-1 < \zeta < 1$), the response has the general form

$$y(t) = \frac{1}{b} \,|K(a + jb)|\, e^{at} \sin(bt + \alpha) + K_1 \tag{6.36}$$

Evaluation of $K(a + jb)$ gives

$$K(a + jb) = \left.\frac{\omega_n^2}{s}\right|_{s=a+jb} = \frac{\omega_n^2}{a + jb} = \frac{\omega_n^2}{\sqrt{a^2 + b^2}\,\angle \tan^{-1} b/a}$$

Thus,

$$|K(a + jb)| = \frac{\omega_n^2}{\sqrt{a^2 + b^2}} = \omega_n \tag{6.37}$$

and

$$\alpha = \measuredangle K(a + jb) = -\tan^{-1}\frac{b}{a} = \tan^{-1}\frac{-b}{a}$$

$$= \tan^{-1}\frac{-\sqrt{1-\zeta^2}}{-\zeta} \tag{6.38}$$

where

$$\sqrt{a^2 + b^2} = \omega_n$$

$$a = -\zeta\omega_n$$

$$b = \omega_n\sqrt{1-\zeta^2}$$

The constant K_1 is evaluated as follows:

$$K_1 = \lim_{s\to 0}\frac{\omega_n^2}{s^2 + 2\zeta\omega_n s + \omega_n^2} = 1$$

Thus, the desired transient response is

$$y(t) = \frac{1}{\sqrt{1-\zeta^2}}e^{-\zeta\omega_n t}\sin\left[(\omega_n\sqrt{1-\zeta^2})t + \alpha\right] + 1 \qquad -1 < \zeta < 1 \tag{6.39}$$

For the case in which $\zeta = 1$, the quadratic term in Eq. (6.35) is

$$s^2 + 2\omega_n s + \omega_n^2 = (s + \omega_n)^2$$

Thus the partial-fraction expansion for $Y(s)$ is

$$Y(s) = \frac{C_2}{(s+\omega_n)^2} + \frac{C_1}{s+\omega_n} + \frac{K_1}{s} \tag{6.40}$$

The constants C_2, C_1, and K_1 are evaluated as follows:

$$C_2 = \lim_{s\to -\omega_n}\frac{\omega_n^2}{s} = -\omega_n$$

$$C_1 = \lim_{s\to -\omega_n}\left[\frac{d}{ds}\left(\frac{\omega_n^2}{s}\right)\right] = \left.\frac{-\omega_n^2}{s^2}\right|_{s=-\omega_n} = -1$$

$$K_1 = \lim_{s\to 0}\frac{\omega_n^2}{s^2 + 2\omega_n s + \omega_n^2} = 1$$

Thus

$$y(t) = (C_2 t + C_1)e^{-\omega_n t} + K_1$$

or

$$y(t) = 1 - (\omega_n t + 1)e^{-\omega_n t} \tag{6.41}$$

In a similar manner, the equation of the time response for $\zeta > 1$ or $\zeta \leq -1$ may also be derived. For these cases the zeros are real, and thus exponential terms are contributed to the response.

In Fig. 6.7 is shown the response $y(t)$ to a step change in the input for various values of the damping ratio ζ. It is to be noted that for $\zeta < 0.4$, there is an excessive

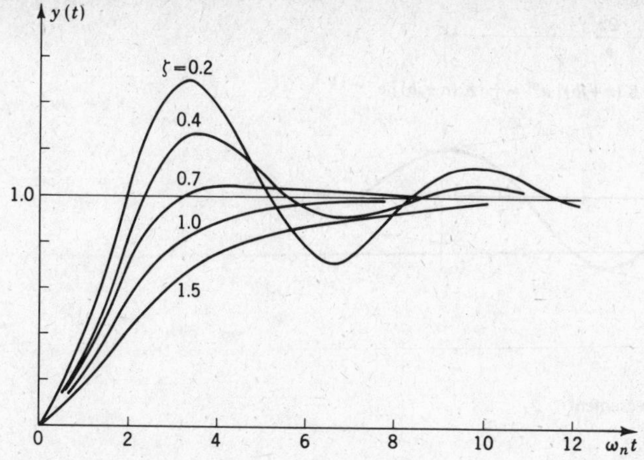

Figure 6.7 Response of a second-order system to a step input.

amount of overshooting and oscillations. For $\zeta > 1$, an excessive amount of time is required to reach the new operating condition. Thus, for most control work, it is desired to have $0.4 < \zeta < 1$.

As shown in Fig. 6.5, the form $a \pm jb$ is the rectangular representation for complex conjugate roots. That is, in rectangular coordinates, the real part a is the horizontal component and the imaginary part b is the vertical component. Similarly, the polar form for complex conjugate roots is specified by the radius $\omega_n = \sqrt{a^2 + b^2}$ and the angle $\beta = \cos^{-1} \zeta$. For computational purposes, the response is usually obtained most readily by using the rectangular form. It is then an easy matter to obtain the polar quantities ω_n and ζ. The polar form has the advantage of providing a more general insight into the actual behavior of the system. For example, Fig. 6.7 shows that the form of the response is determined by ζ. The speed of response is governed by ω_n. That is, Fig. 6.7 shows that for $\zeta = 0.2$, the response $y(t)$ first crosses the value $y(t) = 1$ when $\omega_n t = 2$. Thus, if $\omega_n = 0.1$, the time is $t = 2/\omega_n = 2/0.1 = 20$ s. For $\omega_n = 10$, the time is $t = 2/\omega_n = \frac{2}{10} = 0.2$ s. Hence, the larger the value of ω_n, the faster is the speed of response.

Logarithmic Decrement

For an exponentially damped sinusoid, as shown in Fig. 6.8, the amplitude of the sinusoid after each oscillation changes in a geometric series. At time t_1, the amplitude is $(1/b)|K(a + jb)|e^{at_1}$. The time required to complete one period is $T = 2\pi/b$, and thus the time after one oscillation is completed is $t_2 = t_1 + T = t_1 + 2\pi/b$. The new amplitude is $(1/b)|K(a + jb)|e^{a(t_1 + 2\pi/b)}$, and the ratio of amplitudes is

$$\frac{(1/b)|K(a + jb)|e^{at_1}}{(1/b)|K(a + jb)|e^{at_1}e^{2\pi a/b}} = e^{-2\pi a/b} = e^{2\pi\zeta/\sqrt{(1-\zeta^2)}} \qquad (6.42)$$

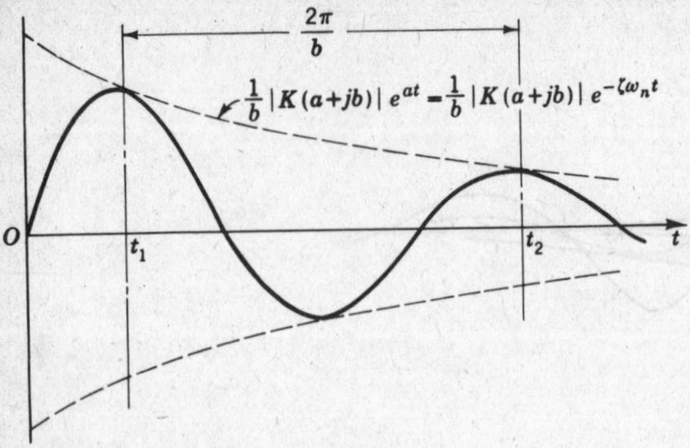

Figure 6.8 Logarithmic decrement.

The ln of this amplitude ratio is $-2\pi a/b = 2\pi\zeta/\sqrt{1-\zeta^2}$, which is called the logarithmic decrement. The amplitude ratio after one oscillation is thus seen to be a function of the damping ratio only.

6.4 TRANSIENT RESPONSE SPECIFICATIONS

A typical response of a second-order system to a step-function input is shown in Fig. 6.9. Depending on the performance criterion for the particular system under investigation, various specifications may be employed. The rise time t_r is the time at which the response first attains its final steady-state value. The percent maximum overshoot is 100 times the maximum amount by which the response overshoots its final steady-state value divided by the final steady-state value. The settling time t_s is the time required before the response does not oscillate more than some small percentage such as 2 or 5 percent from the final steady-state

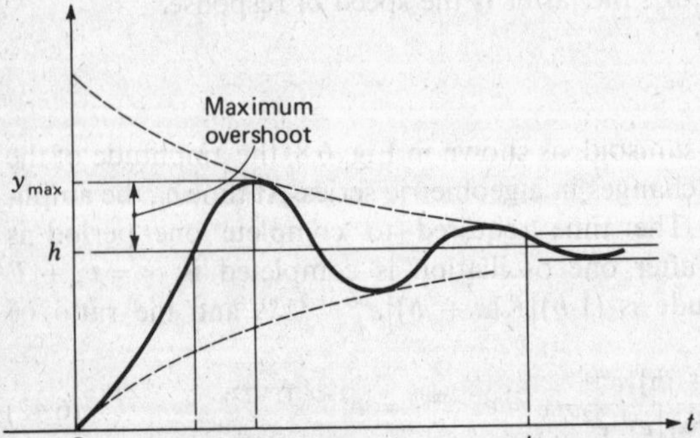

Figure 6.9 System response to a step input.

value. For the case of a step input of height h, the right side of Eq. (6.39) is multiplied by h. That is,

$$y(t) = h + \frac{h}{\sqrt{1-\zeta^2}} e^{-\zeta\omega_n t} \sin\left[(\omega_n\sqrt{1-\zeta^2})t + \alpha\right] \tag{6.43}$$

where α is given by Eq. (6.38). The time t_r such that $y(t) = h$ occurs when the sine term vanishes, that is, when

$$(\omega_n\sqrt{1-\zeta^2})t_r + \alpha = 0$$

Thus, $t_r = \dfrac{-\alpha}{\omega_n\sqrt{1-\zeta^2}} = \dfrac{-\tan^{-1}(-\sqrt{1-\zeta^2}/-\zeta)}{\omega_n\sqrt{1-\zeta^2}} = \dfrac{\tan^{-1}(\sqrt{1-\zeta^2}/-\zeta)}{\omega_n\sqrt{1-\zeta^2}}$

For a given value of ζ, the rise time is inversely proportional to the natural frequency ω_n. A plot of normalized rise time $\omega_n t_r$ versus damping ratio ζ is shown in Fig. 6.10*a*.

Because $\tan\alpha = -\sqrt{1-\zeta^2}/-\zeta$, it follows that $\cos\alpha = -\zeta$ and $\sin\alpha = -\sqrt{1-\zeta^2}$. Thus, Eq. (6.43) may be expressed in the form

$$y(t) = h - \frac{he^{-\zeta\omega_n t}}{\sqrt{1-\zeta^2}}\left[\zeta \sin(\omega_n\sqrt{1-\zeta^2})t + \sqrt{1-\zeta^2}\cos(\omega_n\sqrt{1-\zeta^2})t\right] \tag{6.44}$$

The derivative dy/dt is

$$\frac{dy}{dt} = \frac{\omega_n he^{-\zeta\omega_n t}}{\sqrt{1-\zeta^2}} \sin(\omega_n\sqrt{1-\zeta^2})t$$

Peak values of $y(t)$ occur when $dy/dt = 0$, that is, when

$$(\omega_n\sqrt{1-\zeta^2})t_p = \pi, 2\pi, 3\pi, \ldots$$

The maximum value of $y(t)$ occurs when

$$t_p = \frac{\pi}{\omega_n\sqrt{1-\zeta^2}} \tag{6.45}$$

A plot of normalized peak time $\omega_n t_p$ versus damping ratio ζ is shown in Fig. 6.10*b*. Substitution of $(\omega_n\sqrt{1-\zeta^2})t = \pi$ into Eq. (6.44) yields for the maximum value

$$y_{\max} = h + he^{-\zeta\pi/\sqrt{1-\zeta^2}} \tag{6.46}$$

Subtracting the final steady-state value h, dividing by h, and multiplying by 100 yields for the maximum percent overshoot

$$\text{P.O.} = 100e^{-\zeta\pi/\sqrt{1-\zeta^2}} \tag{6.47}$$

Note that the maximum value and percent overshoot depend on the damping ratio ζ only. A plot of percent overshoot versus damping ratio ζ is shown in Fig. 6.10*c*.

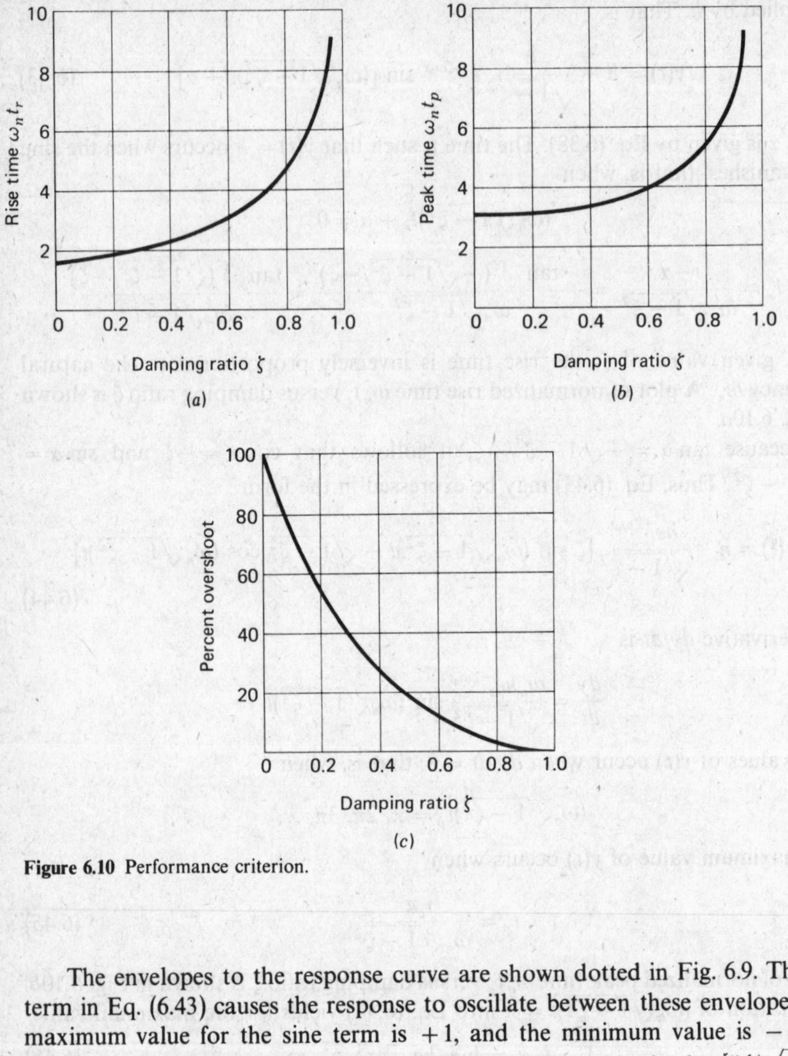

Figure 6.10 Performance criterion.

The envelopes to the response curve are shown dotted in Fig. 6.9. The sine term in Eq. (6.43) causes the response to oscillate between these envelopes. The maximum value for the sine term is $+1$, and the minimum value is -1. The difference between each envelope and the final value is $he^{-\zeta\omega_n t}/\sqrt{1-\zeta^2}$. Each envelope is within 5 percent of the final value when

$$\frac{he^{-\zeta\omega_n t}/\sqrt{1-\zeta^2}}{h} = \frac{e^{-\zeta\omega_n t}}{\sqrt{1-\zeta^2}} \le 0.05$$

Because $e^{-3} = 0.05$, it is customary to approximate the settling time such that the response is within 5 percent of its final value when $\zeta\omega_n t \ge 3$. Thus,

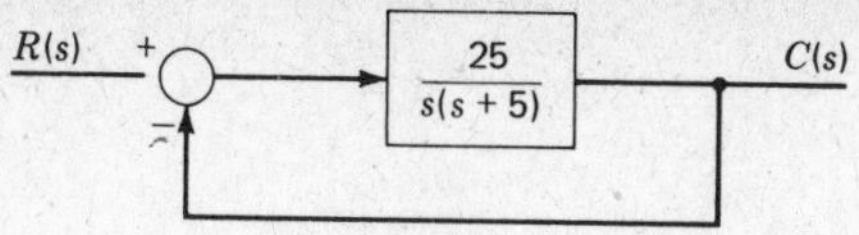

Figure 6.11 Feedback control system.

$$t_s \geq \frac{3}{\zeta\omega_n} \tag{6.48}$$

Similarly, because $e^{-4} = 0.02$, the settling time such that the response is within 2 percent of the final value is approximated by

$$t_s \geq \frac{4}{\zeta\omega_n} \tag{6.49}$$

Illustrative example For the system shown in Fig. 6.11, determine the natural frequency, damping ratio, damped natural frequency, rise time, percent overshoot, and approximate 5 percent settling time.

SOLUTION The characteristic equation for this system is $s^2 + 5s + 25 = 0$. Comparison with the general form given by Eq. (6.30) shows that $\omega_n^2 = 25$ or $\omega_n = 5$ and $2\zeta\omega_n = 5$ or $\zeta = 5/10 = 0.5$. The damped natural frequency is $b = \omega_n\sqrt{1-\zeta^2} = 5\sqrt{3/4} = 4.33$ rad/s. The rise time is

$$t_r = \frac{\tan^{-1}(\sqrt{1-\zeta^2}/-\zeta)}{\omega_n\sqrt{1-\zeta^2}}$$

$$= \frac{\tan^{-1}[(\sqrt{3}/2)/(-1/2)]}{4.33} = \frac{\tan^{-1}(\sqrt{3}/-1)}{4.33} = \frac{2\pi/3}{4.33} = 0.483 \text{ s}$$

The angle whose tangent is $\sqrt{3}/-1$ is located in the second quadrant and is 120°, which is $2\pi/3$ rad.

Application of Eq. (6.47) yields for the percent overshoot

$$\text{P.O.} = 100e^{-\zeta\pi/\sqrt{1-\zeta^2}} = 100e^{-\pi/\sqrt{3}} = 16.3\%$$

The approximate settling time is

$$t_s \approx \frac{3}{\zeta\omega_n} = \frac{3}{(0.5)(5)} = 1.2 \text{ s}$$

6.5 GENERAL FORM OF TRANSIENT RESPONSE

The general form of the transient response can be ascertained directly from the zeros of the transformed function $B(s)$. For example, suppose that the zeros of $B(s)$ are those plotted in Fig. 6.12. It follows that $B(s)$ may be factored in the form

$$B(s) = (s - a_1 - jb_1)(s - a_1 + jb_1)(s - jb_2)(s + jb_2)(s - 0)(s - r_2)(s - r)^2$$

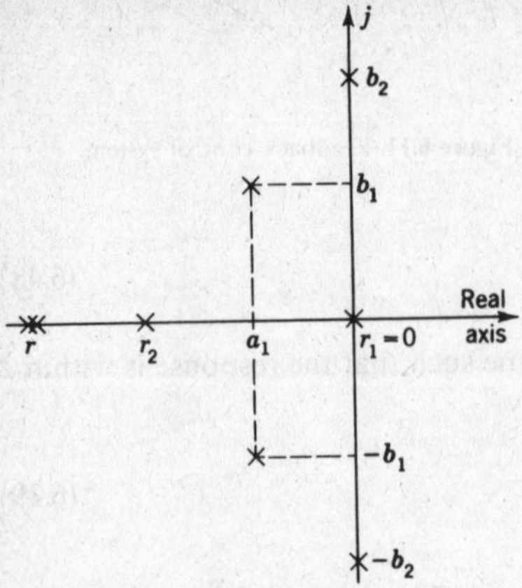

Figure 6.12 Graphical representation of zeros of $B(s)$.

Performing a partial-fraction expansion on $Y(s) = A(s)/B(s)$ yields

$$Y(s) = \frac{K_{c1}}{s - a_1 - jb_1} + \frac{K_{-c1}}{s - a_1 + jb_1} + \frac{K_{c2}}{s - jb_2} + \frac{K_{c2}}{s + jb_2} + \frac{K_1}{s} + \frac{K_2}{s - r_2} + \frac{C_2}{(s - r)^2} + \frac{C_1}{s - r}$$

Taking the inverse transform of the preceding expression yields

$$y(t) = \frac{1}{b_1} |K(a_1 + jb_1)| e^{a_1 t} \sin (b_1 t + \alpha_1) + \frac{1}{b_2} |K(jb_2)| \sin (b_2 t + \alpha_2) + K_1 + K_2 e^{r_2 t} + (C_2 t + C_1) e^{rt}$$

It is to be noted that a pair of complex conjugate zeros yields an exponentially varying sinusoidal term. A pair of complex conjugate zeros on the imaginary axis yields a sinusoid with a constant amplitude. The zero at the origin contributes a constant term. Distinct or multiple zeros on the real axis yield exponential terms.

The term $B(s) = L_n(s) D_{F(s)}$ consists of the zeros of $L_n(s)$ of the characteristic function for the system plus the zeros $D_{F(s)}$ corresponding to the denominator of the transform of the input excitation. If any zero of the characteristic function for the system $L_n(s)$ lies to the right of the imaginary axis, the response contains an increasing time function and will increase without bound. *Thus, if any zero of* $L_n(s)$ *lies in the right half plane (i.e., to the right of the imaginary axis), then the system is basically unstable.* Whether a system is stable or unstable is a basic property of the system $L_n(s)$ itself and not the particular input, or excitation, to the system.

The zeros of $D_{F(s)}$ yield response terms associated with the particular excitation to the system. Take, for example, a ramp function $D_{F(s)} = s^2$, which gives a response term of the form $C_1 t$. It should be noted that the input which is a ramp function eventually becomes infinite, and thus the output of the system has been forced to infinity because of the particular input. As is illustrated by this example, the *zeros of $D_{F(s)}$ do not affect the basic stability of a system* but merely yield response terms appropriate to the particular excitation.

Illustrative example The differential equation of operation for a control system is

$$y(t) = \frac{360(D^2 + D + 1)}{(D^2 + 2D + 5)(D^2 + 6D + 9)(D^2 + 6D + 8)} f(t)$$

Determine the general form of the response equation when the input excitation $f(t)$ is a unit step function.

SOLUTION Because of the unit-step function input, $N_{F(s)} = 1$, $D_{F(s)} = s$, so that $B(s) = L_n(s)D_{F(s)} = L_n(s)s$. Thus

$$Y(s) = \frac{360(s^2 + s + 1)(1) + sI(s)}{(s^2 + 2s + 5)(s^2 + 6s + 9)(s^2 + 6s + 8)s} = \frac{A(s)}{B(s)}$$

The partial-fraction expansion for $Y(s)$ gives

$$Y(s) = \frac{K_c}{s + 1 + j2} + \frac{K_{-c}}{s + 1 - j2} + \frac{C_2}{(s + 3)^2} + \frac{C_1}{s + 3} + \frac{K_1}{s + 2} + \frac{K_2}{s + 4} + \frac{K_3}{s}$$

Thus, the general form of the time solution is

$$y(t) = \tfrac{1}{2}|K(a + jb)|e^{-t} \sin(2t + \alpha) + (C_2 t + C_1)e^{-3t} + K_1 e^{-2t} + K_2 e^{-4t} + K_3$$

It should be noted in all cases that the exponent of each exponential term is equal to the horizontal distance from the imaginary axis to the zero of interest. That is, the exponential factor is equal to the numerical value of the real part of the zero. The terms due to zeros which are located far to the left of the imaginary axis have large exponential decaying factors and tend to decrease very rapidly to negligible quantities. Thus, zeros closer to the imaginary axis usually have more effect on the transient behavior. Accordingly, the analysis of complicated control systems is oftentimes approximated by omitting from the characteristic function zeros which do not affect substantially the performance of the system.

6.6 RESPONSE TO AN EXTERNAL DISTURBANCE

In this section, it is shown that the characteristic function for the differential equation which relates the output of a system to a change in the external disturbance is the same as that for the differential equation which relates the output to a change in the desired input. In Fig. 6.13 is shown the general representation for a feedback control system, in which $d(t)$ represents the external disturbance.

As previously discussed, the effect of the input $r(t)$ and external disturbance $d(t)$ on the output or controlled variable $c(t)$ may be considered individually and then each result added by superposition to obtain the total variation in $c(t)$. The

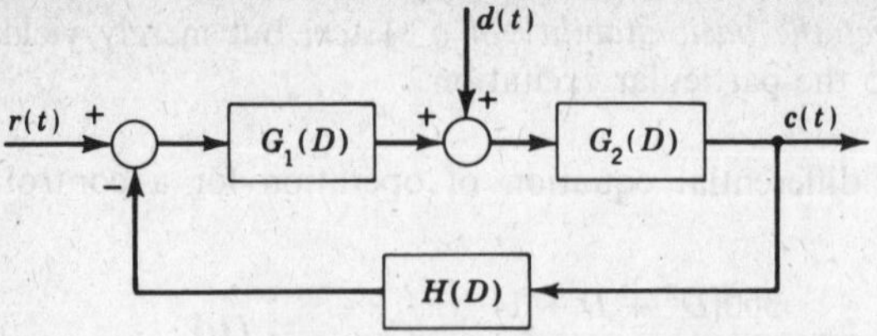

Figure 6.13 General representation for a feedback control system.

block diagram which relates the input $r(t)$ to the output $c(t)$ without regard to the external disturbance is shown in Fig. 6.14. The equation relating $r(t)$ and $c(t)$ is

$$c(t) = \frac{G_1(D)G_2(D)}{1 + G_1(D)G_2(D)H(D)} r(t)$$

By using N_{G_1} to designate the numerator of $G_1(D)$ and D_{G_1} to designate the denominator of $G_1(D)$, etc., the preceding expression may be written in the form

$$c(t) = \frac{N_{G_1} N_{G_2} D_H}{D_{G_1} D_{G_2} D_H + N_{G_1} N_{G_2} N_H} r(t) \tag{6.50}$$

The characteristic function $L_n(D)$ for the system is $D_{G_1} D_{G_2} D_H + N_{G_1} N_{G_2} N_H$.

The block diagram which relates the external disturbance $d(t)$ to the output when $r(t)$ is considered zero is shown in Fig. 6.15. The equation relating $d(t)$ and $c(t)$ is

$$c(t) = \frac{G_2(D)}{1 + G_1(D)G_2(D)H(D)} d(t)$$

$$= \frac{N_{G_2} D_{G_1} D_H}{D_{G_1} D_{G_2} D_H + N_{G_1} N_{G_2} N_H} d(t) \tag{6.51}$$

It can be shown that, if an excitation enters any place in the loop, the differential equation relating the disturbance and the output will always have the same characteristic function $L_n(D)$, which is the product of all the denominator terms plus the product of all the numerator terms. The constants which appear in the partial-fraction expansion depend upon where the disturbance enters the system. Thus, there is but one characteristic function for a system, and this function gives basic information as to the transient behavior of the system.

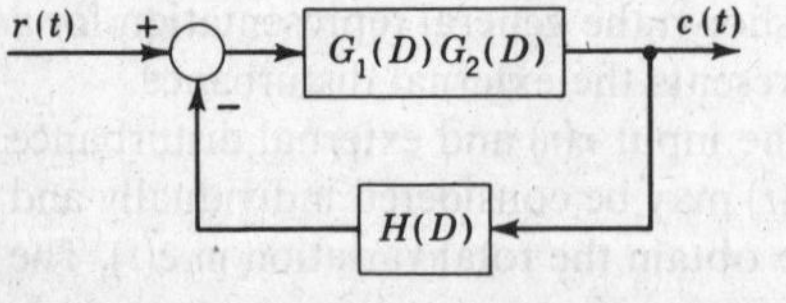

Figure 6.14 Block diagram for consideration of the input $r(t)$.

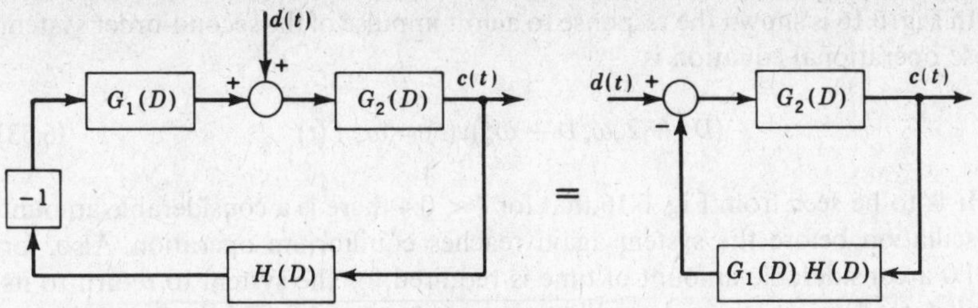

Figure 6.15 Block diagram for consideration of external disturbance $d(t)$.

6.7 IMPULSE RESPONSE

The response of a system to a unit impulse excitation provides a good indication or measure of the general transient behavior of the system. The unit impulse is in effect a momentary disturbance which upsets the initial state of equilibrium of the system. In time, a stable system will return again to its equilibrium position.

Substitution of $F(s) = 1$ into Eq. (6.2) yields the transformed equation for a unit impulse excitation.

$$Y(s) = \frac{L_m(s) + I(s)}{L_n(s)} \tag{6.52}$$

It is to be noted that the basic form of the response of a system to a unit impulse is determined entirely by the zeros of the characteristic function $L_n(s)$. If any zero lies to the right of the imaginary axis, the output increases without bound. Thus the system is basically unstable. For an unstable system, it is impossible to achieve any equilibrium state, because as soon as the power is turned on, the output continually increases with time.

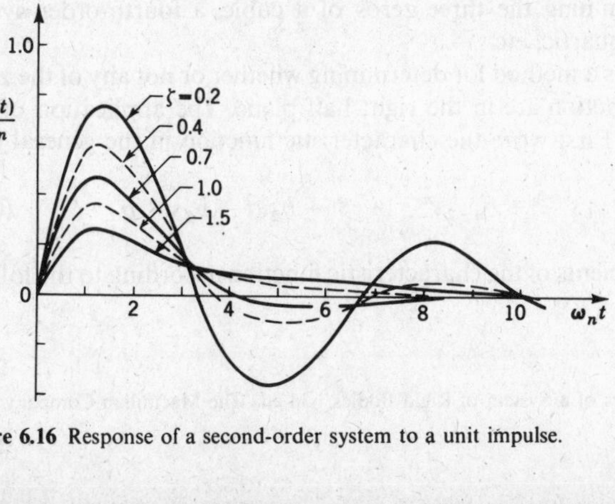

Figure 6.16 Response of a second-order system to a unit impulse.

In Fig. 6.16 is shown the response to a unit impulse of the second-order system whose operational equation is

$$(D^2 + 2\zeta\omega_n D + \omega_n^2)y(t) = \omega_n^2 f(t) \tag{6.53}$$

It is to be seen from Fig. 6.16 that for $\zeta < 0.4$ there is a considerable amount of oscillation before the system again reaches equilibrium operation. Also, for $\zeta > 1.0$ a considerable amount of time is required for the system to return to its initial state. Thus, it seems desirable to have $0.4 < \zeta < 1.0$. This is the result that was obtained from a consideration of the step-function response. Because the scale of the horizontal axis is $\omega_n t$, the speed of response is governed by the natural frequency ω_n, as is described in Sec. 6.3.

6.8 ROUTH'S STABILITY CRITERION

A major difficulty in using the Laplace transform method for determining the transient response of a feedback control system is that it necessitates determining the zeros of the characteristic function. The general form for the characteristic function has previously been shown to be

$$D_{G_1} D_{G_2} D_H + N_{G_1} N_{G_2} N_H \tag{6.54}$$

In determining the block diagram for a system, the terms N_{G_1}, N_{G_2}, N_H, D_{G_1}, D_{G_2}, and D_H are usually obtained in factored form. Because of the plus sign in Eq. (6.54), the zeros of N_{G_1}, N_{G_2}, etc., are not the zeros of the characteristic function. Thus, it becomes necessary to determine the zeros of the general polynomial represented by Eq. (6.54). This presents no difficulty for first- and second-order systems. The zero of a first-order system is immediately obvious, and the two zeros of a quadratic equation are readily solved. However, a third-order system requires determining the three zeros of a cubic, a fourth-order system necessitates solving a quartic, etc.

Routh's criterion[1] is a method for determining whether or not any of the zeros of the characteristic function are in the right half plane. The application of this criterion is as follows: First write the characteristic function in the general form

$$b_n s^n + b_{n-1} s^{n-1} + b_{n-2} s^{n-2} + \cdots + b_2 s^2 + b_1 s + b_0 \tag{6.55}$$

Next arrange the coefficients of the characteristic function according to the following schedule:

[1] E. J. Routh, "Dynamics of a System of Rigid Bodies," 3d ed., The Macmillan Company, New York, 1877.

$$
\begin{array}{llll}
b_n & b_{n-2} & b_{n-4} & b_{n-6} \quad \cdots \\
b_{n-1} & b_{n-3} & b_{n-5} & b_{n-7} \quad \cdots \\
c_1 & c_2 & c_3 & c_4 \quad \cdots \\
d_1 & d_2 & d_3 & \cdots \\
\cdots\cdots & \cdots\cdots & \cdots\cdots & \cdots\cdots \\
e_1 & e_2 & 0 & \\
f_1 & f_2 & 0 & \\
g_1 & 0 & & \\
h_1 & 0 & &
\end{array}
\tag{6.56}
$$

After first arranging the b coefficients as shown, the row of c terms is evaluated as follows:

$$
\begin{aligned}
c_1 &= \frac{b_{n-1}b_{n-2} - b_n b_{n-3}}{b_{n-1}} \\
c_2 &= \frac{b_{n-1}b_{n-4} - b_n b_{n-5}}{b_{n-1}} \\
c_3 &= \frac{b_{n-1}b_{n-6} - b_n b_{n-7}}{b_{n-1}}
\end{aligned}
\tag{6.57}
$$

Examination of Eq. (6.57) reveals the pattern for evaluating the c coefficients. By dropping down a row, the same pattern is used to obtain the d coefficients. That is,

$$
\begin{aligned}
d_1 &= \frac{c_1 b_{n-3} - b_{n-1}c_2}{c_1} \\
d_2 &= \frac{c_1 b_{n-5} - b_{n-1}c_3}{c_1}
\end{aligned}
\tag{6.58}
$$

This process is continued until one more row is obtained than the order of the differential equation. Thus, a third-order equation has four rows, a fourth-order equation has five rows, etc. To illustrate, consider the function

$$s^4 + 3s^3 + s^2 + 6s + 2 \tag{6.59}$$

The first two rows of the following array are obtained directly from the coefficients of Eq. (6.59), and the remaining rows are computed as just described:

$$
\begin{array}{l|rrrr}
s^4 & 1 & 1 & 2 & 0 \\
s^3 & 3 & 6 & 0 & \\
s^2 & -1 & 2 & 0 & \\
s^1 & 12 & 0 & & \\
s^0 & 2 & 0 & &
\end{array}
\tag{6.60}
$$

The left column identifies the row. The first row is indicated by s^4, the second by s^3, etc. The exponent in the first term s^4 is the order of the polynomial. Because there is one more row than the order of the polynomial, the last row is always indicated by s^0.

Routh's criterion states that the number of changes of sign of the coefficients in the first column of the array is equal to the number of zeros of the characteristic function that are located to the right of the imaginary axis. For the preceding example, the signs of the numbers in the first column are seen to go from plus to minus and then back to plus again, so that there are two changes of sign. Thus, there are two zeros located to the right of the imaginary axis.

The number of coefficients in the first column is $n + 1$, where n is the order of the characteristic function. If the Routh array is continued past the last row, it is found that only zeros result. The reason that it is necessary to keep track of the number of pertinent rows is that if the coefficient of the last row is zero, then the characteristic equation has a root at the origin. If the coefficients of the last two pertinent rows are zero, then the characteristic equation has a double root at the origin, etc.

When one of the coefficients in the first column is zero, it may be replaced by a very small number ε for the purpose of computing the remaining coefficients in the array. Thus, consider the characteristic equation

$$s^5 + 2s^4 + 4s^3 + 8s^2 + 10s + 6 = 0 \qquad (6.61)$$

The Routh array is

$$\begin{array}{c|cccc} s^5 & 1 & 4 & 10 & 0 \\ s^4 & 2 & 8 & 6 & 0 \\ s^3 & \varepsilon \approx 0 & 7 & 0 & \\ s^2 & -14/\varepsilon & 6 & 0 & \\ s^1 & 7 & 0 & & \\ s^0 & 6 & 0 & & \end{array}$$

where $d_1 = (8\varepsilon - 14)/\varepsilon = -14/\varepsilon$ is a very large negative number, and $e_1 = (7d_1 - 6\varepsilon)/d_1 = 7$. Because there are two sign changes in the first column, the characteristic equation has two roots located to the right of the imaginary axis.

When some of the roots of the characteristic equation are symmetrically located about the origin, then a row of Routh's array will contain all zeros. This situation occurs when the characteristic equation has a pair of real roots with opposite signs ($\pm r$), complex conjugate roots on the imaginary axis ($\pm j\omega$), or a pair of complex conjugate roots with opposite real parts ($a \pm jb$, $-a \pm jb$). The row preceding the row of zeros is the polynomial of such factors. This polynomial is called the auxiliary equation.

Thus consider the characteristic equation

$$s^6 + 6s^5 + 10s^4 + 12s^3 + 13s^2 - 18s - 24 = 0 \qquad (6.62)$$

The Routh array is

$$\begin{array}{c|ccccc} s^6 & 1 & 10 & 13 & -24 & 0 \\ s^5 & 6 & 12 & -18 & 0 & \\ s^4 & 8 & 16 & -24 & 0 & \\ s^3 & 0 & 0 & 0 & & \end{array}$$

The s^3 row contains all zeros. The auxiliary equation $A(s)$ is obtained from the coefficients of the preceding row as follows:

$$A(s) = 8s^4 + 16s^2 - 24 = 8(s^4 + 2s^2 - 3) = 8(s^2 - 1)(s^2 + 3)$$

The auxiliary equation is always an even order. The power of s for the first coefficient (8) is s^4, the power of s for the next coefficient (16) is s^2, and the power of s for the last coefficient (-24) is $s^0 = 1$. In general, the power of s for the first coefficient is the order of the row, and the power decreases by 2 for each succeeding coefficient. Dividing the polynomial by the known factors $(s^2 - 1)(s^2 + 3)$ yields

$$\begin{array}{r|l}
 & s^2 + 6s + 8 \\
\hline
s^4 + 2s^2 - 3 & s^6 + 6s^5 + 10s^4 + 12s^3 + 13s^2 - 18s - 24 \\
 & s^6 + 2s^4 - 3s^2 \\
\cline{2-2}
 & 6s^5 + 8s^4 + 12s^3 + 16s^2 - 18s \\
 & 6s^5 + 12s^3 - 18s \\
\cline{2-2}
 & 8s^4 + 16s^2 - 24 \\
 & 8s^4 + 16s^2 - 24 \\
\cline{2-2}
\end{array}$$

Thus, the original characteristic equation may be written in the form

$$s^6 + 6s^5 + 10s^4 + 12s^3 + 13s^2 - 18s - 24 = (s^4 + 2s^2 - 3)(s^2 + 6s + 8) = 0$$

The roots of $(s^4 + 2s^2 - 3) = (s^2 - 1)(s^2 + 3)$ consist of the pair of real and opposite roots $(s^2 - 1) = (s - 1)(s + 1)$ and the pair of complex conjugate roots on the imaginary axis $(s^2 + 3) = (s + j\sqrt{3})(s - j\sqrt{3})$.

As another example, consider the characteristic equation

$$s^6 + 3s^5 + 2s^4 + 4s^2 + 12s + 8 = 0 \tag{6.63}$$

The Routh array is

$$\begin{array}{c|cccc}
s^6 & 1 & 2 & 4 & 8 \\
s^5 & 3 & 0 & 12 & 0 \\
s^4 & 2 & 0 & 8 & 0 \\
s^3 & 0 & 0 & 0 &
\end{array}$$

The auxiliary equation is

$$A(s) = 2s^4 + 8 = 2(s^4 + 4)$$

Dividing the characteristic equation by $s^4 + 4$ yields

$$\begin{array}{r|l}
 & s^2 + 3s + 2 \\
\hline
s^4 + 4 & s^6 + 3s^5 + 2s^4 + 0s^3 + 4s^2 + 12s + 8 \\
 & s^6 + 4s^2 \\
\cline{2-2}
 & 3s^5 + 2s^4 + 12s \\
 & 3s^5 + 12s \\
\cline{2-2}
 & 2s^4 + 8 \\
 & 2s^4 + 8
\end{array}$$

The factored form for the original characteristic equation is

$$(s^4 + 4)(s^2 + 3s + 2) = s^6 + 3s^5 + 2s^4 + 4s^2 + 12s + 8 = 0$$

The roots of $(s^4 + 4) = (s^2 + 2s + 2)(s^2 - 2s + 2)$ consist of the complex pair located at $-1 \pm j$ and the pair located at $+1 \pm j$. Such a set of complex conjugate roots is called a quadripole.

It is not necessary to use Routh's criterion if any of the coefficients of the characteristic function are zero or negative, because when this is so, it can be shown that there is at least one zero located on, or to the right of, the imaginary axis.

To determine how many roots of the characteristic equation lie to the right of some vertical line a distance σ from the imaginary axis (i.e., the number of roots that have a real part greater than σ), transform the characteristic equation by substituting $s + \sigma$ for s, and apply Routh's criterion as just described. The number of changes of sign in the first column for this new function is equal to the number of roots which are located to the right of the vertical line through σ.

6.9 SUMMARY

In this chapter it is shown that the transient response of a system is governed primarily by the location of the zeros of $B(s) = L_n(s)D_{F(s)}$. The zeros of $D_{F(s)}$ yield response terms appropriate to the particular excitation to the system. The function $L_n(s)$ is a basic property of the system itself. When all the zeros of $L_n(s)$ are located in the left half plane, the system is stable (i.e., for any bounded input the response is also bounded). If any zero of $L_n(s)$ is located in the right half plane, the system is unstable (i.e., the response is always unbounded). The imaginary axis is the borderline between stable and unstable systems.

Complex imaginary zeros are undesirable because they yield constant sinusoids. A zero of $L_n(s)$ at the origin is also undesirable because it indicates an integration of the input. Note that an integrator in the feedforward elements (which integrates the error signal) does not yield a zero of $L_n(s)$ at the origin because the zeros of $D_{G(s)}$ are not the zeros of $L_n(s)$. When the characteristic function $L_n(s)$ has a zero at the origin, a constant input (i.e., a step function) yields an unbounded time term $C_1 t$ in the output which is the integral of the input.

The basic form of the response due to repeated zeros is the same as that for distinct zeros, with the exception that repeated zeros on the imaginary axis yield increasing time terms rather than time terms with constant amplitudes. Because $B(s) = L_n(s)D_{F(s)}$, the zeros of $L_n(s)$ and $D_{F(s)}$ act independently to yield the time response unless one or more of the zeros of $L_n(s)$ and $D_{F(s)}$ are the same. This introduces repeated zeros in $B(s)$, which affects the basic form of the response equation only if the zeros are on the imaginary axis. For example, a repeated complex imaginary zero results in an increasing sinusoid rather than a constant sinusoid. Similarly, a repeated zero at the origin yields an increasing time function

Table 6.1 Location of zeros and corresponding response functions

Zeros of $B(s) = L_n(s)D_{F(s)}$	Type of response
Left half plane (distinct or repeated)	Decaying exponential and/or decaying sinusoid
Right half plane (distinct or repeated)	Increasing exponential and/or increasing sinusoid
Imaginary axis:	
Distinct	Constant and/or constant sinusoid
Repeated	Increasing time function and/or increasing sinusoid

rather than a constant. To ensure stability, zeros of $L_n(s)$ should be excluded not only from the right half plane but also from the imaginary axis.

Table 6.1 summarizes the types of response terms associated with the zeros of $B(s)$.

PROBLEMS

6.1 Determine the time response $y(t)$ for each of the following transformed equations:

(a) $Y(s) = \dfrac{2s + 12}{s(s + 3)(s + 4)}$ (b) $Y(s) = \dfrac{s^2 + 3s + 8}{(s + 2)(s^2 + 5s + 4)}$ (c) $Y(s) = \dfrac{s + 9}{s(s + 3)^2}$

(d) $Y(s) = \dfrac{s + 30}{s^3(s + 3)}$

6.2 Determine the time response $y(t)$ for each of the following transformed equations:

(a) $Y(s) = \dfrac{5(s + 1)}{s(s^2 + 2s + 5)}$ (b) $Y(s) = \dfrac{4(s + 4)}{(s + 2)(s^2 + 4)}$

6.3 Invert the following to obtain the response $y(t)$:

(a) $Y(s) = \dfrac{10}{s(s^2 + 3s - 10)}$ (b) $Y(s) = \dfrac{25}{s(s^2 - 10s + 25)}$

6.4 Use the Laplace transform method to determine the solution of each of the following differential equations:

(a) $(D + 1)(D + 2)y = e^{-t}$ (b) $(D + 1)(D + 2)y = e^{-2t}$ (c) $(D + 1)(D + 2)y = e^{-t} - e^{-2t}$

6.5 Use the Laplace transform method to solve the following differential equations:

(a) $\dfrac{dy}{dt} + y = 2 \sin t$ (b) $\dfrac{dy}{dt} + y = 2 \cos t$

All the initial conditions are zero.

6.6 For the system shown in Fig. P6.6, determine K and a such that the response to a unit impulse $[r(t) = u_1(t)]$ has the form

$$c(t) = C_1 e^{-t} + C_2 e^{-4t}$$

Evaluate C_1 and C_2 when all the initial conditions are zero.

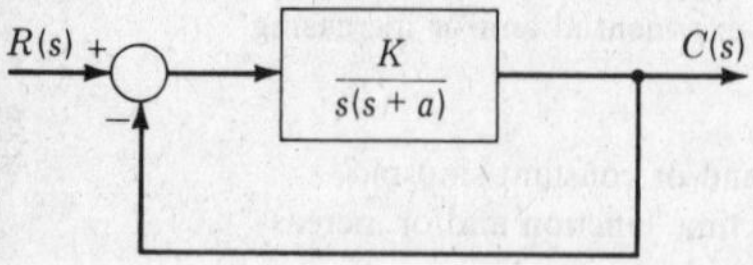

Figure P6.6

6.7 Same as Prob. 6.6, except that it is desired that the impulse response have the form

$$c(t) = (C_0 + C_1 t)e^{-2t}$$

Evaluate C_0 and C_1 when all the initial conditions are zero.

6.8 Same as Prob. 6.6, except that it is desired that the impulse response have the form

$$c(t) = Ce^{-t} \sin (2t + \alpha)$$

Evaluate C and α when all the initial conditions are zero.

6.9 Use the Laplace transform method to solve the following differential equation:

$$y(t) = \frac{25(D + 1)}{D^2 + 10D + 25} f(t)$$

All the initial conditions are zero, and $f(t)$ is a unit step function. Use the initial-value theorem to check $y(0+)$ and $y'(0+)$.

6.10 Use the Laplace transform method to solve the following differential equation:

$$y(t) = \frac{25(D + 1)}{D^2 + 8D + 25} f(t)$$

All the initial conditions are zero, and $f(t)$ is a unit step function. Use the initial-value theorem to check $y(0+)$ and $y'(0+)$.

6.11 A system is described by the differential equation

$$(D^2 + 1)y = f(t)$$

All initial conditions are zero, then a step input $f(t) = 1$ is applied for π seconds $[f(t) = 1$ for $0 < t < \pi$ and $f(t) = 0$ for $t > \pi]$. Determine the response for $0 < t < \pi$ and for $t > \pi$.

6.12 Same as Prob. 5.14 except $K = 4$.

6.13 For the system shown in Fig. 5.10, $K_1 = 1.0$, $K_2 = 0.75$, $\tau = 0.25$, and all initial conditions are zero. Determine the response for each of the following cases:

(*a*) n_{in} is a unit impulse and $u = 0$.

(*b*) u is a unit impulse and $n_{in} = 0$.

6.14 Same as Prob. 6.13 except that $K_2 = 1.25$ rather than 0.75.

6.15 Determine the damping ratio, undamped natural frequency, and damped natural frequency for the system shown in Fig. P6.15. What is the response $c(t)$ of this system to a unit-step-function excitation $r(t) = u(t)$ when all initial conditions are zero?

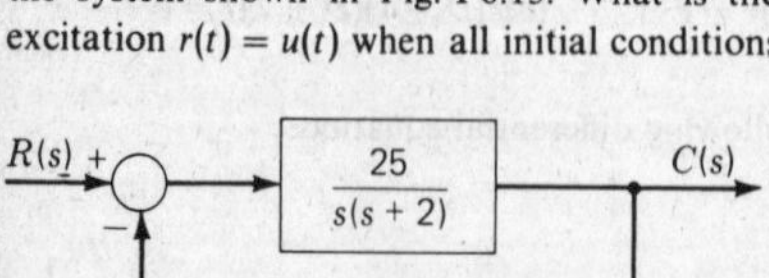

Figure P6.15

6.16 To improve the transient behavior of the system of Fig. P6.15, a controller with proportional and derivative action is added, as shown in Fig. P6.16. Determine the value of K such that the resulting system will have a damping ratio of 0.5. What is the response $c(t)$ of this resulting system to a unit-step-function excitation $r(t) = u(t)$ when all initial conditions are zero?

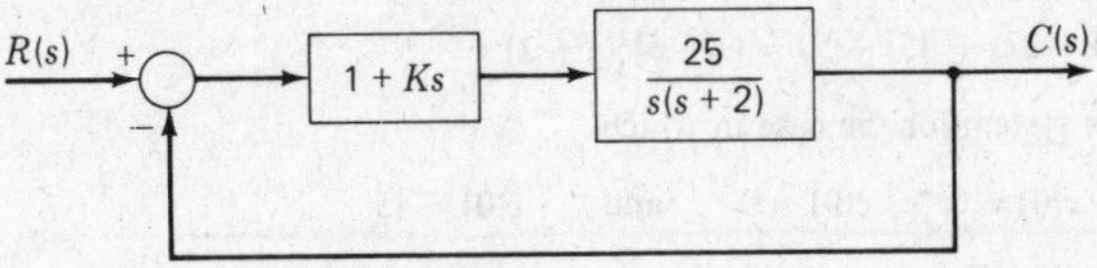

Figure P6.16

6.17 To improve the dynamic performance of the system of Fig. P6.15, derivative action (Ks) is added to the feedback path, as shown in Fig. P6.17. Determine the value of K such that the resulting system will have a damping ratio of 0.5. What is the response $c(t)$ of this resulting system to a unit-step-function excitation $r(t) = u(t)$ when all initial conditions are zero?

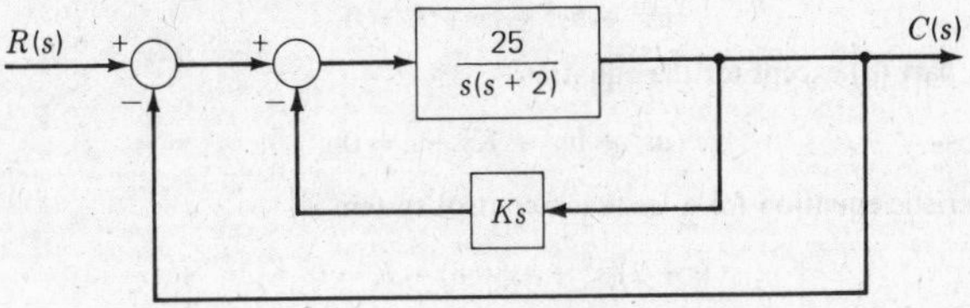

Figure P6.17

6.18 For the system shown in Fig. P6.15, determine the rise time t_r, the peak time t_p, the 2 percent settling time t_s, and the percent overshoot.

6.19 Change the term $s + 2$ in Fig. P6.15 to $s + 10$, then determine the rise time t_r, the peak time t_p, the 2 percent settling time t_s, and the percent overshoot.

6.20 The characteristic function for a control system is known to be

$$L_n(D) = (D + 5)(D^2 + 4D + 13)$$

Determine the general form of the equation for the response $y(t)$ of this system when the input excitation $f(t)$ is

(*a*) An impulse
(*b*) A step function

Is the general form of these response expressions affected by the initial conditions?

6.21 Determine the characteristic function for the control system shown in Fig. P6.21. Use block-diagram algebra to move the constants A and B into the main loop. Does this affect the characteristic function?

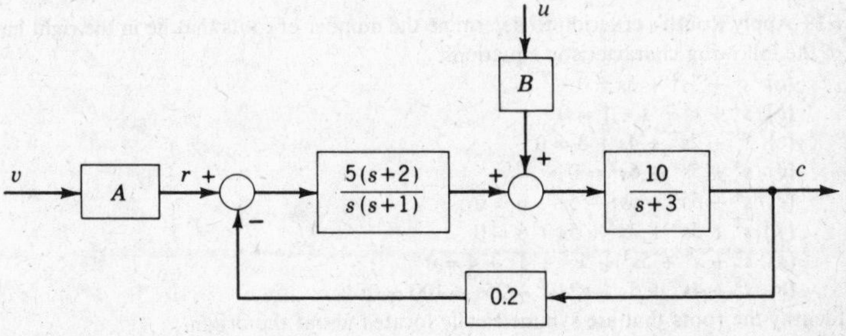

Figure P6.21

6.22 The transfer function $G(s)$ for a unity-feedback control system is

$$G(s) = \frac{K}{s(s^2 + 12s + 45)}$$

When $K = 50$, the roots of the characteristic equation are -5, -5, and -2. Thus,

$$s(s^2 + 12s + 45) + 50 = (s + 5)^2(s + 2)$$

Determine the response $c(t)$ of this system for the case in which

$$r(t) = 0 \qquad c(0) = 0 \qquad \dot{c}(0) = 0 \qquad \text{and} \qquad \ddot{c}(0) = 45.$$

6.23 Same as Prob. 6.22 except $K = 104$. For this case the roots of the characteristic equation are -8, $-2 + j3$, and $-2 - j3$. Thus,

$$s(s^2 + 12s + 45) + 104 = (s + 8)(s^2 + 4s + 13)$$

6.24 (*a*) Apply Routh's criterion to determine an equation for K in terms of a, b, and c such that the cubic equation given below will have no roots with positive real parts.

$$as^3 + bs^2 + cs + K = 0$$

(*b*) Same as part (*a*) except for the equation

$$as^3 + bs^2 + Ks + c = 0$$

6.25 The characteristic equation for a feedback control system is

$$(s + 2)(s^2 + 4s + 8) + K = 0$$

Use Routh's criterion to determine the range of values of K for which the system is stable.

6.26 The characteristic equation for a control system is

$$s(s^2 + 8s + a) + 4(s + 8) = 0$$

Use Routh's criterion to obtain the range of values of a for which the system is stable.

6.27 For each of the characteristic functions given below:

(*a*) Determine the number of zeros that lie on or to the right of the imaginary axis.

$$s^3 + 2s^2 + 5s + 24 \qquad s^4 + 2s^3 + 6s^2 + 2s + 5$$

$$s^4 + 3s^3 + 4s^2 + 6s$$

(*b*) Determine the number of zeros that have a real part greater than or equal to -4.

6.28 The characteristic equation for a certain system is

$$s(s^3 + 4s^2 + 2s + 3) + K(s + 1) = 0$$

Using Routh's criterion, determine the range of values of K for which the system is stable.

6.29 Apply Routh's criterion to determine the number of roots that lie in the right half plane for each of the following characteristic equations:

(*a*) $s^3 + 5s^2 + 6s = 0$
(*b*) $s^3 + s^2 - s - 1 = 0$
(*c*) $s^3 + 2s^2 + 4s + 8 = 0$
(*d*) $s^4 + 5s^3 + 6s^2 = 0$
(*e*) $s^4 + 5s^3 + 5s^2 - 5s - 6 = 0$
(*f*) $s^4 + 5s^3 + 7s^2 + 5s + 6 = 0$
(*g*) $s^5 + s^4 + 5s^3 + 5s^2 + 4s + 4 = 0$
(*h*) $s^5 + 4s^4 + 6s^3 + 24s^2 + 25s + 100 = 0$

Identify the roots that are symmetrically located about the origin.

6.30 The characteristic equation for a system is

$$s(s^2 + 6s + 13) + K = 0$$

(*a*) Determine the value of K such that the characteristic equation has a pair of complex conjugate roots on the imaginary axis. Write the factored form of the characteristic equation for this case.

(*b*) Determine the value of K such that the characteristic equation has a pair of complex conjugate roots whose real part is -1. Write the factored form of the characteristic equation for this case.

CHAPTER

SEVEN

THE ROOT-LOCUS METHOD

The root-locus method was developed by W. R. Evans.[1,2] This method enables one to determine the roots of the characteristic equation (i.e., the zeros of the characteristic function) by knowing the factored form of the feedforward and feedback elements of a control system. As is discussed in Chap. 6, the transient behavior of a system is governed primarily by the roots of the characteristic equation for the system. Neither the initial conditions nor the particular excitation affects the basic operation of a system.

7.1 SIGNIFICANCE OF ROOT LOCI

Consider the control system represented by Fig. 7.1*a*. The general form for the characteristic equation is

$$D_G D_H + N_G N_H = 0 \tag{7.1}$$

From Fig. 7.1*a* it follows that $N_G = K$, $D_G = s(s+4)$, $N_H = 1$, and $D_H = 1$. Thus, the characteristic equation for this system is

$$s(s+4) + K = s^2 + 4s + K = 0 \tag{7.2}$$

The roots of the characteristic equation depend upon the value of K, which is the *static loop sensitivity*. As is shown in Fig. 7.1*a*, the static loop sensitivity K is the

[1] W. R. Evans, Graphical Analysis of Control Systems, *Trans. AIEE*, **67:** 547–551 (1948).
[2] W. R. Evans, "Control-system Dynamics," McGraw-Hill Book Company, New York, 1954.

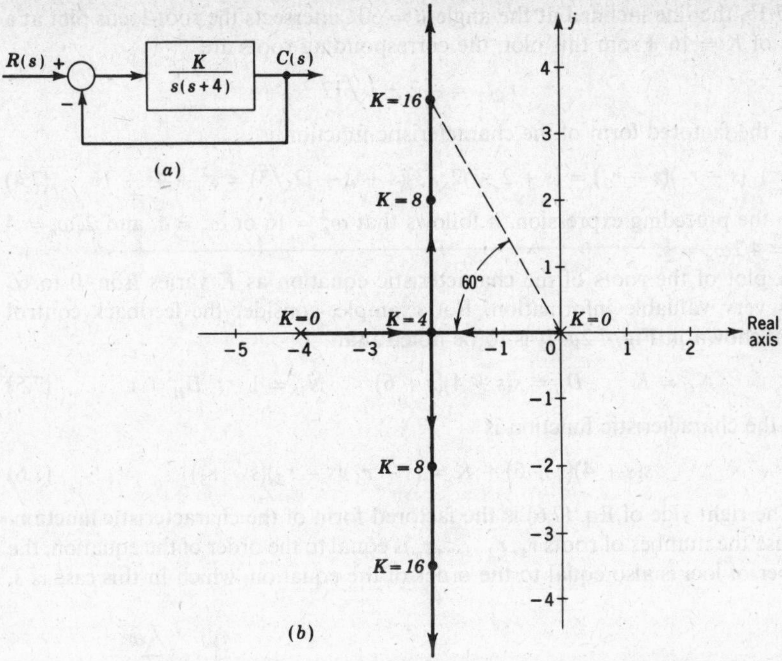

Figure 7.1 Root-locus plot for $s(s + 4) + K = 0$.

product of all the constant terms in the control loop when the coefficient of each s term is unity.

Because Eq. (7.2) is a quadratic, the roots are $r_{1,2} = a \pm jb$, in which $-2a = 4$ or $a = -2$ and $b = \sqrt{K - a^2} = \sqrt{K - 4}$. Thus

$$\begin{aligned} &\text{For} \quad K > 4 \qquad r_{1,2} = -2 \pm j\sqrt{K-4} \\ &\text{For} \quad K = 4 \qquad r_1 = r_2 = -2 \\ &\text{For} \quad K < 4 \qquad r_{1,2} = -2 \pm j\sqrt{K-4} = -2 \mp \sqrt{4-K} \end{aligned} \tag{7.3}$$

In this last case, the roots are real and unequal. The heavy lines in Fig. 7.1*b* are a plot of the roots of this characteristic equation for various values of K. When $K = 0$, the roots are $r_{1,2} = 0, -4$; when $K = 4$, the roots are $r_1 = r_2 = -2$; when $K = 16$, the roots are $r_{1,2} = -2 \pm j\sqrt{12}$; etc.

Such a plot of the roots of the characteristic equation for each value of K as K varies from 0 to ∞ is a root-locus plot. From such a root-locus plot, it is an easy matter to select the value of K to yield the desired roots of the characteristic equation. For example, let it be desired to have a damping ratio $\zeta = 0.5$. As discussed in the preceding chapter, $\beta = \cos^{-1} \zeta = \cos^{-1} 0.5 = 60°$. As is shown in

Fig. 7.1*b*, the line inclined at the angle $\beta = 60°$ intersects the root-locus plot at a value of $K = 16$. From this plot, the corresponding roots are

$$r_{1,2} = -2 \pm j\sqrt{12}$$

Thus, the factored form of the characteristic function is

$$(s - r_1)(s - r_2) = (s + 2 - j2\sqrt{3})(s + 2 + j2\sqrt{3}) = s^2 + 4s + 16 \qquad (7.4)$$

From the preceding expression, it follows that $\omega_n^2 = 16$ or $\omega_n = 4$, and $2\zeta\omega_n = 4$ or $\zeta = 4/2\omega_n = \frac{1}{2}$.

A plot of the roots of the characteristic equation as K varies from 0 to ∞ yields very valuable information. For example, consider the feedback control system shown in Fig. 7.2*a*. It is to be noted that

$$N_G = K \qquad D_G = s(s + 4)(s + 6) \qquad N_H = 1 \qquad D_H = 1 \qquad (7.5)$$

Thus the characteristic function is

$$s(s + 4)(s + 6) + K = (s - r_1)(s - r_2)(s - r_3) \qquad (7.6)$$

The right side of Eq. (7.6) is the factored form of the characteristic function. Because the number of roots $r_1, r_2, \ldots, r_n$ is equal to the order of the equation, the number of loci is also equal to the order of the equation, which in this case is 3.

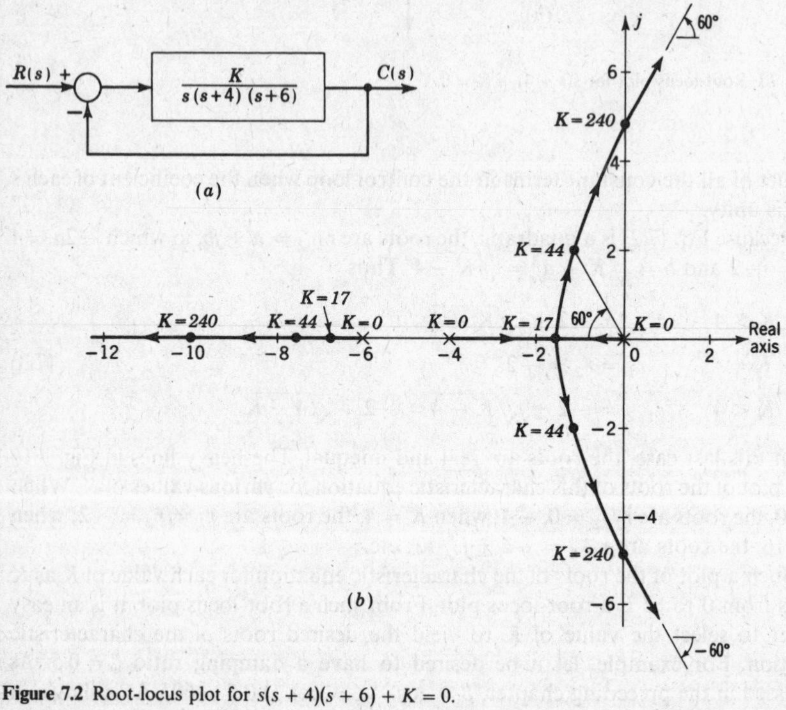

Figure 7.2 Root-locus plot for $s(s + 4)(s + 6) + K = 0$.

For each value of K, there corresponds a particular value of r_1, r_2, and r_3. Thus, for each value of K from 0 to ∞ one may plot the loci of corresponding values of r_1, r_2, and r_3. The three loci for Eq. (7.6) are drawn in Fig. 7.2*b*. One locus starts at $r_1 = -6$ for $K = 0$ and proceeds out the negative real axis as K increases. Another locus starts at $r_2 = -4$ and goes to the right along the real axis to the point $r_2 = -1.57$ and then leaves the real axis and proceeds out along a 60° asymptote toward infinity. The third locus starts at $r_3 = 0$ and moves along the negative real axis to $r_3 = -1.57$. This locus then leaves the real axis and proceeds toward infinity along a $-60°$ asymptote. In the construction of the loci, the three loci are determined without regard to which is considered the r_1, the r_2, or the r_3 locus. That is, from the similarity of the terms on the right side of Eq. (7.6), it is seen that the particular subscripts 1, 2, and 3 may be used interchangeably.

From Fig. 7.2*b* it is to be noted that, if K is 240, then the three roots of the characteristic equation are

$$r_1 = -10 \qquad r_2 = j4.9 \qquad r_3 = -j4.9$$

Thus, the characteristic function may be written in the following factored form:

$$s(s+4)(s+6) + 240 = (s+10)(s-j4.9)(s+j4.9) \tag{7.7}$$

For $K = 240$, a pair of roots lie on the imaginary axis, which would yield a sinusoidal response term of constant amplitude. From the root-locus plot, it is to be noted that, for $K > 240$, a pair of roots will always lie in the right half plane, thus making the system unstable.

For each value of K the corresponding roots of the characteristic equation may be determined directly from the root-locus plot. These roots in turn govern the transient behavior. From the root-locus plot, the designer may select the value of K such that the system will have a desired transient behavior. For example, let it be desired to have a damping ratio of 0.5. The intersection of the line drawn at the angle $\beta = 60°$ with the loci determines the value of $K = 44$. It is to be noted that the loci are always symmetrical with respect to the real axis because complex roots always occur as conjugate pairs.

Illustrative example For the control system shown in Fig. 7.2, determine

1. The differential equation relating $c(t)$ and $r(t)$.
2. The transformed equation relating $C(s)$ and $R(s)$.
3. The response $c(t)$ of this system for the case in which $K = 44$, the input $r(t)$ is a unit impulse, and all the initial conditions are zero.

SOLUTION

1. Replacing s by D in the block diagram and then applying Eq. (3.70) gives for the differential equation

$$c(t) = \frac{Kr(t)}{D(D+4)(D+6)+K} = \frac{Kr(t)}{D^3 + 10D^2 + 24D + K}$$

2. The transform is

$$C(s) = \frac{KR(s) + [s^2c(0) + sc'(0) + c''(0)] + 6[sc(0) + c'(0)] + 24c(0)}{s^3 + 10s^2 + 24s + K}$$

3. For $K = 44$, the root-locus plot shows that the roots of the characteristic equation are $a \pm jb = -1.2 \pm j2.1$ and $r = -7.6$. Hence, the factored form of the characteristic equation is

$$s^3 + 10s^2 + 24s + K = (s^2 + 2.4s + 5.85)(s + 7.6)$$

For $R(s) = 1$ and all the initial conditions zero, the transformed equation becomes

$$C(s) = \frac{44}{(s + 7.6)(s^2 + 2.4s + 5.85)}$$

The general form of the response is

$$c(t) = K_1 e^{-7.6t} + \frac{|K(a + jb)|}{b} e^{at} \sin (bt + \alpha)$$

The value of K_1 is

$$K_1 = \lim_{s \to -7.6} \frac{44}{s^2 + 2.4s + 5.85} = \frac{44}{81.85} = 0.54$$

The value of $K(a + jb)$ is

$$K(a + jb) = \lim_{s \to -1.2 + j2.1} \frac{44}{s + 7.6} = \frac{44}{6.4 + j2.1} = \frac{44}{6.74 \underline{/ 18.2^\circ}}$$

$$= 6.53 \underline{/ -18.2^\circ}$$

Thus, the desired solution is

$$c(t) = 0.54e^{-7.6t} + 3.11e^{-1.2t} \sin (2.1t - 18.2^\circ)$$

It is to be noted that regardless of the particular problem being solved, the general form of the transient response is determined by the roots of the characteristic equation. For a given value of K these roots are ascertained directly from the root-locus plot.

7.2 CONSTRUCTION OF LOCI

By determining certain points and asymptotes, the loci may be sketched in quite readily. The loci always originate, or begin, at $K = 0$, in which case the value of the roots is obtained directly from the characteristic equation. For example, from Eq. (7.6), when $K = 0$, the roots are 0, -4, and -6.

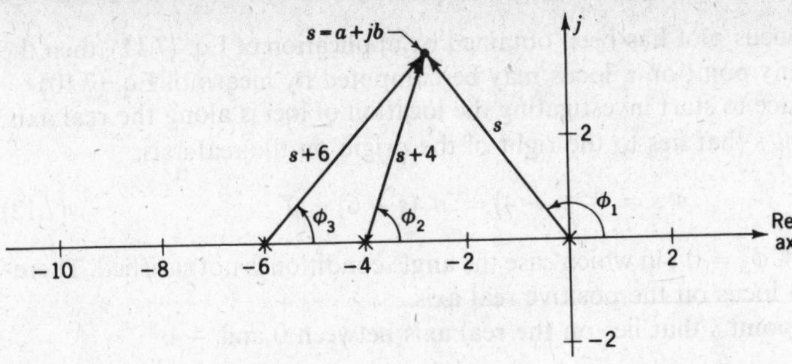

Figure 7.3 Application of angle condition to a trial point.

The roots $r_1, r_2, \ldots, r_n$ of a characteristic equation are those values of s which make the characteristic function equal to zero, i.e.,

$$s(s+4)(s+6) + K = (s - r_1)(s - r_2)(s - r_3) = 0 \tag{7.8}$$

Thus, a root $r_1, r_2, \ldots, r_n$ of a characteristic equation is a value of s such that

$$s(s+4)(s+6) + K = 0$$

or

$$s(s+4)(s+6) = -K \tag{7.9}$$

In Fig. 7.3, it is to be noted that the term s in Eq. (7.9) may be represented as a vector drawn from the origin to any point $s = a + jb$ in the s plane. The term $s + 4$ is the vector sum of the vector drawn from the -4 point to the origin plus the vector from the origin to the point s. This vector sum is equal to the vector drawn directly from the -4 point to s. Similarly, $s + 6$ is the vector drawn from -6 to s. Thus, Eq. (7.9) may be regarded as a vector equation. The length or magnitude of each vector satisfies the magnitude condition

$$|s|\,|s+4|\,|s+6| = |-K| = K \tag{7.10}$$

where $|s|$ is the length of the s vector in Fig. 7.3, $|s+4|$ is the length of the $s + 4$ vector, etc. In addition, the angle of each vector must satisfy the angle condition

$$\measuredangle s + \measuredangle (s+4) + \measuredangle (s+6) = \measuredangle(-K) = 180^\circ \pm k360^\circ \tag{7.11}$$

where $k = 0, 1, 2, 3, \ldots$

$$\measuredangle s = \phi_1$$
$$\measuredangle (s+4) = \phi_2$$
$$\measuredangle (s+6) = \phi_3$$

The angles ϕ_1, ϕ_2, and ϕ_3 are illustrated in Fig. 7.3.

The term $-K$ is a negative number which may be represented as being at the point $-K$ on the negative real axis such that $\measuredangle(-K)$ is $180^\circ \pm k360^\circ$.

In order that a point in the s plane be a root of the characteristic equation and thus lie on a locus of the roots, it is necessary that the point be located so that Eq. (7.11) is satisfied. Thus, the paths of the loci are determined from Eq. (7.11).

After the root-locus plot has been obtained by application of Eq. (7.11), then the value of K at any point on a locus may be computed by means of Eq. (7.10).

The first place to start investigating the location of loci is along the real axis. For a trial point s that lies to the right of the origin on the real axis,

$$\angle s = \angle (s+4) = \angle (s+6) = 0^\circ \tag{7.12}$$

Thus, $\phi_1 + \phi_2 + \phi_3 = 0^\circ$, in which case the angle condition is not satisfied. Therefore, there is no locus on the positive real axis.

For a trial point s that lies on the real axis between 0 and -4,

$$\angle s = 180^\circ \qquad \angle (s+4) = 0^\circ \qquad \angle (s+6) = 0^\circ \tag{7.13}$$

Because $\phi_1 + \phi_2 + \phi_3 = 180^\circ$ satisfies the angle condition, there is a locus on the real axis between 0 and -4.

For the region from -4 to -6, it follows that

$$\angle s = 180^\circ \qquad \angle (s+4) = 180^\circ \qquad \angle (s+6) = 0^\circ \tag{7.14}$$

Thus, $\phi_1 + \phi_2 + \phi_3 = 360^\circ$ does not satisfy the angle condition. Finally, for the region from -6 to $-\infty$ on the negative real axis,

$$\phi_1 + \phi_2 + \phi_3 = 180^\circ + 180^\circ + 180^\circ = 540^\circ$$

so that Eq. (7.11) is again satisfied, which signifies a locus in this region.

The next step in the construction of the loci is to determine the asymptotes as s approaches infinity. For very large values of s, the terms 0, 4, and 6 in Eq. (7.9) become negligible compared with the value of s, so that Eq. (7.9) becomes

$$s(s+4)(s+6) \approx s(s)(s) = s^3 = -K \tag{7.15}$$

The angle condition is

$$\angle s^3 = 3 \angle s = 180^\circ \pm k360^\circ$$

or

$$\angle s = \frac{180^\circ \pm k360^\circ}{3} = 60^\circ \pm k120^\circ \tag{7.16}$$

Only three distinct angles, 60°, -60°, 180°, are obtained from Eq. (7.16).

In order to locate the asymptotes, it is necessary to know where they intersect the real axis. The point σ_c where the asymptotes cross the real axis is determined from the general equation

$$\sigma_c = \frac{\sum \text{zeros of } D_G D_H - \sum \text{zeros of } N_G N_H}{(\text{no. of zeros of } D_G D_H) - (\text{no. of zeros of } N_G N_H)} \tag{7.17}$$

To verify Eq. (7.17), first write the characteristic equation [i.e., Eq. (7.1)] in the form

$$(s-p_1)(s-p_2)\cdots(s-p_n) + K(s-z_1)(s-z_2)\cdots(s-z_m) = 0$$

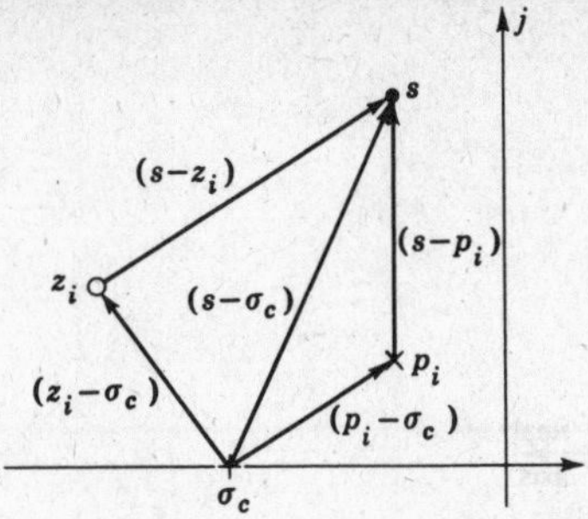

Figure 7.4 Asymptote crossing σ_c.

where $p_1, p_2, \ldots, p_n$ are the roots of $D_G D_H$ and $z_1, z_2, \ldots, z_m$ are the roots of $N_G N_H$. Solving for $-K$ gives

$$-K = \frac{(s-p_1)\cdots(s-p_n)}{(s-z_1)\cdots(s-z_m)} = \frac{s^n - (p_1 + \cdots + p_n)s^{n-1} + \cdots}{s^m - (z_1 + \cdots + z_m)s^{m-1} + \cdots} \tag{7.18}$$

It is to be noted that the coefficient of the second term in a polynomial is the negative of the sum of the roots.

Each numerator factor and each denominator factor may be written in the following form:

$$s - p_i = (s - \sigma_c) - (p_i - \sigma_c)$$

$$s - z_i = (s - \sigma_c) - (z_i - \sigma_c)$$

In Fig. 7.4, the point s is indicated by a dot, p_i by a $\times$, z_i by a circle, and σ_c by a $+$. The various vector quantities are indicated on this diagram. For a given value of p_i the vector $p_i - \sigma_c$ remains constant. Hence, as s becomes infinite, $s - \sigma_c \gg p_i - \sigma_c$. Thus, for very large s,

$$s - p_i \approx s - \sigma_c$$

Similarly, as s becomes infinite it follows that

$$s - z_i \approx s - \sigma_c$$

Thus

$$-K \approx \frac{(s-\sigma_c)^n}{(s-\sigma_c)^m} = (s-\sigma_c)^{n-m} = s^{n-m} - \sigma_c(n-m)s^{n-m-1} + \cdots$$

Performing the division indicated in Eq. (7.18) gives

$$-K = s^{n-m} - [(p_1 + p_2 + \cdots + p_n) - (z_1 + z_2 + \cdots + z_m)]s^{n-m-1} + \cdots$$

Equating the coefficients of the second terms in the two preceding equations for $-K$ and solving for σ_c verifies the result given by Eq. (7.17). For the system under consideration Eq. (7.17) becomes

$$\sigma_c = \frac{[(0) + (-4) + (-6)] - 0}{3 - 0} = \frac{-10}{3} = -3\tfrac{1}{3} \tag{7.19}$$

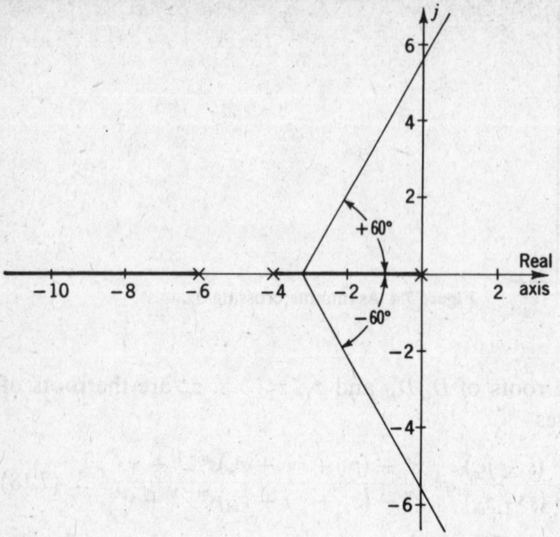

Figure 7.5 Location of loci on real axis and the asymptotes.

The information thus far obtained concerning the location of the roots is shown graphically in Fig. 7.5. By knowing the point at which the locus between 0 and -4 breaks away from the real axis, one can construct a reasonably good sketch of the locus. This breakaway point σ_b is determined as follows: Consider in Fig. 7.6 a point s which is a small vertical distance Δ above the real axis. The equation for each angle is

$$\phi_1 = \pi - \tan^{-1} \frac{\Delta}{0 - \sigma_b}$$

$$\phi_2 = \tan^{-1} \frac{\Delta}{\sigma_b - (-4)} \tag{7.20}$$

$$\phi_3 = \tan^{-1} \frac{\Delta}{\sigma_b - (-6)}$$

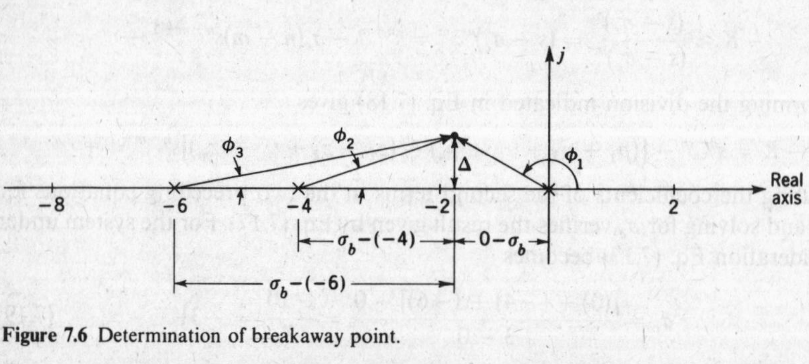

Figure 7.6 Determination of breakaway point.

For small values of Δ, $\tan^{-1}(\Delta/-\sigma_b) \approx -\Delta/\sigma_b$, etc. From Fig. 7.6, it is to be seen that, as Δ approaches zero, $\phi_1 + \phi_2 + \phi_3 \approx \pi + 0 + 0 = \pi$. Thus

$$\phi_1 + \phi_2 + \phi_3 = \pi + \frac{\Delta}{\sigma_b} + \frac{\Delta}{4 + \sigma_b} + \frac{\Delta}{6 + \sigma_b} = \pi$$

or

$$\frac{\Delta}{\sigma_b} + \frac{\Delta}{\sigma_b + 4} + \frac{\Delta}{\sigma_b + 6} = 0 \tag{7.21}$$

After eliminating Δ and obtaining a common denominator, the preceding expression becomes

$$3\sigma_b^2 + 20\sigma_b + 24 = 0$$

whence

$$\sigma_b = -1.57 \tag{7.22}$$

The value of K at the point where the locus breaks away from the real axis is the maximum value that K attains between the points 0 and -4. Thus, an alternative method for determining σ_b is first to solve the characteristic equation for K:

$$K = -s(s+4)(s+6) = -(s^3 + 10s^2 + 24s) \tag{7.23}$$

Differentiation to obtain the value of $s = \sigma_b$ at which K is a maximum gives

$$\frac{dK}{ds} = -\frac{d}{ds}(s^3 + 10s^2 + 24s) = -(3s^2 + 20s + 24) = 0 \tag{7.24}$$

Equation (7.24) is the result that was obtained by the preceding geometric evaluation. The occurrence of a breakaway point is ascertained by the fact that *there is always a breakaway point between any two adjacent* $\times$*'s on the real axis which are connected by a locus.* A $\times$ is used to designate a zero of $D_G D_H$.

With the information obtained thus far, the root-locus plot may be sketched in quite accurately, as is shown in Fig. 7.7. For better accuracy in constructing the path of the loci from the breakaway point to the asymptote, it is necessary by trial and error to select trial points in this region and apply the angle condition. Trial points which satisfy the angle condition are points on the locus. It is a good idea to start by choosing all trial points on the same horizontal line until the point on the loci is obtained. For a trial point on one side of the loci, the angle condition will yield an angle greater than 180°, and for a trial point on the other side, an angle less than 180° is indicated. This information indicates in what direction a new trial point should be taken. The use of a spirule, which is a commercially available device, saves much effort in finding the angle of a trial point.

To illustrate the application of the magnitude condition, consider the point shown on the locus in Fig. 7.7. The value of s at this point is

$$s = -1.2 + j2.1$$

From Eq. (7.10), it follows that

$$K = |s||s+4||s+6|$$
$$= \sqrt{-1.2^2 + 2.1^2}\sqrt{2.8^2 + 2.1^2}\sqrt{4.8^2 + 2.1^2} = 44$$

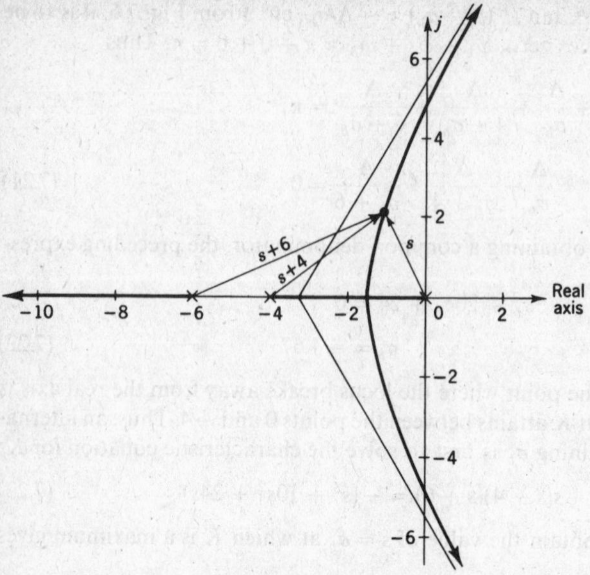

Figure 7.7 Application of magnitude condition.

In summary, the path of the locus plots is obtained entirely from the angle condition [Eq. (7.11)], and the values of K along the loci are determined from the magnitude condition [Eq. (7.10)].

The value of K at which the locus crosses the imaginary axis may be computed by Routh's method. That is, application of Routh's criterion to the characteristic function $s^3 + 10s^2 + 24s + K$ gives the following array:

$$\begin{array}{c|ccc} s^3 & 1 & 24 & 0 \\ s^2 & 10 & K & 0 \\ s^1 & \dfrac{240 - K}{10} = \varepsilon & 0 & \\ s^0 & \dfrac{K\varepsilon}{\varepsilon} = K & & \end{array}$$

The value of K which makes the s^1 row vanish is $K = 240$. The auxiliary equation is $10s^2 + K = 10(s^2 + 24)$. Thus, the characteristic function has complex conjugate zeros located at $r_{1,2} = \pm j\sqrt{24} = \pm j4.9$.

Complex Conjugate Terms

The application of the root-locus method is now illustrated for the system shown in Fig. 7.8. The characteristic equation for this system is

$$(s + 1)(s^2 + 6s + 13) + K(s + 4) = (s - r_1)(s - r_2)(s - r_3) = 0 \qquad (7.25)$$

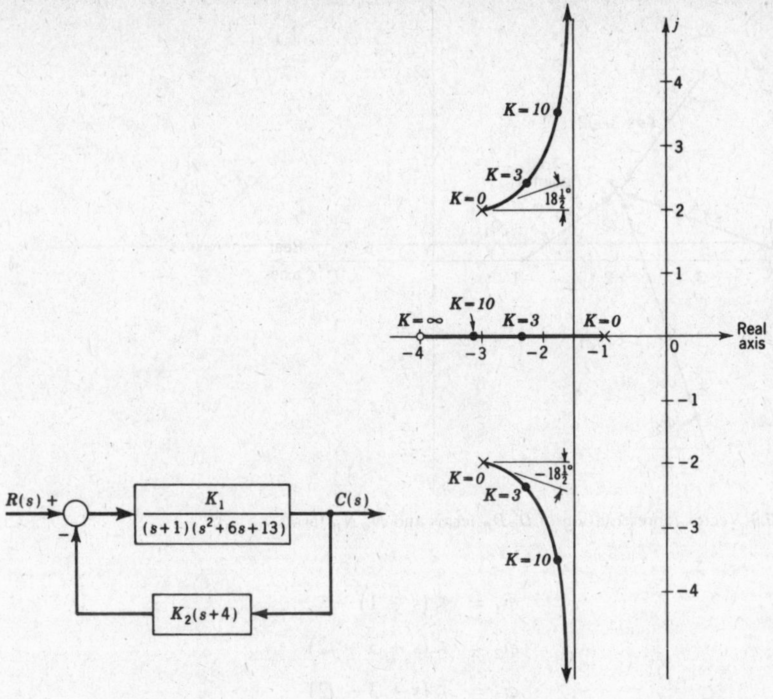

Figure 7.8 Root-locus plot for $(s + 1)(s^2 + 6s + 13) + K(s + 4) = 0$.

where $K = K_1 K_2$. The characteristic equation is now written in the form

$$\frac{(s+1)(s+3+j2)(s+3-j2)}{s+4} = -K \tag{7.26}$$

The zeros of $D_G D_H$ are -1, $-3 - j2$, and $-3 + j2$. The zero of $N_G N_H$ is -4. To begin to construct a locus, first plot the zeros of $D_G D_H$ and the zeros of $N_G N_H$. As is shown in Fig. 7.9, the locations of the zeros of $D_G D_H$ are indicated by crosses ($\times$), and the zeros of $N_G N_H$ are indicated by circles ($\odot$). Also, it is to be noted that the vector drawn from each $\times$ to a point s is the corresponding term in the numerator of Eq. (7.26). Similarly, the vector drawn from the circle ($\odot$) to the point s is the corresponding term in the denominator of Eq. (7.26). The angle condition is

$$\measuredangle(s+1) + \measuredangle(s+3+j2) + \measuredangle(s+3-j2) - \measuredangle(s+4) = 180° \pm k360° \tag{7.27}$$

or

$$\phi_1 + \phi_2 + \phi_3 - \phi_4 = 180° \pm k360°$$

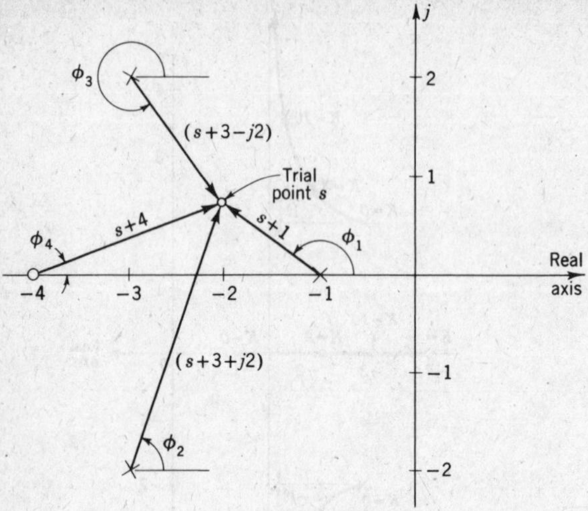

Figure 7.9 Vector representation of $D_G D_H$ terms and $N_G N_H$ terms.

where
$$\phi_1 = \measuredangle(s+1)$$
$$\phi_2 = \measuredangle(s+3+j2)$$
$$\phi_3 = \measuredangle(s+3-j2)$$
$$\phi_4 = \measuredangle(s+4)$$

As usual, the first place to investigate the possible location of loci is along the real axis. As is illustrated in Fig. 7.10, the value of $\phi_2 + \phi_3$ will always be 360° when s is on the real axis. For any trial point s on the real axis, the sum of the

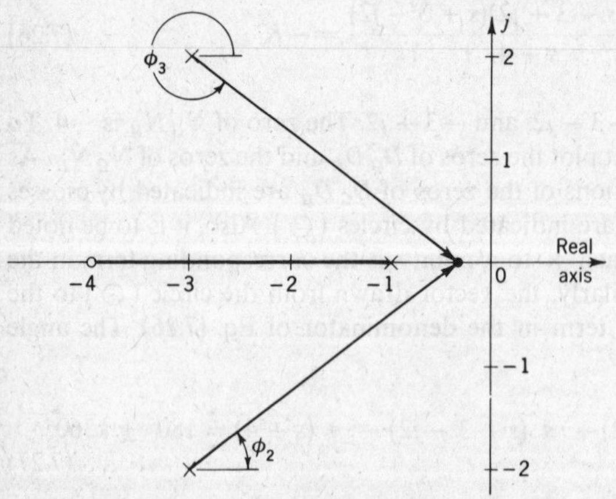

Figure 7.10 Location of loci on real axis.

angular contribution $\phi_2 + \phi_3$ for any complex conjugate $\times$'s (zeros of $D_G D_H$) or $\odot$'s (zeros of $N_G N_H$) will always be 360°. Thus, *the location of the loci along the real axis is determined only by the $\times$'s and $\odot$'s which lie on the real axis.* When s is to the right of the -1 point, $\phi_1 = \phi_4 = 0°$. Thus, there is no locus located to the right of the -1 point. When s is between -1 and -4,

$$\phi_1 - \phi_4 = 180° - 0° = 180°$$

so that a locus is located in this region. Similarly, it can be established that there is no locus to the left of the -4 point.

The next step in the construction of the loci is to determine the asymptotes for very large values of s. In Eq. (7.27), the terms 1, $3 + j2$, $3 - j2$, and 4 become negligible compared with the value of s, so that Eq. (7.27) becomes

$$\angle s + \angle s + \angle s - \angle s = 180° \pm k360° \qquad k = 0, 1, 2, \ldots \tag{7.28}$$

or

$$3\angle s - \angle s = 2\angle s = 180° \pm k360°$$

$$\angle s = \frac{180° \pm k360°}{2} = 90° \pm k180° = \pm 90° \tag{7.29}$$

In general, it follows that the angle of the asymptotes is

$$\angle s = \frac{180° \pm k360°}{n - m} \qquad k = 0, 1, 2, \ldots \tag{7.30}$$

where n = highest power of s in $D_G D_H$ = no. of $\times$'s
m = highest power of s in $N_G N_H$ = no. of $\odot$'s

The number of distinct asymptotes is equal to $n - m$. Although it would appear from Eq. (7.30) that there are more asymptotes, the angles repeat for other values of k after $n - m$ distinct angles have been determined. In Fig. 7.11 is shown

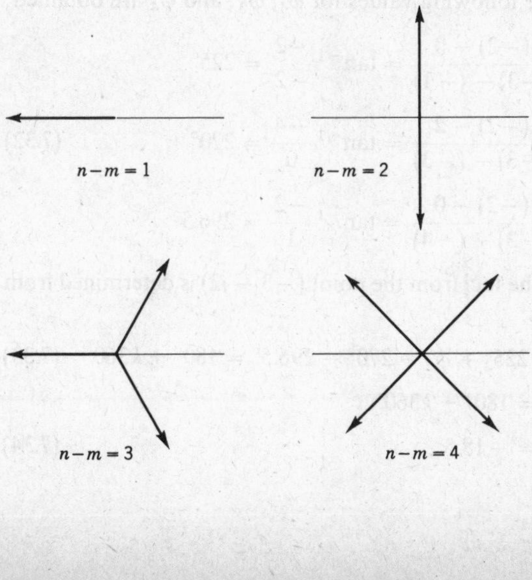

Figure 7.11 Asymptotes for $n - m = 1, 2, 3$, and 4.

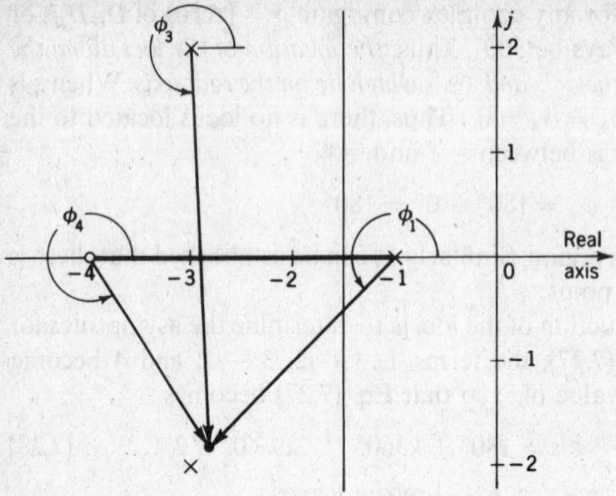

Figure 7.12 Determination of angle of departure.

a plot of the asymptotes for the cases in which $n - m = 1$, 2, 3, and 4. For $n - m = 1$ the angle is $-180°$, for $n - m = 2$ the angles are $\pm 90°$, for $n - m = 3$ the angles are $-180°$ and $\pm 60°$, and for $n - m = 4$ the angles are $\pm 45°$ and $\pm 135°$.

For the system under consideration, the intersection of the asymptotes with the real axis is found as follows by application of Eq. (7.17):

$$\sigma_c = \frac{[(-1) + (-3 - j2) + (-3 + j2)] - (-4)}{3 - 1} = -1.5 \qquad (7.31)$$

The information thus far obtained is sketched in Fig. 7.12. The next step is to determine the angle of departure of the loci from the complex conjugate zeros of $D_G D_H$. To do this a trial point s is taken which is located very close to the point $(-3 - j2)$. From Fig. 7.12, the following values for ϕ_1, ϕ_3, and ϕ_4 are obtained:

$$\phi_1 = \tan^{-1} \frac{(-2) - 0}{(-3) - (-1)} = \tan^{-1} \frac{-2}{-2} = 225°$$

$$\phi_3 = \tan^{-1} \frac{(-2) - 2}{(-3) - (-3)} = \tan^{-1} \frac{-4}{0} = 270° \qquad (7.32)$$

$$\phi_4 = \tan^{-1} \frac{(-2) - 0}{(-3) - (-4)} = \tan^{-1} \frac{-2}{1} = 296.5°$$

The angle ϕ_2 of departure of the loci from the point $(-3 - j2)$ is determined from the angle condition as follows:

$$\phi_1 + \phi_2 + \phi_3 - \phi_4 = 225° + \phi_2 + 270° - 296.5° = 180° \pm k360° \qquad (7.33)$$

Thus $\qquad \phi_2 + 198.5° = 180° \pm k360°$

or $\qquad \phi_2 = -18.5° \pm k360° = -18.5° \qquad (7.34)$

Because the loci are symmetrical about the real axis, the angle of departure from the other conjugate zero will be $+18.5°$. The complete root-locus plot may now be sketched in as shown in Fig. 7.8. The value of K at any place along the loci is determined by application of the magnitude condition.

From Eq. (7.26), it is to be noted that for $s = -1, -3 - j2$, or $-3 + j2$, the value of K is 0. These values of s are the zeros of $D_G D_H$. In general, one locus begins at each zero of $D_G D_H$ (that is, each $\times$). Similarly, for $s = -4$, $K = \infty$. The value $s = -4$ is a zero of $N_G N_H$. In general, one locus terminates at each zero of $N_G N_H$ (that is, each $\odot$). If n is the number of $\times$'s and m the number of $\odot$'s, then the remaining $n - m$ loci terminate along asymptotes at infinity.

7.3 GENERAL PROCEDURE

In the preceding section, it was shown that the loci could be sketched in quite accurately by knowing a few critical points, asymptotes, and angle of departure from complex conjugate zeros, etc. The general procedure for constructing root loci is summarized as follows.

1. *Origin.* When K is zero, the zeros of the characteristic function are the zeros of $D_G D_H$. Thus, *each locus originates at a zero of $D_G D_H$ (designated by $\times$'s) and the number of individual loci is equal to n, the number of zeros of $D_G D_H$.*
2. *Terminus.* As K becomes very large, m loci (m is the number of zeros of $N_G N_H$) will approach the m zeros of $N_G N_H$. That is, *one locus will terminate at each of the m zeros of $N_G N_H$. The remaining n − m loci will approach infinity along asymptotes.*
3. *Asymptotes.* The angle at which each of the $n - m$ loci approaches infinity is determined from Eq. (7.30); i.e.,

$$\measuredangle s = \frac{180° \pm k360°}{n - m}$$

The point σ_c at which the asymptotes intersect or cross the real axis is computed by Eq. (7.17); i.e.,

$$\sigma_c = \frac{\sum (\text{zeros of } D_G D_H) - \sum (\text{zeros of } N_G N_H)}{n - m}$$

4. *Loci on real axis.* Complex conjugate zeros of $D_G D_H$ or $N_G N_H$ have no effect on the location of loci on the real axis. The place at which the loci are located along the real axis is determined by considering only zeros of $D_G D_H$ and $N_G N_H$ which lie on the real axis. As is illustrated in Fig. 7.13, there is never a locus to the right of the first $\odot$ or $\times$ on the real axis, but there is always a locus to the left of the first $\odot$ or $\times$, there is never a locus to the left of the second $\odot$ or $\times$, there is always a locus to the left of the third $\odot$ or $\times$, never left of fourth, always left of fifth, and so on, alternating.

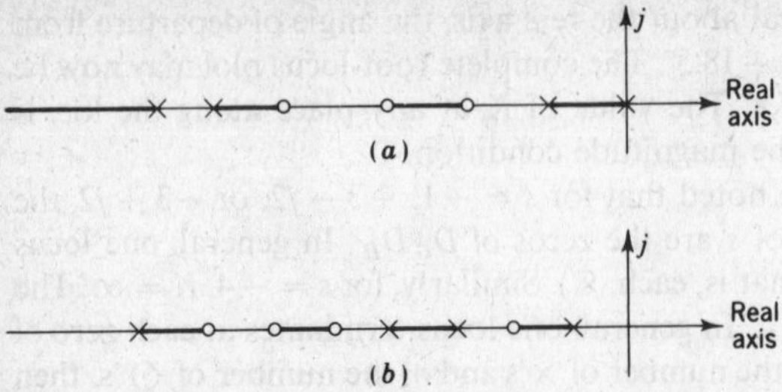

Figure 7.13 Loci on real axis.

5. *Angle of departure.* The angle of departure of a locus from a complex conjugate zero of $D_G D_H$ is obtained by selecting a trial point very close to this zero and applying the angle condition.
6. *Angle of arrival.* The angle at which a locus will terminate at a complex conjugate zero of $N_G N_H$ is determined by taking a trial point which is close to this zero and applying the angle condition. This process is similar to that used to obtain the angle of departure from a zero of $D_G D_H$.
7. *Breakaway or break-in points.* The point σ_b at which the locus breaks away from or breaks into the real axis is obtained by applying the angle condition to an arbitrarily chosen point which is a small vertical distance Δ from the real axis and then solving this resultant equation for the only unknown term σ_b. This may also be determined by finding the real value $s = \sigma_b$ at which $dK/ds = 0$.

A breakaway point is located where K is a maximum, and a break-in point is located where K is a minimum. A break-in point is similar to a breakaway point with the exception that a pair of loci comes into the real axis rather than leaving it. A break-in point is illustrated in Fig. 7.14. This is the system shown in Fig. 7.1, with the addition of the $s + 6$ term in N_G. The characteristic equation for the system of Fig. 7.14 is

$$s(s + 4) + K(s + 6) = 0 \tag{7.35}$$

Application of rule 4 to determine the loci on the real axis yields the location of loci along the real axis as shown in Fig. 7.14.

The breakaway and break-in points are evaluated as follows:

$$\frac{dK}{ds} = -\frac{d}{ds}\frac{s(s+4)}{s+6} = -\left[\frac{(s+6)(2s+4) - s(s+4)}{(s+6)^2}\right] = 0 \tag{7.36}$$

Thus, $$s^2 + 12s + 24 = 0$$

whence $$s = -6 \pm 2\sqrt{3} = -2.54, -9.46 \tag{7.37}$$

Further investigation shows that the value -2.54 makes K a maximum in the region $-4 < s < 0$; thus this is the breakaway point. The value -9.46 makes K a minimum in the range $-\infty < s < -6$; thus this is a break-in point.

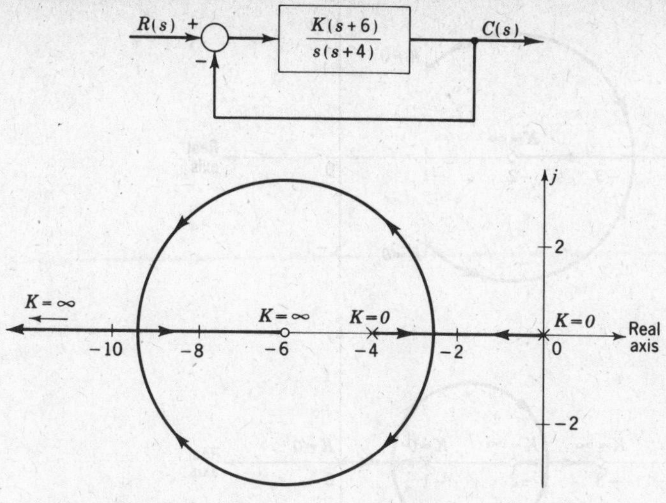

Figure 7.14 Root-locus plot for $s(s+4) + K(s+6) = 0$.

The occurrence of a breakaway or break-in point can be recognized from a consideration of the $\times$'s and $\odot$'s which lie on the real axis. Every locus begins at an $\times$ and terminates at a $\odot$ or along an asymptote at ∞. Thus, *there must be a breakaway point between any two adjacent* $\times$*'s on the real axis which are connected by a locus. Similarly, a break-in point is required if a* $\odot$ *on the real axis is not connected to an adjacent* $\times$ *on the real axis by a locus.* Thus, if the locus is not located entirely on the real axis between an adjacent $\odot$ and $\times$, it is necessary that it come into the real axis from elsewhere. The preceding rules may be verified for the root-locus plots shown in Fig. 7.15.

When the equation for dK/ds is a cubic, quartic, or higher-degree polynomial, solving for the break-in or breakaway point is a very laborious process. A plot of dK/ds versus s would yield the desired breakaway or break-in point as the value of s at which $dK/ds = 0$. However, construction of such a plot is quite time-consuming. For this type of situation, the method of taking a point a small vertical distance Δ from the real axis also results in a cubic, quartic, or higher-degree equation.

A technique for obtaining a close approximation to the break-in or breakaway point for such cases is explained in the following.

Newton's Method and the Remainder Theorem

Let $P(s)$ be the numerator of dK/ds. Thus when $P(s) = 0$, then $dK/ds = 0$. In Fig. 7.16 is shown a plot of $P(s)$ versus s. The tangent to this curve at $s = s_1$ is

$$P'(s_1) = \frac{P(s_1)}{s_1 - s_2}$$

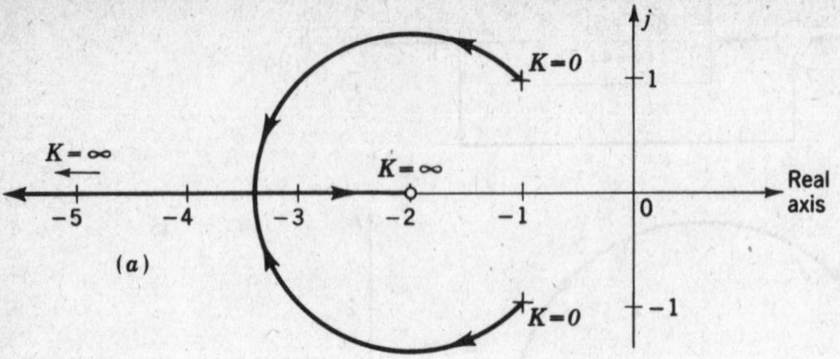

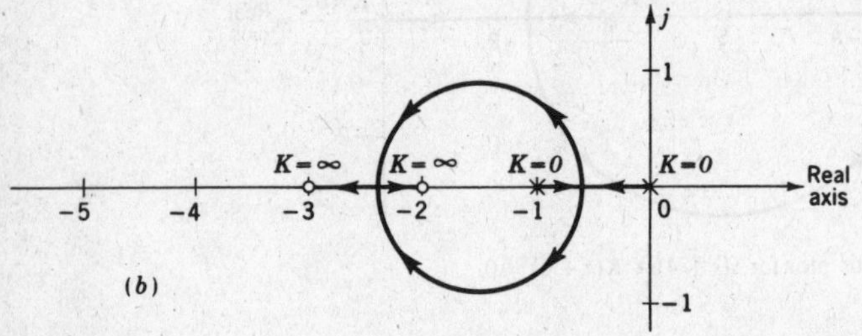

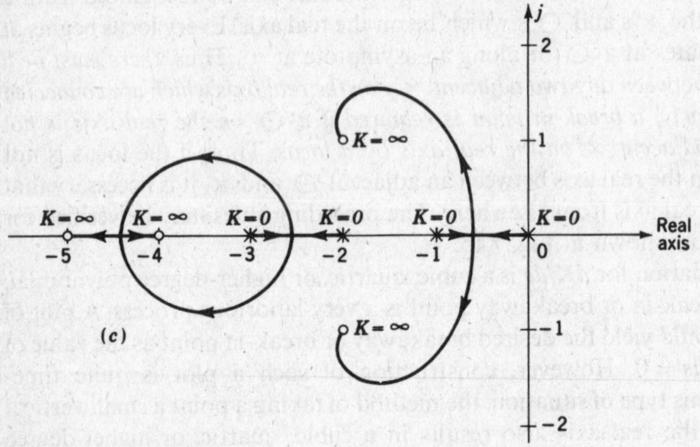

Figure 7.15 Root-locus plots.

Solving for s_2 gives

$$s_2 = s_1 - \frac{P(s_1)}{P'(s_1)} \tag{7.38}$$

The point s_2, which is the intersection of the tangent and the horizontal axis, is a closer approximation to σ_b than is s_1. After evaluating s_2, then applying the same process yields a closer approximation s_3, etc. Usually one trial yields sufficient

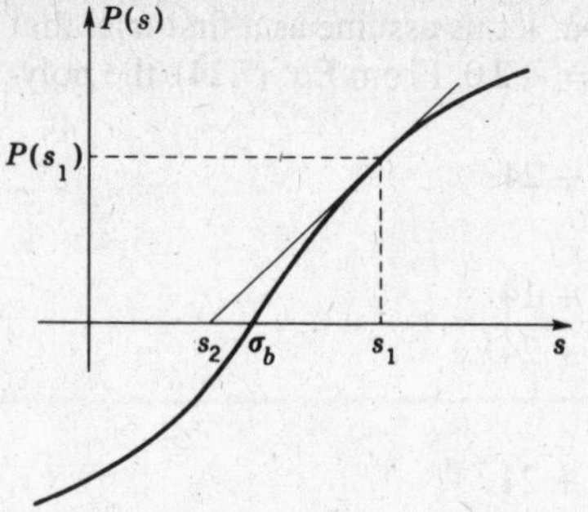

Figure 7.16 Typical plot of $P(s)$ versus s.

accuracy for constructing the root-locus plot. It is now shown how $P(s_1)/P'(s_1)$ may be obtained by use of the remainder theorem.

Dividing $P(s)$ by $(s - s_1)$ gives

$$\frac{P(s)}{s - s_1} = Q(s) + \frac{R_1}{s - s_1}$$

where R_1 is the remainder that results when $P(s)$ is divided by $s - s_1$. Multiplying through by $s - s_1$ gives

$$P(s) = (s - s_1)Q(s) + R_1 \tag{7.39}$$

Taking the limit as s approaches s_1 shows that

$$P(s_1) = R_1 \tag{7.40}$$

By similarly dividing $Q(s)$ by $s - s_1$, it follows that

$$\frac{Q(s)}{s - s_1} = T(s) + \frac{R_2}{s - s_1} \tag{7.41}$$

where R_2 is the remainder that results when $Q(s)$ is divided by $s - s_1$. Multiplying through Eq. (7.41) by $(s - s_1)$ and then taking the limit as s approaches s_1 shows that

$$Q(s_1) = R_2 \tag{7.42}$$

To show that $Q(s_1) = P'(s_1)$, first differentiate Eq. (7.39) with respect to s:

$$P'(s) = (s - s_1)Q'(s) + Q(s)$$

Taking the limit as s approaches s_1 verifies the fact that

$$P'(s_1) = Q(s_1) = R_2 \tag{7.43}$$

Equation (7.38) may now be expressed in the form

$$s_2 = s_1 - \frac{R_1}{R_2} \tag{7.44}$$

To illustrate the application of this method, let us assume as a first trial that the breakaway point for Fig. 7.7 occurs at $s_1 = -2.0$. From Eq. (7.24), the polynomial $P(s)$ is

$$P(s) = 3s^2 + 20s + 24$$

Division by $s - s_1 = s + 2$ yields

$$\begin{array}{r@{\;}l}
 & 3s + 14 \\
s + 2 & \overline{)\,3s^2 + 20s + 24} \\
 & \underline{3s^2 + 6s} \\
 & 14s + 24 \\
 & \underline{14s + 28} \\
 & -4
\end{array}$$

Hence, $Q(s) = 3s + 14$ and $R_1 = -4$. Dividing $Q(s)$ by $s - s_1$ gives

$$\begin{array}{r@{\;}l}
 & 3 \\
s + 2 & \overline{)\,3s + 14} \\
 & \underline{3s + 6} \\
 & 8
\end{array}$$

Hence, $T(s) = 3$ and $R_2 = 8$. Application of Eq. (7.44) yields the closer approximation

$$s_2 = -2 - \frac{-4}{8} = -1.5$$

The preceding divisions are simplified by the use of synthetic division, as is illustrated below.

$$\begin{array}{rrrl}
3 & 20 & 24 & \underline{/-2} \\
 & -6 & -28 & \\
\hline
3 & 14 & \textcircled{-4} &
\end{array}$$

The first row consists of the coefficients of the polynomial $P(s)$ and the root -2. The first coefficient 3 is brought below the line; then multiplying 3 by -2 yields -6 as shown. Adding 20 and -6 gives 14 as shown. Multiplying 14 by -2 yields the -28 term. Finally, adding 24 and -28 yields the remainder $R_1 = -4$, which is circled. It is to be noted that the coefficients of $Q(s)$ appear to the left of the circled remainder. The remainder R_2 is now obtained by similarly applying synthetic division to the $Q(s)$ polynomial. That is

$$\begin{array}{rrl}
3 & 14 & \underline{/-2} \\
 & -6 & \\
\hline
3 & \textcircled{8} &
\end{array}$$

Thus, the remainder R_2 is 8 and $T(s)$ is simply 3.

Let us now take -1.5 as the new trial root, and then employ synthetic division to obtain the next closer approximation. Thus

$$\begin{array}{rrrl} 3.00 & 20.00 & 24.00 & \underline{/-1.50} \\ & -4.50 & -23.25 & \\ \hline 3.00 & 15.50 & \boxed{0.75} & \\ & -4.50 & & \\ \hline 3.00 & \boxed{11.00} & & \end{array}$$

Thus, $R_1 = 0.75$, $R_2 = 11.00$, $Q(s) = 3s + 15.50$, and $T(s) = 3$. The closer approximation is

$$s_3 = s_2 - \frac{R_1}{R_2} = -1.50 - \frac{0.75}{11.00} = -1.57$$

7.4 LOCI EQUATIONS

In studying control systems, one frequently encounters the case in which there are two $\times$'s and one $\odot$, as shown in Fig. 7.17. It is now shown that when a locus leaves the real axis, it follows a circular path. The characteristic equation for this case is

$$(s - p_1)(s - p_2) + K(s - z) = 0 \tag{7.45}$$

As shown in Fig. 7.17*a*, a trial point s may be expressed in the form $s = x + jy$. The substitution of $s = x + jy$ in the preceding equation gives

$$(x^2 + 2jxy - y^2) - (p_1 + p_2 - K)(x + jy) + p_1 p_2 - Kz = 0$$

In order that this equation equal zero, it is necessary that both the real parts and the imaginary parts (i.e., j components) be zero. Thus,

$$x^2 - y^2 - (p_1 + p_2 - K)x + p_1 p_2 - Kz = 0$$

$$2xy - (p_1 + p_2 - K)y = 0$$

To eliminate K between the two preceding equations, first solve each for K. That is,

$$K = \frac{(x^2 - y^2) - (p_1 + p_2)x + p_1 p_2}{z - x} \tag{7.46}$$

$$K = (p_1 + p_2) - 2x \tag{7.47}$$

The term K is now eliminated by equating the right sides of the preceding expressions. Thus

$$x^2 + y^2 = p_1 p_2 + [2x - (p_1 + p_2)]z \tag{7.48}$$

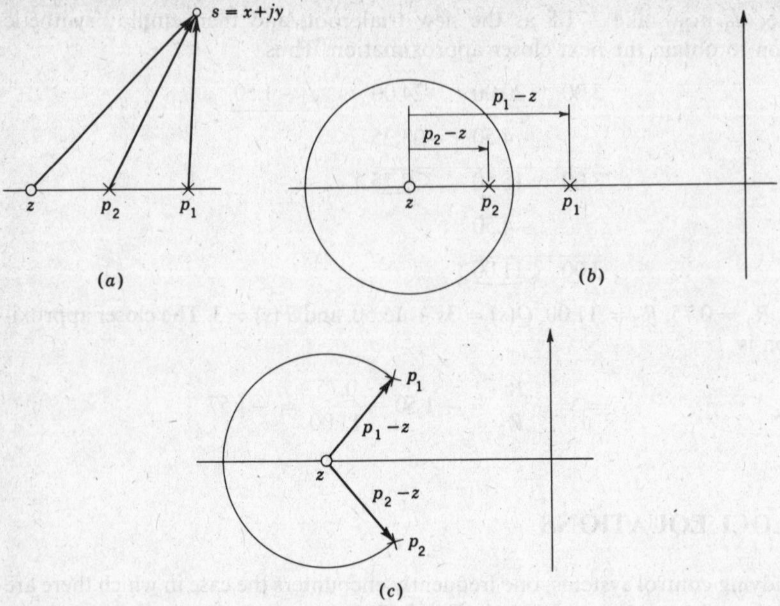

Figure 7.17 Circular loci.

Completing the square gives

$$(x - z)^2 + y^2 = (p_1 - z)(p_2 - z) \tag{7.49}$$

This is recognized as the equation of a circle with center at z. The radius is the square root of the product of the distance from z to p_1 and the distance z to p_2. That is,

$$R = \sqrt{(p_1 - z)(p_2 - z)} \tag{7.50}$$

A typical root-locus plot for the case in which p_1 and p_2 are real is shown in Fig. 7.17*b*. For the case in which p_1 and p_2 are complex conjugate roots, then the distance from z to p_1 equals the distance from z to p_2. Thus, the radius is simply the distance from z to either of the complex conjugate roots, as is shown in Fig. 7.17*c*.

Equation (7.47) may be used to determine the gain K for points on the loci in the complex plane (i.e., off the real axis). For loci on the real axis, $y = 0$. Thus, letting $y = 0$ in Eq. (7.46) yields an equation for evaluating the gain K for loci points on the real axis.

Illustrative example Construct the root-locus plot for the system shown in Fig. 7.18*a*, and then determine the gain K at $x = -4$ and at $x = -8$.

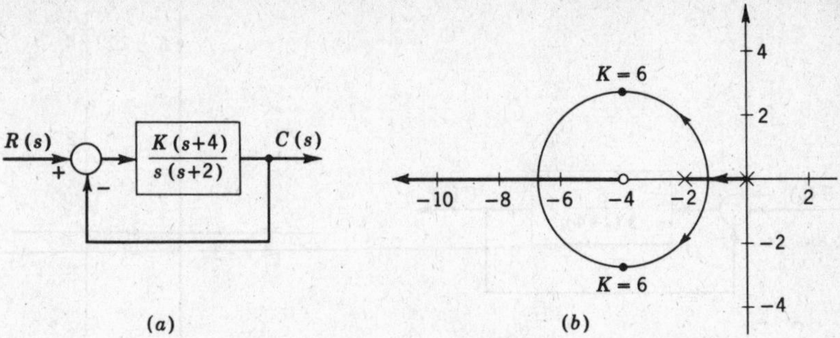

Figure 7.18 Root-locus plot for $s(s+2)+K(s+4)=0$.

SOLUTION The characteristic equation for this system is

$$s(s+2)+K(s+4)=0$$

Thus, $z=-4$, $p_1=0$, and $p_2=-2$.

The location of the loci on the real axis may be drawn as shown in Fig. 7.18*b*. Because there are two ×'s and a ⊙, then in the complex plane (i.e., off the real axis) the loci form a circle with center at $z=-4$ and radius

$$R=\sqrt{(p_1-z)(p_2-z)}=\sqrt{(4)(2)}=\sqrt{8}$$

The application of Eq. (7.47) to determine the gain K at $x=-4$ gives

$$K=(p_1+p_2)-2x=(0-2)-2(-4)=6$$

For the loci on the real axis at $x=-8$, application of Eq. (7.46) in which $y=0$ gives

$$K=\frac{x^2-(p_1+p_2)x+p_1p_2}{z-x}=\frac{64-(-2)(-8)}{-4-(-8)}=\frac{48}{4}=12$$

The preceding method for obtaining the equation for a circular locus may be applied to any locus. The method is to replace s by $x+jy$ in the characteristic equation. Because both the real and imaginary parts must be zero, two equations are obtained. One equation gives values of gain K for loci on the real axis, and the other equation gives values of gain K for loci in the complex plane. Eliminating K between these two equations yields a general equation in x and y for the loci. Corresponding values of x and y that satisfy this equation are points on the loci. In the preceding example the equation was recognized as that of a circle. However, for more complex systems, it may be necessary to use a digital computer to ascertain the corresponding values of x and y that satisfy the equation, and thus are points on the locus. For most engineering work, the spirule provides sufficient accuracy for sketching the loci in the complex plane.

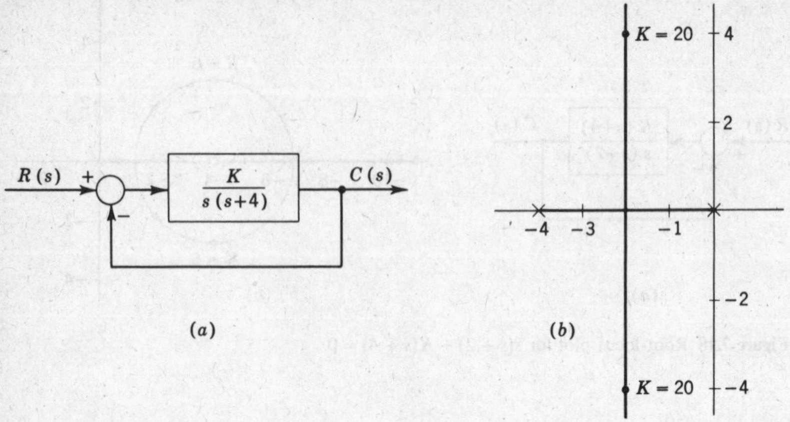

Figure 7.19 Root-locus plot for $s(s+4)+K=0$.

7.5 VARIATION OF PARAMETERS

Thus far the discussion of root locus has been concerned with the case in which the gain K is the variable parameter. By algebraically rearranging the characteristic equation, the effect of the change of any parameter can be investigated.

To illustrate this procedure, consider the system shown in Fig. 7.19*a*. The characteristic equation for this system is

$$s(s+4)+K=0$$

The basic root-locus plot is shown in Fig. 7.19*b*. For $K=20$, it is to be noted that the roots of the characteristic equation are $-2 \pm j4$. Thus

$$s(s+4)+20=[s-(-2-j4)][s-(-2+j4)]=0$$

Let it now be desired to investigate the effect of varying the parameter 4 when $K=20$. Replacing the parameter 4 by $4+\Delta$, where Δ is the change in the parameter, yields for the new characteristic equation

$$\begin{aligned} s[s+(4+\Delta)]+20 &= [s(s+4)+20]+s\Delta \\ &= [s-(-2-j4)][s-(-2+j4)]+s\Delta=0 \qquad (7.51) \end{aligned}$$

This equation has the familiar form except that Δ is now the variable rather than K. The new root-locus plot begins at the value of the roots on the basic plot for $K=20$. Equation (7.51) shows that the $\times$'s for the new plot are at $s=-2\pm j4$ and there is a $\odot$ at the origin. The corresponding root-locus plot for positive values of Δ is shown in Fig. 7.20*a*.

In investigating the effect of a change in a parameter, it is desired to know the effect of decreasing as well as increasing the parameter. Thus far, root-locus plots

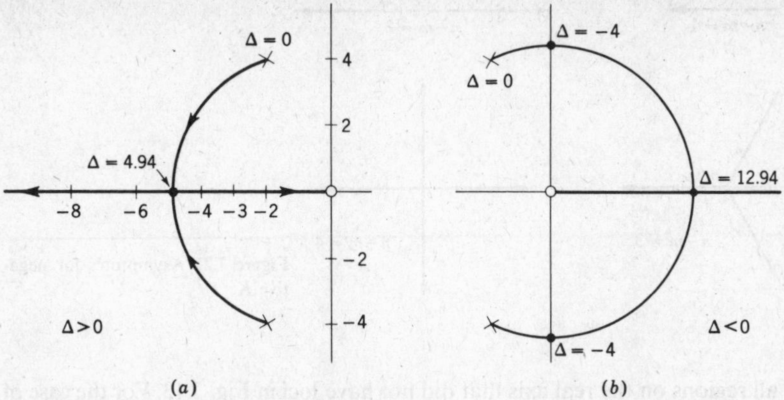

Figure 7.20 Root-locus plot for $[s(s+4)+20]+\Delta s=0$.

have been constructed for positive values of K only. From Eq. (7.11), it follows that when K (or Δ) is positive, the summation of the angles is $180° \pm k360°$. When K (or Δ) is a negative number, then $(-K)$ is a positive number which may be represented by a point on the positive real axis. For negative K the angle is

$$\measuredangle(-K) = 0° \pm k360°$$

The following rules for constructing a root-locus plot for negative values of K (or Δ) are very similar to those given in Sec. 7.3 for positive values of K.

1. *Origin.* One locus begins at each ×, as was the case for positive K.
2. *Terminus.* One locus ends at each ⊙, as was the case for positive K. The remaining $n-m$ loci terminate at asymptotes.
3. *Asymptotes.* The angle at which each $n-m$ locus approaches infinity is

$$\measuredangle s = \frac{0° \pm k360°}{n-m}$$

The corresponding asymptotes for $n-m=1$, 2, 3, and 4 are shown in Fig. 7.21. For $n-m=1$ the angle is 0°, for $n-m=2$ the angles are 0° and 180°, for $n-m=3$ the angles are 0° and $\pm 120°$, and for $n-m=4$ the angles are 0°, $\pm 90°$, and 180°.

The point σ_c at which the asymptotes intersect the real axis is obtained by Eq. (7.17) in the same manner as for positive K.

4. *Loci on the real axis.* The location of loci on the real axis is determined by the ×'s and ⊙'s that lie on the real axis. The summation of angles at any point on the real axis is either 0° or 180°. For positive K the loci are regions on the real axis where the angle is 180°. The remaining regions on the real axis must be places where the angle is 0°, and thus these are the regions of the loci for negative values of K. In Fig. 7.22 is shown the location of loci on the real axis for negative K for the same × and ⊙ pattern as Fig. 7.13. The loci now appear

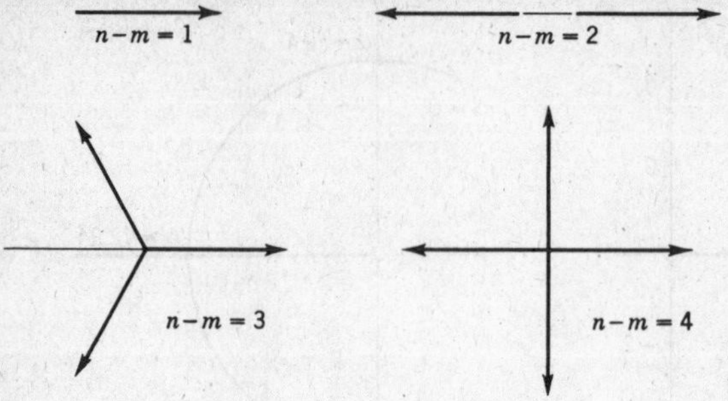

Figure 7.21 Asymptotes for negative *K*.

at all regions on the real axis that did not have loci in Fig. 7.13. For the case of negative *K*, a locus always appears to the right of the first ⊙ or × on the real axis, there is never a locus to the left of the first ⊙ or ×, there is always a locus to the left of the second ⊙ or ×, there is never a locus to the left of the third ⊙ or ×, and so on alternating.

5. *Angle of departure.* Because the summation of angles is now 0° rather than 180°, the angle of departure for negative *K* is always 180° different from that obtained for positive *K*.
6. *Angle of arrival.* The angle of arrival for negative *K* is always 180° different from that obtained for positive *K*.
7. *Breakaway or break-in points.* These are determined in the same way as for positive *K*. In determining the breakaway or break-in points for positive *K*, oftentimes extra or extraneous values were obtained. Actually, these values are the ones for the case of negative *K*.

In Fig. 7.20*b* is shown the root-locus plot for negative values of Δ. Because there are two ×'s and one ⊙, the loci form a circle in the complex plane. The system becomes unstable when the locus crosses the imaginary axis, which occurs at $\Delta = -4$. The preceding concepts are further illustrated in the following example.

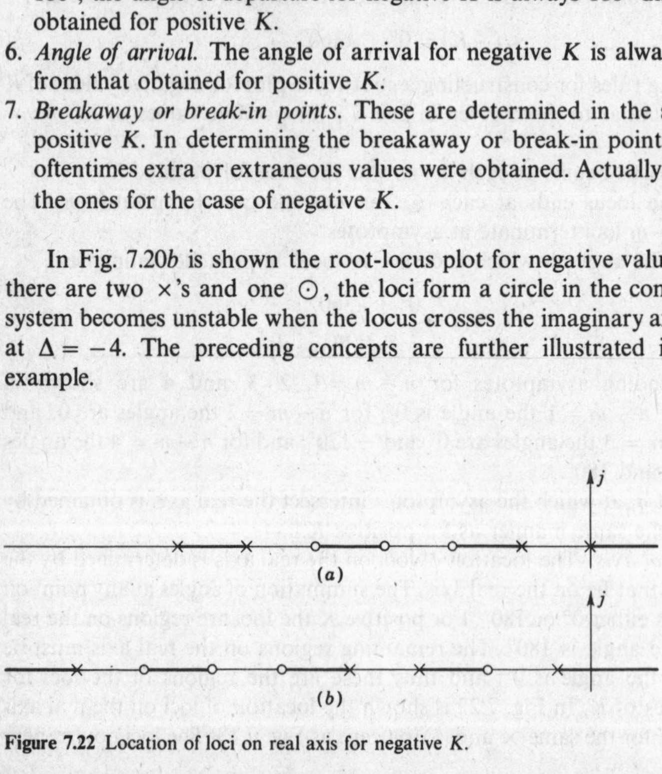

Figure 7.22 Location of loci on real axis for negative *K*.

Illustrative example Suppose that for the system shown in Fig. 7.2 the gain K must be maintained at 240 to achieve satisfactory steady-state operation. For $K = 240$ the roots of the characteristic equation are $s = \pm j\sqrt{24}$ and $s = -10$. Hence, the factored form of the characteristic equation is

$$s(s + 4)(s + 6) + 240 = (s + 10)(s^2 + 24)$$

Determine whether or not this system can be stabilized and good dynamic behavior achieved by changing the parameter 4 in the term $s + 4$.

SOLUTION Replacing 4 by $4 + \Delta$ yields, for the new characteristic equation,

$$s[(s + 4) + \Delta](s + 6) + 240 = [s(s + 4)(s + 6) + 240] + s(s + 6)\Delta = 0$$
$$= (s + 10)(s^2 + 24) + s(s + 6)\Delta = 0$$

To construct the root-locus plot for positive values of Δ, first draw the loci on the real axis as shown in Fig. 7.23*a*. Next the angle of departure from the $\times$ at $s = j\sqrt{24}$ is

$$\left(\phi_d + 90° + \tan^{-1}\frac{\sqrt{24}}{10}\right) - \left(90° + \tan^{-1}\frac{\sqrt{24}}{6}\right) = 180°$$

Solving for ϕ_d gives $\phi_d = 193.1°$.

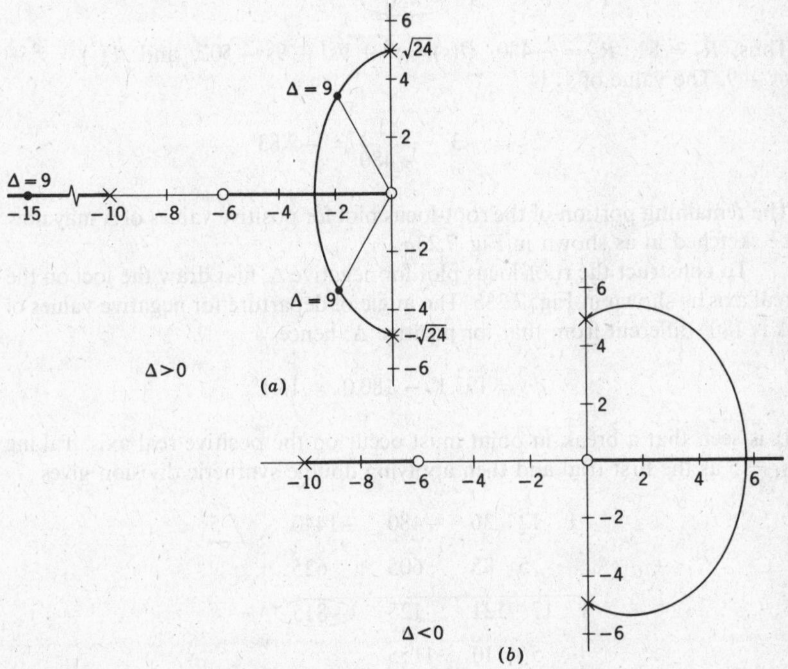

Figure 7.23 Root-locus plot for $[s(s + 4)(s + 6) + 240] + s(s + 6)\Delta = 0$.

A break-in point is seen to occur between 0 and -6 on the real axis, As a first trial, let s_1 be the midpoint -3. To apply Newton's method, first solve the characteristic equation for Δ.

$$\Delta = \frac{(s+10)(s^2+24)}{s(s+6)}$$

Differentiation to obtain $d\Delta/ds$ gives

$$\frac{d\Delta}{ds} = -\frac{s^4 + 12s^3 + 36s^2 - 480s - 1440}{(s^2+6s)^2} = 0$$

The polynomial $P(s)$ is taken as the numerator of $d\Delta/ds$. Thus, application of double synthetic division to obtain the remainders yields

1	12	36	−480	−1440	$\angle -3$
	−3	−27	−27	1521	
1	9	9	−507	(81)	
	−3	−18	27		
1	6	−9	(−480)		

Thus, $R_1 = 81$, $R_2 = -480$, $Q(s) = s^3 + 9s^2 + 9s - 507$, and $T(s) = s^2 + 6s - 9$. The value of s_2 is

$$s_2 = -3 - \frac{81}{-480} = -2.83$$

The remaining portion of the root-locus plot for positive values of Δ may now be sketched in as shown in Fig. 7.23*a*.

To construct the root-locus plot for negative Δ, first draw the loci on the real axis as shown in Fig. 7.23*b*. The angle of departure for negative values of Δ is 180° different from that for positive Δ; hence

$$\phi_d = 193.1° - 180.0° = 13.1°$$

It is seen that a break-in point must occur on the positive real axis. Taking $s_1 = 5$ as the first trial and then applying double synthetic division gives

1	12	36	−480	−1440	$\angle 5$
	5	85	605	625	
1	17	121	125	(−815)	
	5	110	1155		
1	22	231	(1280)		

Thus, $R_1 = -815$, $R_2 = 1280$, $Q(s) = s^3 + 17s^2 + 121s + 125$, and $T(s) = s^2 + 22s + 231$. Application of Eq. (7.24) to obtain the closer approximation to the break-in point gives

$$s_2 = 5.0 - \frac{-815}{1280} = 5.64$$

From the root-locus plot it is seen that good dynamic behavior is obtained for $\Delta = 9$, in which case the three roots are $-2 \pm j\sqrt{12}$ and -15. For the complex conjugate roots, $\zeta = 0.5$ and $\omega_n = 4$.

7.6 SENSITIVITY

The parameters used in the design of control systems vary due to factors such as wear, aging, variations in the operating point, temperature, etc. It is thus desired to know the effect of small variations in these parameters upon the dynamic response of the system. In Sec. 7.5, it was shown how to determine the effect of such variations upon the location of the roots of the characteristic equation. The sensitivity method is described in the following.

The sensitivity S is defined as the percentage change in the system transmittance T compared to the percentage change in the parameter K. That is,

$$S_K^T = \frac{dT/T}{dK/K} = \frac{K\,dT}{T\,dK} = \frac{d\ln T}{d\ln K}$$

where $T(s) = C(s)/R(s)$ is the closed-loop transfer function for the system. The term K may represent any parameter, such as gain, time constant, damping ratio, natural frequency, etc. To have the transmittance T which represents the system dynamics insensitive to variations in a parameter, then the sensitivity S should be zero, or as small as possible.

The transfer function for the system of Fig. 7.19 may be expressed in the general form

$$G(s) = \frac{K}{s(s+a)} = \frac{K}{s(s+1/\tau)}$$

where $a = 1/\tau$ in which τ is the time constant. As indicated in the following, for computational purposes it is easier to work with a. It is an easy matter to convert the resulting answer from a to τ if so desired.

The transmittance T is

$$T(s) = \frac{C(s)}{R(s)} = \frac{G(s)}{1+G(s)} = \frac{K}{s(s+a)+K}$$

The sensitivity with respect to the gain K is

$$S_K^T = \frac{K\,dT}{T\,dK} = \frac{K[s(s+a)+K]}{K}\frac{[s(s+a)+K]-K}{[s(s+a)+K]^2}$$

$$= \frac{s(s+a)}{s(s+a)+K} \tag{7.52}$$

The sensitivity with respect to the parameter a is

$$S_a^T = \frac{a\,dT}{T\,da} = \frac{a[s(s+a)+K]}{K}\frac{-sK}{[s(s+a)+K]^2}$$

$$= \frac{-as}{s(s+a)+K} \tag{7.53}$$

The steady-state sensitivity is obtained by letting $s = 0$. For both Eqs. (7.52) and (7.53), the steady-state sensitivity obtained by letting $s = 0$ is $S_K^T = S_a^T = 0$. The dynamic sensitivity is obtained by replacing s by $j\omega$ in the sensitivity equations, and then making plots of the sensitivity as a function of the frequency ω. The significance of replacing s by $j\omega$ is explained in Chaps. 11 and 12.

By defining sensitivity in a slightly different manner, it is possible to determine the change in the roots of the characteristic equation for small variations of a parameter. Thus, sensitivity is now defined as the rate of change of the root location with respect to the parameter. That is,

$$S_K^s = \frac{ds}{dK} \tag{7.54}$$

where ds/dK is the rate of change of the root location s in the characteristic equation with respect to K. For the system of Fig. 7.19, the characteristic equation is

$$s(s+a) + K = (s - r_1)(s - r_2) = 0$$

The derivative with respect to K is

$$2s\frac{ds}{dK} + a\frac{ds}{dK} + 1 = 0$$

Thus, the sensitivity with respect to the parameter K is

$$S_K^s = \frac{ds}{dK} = \frac{-1}{a+2s}$$

At the reference operating condition $a = 4$ and $K = 20$, the roots are $r_1 = -2 + j4$ and $r_2 = -2 - j4$. The sensitivity of the location of the root r_1 is obtained by evaluating S_K^s at $s = r_1$. Thus,

$$S_K^{r_1} = \frac{dr_1}{dK} = \frac{-1}{4 + 2(-2 + j4)} = \frac{-1}{j8} = \frac{j}{8}$$

Because $dr_1 = (dr_1/dK)\,dK = S_K^{r_1}\,dK$, then

$$\Delta r_1 \approx S_K^{r_1}\,\Delta K = \frac{j}{8}\Delta K \tag{7.55}$$

If ΔK is 4, then $\Delta r_1 \approx 0.5j$. Hence, for $K = 20 + \Delta K = 24$, then $r_1 \approx (-2 + j4) + 0.5j = -2 + j4.50$. From the characteristic equation, the exact value of r_1 is found to be $-2 + j\sqrt{20} = -2 + j4.47$. In a similar manner, the change in the location of the root r_2 may also be found.

The sensitivity of the location of the roots with respect to the parameter a is

$$S_a^s = \frac{ds}{da}$$

The derivative of the characteristic equation with respect to a is

$$2s\frac{ds}{da} + a\frac{ds}{da} + a\frac{da}{da} = 0$$

Thus, the sensitivity ds/da is

$$S_a^s = \frac{ds}{da} = \frac{-s}{a + 2s}$$

The root sensitivity at $s = r_1$ is

$$S_a^{r_1} = \frac{dr_1}{da} = \frac{-(-2 + j4)}{4 + 2(-2 + j4)} = -\frac{2 + j}{4}$$

Thus

$$\Delta r_1 \approx -\frac{2 + j}{4}\Delta a \tag{7.56}$$

Because $a = 1/\tau$, if the time constant τ is changed from $\frac{1}{4}$ to $\frac{1}{2}$, then $\Delta a = 4 - 2 = 2$. Thus

$$r_1 \approx (-2 + j4) - \frac{(2 + j)}{4}2 = -3 + j3.50$$

From the characteristic equation (for $a = 4 + 2 = 6$ and $K = 20$) the exact value of r_1 is found to be $-3 + j\sqrt{11} = -3 + j3.32$.

When the sensitivity is expressed in the polar form, then Eqs. (7.55) and (7.56) become

$$\Delta r_1 \approx 0.125\,\Delta K\,\underline{/90^\circ}$$

$$\Delta r_1 \approx -\sqrt{5}\frac{\Delta a}{4}\,\underline{/206.6^\circ}$$

The angles indicate the direction that the roots leave the reference value for positive variations in ΔK or Δa. The direction is reversed by 180° for negative variations.

If both K and a change simultaneously, then

$$\Delta s \approx \frac{\partial s}{\partial K}\Delta K + \frac{\partial s}{\partial a}\Delta a = S_K^s \Delta K + S_a^s \Delta a$$

Thus, the effects add when more than one parameter varies. For example, if $\Delta K = 4$ and $\Delta a = 2$, then the change Δr_1 is

$$\Delta r_1 \approx \frac{j}{8}4 - \frac{2+j}{4}2 = -1$$

The new value of r_1 is $(-2 + j4) - 1 = -3 + j4$. From the characteristic equation for $K = 20 + 4 = 24$ and $a = 4 + 2 = 6$, the exact value is found to be $-3 + j\sqrt{15} = -3 + j3.87$.

PROBLEMS

7.1 The root-locus plot for the system of Fig. 7.1*a* is given in Fig. 7.1*b*. Determine the response equation $c(t)$ for the case in which $r(t)$ is a unit step function and $K = 8$. All the initial conditions are zero.

7.2 The root-locus plot for the system of Fig. 7.2*a* is given in Fig. 7.2*b*. Determine the response $c(t)$ for the case in which $r(t)$ is a unit impulse and $K = 17$. All the initial conditions are zero.

7.3 Sketch the root-locus plot for the system shown in Fig. P7.3. Determine the value K to yield a damping ratio of 0.5.

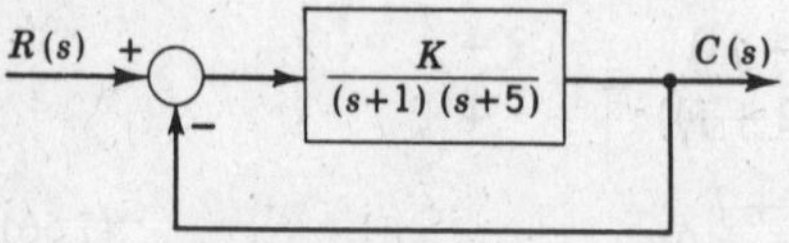

Figure P7.3

7.4 The block diagram and corresponding root-locus plot for a control system are shown in Fig. P7.4.

(*a*) Determine the differential equation relating the output $c(t)$ and the input $r(t)$.

(*b*) Determine the response $c(t)$ for the case in which all the initial conditions are zero, $K = 20$, and the input excitation $r(t)$ is a unit impulse.

(*c*) Use Routh's criterion to determine the value of the gain K at which the system becomes unstable.

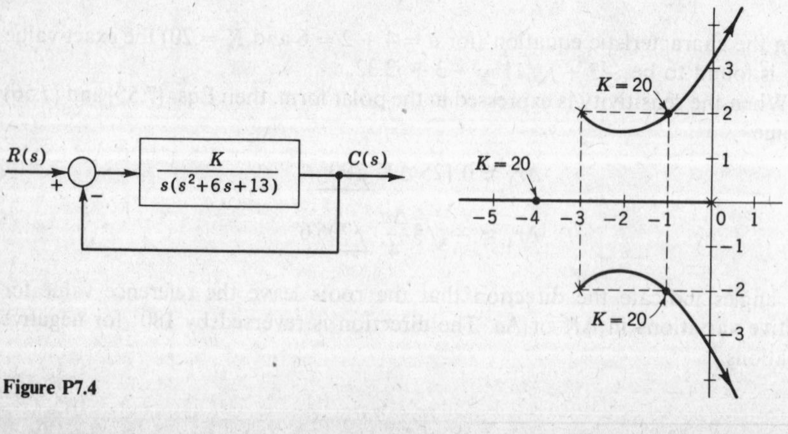

Figure P7.4

7.5 The block diagram for a control system is shown in Fig. P7.5. The controller is represented by the block $G_c(s)$. Determine the characteristic equation, and then sketch the corresponding root-locus plot for each of the following cases.

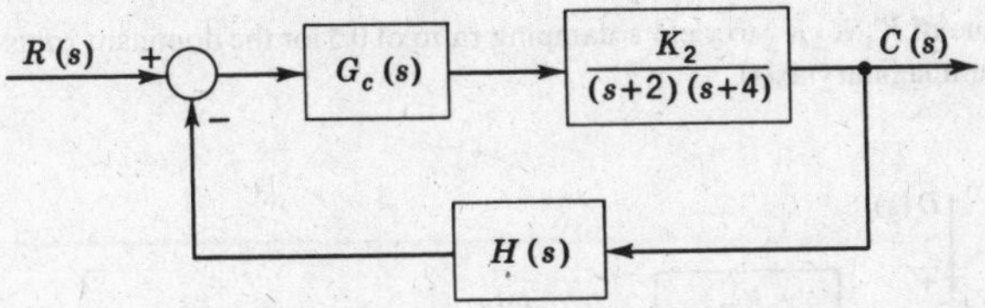

Figure P7.5

(*a*) Proportional controller, $G_c(s) = K_1$ and $H(s) = 1$.
(*b*) Integral controller, $G_c(s) = K_1/s$ and $H(s) = 1$.
(*c*) Proportional plus integral controller, $G_c(s) = K_1(1 + 1/s)$ and $H(s) = 1$.
(*d*) Proportional plus rate feedback, $G_c(s) = K_1$ and $H(s) = K_3(1 + s)$.

7.6 Sketch the root-locus plot for each of the systems shown in Fig. P7.6.

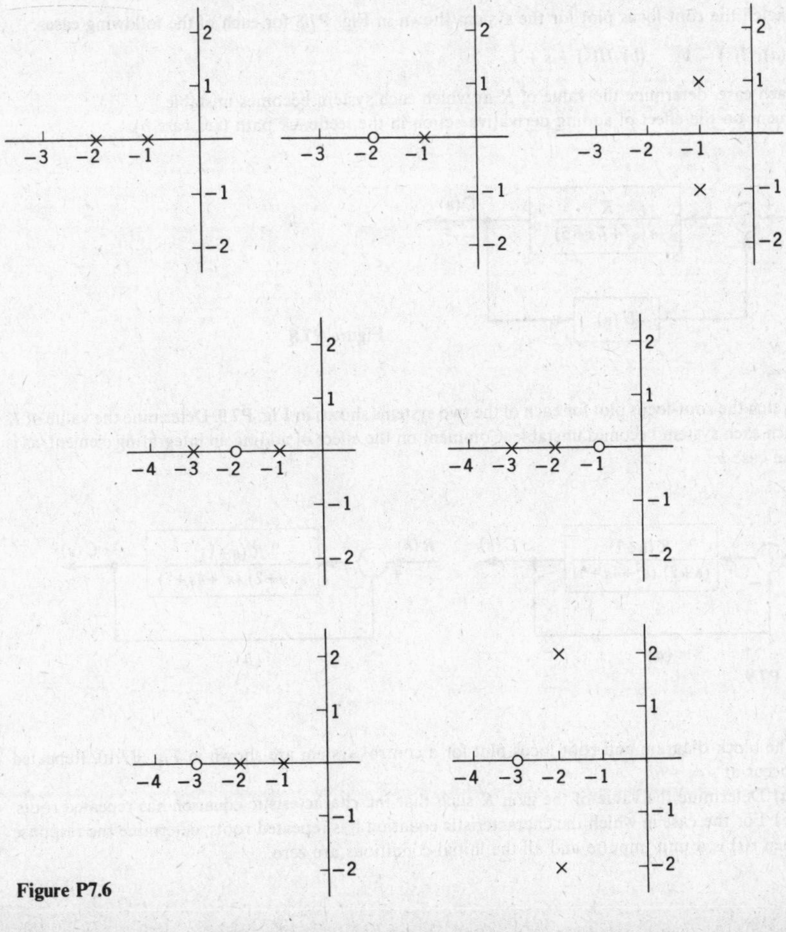

Figure P7.6

7.7 Sketch the root-locus plot for the system shown in Fig. P7.7 for each of the following cases:

(a) $G_1(s) = \dfrac{K_1}{s}$ (b) $G_1(s) = \dfrac{K_1}{s+4}$

For each case, determine the value of $K_1 K_2 K_3$ to yield a damping ratio of 0.5 for the dominant roots (i.e., the ones located nearest the imaginary axis).

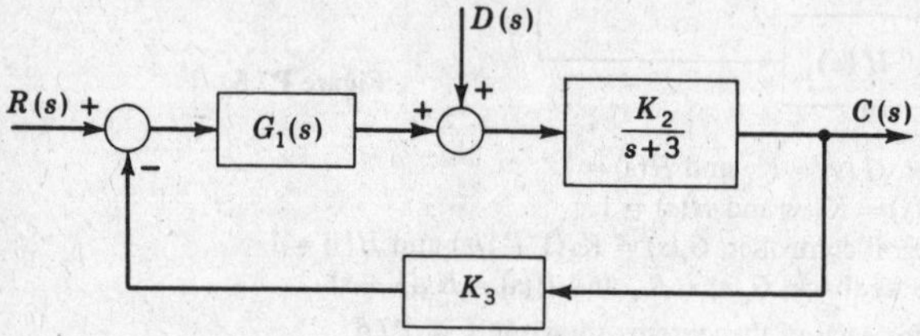

Figure P7.7

7.8 Sketch the root-locus plot for the system shown in Fig. P7.8 for each of the following cases:

(a) $H(s) = 1$ (b) $H(s) = s + 1$

For each case, determine the value of K at which each system becomes unstable. Comment on the effect of adding derivative action in the feedback path (i.e., case b).

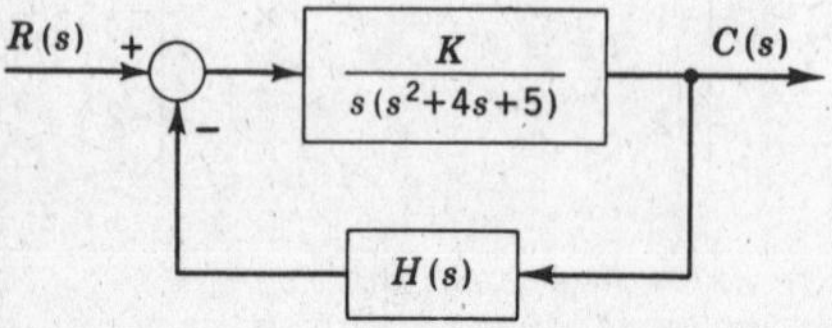

Figure P7.8

7.9 Sketch the root-locus plot for each of the two systems shown in Fig. P7.9. Determine the value of K at which each system becomes unstable. Comment on the effect of adding an integrating element, as is done in case b.

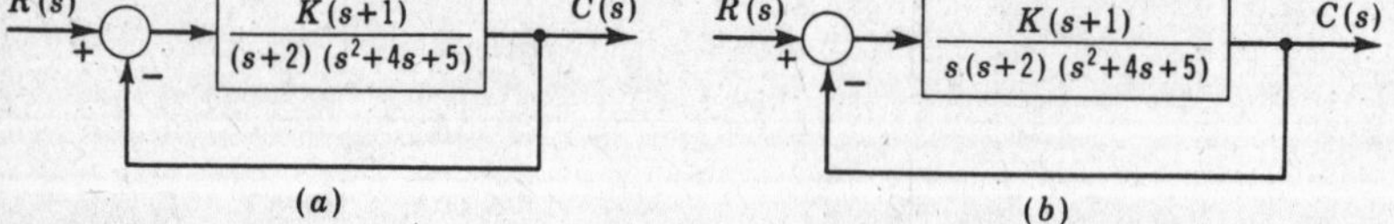

Figure P7.9

7.10 The block diagram and root-locus plot for a control system are shown in Fig. P7.10. Repeated roots occur at $s = -6$.

(a) Determine the value of the gain K such that the characteristic equation has repeated roots.

(b) For the case in which the characteristic equation has repeated roots, determine the response $c(t)$ when $r(t)$ is a unit impulse and all the initial conditions are zero.

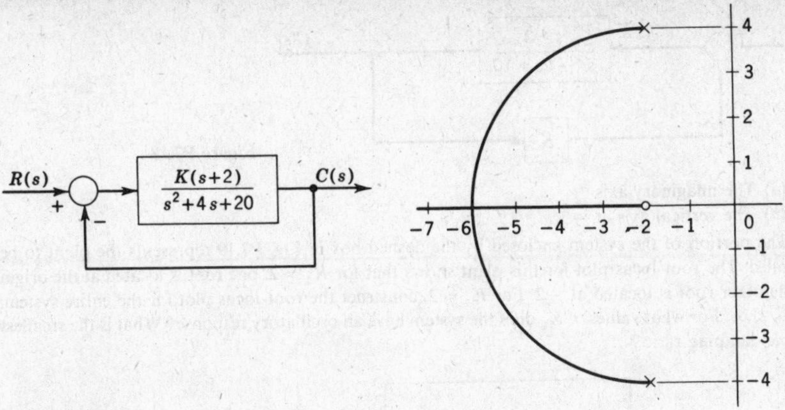

Figure P7.10

7.11 Sketch the root-locus plot for each of the following characteristic equations:

(*a*) $s(s^2 + 8s + 25) + K = 0$ (*b*) $s(s^2 + 8s + 25) + K(s + 2) = 0$

(*c*) $s(s^2 + 8s + 25) + K(s + 2)(s + 4) = 0$

7.12 Sketch the root-locus plot for each of the following characteristic equations:

(*a*) $(s + 2)^2 + K(s + 4) = 0$ (*b*) $(s + 2)^3 + K(s + 4) = 0$

(*c*) $s(s^2 + 10s + 26) + K = 0$ (*d*) $(s + 3)^2 + K(s^2 + 10s + 26) = 0$

7.13 The characteristic equation of Fig. 7.2 is given by Eq. (7.6). If a zero is added to the system, the characteristic equation becomes

$$s(s + 4)(s + 6) + (s + 2)K = 0$$

Sketch the root-locus plot for this new system.

7.14 Sketch the root-locus plot for each of the characteristic equations given below:

(*a*) $s^2(s + 8) + K = 0$ (*b*) $s^2(s + 8) + (s + 2)K = 0$

7.15 A certain system has the characteristic equation

$$s(s^2 + 12s + 45) + K = 0$$

Determine the location of the breakaway and break-in points and the value of K at each point, then proceed to construct the root-locus plot for this system. Determine the range of K so that the system does not oscillate.

7.16 A certain system has the characteristic equation

$$s(s^2 + 8s + 20) + K(s + 8) = 0$$

Construct the root-locus plot for this system. Determine the value of the gain K when the characteristic equation has a pair of complex conjugate roots whose real part is -2.

7.17 Construct the root-locus plot for the system shown in Fig. P6.16. Determine the value of K so that the resulting system will have a damping ratio of 0.6.

7.18 It is desired to design a compensator to stabilize the system shown in Fig. P7.18. The only means available is a constant multiplier K which can be inserted in the feedback loop as shown. Sketch the root-locus plot and then use Routh's criterion to determine the gain K such that the roots of the characteristic equation lie on

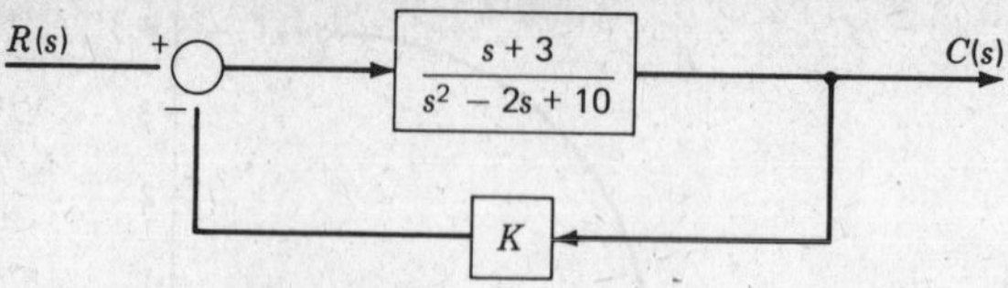

Figure P7.18

(*a*) The imaginary axis
(*b*) The vertical axis at -3

7.19 The portion of the system enclosed by the dashed box in Fig. P7.19 represents the plant to be controlled. The root-locus plot for this plant shows that for $K_1 = 2$, one root is located at the origin and the other root is located at -2. For $K_1 = 2$, construct the root-locus plot for the entire system, $0 < K_2 < \infty$. For what values of K_2 does the system have an oscillatory response? What is the smallest possible damping ratio?

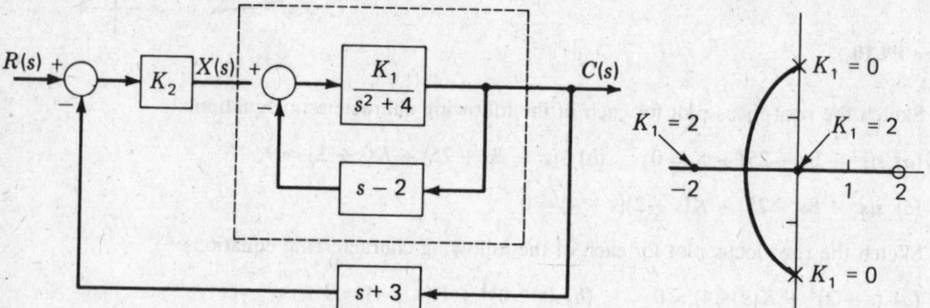

Figure P7.19

7.20 The root-locus plot for the system whose characteristic equation is $s(s + 2) + K(s + 4) = 0$ is shown in Fig. 7.18. When $K = 6$, the roots are $-4 \pm j\sqrt{8}$. Hence, for $K = 6$, the factored form of the characteristic equation is

$$s(s + 2) + 6(s + 4) = s^2 + 8s + 24$$

To investigate the effect of changing the parameter 4, replace 4 by $4 + \Delta$ and then:

(*a*) Sketch the root-locus plot for positive Δ.
(*b*) Sketch the root-locus plot for negative Δ.

7.21 Same as Prob. 7.20 except vary the parameter 2 instead of 4.

7.22 A feedback control system and its root-locus plot are shown in Fig. P7.22. (This is the same system discussed in Probs. 6.22 and 6.23.)

Figure P7.22

(*a*) When $K = 50$, the roots of the characteristic equation are located at -5, -5, and -2. Replace the parameter 45 in the characteristic equation by $45 + \Delta$ and proceed to construct the root-locus plot for $\Delta > 0$ and the root-locus plot for $\Delta < 0$.

(*b*) When $K = 104$, the roots of the characteristic equation are located at -8, $-2 + j3$, and $-2 - j3$. Replace the parameter 45 by $45 + \Delta$ and proceed to construct the root-locus plot for $\Delta > 0$ and the root-locus plot for $\Delta < 0$.

7.23 For the system of Prob. 7.4, it is desired to investigate the effect of varying the parameter 13 when $K = 20$. Thus replace the parameter 13 by $13 + \Delta$ in the characteristic equation, then sketch the resulting root-locus plot for $\Delta > 0$ and the root-locus plot for $\Delta < 0$.

7.24 For the system of Prob. 7.4, it is desired to investigate the effect of varying the parameter 6 when $K = 20$. Thus replace the parameter 6 by $6 + \Delta$, then sketch the resulting root-locus plot for $\Delta > 0$ and the root-locus plot for $\Delta < 0$.

7.25 The feedforward transfer function for a unity-feedback control system is

$$G(s) = \frac{K(s + 8)}{s(s^2 + 8s + 20)}$$

The root-locus plot for this system is shown in Fig. P7.25. When the gain K is 4, the roots of the

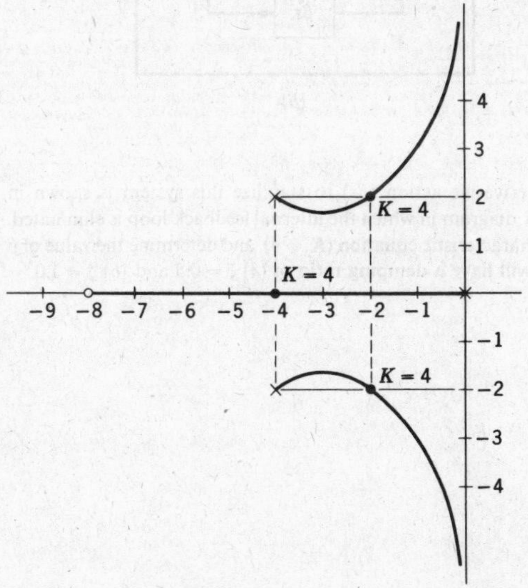

Figure P7.25

characteristic equation are -4, $-2 + j2$, and $-2 - j2$. For $K = 4$, investigate the effect of varying the parameter 20 in the transfer function $G(s)$. Sketch the resulting loci for both positive and negative values of Δ.

7.26 The transfer function for a unity-feedback control system is

$$G(s) = \frac{K}{s^2 + 2\zeta\omega_n s + \omega_n^2} = \frac{15}{s^2 + 4s + 5}$$

The roots of the characteristic equation are $r_{1,2} = -2 \pm j4$. Determine the equation for the change Δr_1 in the root r_1 due to a change in (*a*) K, (*b*) ω_n, and (*c*) ζ.

7.27 In Fig. P7.27 is shown a feedback control system with internal feedback. Construct the root-locus plot for the basic system without the internal feedback ($\beta = 0$), and then construct the root-locus plot

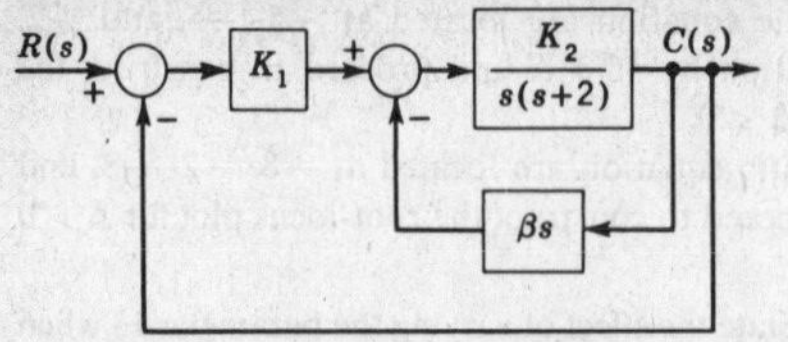

Figure P7.27

for the modified system in which β is the variable parameter, $K_1 = 2$, and $K_2 = 5$. Determine the value of β such that the resulting system will have a damping ratio of (*a*) $\zeta = 0.5$ and (*b*) $\zeta = 1.0$.

7.28 The block diagram for controlling the azimuth angle ϕ of the stable platform of an inertial guidance system is shown in Fig. P7.28*a*. Construct the root-locus plot, and determine the roots of the characteristic equation when $K = 4$.

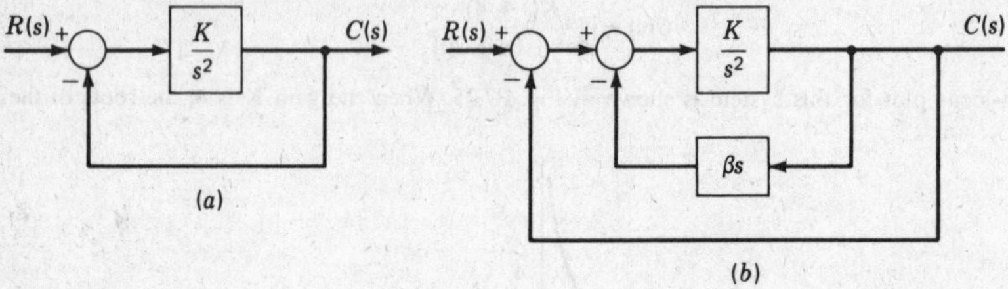

Figure P7.28

The use of internal feedback with derivative action (βs) to stabilize this system is shown in Fig. P7.28*b*. Construct the equivalent block diagram in which the internal feedback loop is eliminated. Construct the root-locus plot for the new characteristic equation ($K = 4$), and determine the value of β such that the new characteristic equation will have a damping ratio of (*a*) $\zeta = 0.5$ and (*b*) $\zeta = 1.0$.

CHAPTER

EIGHT

ANALOG COMPUTERS

The use of computers has played a major role in the recent advances in the design of automatic control systems. These computers may be divided into two types, analog computers and digital computers.

An analog computer is one in which the equation describing the operation of the computer is analogous to that for the actual system. The most commonly used analog computer is the electronic analog computer, in which voltages at various places within the computer are proportional to the variable terms in the actual system. As is shown in this chapter, the operation of a control system can be simulated by the use of an analog computer.

Basically a digital computer can only add and subtract. Thus it is necessary to reduce all problems to rather elementary mathematical manipulations. This process is called programming. The programming of a problem for solution on a digital computer makes extensive use of the methods of " numerical analysis " to convert the problem to the numerical operations which the computer can perform. It may require weeks or even months to program a problem for a computer, which in turn completes the solution in a few minutes or seconds. A digital computer has been referred to as an " energetic moron " in that it is capable of performing thousands of simple additions and subtractions in a second. A digital computer must store information for use in later computations. This is usually done by means of a magnetic drum, which acts as a memory device.

The input to a digital computer consists of numbers and instructions for the operation of the machine on these numbers. These numbers and instructions may be fed into the machine by various methods, such as punched cards, tape, typewriter, etc.

Because of the ability of both digital and analog computers to solve complicated mathematical equations almost instantaneously, they are often incorporated as part of a control system to compute desired information. This information may then be used immediately to improve the control of the particular system. For example, in an inertial guidance system, the output of three mutually perpendicular accelerometers is fed into a computer, which in turn calculates the position of the vehicle. Thus, the output of this computer is the actual position of the vehicle, which is compared with the desired position to yield an error signal for actuating the steering mechanism.

The electronic analog computer is a very powerful tool for investigating the performance of control systems. For more complex systems, the advantages of the analog computer become more apparent. Analog computers are used for many purposes besides that of investigating linear and nonlinear control systems. For example, they are used to solve nonlinear differential equations, partial differential equations, systems of differential or partial differential equations, matrix and eigenvalue problems, operational research problems, etc. New applications and uses for this versatile computing device are continually being discovered.

This chapter is primarily concerned with the use of these computers for simulating control systems. For this purpose, the equation describing the operation of the analog computer is analogous to that which represents the actual physical system. The variable quantities of the actual system, such as the output, input, error, etc., are represented by voltages at various places within the analog computer. Permanent records of these voltages may be obtained by using recording equipment. By using potentiometers or variable capacitors to vary the resistance or capacitance at various places within the computer, the effect upon system performance of changing the corresponding parameters in the actual system (e.g., gain, time constants, damping ratio, etc.) may be determined immediately.

8.1 COMPUTER OPERATIONS

To solve any linear differential equation with constant coefficients, it is necessary only to make use of the processes of integration, summation, and multiplication by a constant. This is illustrated by the block diagram of Fig. 8.1 for the equation

$$M\ddot{y} + B\dot{y} + Ky = f(t) \tag{8.1}$$

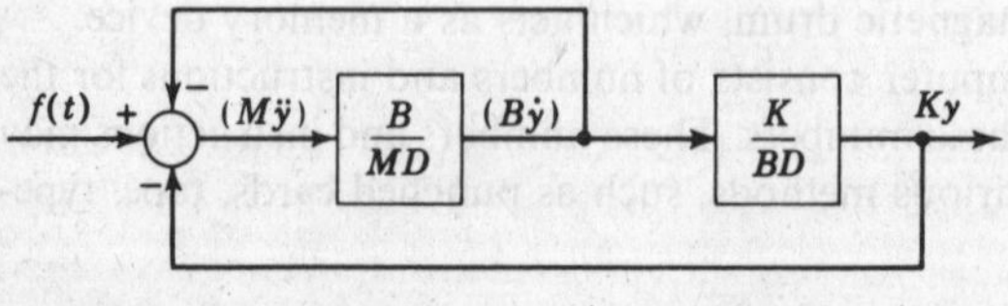

Figure 8.1 Block diagram for $M\ddot{y} + B\dot{y} + Ky = f(t)$.

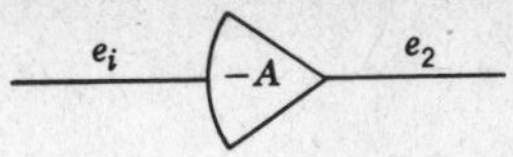

Figure 8.2 Schematic representation for an operational amplifier.

To set up the block-diagram representation for a differential equation, first solve for the highest-order differential appearing in the original equation. The highest-order term appearing in Eq. (8.1) is $M\ddot{y}$. Solving Eq. (8.1) for $M\ddot{y}$ yields

$$M\ddot{y} = f(t) - B\dot{y} - Ky \tag{8.2}$$

Successive integration of the highest-order differential and multiplication by appropriate constants yields the other lower-order terms. That is,

$$\begin{aligned} \frac{B/M}{D}(M\ddot{y}) &= B\dot{y} \\ \frac{K/B}{D}(B\dot{y}) &= Ky \end{aligned} \tag{8.3}$$

Each term on the right side of Eq. (8.2) goes into the summer of Fig. 8.1, so that the output of the summer is proportional to the acceleration. Successive integration of this acceleration yields the velocity and displacement.

The heart of the electronic analog computer is the operational amplifier, which is a very-high-gain dc amplifier. This device may be used as an integrator, summer, or multiplier. The particular mathematical operation depends upon the particular network of resistors and capacitors which are placed around it.

In Fig. 8.2 is shown the schematic representation of an operational amplifier. The input voltage is e_i, the output is e_2, and the amplification is $-A$. Thus

$$e_2 = -Ae_i \tag{8.4}$$

The reason for the minus sign is that the amplifier reverses the phase of the input. For most operational amplifiers, the value of A is very large. Values of A may range from 100×10^3 to 100×10^6.

Multiplication by a Constant

By feeding the input voltage through a resistor R_1 and by putting a resistor R_2 in parallel with the amplifier as shown in Fig. 8.3, a circuit for multiplication by a constant is obtained. Because the input grid of the amplifier draws little or no current (a typical value is 10^{-9} A), then

$$i_1 \approx i_2 \tag{8.5}$$

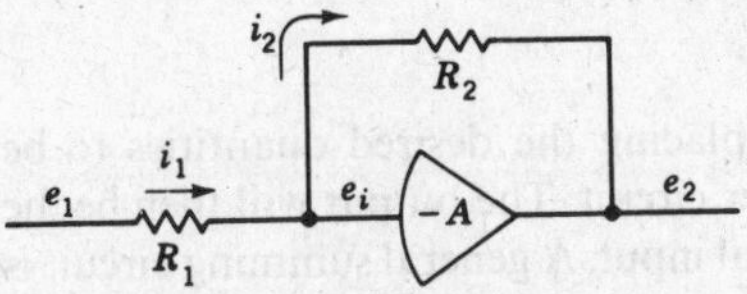

Figure 8.3 Operational amplifier circuit for multiplying by a constant.

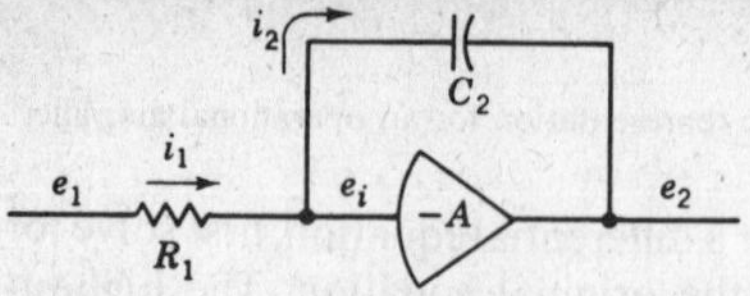

Figure 8.4 Operational amplifier circuit for integrating.

The values of i_1 and i_2 are

$$i_1 = \frac{e_1 - e_i}{R_1} \qquad i_2 = \frac{e_i - e_2}{R_2} \tag{8.6}$$

Equating i_1 and i_2 yields

$$\frac{e_1 - e_i}{R_1} = \frac{e_i - e_2}{R_2} \tag{8.7}$$

Usually e_2 is less than 10 V; so for very large values of A, it follows from Eq. (8.4) that $e_i = -e_2/A \approx 0$. The substitution of $e_i \approx 0$ into Eq. (8.7) gives

$$e_2 = -\frac{R_2}{R_1} e_1 \tag{8.8}$$

The value of the multiplication constant is $-R_2/R_1$. When $R_2 = R_1$, the constant is -1, which means simply that the phase of the input signal has been inverted.

Integration

By replacing the resistor R_2 of Fig. 8.3 by a capacitor as shown in Fig. 8.4, an integrating circuit is obtained. The current i_2 flowing through this capacitor is

$$i_2 = C_2 D(e_i - e_2) \tag{8.9}$$

By equating i_1 and i_2 as before, it follows that

$$\frac{e_1 - e_i}{R_1} = C_2 D(e_i - e_2) \tag{8.10}$$

Because $e_i \approx 0$, the preceding expression reduces to

$$e_2 = \frac{-e_1}{R_1 C_2 D} = \frac{-1}{R_1 C_2} \int_0^t e_1 \, dt + e_2(0) \tag{8.11}$$

where $e_2(0)$ is the value of e_2 when $t = 0$. In addition to integration, the circuit of Fig. 8.4 also multiplies by the constant $-1/R_1 C_2$.

Summation

The effect of a summation is obtained by placing the desired quantities to be added in parallel at the input to the computer circuit. The output will then be the summation of the effect due to each individual input. A general summing circuit is

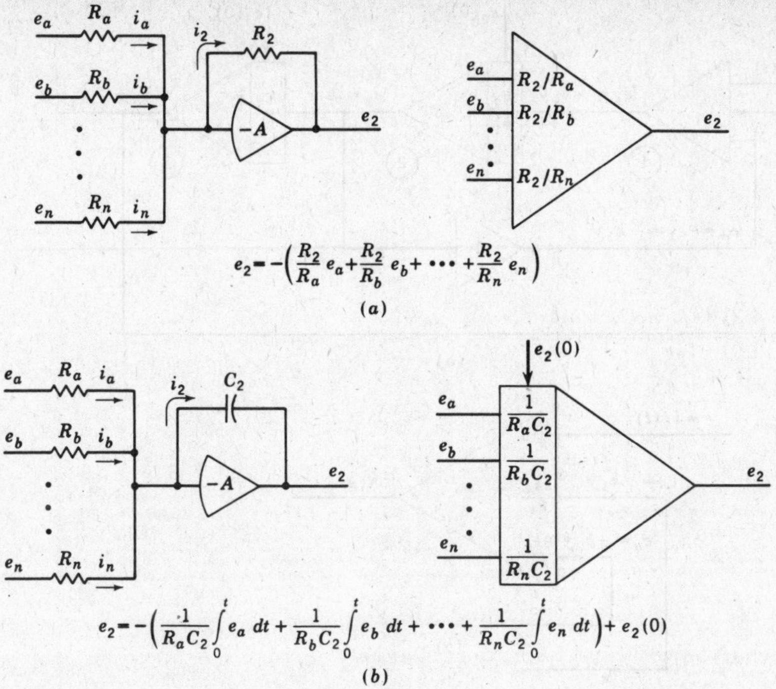

Figure 8.5 General summing circuits.

shown in Fig. 8.5*a*, and a circuit to integrate more than one quantity is shown in Fig. 8.5*b*. A simplified notation for these various computer elements is also shown in Fig. 8.5*a* and *b*. This schematic notation saves much effort in drawing the computer diagram for a circuit.

8.2 DIRECT PROGRAMMING

Let it be desired to determine the computer diagram for solving the following equation:

$$\ddot{y} + 8\dot{y} + 2y = f(t) \tag{8.12}$$

The initial conditions are $y(0) = 0.2$ m and $\dot{y}(0) = 0.5$ m/s. The expected maximum values are $y_m = 0.5$ m, $\dot{y}_m = 1.0$ m/s, $\ddot{y}_m = 2.0$ m/s^2, and $f(t)_m = 2.0$ N. The general computer diagram is shown in Fig. 8.6*a*. Solving Eq. (8.12) for the highest-order derivative yields

$$\ddot{y} = f(t) - 8\dot{y} - 2y \tag{8.13}$$

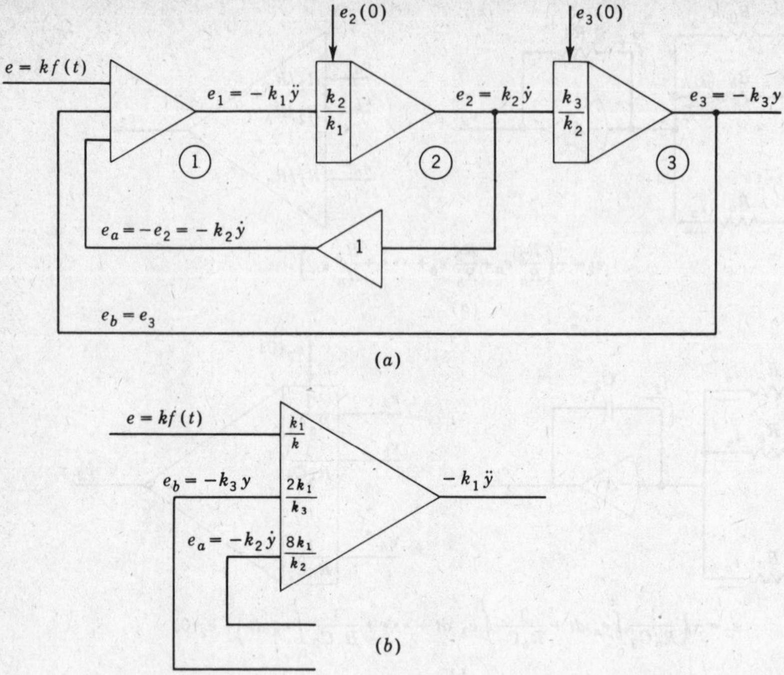

Figure 8.6 Computer diagram for $\ddot{y} + 8\dot{y} + 2y = f(t)$.

Because an amplifier reverses the sign from the input to the output, the sign in front of each scale factor alternates in going from one amplifier to the next. As shown in Fig. 8.6*a*, the output of the first amplifier is $e_1 = -k_1\ddot{y}$, the output of the second is $e_2 = k_2\dot{y}$, and the output of the third is $e_3 = -k_3 y$. A more detailed diagram of the first amplifier is shown in Fig. 8.6*b*. The first amplifier yields the highest-order derivative. The remaining amplifiers integrate to yield lower-order derivatives.

The voltage relationship for the first amplifier is

$$e_1 = -\frac{R_2}{R}e - \frac{R_2}{R_a}e_a - \frac{R_2}{R_b}e_b \tag{8.14}$$

Multiplying through Eq. (8.13) by $-k_1$ gives

$$-k_1\ddot{y} = -k_1 f(t) + 8k_1\dot{y} + 2k_1 y$$

This may be written in the form

$$-k_1\ddot{y} = -\frac{k_1}{k}[kf(t)] - \frac{8k_1}{k_2}(-k_2\dot{y}) - \frac{2k_1}{k_3}(-k_3 y) \tag{8.15}$$

Equation (8.14) is the voltage relationship for the amplifier, and Eq. (8.15) is the corresponding physical relationship.

Termwise comparison of Eqs. (8.14) and (8.15) shows that to have the voltage relationships $e_1 = -k_1\ddot{y}$, $e = kf(t)$, $e_a = -k_2\dot{y} = -e_2$, $e_b = -k_3 y = e_3$, then the following relationships must hold:

$$\frac{R_2}{R} = \frac{k_1}{k} \qquad \frac{R_2}{R_a} = \frac{8k_1}{k_2} \qquad \frac{R_2}{R_b} = \frac{2k_1}{k_3} \tag{8.16}$$

Because the output of the second amplifier is $e_2 = k_2\dot{y}$, it is necessary to use a sign changer to obtain $e_a = -e_2 = -k_2\dot{y}$. The voltage $e_b = e_3 = -k_3 y$ may be fed back directly.

The voltage relationship for the second amplifier, which is an integrator, is

$$e_2 = \frac{-1}{(R_1 C_2)_2}\int_0^t e_1\,dt + e_2(0) \tag{8.17}$$

where $(R_1 C_2)_2$ is the product of the resistance and capacitance for amplifier 2. Because the integral of acceleration is velocity, it follows that

$$\dot{y} = \int_0^t \ddot{y}\,dt + \dot{y}(0)$$

Multiplication of the preceding expression by k_2 yields

$$k_2\dot{y} = -\frac{k_2}{k_1}\int_0^t (-k_1\ddot{y})\,dt + k_2\dot{y}(0) \tag{8.18}$$

Equation (8.17) is the voltage relationship for the amplifier, and Eq. (8.18) is the corresponding physical relationship. To have $e_2 = k_2\dot{y}$ and $e_1 = -k_1\ddot{y}$, termwise comparison of Eqs. (8.17) and (8.18) shows that

$$\frac{1}{(R_1 C_2)_2} = \frac{k_2}{k_1} \quad \text{and} \quad e_2(0) = k_2\dot{y}(0) \tag{8.19}$$

The voltage equation for the third amplifier circuit is

$$e_3 = \frac{-1}{(R_1 C_2)_3}\int_0^t e_2\,dt + e_3(0) \tag{8.20}$$

Because the integral of velocity is displacement,

$$y = \int_0^t \dot{y}\,dt + y(0)$$

Multiplication of the preceding expression by $-k_3$ gives

$$-k_3 y = -\frac{k_3}{k_2}\int_0^t (k_2\dot{y})\,dt - k_3 y(0) \tag{8.21}$$

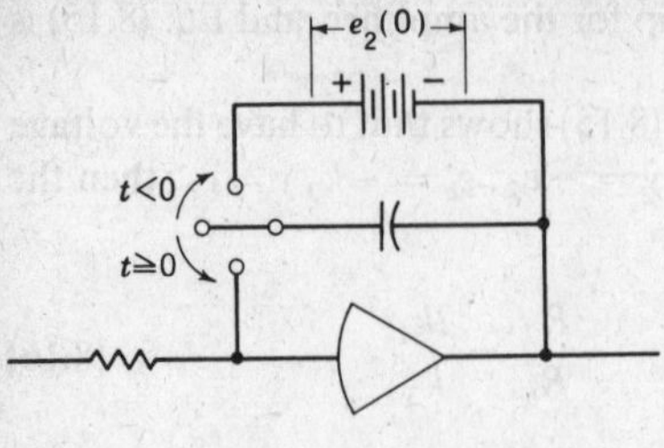

Figure 8.7 Circuit for obtaining initial conditions.

To have $e_3 = -k_3 y$ and $e_2 = k_2 \dot{y}$, termwise comparison of Eqs. (8.20) and (8.21) shows that

$$\frac{1}{(R_1 C_2)_3} = \frac{k_3}{k_2} \quad \text{and} \quad e_3(0) = -k_3 y(0) \tag{8.22}$$

Each integrator may be initially biased by a dc voltage to give the effect of initial conditions, as is represented diagrammatically at the top of each integrator in Fig. 8.6*a*. In practice, the initial condition is obtained by placing a source of constant potential such as a battery of potential $e_2(0)$ in parallel with the capacitor, as is shown in Fig. 8.7. For $t < 0$, the switch is up so that the battery can charge the capacitor to the desired initial value. At $t = 0$, the switch moves down to disconnect the battery so that the integrator circuit functions as previously discussed. There is never any need to apply an initial voltage $e(0)$ to account for initial conditions when an amplifier is used to multiply by a constant. Only integration requires initial conditions.

Scale Factors

Because the voltages e, e_1, e_2, and e_3 correspond to values of quantities in the physical system [$e = kf(t)$, $e_1 = -k_1 \ddot{y}$, $e_2 = k_2 \dot{y}$, $e_3 = -k_3 y$], it is necessary to select the value of the scale factors k, k_1, k_2, and k_3 in order to interpret the results. For many computers, the voltages e, e_1, e_2, and e_3 should be limited to within 10 V. Thus, the scale factor may be obtained from the equation

$$\text{Scale factor} = \frac{10}{\text{maximum value of parameter}} \tag{8.23}$$

From the originally given information, the scale factors are computed as follows:

$$\begin{aligned} k &= \frac{10}{f(t)_m} = \frac{10}{2.0} = 5 \text{ V/N} \\ k_1 &= \frac{10}{\ddot{y}_m} = \frac{10}{2.0} = 5 \text{ V} \cdot \text{s}^2/\text{m} \\ k_2 &= \frac{10}{\dot{y}_m} = \frac{10}{1.0} = 10 \text{ V} \cdot \text{s/m} \\ k_3 &= \frac{10}{y_m} = \frac{10}{0.5} = 20 \text{ V/m} \end{aligned} \tag{8.24}$$

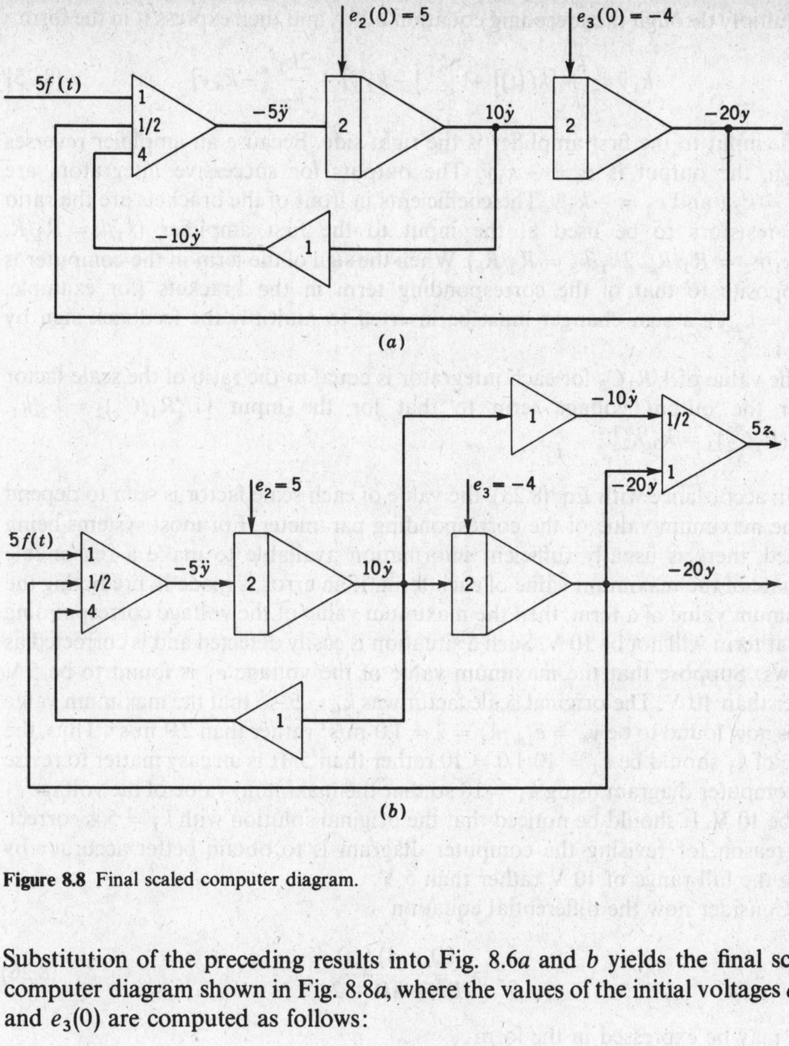

Figure 8.8 Final scaled computer diagram.

Substitution of the preceding results into Fig. 8.6*a* and *b* yields the final scaled computer diagram shown in Fig. 8.8*a*, where the values of the initial voltages $e_2(0)$ and $e_3(0)$ are computed as follows:

$$e_2(0) = k_2\,\dot{y}(0) = 10(0.5) = 5 \text{ V}$$

$$e_3(0) = -k_3\,y(0) = -20(0.2) = -4 \text{ V}$$

The general procedure for setting up an electronic analog computer to solve a differential equation of order n may be summarized as follows.

1. Solve the differential equation for the highest-order derivative. For the preceding example,

$$\ddot{y} = f(t) - 8\dot{y} - 2y$$

2. Multiply through the preceding equation by k_1, and then express it in the form

$$k_1\ddot{y} = \frac{k_1}{k}[kf(t)] + \frac{8k_1}{k_2}[-k_2\dot{y}] + \frac{2k_1}{k_3}[-k_3 y] \tag{8.25}$$

The input to the first amplifier is the right side. Because an amplifier reverses sign, the output is $e_1 = -k_1\ddot{y}$. The outputs for successive integrators are $e_2 = k_2\dot{y}$ and $e_3 = -k_3 y$. The coefficients in front of the brackets are the ratio of resistors to be used at the input to the first amplifier ($k_1/k = R_2/R$, $8k_1/k_2 = R_2/R_a$, $2k_1/k_3 = R_2/R_b$). When the sign of the term in the computer is opposite to that of the corresponding term in the brackets (for example, $e_2 = k_2\dot{y}$), a sign changer must be inserted to multiply the feedback sign by -1.

3. The value of $1/R_1C_2$ for each integrator is equal to the ratio of the scale factor for the output voltage term to that for the input $[1/(R_1/C_2)_2 = k_2/k_1$, $1/(R_1C_2)_3 = k_3/k_2]$.

In accordance with Eq. (8.23), the value of each scale factor is seen to depend on the maximum value of the corresponding parameter. For most systems being studied, there is usually sufficient information available to make a reasonable estimate of the maximum value of each term. If an error is made in predicting the maximum value of a term, then the maximum value of the voltage corresponding to that term will not be 10 V. Such a situation is easily detected and is corrected as follows: Suppose that the maximum value of the voltage e_1 is found to be 5 V rather than 10 V. The original scale factor was $k_1 = 5$, so that the maximum value of $\ddot{y}$ is now found to be $\ddot{y}_m = e_{1m}/k_1 = \frac{5}{5} = 1.0\ \text{m/s}^2$ rather than $2.0\ \text{m/s}^2$. Thus, the value of k_1 should be $k_1 = 10/1.0 = 10$ rather than 5. It is an easy matter to revise the computer diagram using $k_1 = 10$ so that the maximum value of the voltage e_1 will be 10 V. It should be noticed that the original solution with $k_1 = 5$ is correct. The reason for revising the computer diagram is to obtain better accuracy by using the full range of 10 V rather than 5 V.

Consider now the differential equation

$$z = \frac{(D+4)f(t)}{D^2 + 8D + 2} \tag{8.26}$$

This may be expressed in the form

$$z = (D+4)y = \dot{y} + 4y \tag{8.27}$$

where

$$y = \frac{f(t)}{D^2 + 8D + 2} \tag{8.28}$$

The differential equation for y is the same as Eq. (8.12), and the corresponding computer diagram is shown in Fig. 8.8*a*. In Fig. 8.8*b* is shown the modified computer diagram for the case in which $z_m = 2.0$ and thus the output is $5z = 5(\dot{y} + 4y)$.

When the initial conditions are given in terms of z, it is necessary to convert them to y in order to obtain the computer diagram for y. Equations relating $\dot{y}$ and $\dot{y}$ to z and $\dot{z}$ are obtained from the original equation for the system as follows:

$$z = \dot{y} + 4y$$

$$\dot{z} = \ddot{y} + 4\dot{y} = [-8\dot{y} - 2y + f(t)] + 4\dot{y}$$
$$= -4\dot{y} - 2y + f(t)$$

Solving for y and $\dot{y}$ in terms of z and $\dot{z}$ gives

$$y = \frac{\dot{z} + 4z - f(t)}{14}$$
$$\dot{y} = -\frac{2\dot{z} + z - 2f(t)}{7} \tag{8.29}$$

8.3 TIME SCALE

For many problems, it is desired that the speed at which the analog computer solves the problem be different from the speed at which the phenomena actually occur. For example, various phenomena of astronomy require years; so obviously it is desirable to increase the speed at which such problems are solved on the computer. For other phenomena which take place very rapidly, it is necessary to slow down the speed at which such problems are simulated by the computer. Letting t represent the time at which a phenomenon actually occurs and the term τ represent the time required for this phenomenon to occur on the computer, $\tau = at$ relates the actual time t to the computer or machine time τ. For $a < 1$ the phenomenon occurs faster in the computer than it does in nature. For example, if $a = 0.1$, something which actually requires 10 s to complete is completed by the computer in $\tau = 0.1t = 0.1 \times 10 = 1$ s. Similarly, if $a > 1$, the phenomenon is slowed down by the computer.

Illustrative example Let it be desired to slow down the computer solution of Eq. (8.12) by a factor of 5.

SOLUTION The first step in the solution of this problem is to transform the original equation from a function of actual time t to a function of machine time τ. This is accomplished by noting that

$$\tau = at \tag{8.30}$$

and

$$\frac{d\tau}{dt} = a \tag{8.31}$$

Thus

$$\dot{y} = \frac{dy}{dt} = \frac{d\tau}{dt}\frac{dy}{d\tau} = a\frac{dy}{d\tau}$$
$$\ddot{y} = \frac{d^2y}{dt^2} = \frac{d}{dt}\left(\frac{dy}{dt}\right) = \frac{d\tau}{dt}\frac{d}{d\tau}\left(a\frac{dy}{d\tau}\right) = a^2\frac{d^2y}{d\tau^2} \tag{8.32}$$

Similarly, it may be shown that in general

$$\frac{d^n y}{dt^n} = a^n \frac{d^n y}{d\tau^n} \tag{8.33}$$

Application of the preceding rules to convert the original time expression given by Eq. (8.12) from a function of t to a function of τ gives

$$a^2 \frac{d^2 y}{d\tau^2} + 8a \frac{dy}{d\tau} + 2y = f\left(\frac{\tau}{a}\right) \tag{8.34}$$

where $f(\tau/a)$ is obtained by substitution of τ/a for t in the original function $f(t)$. Because of the change of variable, the term y in Eq. (8.34) is now a function of τ rather than t. To slow down the solution by a factor of 5, the value of a is 5, so that Eq. (8.34) becomes

$$25 \frac{d^2 y}{d\tau^2} + 40 \frac{dy}{d\tau} + 2y = f\left(\frac{\tau}{5}\right) \tag{8.35}$$

The transformed initial conditions are

$$\left.\frac{dy}{d\tau}\right|_{\tau=0} = \left.\frac{1}{a}\frac{dy}{dt}\right|_{t=0} = \frac{1}{5}(0.5) = 0.1 \text{ m/s} \tag{8.36}$$

Similarly, the transformed maximum values are

$$\begin{aligned} \left(\frac{d^2 y}{d\tau^2}\right)_m &= \frac{1}{a^2}\left(\frac{d^2 y}{dt^2}\right)_m = \frac{2.0}{25} = 0.08 \text{ m/s}^2 \\ \left(\frac{dy}{d\tau}\right)_m &= \frac{1}{a}\left(\frac{dy}{dt}\right)_m = \frac{1.0}{5} = 0.2 \text{ m/s} \end{aligned} \tag{8.37}$$

As is shown in Fig. 8.9, the function $f(\tau/5)$ is obtained by multiplying the original time scale by the factor $a = 5$. Thus, a time-scale change does not affect the initial and maximum values of $f(\tau/a)$. Similarly, the initial and maximum values for y are unaffected by a change in the time scale.

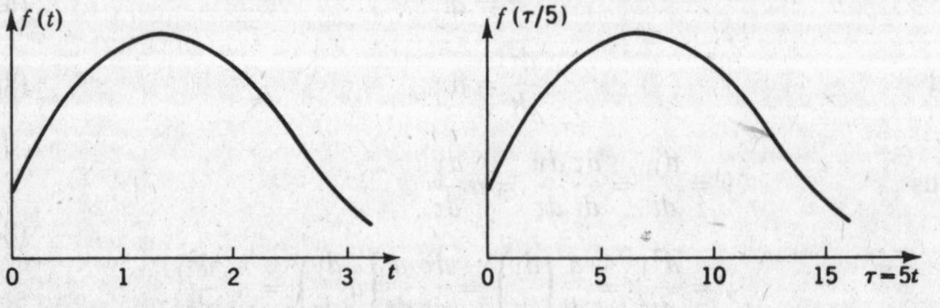

Figure 8.9 Graphs of $f(t)$ versus t and $f(\tau/5)$ versus τ.

The new scale factors are computed as follows:

$$
\begin{aligned}
k &= \frac{10}{f(\tau/a)_m} = \frac{10}{2.0} = 5 \text{ V/N} \\
k_1 &= \frac{10}{(d^2y/d\tau^2)_m} = \frac{10}{0.08} = 125 \text{ V} \cdot \text{s}^2/\text{m} \\
k_2 &= \frac{10}{(dy/d\tau)_m} = \frac{10}{0.2} = 50 \text{ V} \cdot \text{s/m} \\
k_3 &= \frac{10}{y_m} = \frac{10}{0.5} = 20 \text{ V/m}
\end{aligned}
\tag{8.38}
$$

The computer diagram is now obtained by application of the general procedure given in the preceding section. Solving Eq. (8.35) for $d^2y/d\tau^2$ and multiplying by $k_1 = 125$ gives

$$
k_1 \frac{d^2y}{d\tau^2} = 125 \frac{d^2y}{d\tau^2} = 5f\left(\frac{\tau}{5}\right) - 200 \frac{dy}{d\tau} - 10y \tag{8.39}
$$

This is now written in the form

$$
\begin{aligned}
125 \frac{d^2y}{d\tau^2} &= \frac{5}{k} kf\left(\frac{\tau}{5}\right) + \frac{200}{k_2}\left(-k_2 \frac{dy}{d\tau}\right) + \frac{10}{k_3}(-k_3 \dot{y}) \\
&= 5f\left(\frac{\tau}{5}\right) + 4\left(-50 \frac{dy}{d\tau}\right) + 0.5(-20y)
\end{aligned}
\tag{8.40}
$$

The resulting computer diagram is shown in Fig. 8.10*a*.

The coefficients of the terms of Eq. (8.40) are the effective input multipliers at the first amplifier. The multiplication factors for the second and third amplifiers are obtained as follows:

$$
\left(\frac{1}{R_1 C_2}\right)_2 = \frac{k_2}{k_1} = \frac{50}{125} = 0.4 \tag{8.41}
$$

$$
\left(\frac{1}{R_1 C_2}\right)_3 = \frac{k_3}{k_2} = \frac{20}{50} = 0.4 \tag{8.42}
$$

The values of the initial voltages $e_2(0)$ and $e_3(0)$ are computed in the following manner:

$$
\begin{aligned}
e_2(0) &= k_2 \frac{dy}{d\tau}\bigg|_{\tau=0} = 50(0.1) = 5 \text{ V} \\
e_3(0) &= -k_3 y\bigg|_{\tau=0} = -20(0.2) = -4 \text{ V}
\end{aligned}
\tag{8.43}
$$

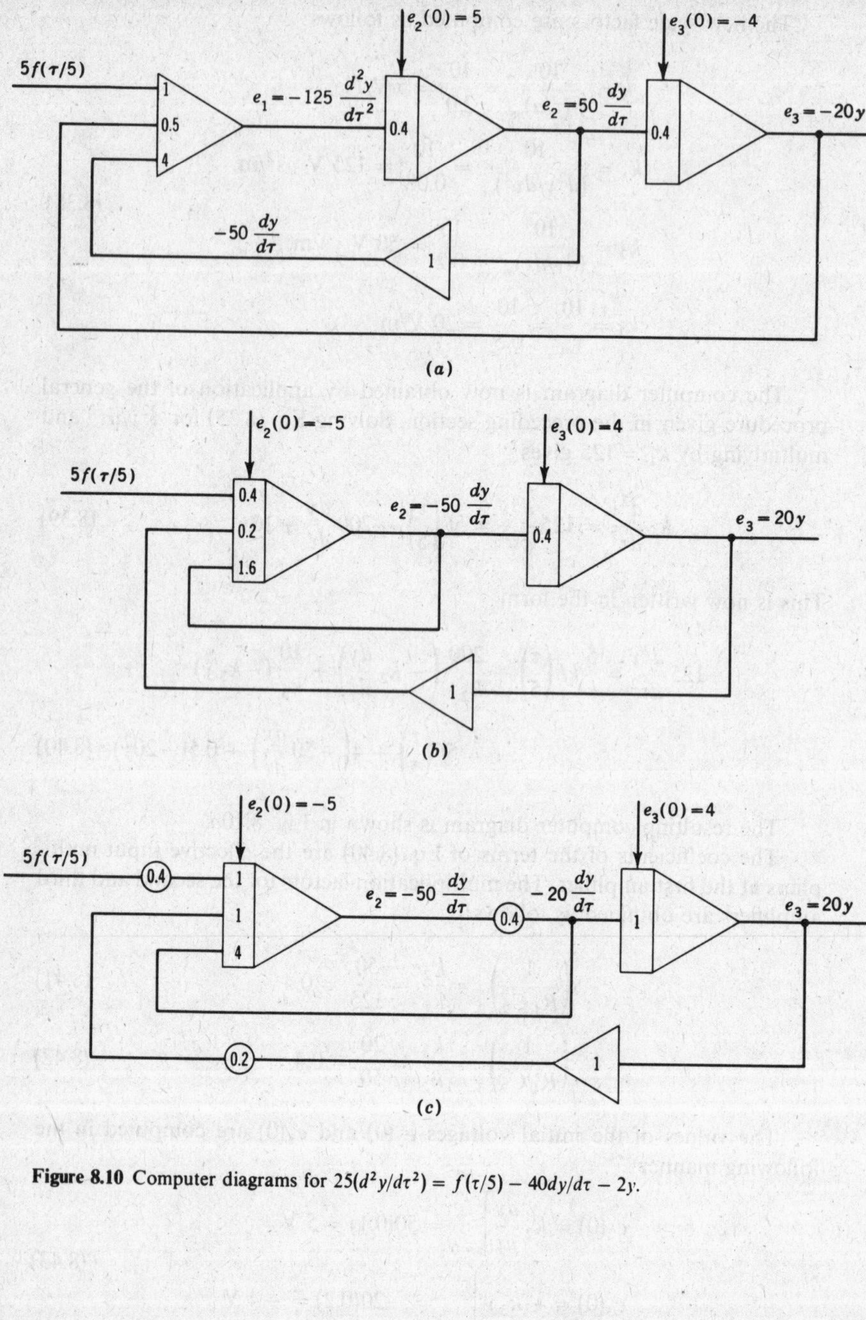

Figure 8.10 Computer diagrams for $25(d^2y/d\tau^2) = f(\tau/5) - 40dy/d\tau - 2y$.

Comparison of Figs. 8.8*a* and 8.10*a* shows that the gains in the operational amplifiers which multiply by a constant are unaffected by a time scale change. Only the gains of the integrating amplifiers are affected. It is to be noted that the value of the gain in the integrators of Fig. 8.10*a* is equal to that in Fig. 8.8*a* divided by the scale constant a (i.e., $2/a = \frac{2}{5} = 0.4$). Thus, the easiest way to obtain the computer diagram for a time scale change is to first of all obtain the diagram for the case of no time change and then to divide the gain in each integrator by a. The scale factors are most readily obtained by first noting that the scale factor for the y term is unaffected by a time scale change (i.e., $e_3 = -20y$). Thus, dividing $k_3 = 20$ by the amplifier gain 0.4 yields the scale factor $k_2 = 50$ shown in Fig. 8.10*a*. Similarly, dividing $k_2 = 50$ by 0.4 yields the scale factor $k_1 = 125$.

If it is not necessary to measure $d^2y/d\tau^2$, the first amplifier may be eliminated by multiplying the input constants of the first summer by the factor 0.4 for the next amplifier [that is, $(1)(0.4) = 0.4$, $(0.5)(0.4) = 0.2$, $(4)(0.4) = 1.6$], as shown in Fig. 8.10*b*. The elimination of this amplifier changes the signs of the resulting voltages, and thus the sign of each feedback quantity must be reversed. Similarly the sign of each initial condition voltage must be changed.

Some operational amplifiers use standard resistors of 1×10^6, 0.25×10^6, and 0.10×10^6 ohms and a standard capacitor of 1×10^{-6} F. Thus, only gains of $1/RC$ equal to 1, 4, or 10 are readily available for each integrator. It is possible to put two resistors in parallel or series at the input to obtain some other effective value of resistance. For example, two 1×10^6 ohm resistors in series yield a 2×10^6 ohm resistance, while two 1×10^6 ohm resistors in parallel yield a 0.5×10^6 ohm resistance.

In general, it is necessary to use a potentiometer to obtain the desired effective resistance. Figure 8.11 shows a schematic diagram of a potentiometer. The voltage relationship is

$$e_o = \frac{R_b}{R_a} e_{\text{in}} = k e_{\text{in}} \tag{8.44}$$

where

$$k = \frac{R_b}{R_a} \le 1$$

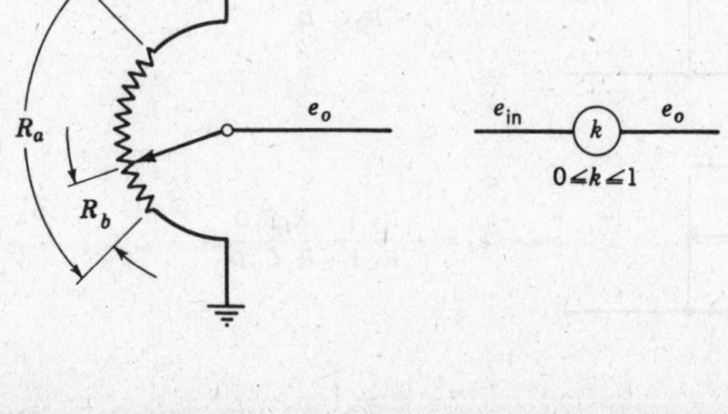

Figure 8.11 Potentiometer.

The computer diagram of Fig. 8.10*b* may be modified by the addition of three potentiometers as shown in Fig. 8.10*c* such that only gains of 1, 4, or 10 are necessary at each amplifier. By comparison of Fig. 8.10*b* and *c*, it is to be noted that the effective gain of an amplifier is the product of the gain of the amplifier and the value of k for the potentiometer in front of the amplifier.

8.4 SIMULATION

A very important application of the analog computer is the simulation of automatic control systems. One method that could be used to simulate a control system would be to determine the overall differential equation and solve this on the computer. Usually though, one is interested in determining the effect on the system performance when certain parameters are varied. Using the preceding technique would mean solving a new differential equation for each change.

Because of the similarity between a block diagram and a computer diagram, it is customary to simulate each portion of the system and then interconnect each of these elements. Thus, the effect of changing one of the terms in the original block diagram may be achieved by changing the corresponding quantity in the computer diagram.

Table 8.1

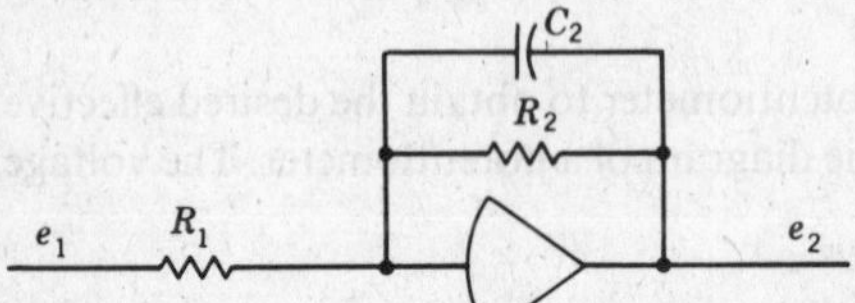

$$e_2 = \frac{-R_2}{R_1(1 + R_2 C_2 D)} e_1$$

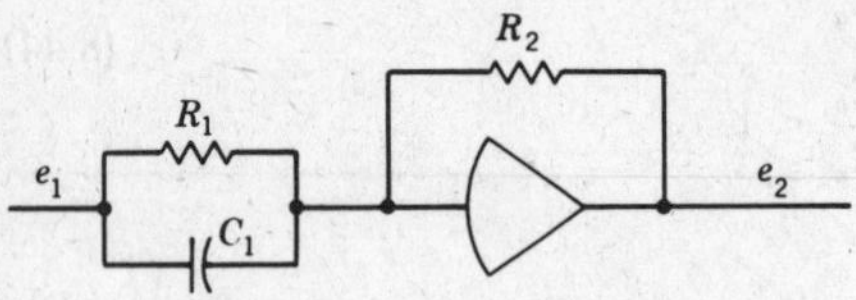

$$e_2 = -\frac{R_2}{R_1}(1 + R_1 C_1 D)\, e_1$$

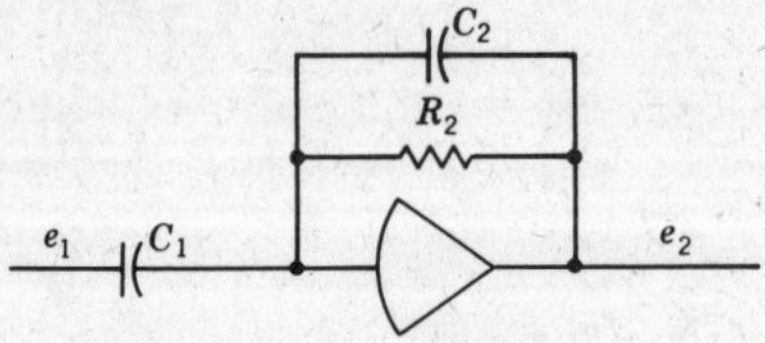

$$e_2 = \frac{-R_2 C_1 D}{1 + R_2 C_2 D} e_1$$

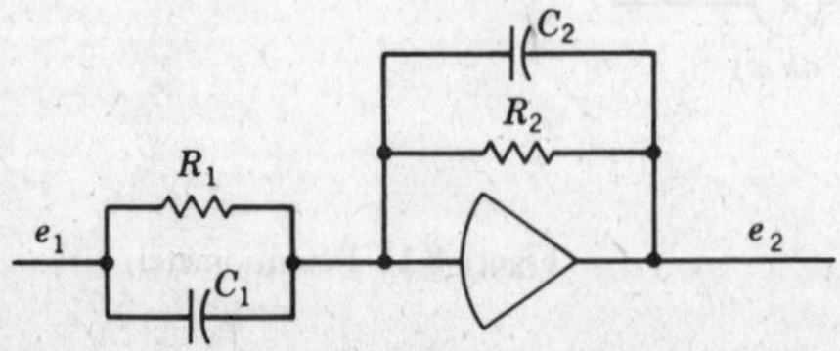

$$e_2 = -\frac{R_2}{R_1}\frac{1 + R_1 C_1 D}{1 + R_2 C_2 D} e_1$$

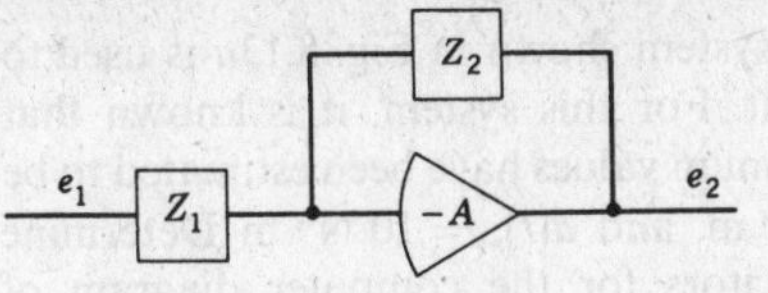

Figure 8.12 General schematic representation of an operational amplifier.

In Fig. 8.12 is shown a schematic representation of an operational amplifier in which the input impedance is Z_1 and the parallel impedance is Z_2. The equation of operation for this amplifier is

$$\frac{e_2}{e_1} = -\frac{Z_2}{Z_1} \tag{8.45}$$

When the input impedance is a resistor R_1 and the parallel impedance is a resistor R_2, the preceding expression reduces to the result given by Eq. (8.8). For the case in which $Z_1 = R_1$ and $Z_2 = 1/C_2 D$, the result given by Eq. (8.11) is verified.

In Table 8.1 is shown a number of computer circuits for simulating various transfer functions. For the first circuit, $Z_1 = R_1$ and $Z_2 = 1/(1/R_2 + C_2 D) = R_2/(1 + R_2 C_2 D)$. Substitution of the values of these impedances into Eq. (8.45) gives the equation of operation for this computer circuit, i.e.,

$$e_2 = -\frac{R_2}{R_1(1 + R_2 C_2 D)} e_1 \tag{8.46}$$

In Fig. 8.13*a* is shown a typical block diagram, and the corresponding computer diagram is shown in Fig. 8.13*b*.

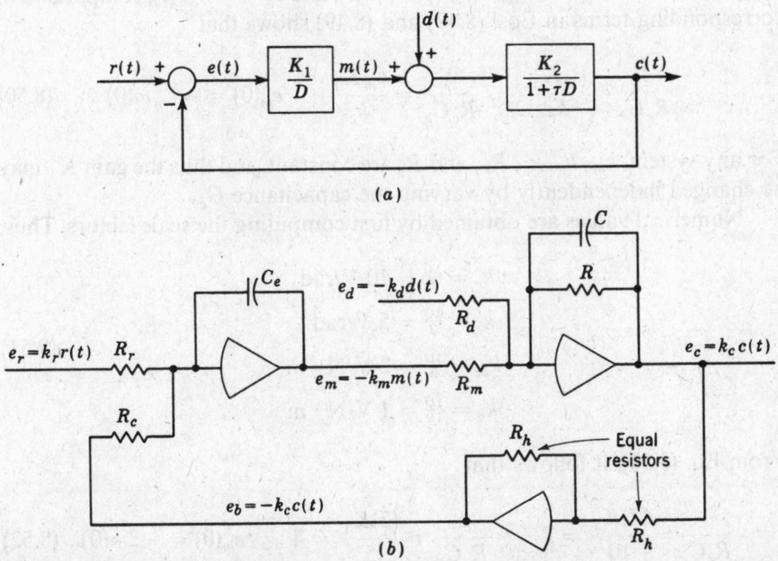

Figure 8.13 Block diagram and corresponding computer diagram.

Illustrative example Suppose that the system shown in Fig. 8.13*a* is used to control the angular position of a shaft. For this system, it is known that $K_1 = 10$, $K_2 = 5$, and $\tau = 1.0$ The maximum values have been estimated to be $c(t)_m = 2$ rad, $r(t)_m = 1$ rad, $m_m = 5$ N · m, and $d(t)_m = 10$ N · m Determine the values of the resistors and capacitors for the computer diagram of Fig. 8.13*b*.

SOLUTION The voltage equation for the first amplifier is

$$e_m = \frac{-1}{R_r C_e}\int_0^t e_r\,dt - \frac{1}{R_c C_e}\int_0^t e_b\,dt + e_m(0) \tag{8.47}$$

The equation which describes the operation of the corresponding portion of the actual system is

$$\begin{aligned} m(t) &= K_1 \int_0^t [r(t) - c(t)]\,dt + m(0) \\ &= K_1 \int_0^t r(t)\,dt - K_1 \int_0^t c(t)\,dt + m(0) \end{aligned} \tag{8.48}$$

Multiplication of Eq. (8.48) by $-k_m$ gives

$$-k_m m(t) = -\frac{k_m K_1}{k_r}\int_0^t k_r r(t)\,dt + \frac{k_m K_1}{k_c}\int_0^t k_c c(t)\,dt - k_m m(0) \tag{8.49}$$

In order that $e_m = -k_m m(t)$, $e_r = k_r r(t)$, and $e_b = -k_c c(t)$, comparison of corresponding terms in Eqs. (8.47) and (8.49) shows that

$$\frac{1}{R_r C_e} = \frac{k_m K_1}{k_r} \qquad \frac{1}{R_c C_e} = \frac{k_m K_1}{k_c} \qquad e_m(0) = -k_m m(0) \tag{8.50}$$

For any system, k_m, k_r, k_c, R_r, and R_c are constant, and thus the gain K_1 may be changed independently by varying the capacitance C_e.

Numerical values are obtained by first computing the scale factors. Thus,

$$\begin{aligned} k_r &= \tfrac{10}{1} = 10 \text{ V/rad} \\ k_c &= \tfrac{10}{2} = 5 \text{ V/rad} \\ k_m &= \tfrac{10}{5} = 2 \text{ V/N} \cdot \text{m} \\ k_d &= \tfrac{10}{10} = 1 \text{ V/N} \cdot \text{m} \end{aligned} \tag{8.51}$$

From Eq. (8.50), it follows that

$$\frac{1}{R_r C_e} = \frac{(2)K_1}{10} = 2 \qquad \frac{1}{R_c C_e} = \frac{(2)K_1}{5} = 4 \qquad e_m(0) = -2m(0) \tag{8.52}$$

If a 1-μF capacitor is used for C_e, then

$$R_r = \frac{1}{2C_e} = \frac{1}{2 \times 10^{-6}} = 500{,}000 \text{ ohms} \tag{8.53}$$

$$R_c = \frac{1}{4C_e} = 250{,}000 \text{ ohms} \tag{8.54}$$

From Table 8.1, it follows that the voltage equation for the second amplifier is

$$e_c = -\frac{R}{R_m(1 + RCD)} e_m - \frac{R}{R_d(1 + RCD)} e_d \tag{8.55}$$

The equation for the corresponding portion of the actual system is

$$c(t) = \frac{K_2}{1 + \tau D}[m(t) + d(t)] \tag{8.56}$$

Multiplication by k_c gives

$$k_c c(t) = \frac{k_c K_2}{k_m(1 + \tau D)} k_m m(t) + \frac{k_c K_2}{k_d(1 + \tau D)} k_d d(t) \tag{8.57}$$

By comparison of corresponding terms in Eqs. (8.55) and (8.57), it follows that, to have $e_c = k_c c(t)$, $e_m = -k_m m(t)$, and $e_d = -k_d d(t)$, the following relationships must hold:

$$\frac{Rk_m}{R_m} = k_c K_2 \qquad \frac{Rk_d}{R_d} = k_c K_2 \qquad \tau = RC \tag{8.58}$$

The substitution of numerical values gives

$$RC = \tau = 1 \tag{8.59}$$

$$\frac{R}{R_m} = \frac{k_c K_2}{k_m} = \frac{(5)(5)}{2} = 12.5 \tag{8.60}$$

$$\frac{R}{R_d} = \frac{k_c K_2}{k_d} = \frac{(5)(5)}{1} = 25 \tag{8.61}$$

If a 1-μF capacitor is used for C, then

$$R = \frac{1}{C} = 1{,}000{,}000 \text{ ohms}$$

$$R_m = \frac{R}{12.5} = 80{,}000 \text{ ohms} \tag{8.62}$$

$$R_d = \frac{R}{25} = 40{,}000 \text{ ohms}$$

Because C appears only in Eq. (8.59), τ may be varied independently by varying C. A variable capacitor provides a convenient means for varying C. From Eqs. (8.60) and (8.61) it follows that to change the value of K_2, both R_m and R_d must be changed accordingly. Because the output e_c is to be subtracted from the input e_r, it is necessary to multiply the output by -1, as shown in the feedback path of Fig. 8.13b.

If, in testing, it is found that $e_{c_m} \neq 10$ V, this is evidence that the originally estimated value for $c(t)_m$ is not correct. Because $e_c = k_c c(t)$, the actual value of $c(t)_m$ is now easily found to be

$$c(t)_m = \frac{e_{c_m}}{k_c} \tag{8.63}$$

When the maximum value of $c(t)$ is near 10 V, there is no need to change the value of k_c. However, if the maximum voltage is quite small, then it is desirable to increase the accuracy with which the output voltage can be read by using a new value of k_c based on the value of $c(t)_m$ obtained from Eq. (8.63). Similarly, if e_{c_m} was sufficiently greater than 10 V to cause overloading, then it would be necessary to decrease the value of k_c. For most amplifiers, an overload light turns on when the maximum voltage is high enough to overload an amplifier.

A time-scale change $\tau = at$ is readily effected by substituting aD for D in the block diagram of Fig. 8.13a.

A major application of analog computers is in the design of systems with nonlinear components. Standard electronic circuits are available for simulating commonly encountered nonlinear effects such as coulomb friction, backlash, dead zone, saturation, continuous nonlinear functions, etc.

PROBLEMS

8.1 Derive the equation of operation for each circuit shown in Fig. 8.5.

8.2 Determine the computer diagram for the following first-order equation:

$$(0.5D + 1)y = f(t)$$

The initial condition is $y(0) = 0.2$ m, and the maximum expected values are $f(t)_m = 1$ N, $y_m = 0.5$ m, and $\dot{y}_m = 2$ m/s.

8.3 Determine the computer diagram for the following differential equation:

$$\ddot{y} + 6\dot{y} + 5y = f(t)$$

The maximum expected values are $y_m = 0.5$, $\dot{y}_m = 1.0$, $\ddot{y}_m = 2.0$, and $f_m = 5.0$. The initial conditions are $y(0) = 0.2$ and $\dot{y}(0) = -0.2$.

8.4 Determine the computer diagram for the following differential equation:

$$\ddot{y} + 25y = f(t)$$

The maximum expected values are $y_m = 0.1$, $\dot{y}_m = 0.5$, $\ddot{y}_m = 2.5$, and $f_m = 1.0$. The initial conditions are $y(0) = 0$ and $\dot{y}(0) = 0.5$.

8.5 Determine the computer diagram to solve the following differential equation:

$$\ddot{y} + 2y = 5f(t)$$

The initial conditions are $y(0) = 3$ and $\dot{y}(0) = 2$. The maximum expected values are $y_m = 10$, $\dot{y}_m = 20$, $\ddot{y}_m = 50$, $f(t)_m = 2$.

8.6 (*a*) Determine the computer diagram for the following third-order differential equation:

$$(D^3 + 2D^2 + 5D + 10)y = f(t)$$

The initial conditions are $y(0) = 0.5$, $\dot{y}(0) = 0$, and $\ddot{y}(0) = 1.0$. The maximum expected values are $f(t)_m = 2.5$, $y_m = 1.0$, $\dot{y}_m = 2.0$, $\ddot{y}_m = 5.0$, and $\dddot{y}_m = 10$.

(*b*) Suppose that in part (*a*) it is found that $e_{3m} = k_3 \dot{y}_m = 2.5$ V rather than 10 V. What is the actual value of $\dot{y}_m$? Revise the computer diagram so that e_{3m} will be 10 V.

8.7 Let it be desired to speed up the computer solution for Prob. 8.2 by a factor of 5. Determine the computer diagram for this case.

8.8 Determine the diagram which speeds up the solution of Prob. 8.3 by a factor of 5.

8.9 Let is be desired to slow down the computer solution for Prob. 8.6 by a factor of 2. Determine the computer diagram for this case.

8.10 (*a*) Determine the computer diagram to solve the following differential equation:

$$\dddot{y} + 8\ddot{y} + 25\dot{y} + 20y = f(t)$$

The initial conditions are $\ddot{y}(0) = 3$, $\dot{y}(0) = 1$, $y(0) = 1$. The maximum expected values are $\dddot{y}_m = 10$. $\ddot{y}_m = 5$, $\dot{y}_m = 2$, $y_m = 1$, $f(t)_m = 40$.

(*b*) Determine the computer diagram which will speed up the solution of part (*a*) by a factor of 2.

8.11 Determine the differential equation that is being solved by the computer diagram shown in Fig. P8.11.

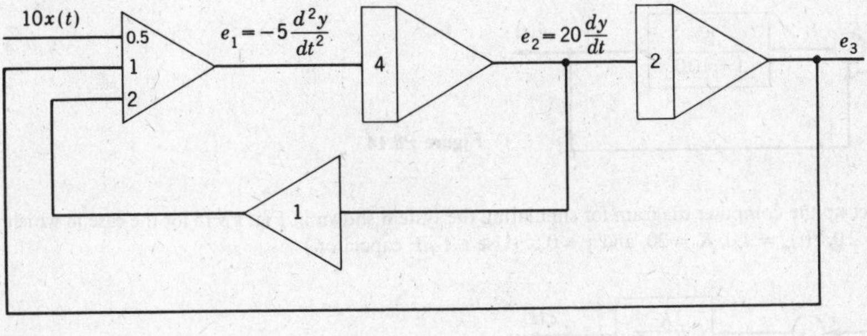

Figure P8.11

8.12 (*a*) Determine the differential equation that is being solved by the analog computer shown in Fig. P8.12.

(*b*) For the first amplifier,

$$\frac{bk_1}{k_3} = \frac{R_2}{R_b} \qquad \frac{ak_1}{k_2} = \frac{R_2}{R_a}$$

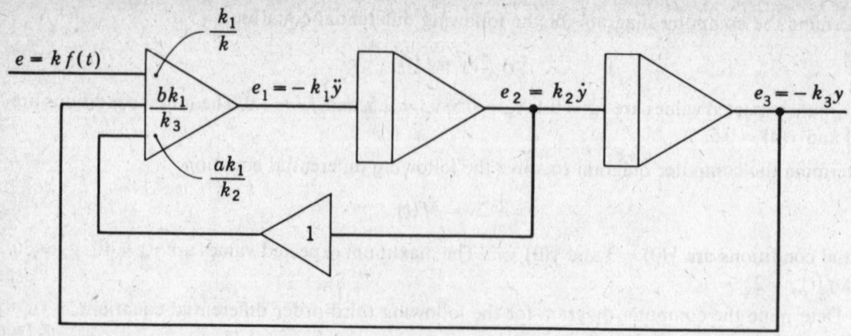

Figure P8.12

Let $a = 2\zeta\omega_n$ and $b = \omega_n^2$. Solve for ζ and ω_n in terms of these electrical constants and scale factors. Can either ζ or ω_n be varied independently?

8.13 Derive the equation of operation for the amplifier circuit shown in Fig. P8.13.

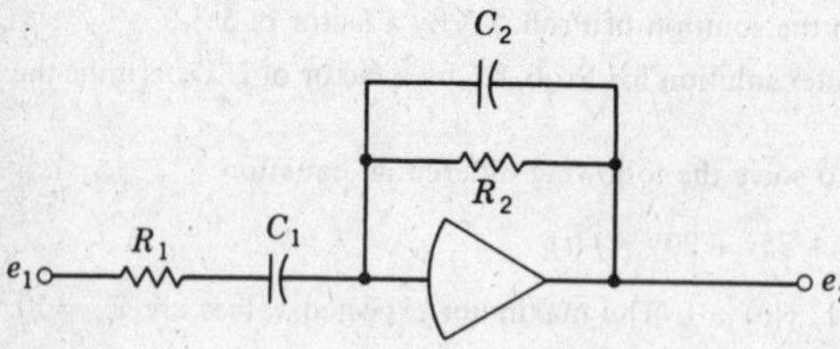

Figure P8.13

8.14 Construct the computer diagram for simulating the control system shown in Fig. P8.14. The maximum expected values are $r_m = 2.0$ and $c_m = 1.0$.

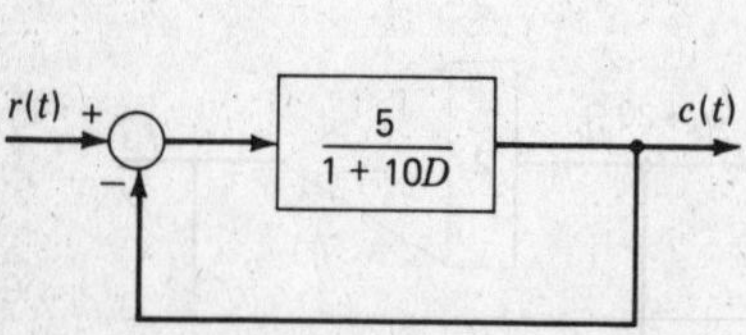

Figure P8.14

8.15 Set up the computer diagram for simulating the system shown in Fig. P8.15 for the case in which $r(t)_m = 2.0$, $c(t)_m = 1.0$, $K = 20$, and $\tau = 0.5$. (Use a 1-μF capacitor.)

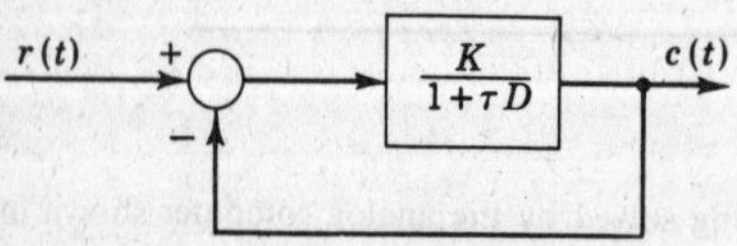

Figure P8.15

8.16 A control system and the corresponding computer diagram for simulating the control system are shown in Fig. P8.16. For $e_r = 5r$, $e_c = -10c$, $C_2 = 1\ \mu$F, $R_2 = 1$ megohm, $R_r = 0.1$ megohm, and $R_c = 0.2$ megohm, determine the corresponding values of K_1, K_2, and τ.

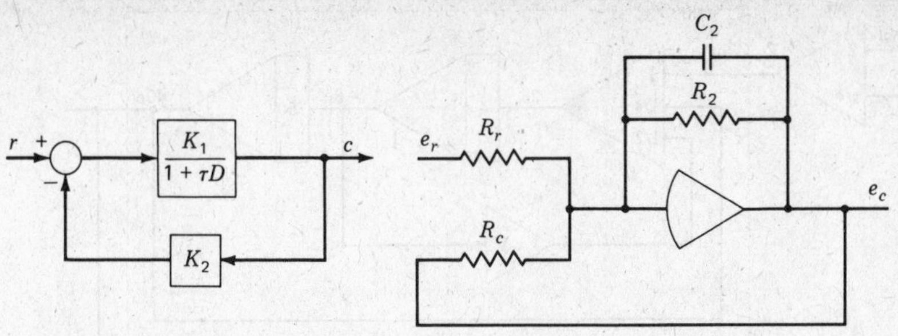

Figure P8.16

8.17 Determine the block-diagram representation for the control system which is being simulated by the analog computer shown in Fig. P8.17.

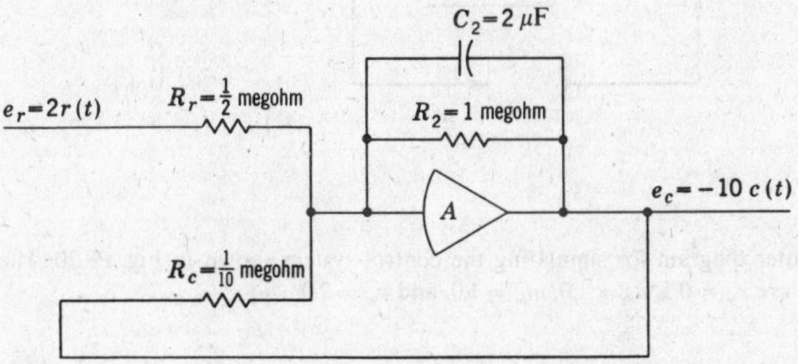

Figure P8.17

8.18 Construct the computer diagram for simulating the control system shown in Fig. P8.18. For this system $K_1 = 5$, $K_2 = 2$, and $\tau = 1$. The maximum expected values are $r(t)_m = 1.0$ and $c(t)_m = 2.0$. (Let $C_2 = 1\ \mu F$.)

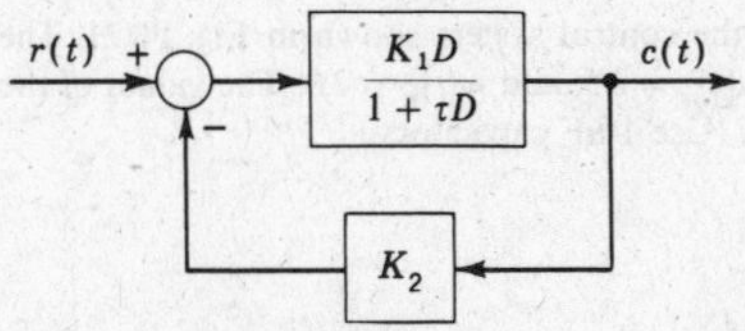

Figure P8.18

8.19 (*a*) Determine the block diagram for the system which is being simulated by the analog computer diagram shown in Fig. P8.19. HINT: First obtain the block diagram for the portion of the circuit enclosed by dashed lines, that is, the block diagram relating the input x to output c.

(*b*) Draw directly the new computer diagram for speeding up the solution of the above problem by a factor of 2.

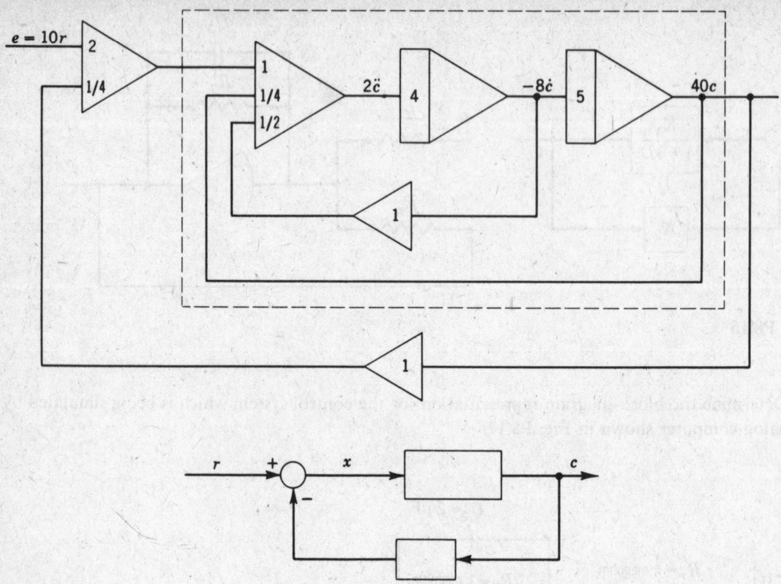

Figure P8.19

8.20 Determine the computer diagram for simulating the control system shown in Fig. P8.20. The maximum expected values are $r_m = 0.5$, $d_m = 1.0$, $m_m = 1.0$, and $c_m = 2.0$.

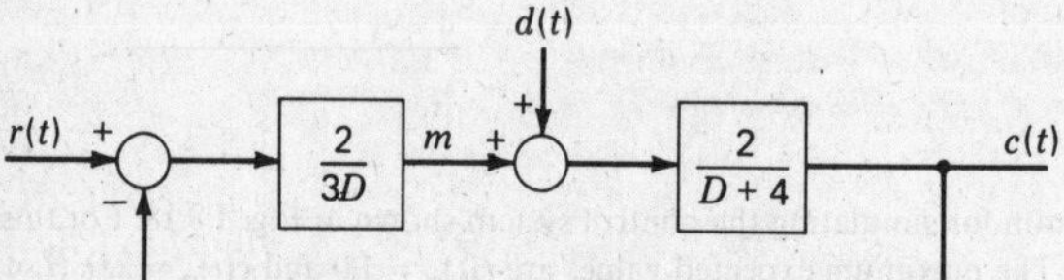

Figure P8.20

8.21 Determine the computer diagram for simulating the control system shown in Fig. P8.21. The maximum expected values are $r(t)_m = 0.5$, $c(t)_m = 1.0$, $d(t)_m = 2.5$, and $m(t)_m = 2.0$. The values of the constants are $K_1 = 10$, $K_2 = 20$, $\tau_1 = 0.2$, and $\tau_2 = 1.0$. (Use 1-μF capacitors.)

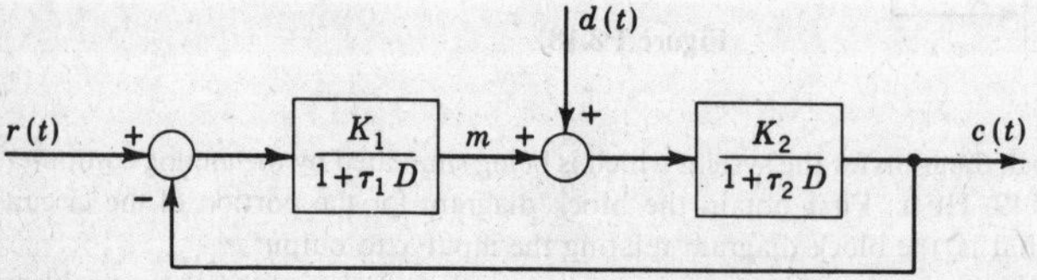

Figure P8.21

8.22 A system is described by the two simultaneous equations

$$\dot{x} + 4x + 2y = f(t)$$

$$2x + 4y + \dot{y} = 0$$

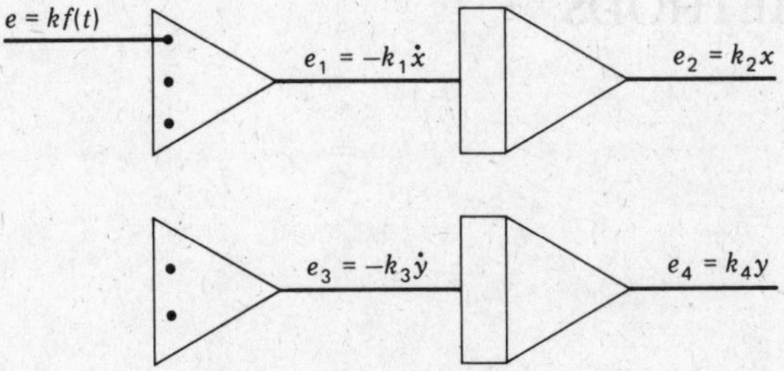

Figure P8.22

Solve the first differential equation for $\dot{x}$ and the second for $\dot{y}$, then proceed to complete the computer diagram shown in Fig. P8.22. That is, indicate the various amplifier gains and hook up the appropriate interconnecting and feedback signals. The maximum expected values are $f_m = 2.0$, $x_m = 0.5$, $\dot{x}_m = 1.0$, $y_m = 1.0$, and $\dot{y}_m = 2.0$. The initial conditions are $x(0) = 0.2$ and $y(0) = 0.1$.

8.23 Construct the computer diagram for solving the two simultaneous differential equations

$$\dot{x} + 5x = y + f(t)$$

$$\ddot{y} + 10y = 2x$$

The initial conditions are $x(0) = 1$, $\dot{y}(0) = 0$, and $y(0) = 0.2$. The maximum expected values are $x_m = 4$, $\dot{x}_m = 10$, $y_m = 1$, $\dot{y}_m = 2$, $\ddot{y}_m = 4$, and $f(t)_m = 10$.

CHAPTER

NINE

STATE-SPACE METHODS

State-space methods provide a generalized technique for investigating the behavior of control systems. This approach is especially well suited to the analysis of more complex and nonlinear control systems. A feature of state-space methods is that they lend themselves to solution by either digital or analog computers.

9.1 SYSTEM REPRESENTATION

Common techniques employed for obtaining the state-space representation for a control system are direct programming, parallel programming, series programming, and general programming. The choice of the state-space representation depends on the nature of the particular problem to be solved.

Direct Programming

To illustrate this method, consider the differential equation

$$c(t) = \frac{D+3}{(D+1)(D+2)} f(t) \tag{9.1}$$

This may be written in the form

$$c(t) = (D+3)x_1$$

where

$$x_1 = \frac{1}{(D+1)(D+2)} f(t)$$

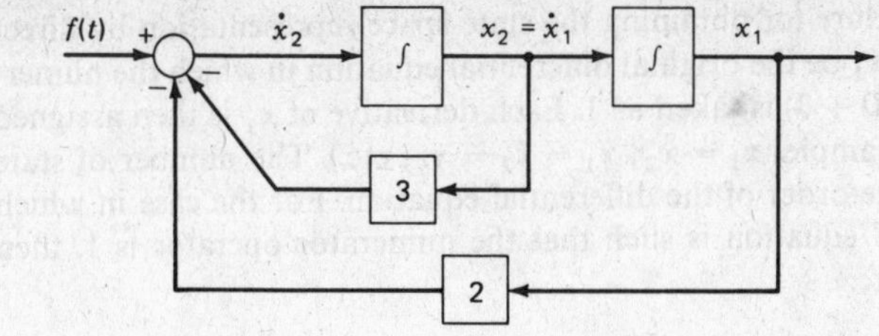

(a)

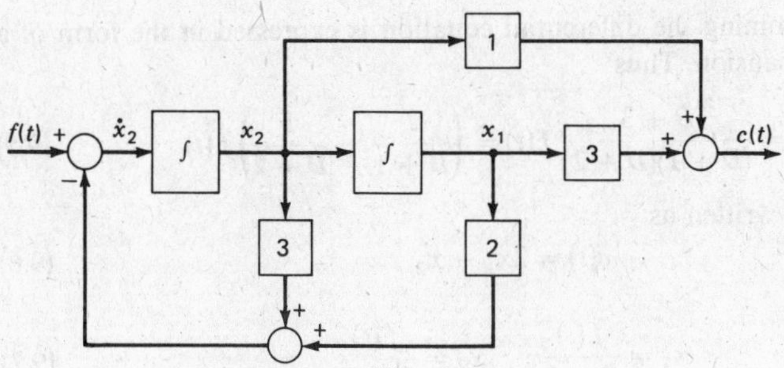

(b)

Figure 9.1 Computer diagram by direct programming.

By letting $\dot{x}_1 = x_2$, then

$$c(t) = 3x_1 + x_2 \tag{9.2}$$

$$\dot{x}_2 = -2x_1 - 3x_2 + f(t) \tag{9.3}$$

The block diagram for obtaining the computer solution of Eq. (9.3) is shown in Fig. 9.1*a*. Note that the output of the summer (indicated by the circle) is $\dot{x}_2$. Successive integration of $\dot{x}_2$ yields in turn $x_2 = \dot{x}_1$ and x_1. The final computer diagram for obtaining $c(t)$ from x_1 and x_2 using Eq. (9.2) is shown in Fig. 9.1*b*.

The state-space representation for the differential equation, Eq. (9.1), is given by Eqs. (9.2) and (9.3). These system equations may be expressed in the matrix form:

$$\begin{aligned} \begin{bmatrix} \dot{x}_1 \\ \dot{x}_2 \end{bmatrix} &= \begin{bmatrix} 0 & 1 \\ -2 & -3 \end{bmatrix} \begin{bmatrix} x_1 \\ x_2 \end{bmatrix} + \begin{bmatrix} 0 \\ 1 \end{bmatrix} f(t) \\ c &= [3 \quad 1] \begin{bmatrix} x_1 \\ x_2 \end{bmatrix} \end{aligned} \tag{9.4}$$

The x's are referred to as the state variables. Note that the output of each integrator in Fig. 9.1 is a state variable.

The general procedure for obtaining the state-space representation by direct programming is to let x_1 be the original differential equation in which the numerator operator (that is, $D + 3$) is taken as 1. Each derivative of x_1 is then assigned a state variable (for example, $\dot{x}_1 = x_2$, $\ddot{x}_1 = \dot{x}_2 = x_3$, etc.). The number of state variables is equal to the order of the differential equation. For the case in which the original differential equation is such that the numerator operator is 1, then $c = x_1$, $\dot{c} = \dot{x}_1 = x_2$, etc.

Parallel Programming

In parallel programming the differential equation is expressed in the form of a partial-fraction expansion. Thus

$$c(t) = \frac{D+3}{(D+1)(D+2)} f(t) = \left(\frac{2}{D+1} - \frac{1}{D+2} \right) f(t) \tag{9.5}$$

This result may be written as

$$c(t) = 2x_1 - x_2 \tag{9.6}$$

where

$$x_1 = \frac{f(t)}{D+1} \qquad x_2 = \frac{f(t)}{D+2} \tag{9.7}$$

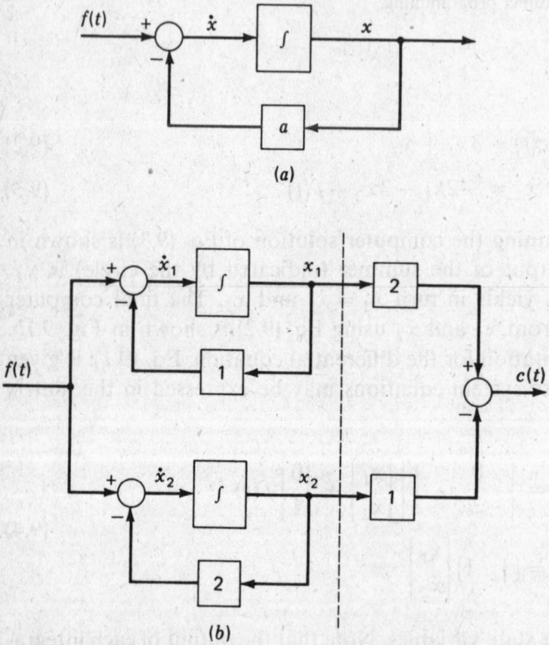

Figure 9.2 Computer diagram by parallel programming.

In Fig. 9.2*a* is shown the computer diagram for generating the basic term

$$x = \frac{f(t)}{D + a}$$

or

$$\dot{x} = f(t) - ax$$

The computer diagram for generating the state variables as defined in Eq. (9.7) is shown to the left of the dotted partition in Fig. 9.2*b*. To the right of the dotted partition is indicated the manner in which the state variables are combined in Eq. (9.6) to yield the desired solution $c(t)$. Equations (9.6) and (9.7) make up a state-space representation for the system, Eq. (9.1). In terms of matrix notation, Eqs. (9.6) and (9.7) become

$$\begin{bmatrix} \dot{x}_1 \\ \dot{x}_2 \end{bmatrix} = \begin{bmatrix} -1 & 0 \\ 0 & -2 \end{bmatrix} \begin{bmatrix} x_1 \\ x_2 \end{bmatrix} + \begin{bmatrix} 1 \\ 1 \end{bmatrix} f(t)$$
$$c(t) = [2 \quad -1] \begin{bmatrix} x_1 \\ x_2 \end{bmatrix} \tag{9.8}$$

Series Programming

Consider the general nth-order differential equation

$$(D^n + a_1 D^{n-1} + \cdots + a_{n-1} D + a_n)c(t) = (b_1 D^{n-1} + b_2 D^{n-2} + \cdots + b_{n-1} D + b_n) f(t) \tag{9.9}$$

This differential equation may be written in the matrix form

$$\begin{bmatrix} \dot{x}_1 \\ \dot{x}_2 \\ \vdots \\ \dot{x}_n \end{bmatrix} = \begin{bmatrix} -a_1 & 1 & 0 & \cdots & 0 \\ -a_2 & 0 & 1 & \cdots & 0 \\ \vdots & \vdots & \vdots & & \vdots \\ -a_n & 0 & 0 & \cdots & 0 \end{bmatrix} \begin{bmatrix} x_1 \\ x_2 \\ \vdots \\ x_n \end{bmatrix} + \begin{bmatrix} b_1 \\ b_2 \\ \vdots \\ b_n \end{bmatrix} f(t) \tag{9.10}$$

where $c(t) = x_1$.

For Eq. (9.1), it follows that $a_1 = 3$, $a_2 = 2$, $b_1 = 1$, and $b_2 = 3$. The resulting matrix representation is

$$\begin{bmatrix} \dot{x}_1 \\ \dot{x}_2 \end{bmatrix} = \begin{bmatrix} -3 & 1 \\ -2 & 0 \end{bmatrix} \begin{bmatrix} x_1 \\ x_2 \end{bmatrix} + \begin{bmatrix} 1 \\ 3 \end{bmatrix} f(t)$$
$$c(t) = [1 \quad 0] \begin{bmatrix} x_1 \\ x_2 \end{bmatrix} \tag{9.11}$$

To prove that this matrix representation satisfies Eq. (9.1), first write the matrix equations in the form

$$\dot{x}_1 = -3x_1 + x_2 + f(t)$$
$$\dot{x}_2 = -2x_1 + 3f(t)$$

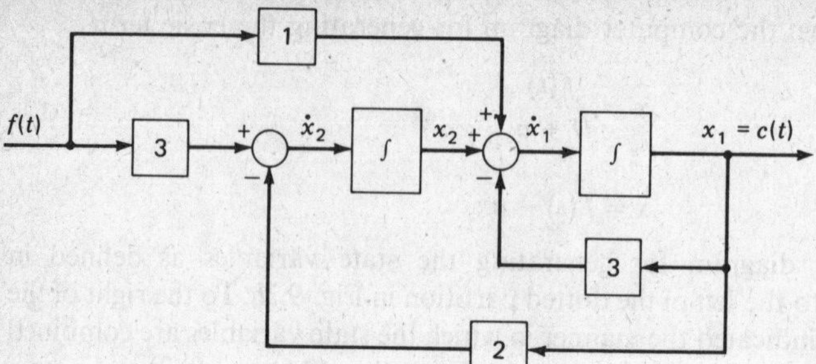

Figure 9.3 Computer diagram by series programming.

Differentiating the first equation, then substituting the resulting expression for $\dot{x}_2$ into the second gives

$$\dot{x}_2 = \ddot{x}_1 + 3\dot{x}_1 - f'(t) = -2x_1 + 3f(t)$$

or

$$\ddot{x}_1 + 3\dot{x}_1 + 2x_1 = f'(t) + 3f(t)$$

This is identical to Eq. (9.1), with $x_1 = c(t)$. The block-diagram representation for the matrix equations is shown in Fig. 9.3.

General Programming

Consider the differential equation

$$(D^2 + a_1 D + a_2)c(t) = (b_0 D^2 + b_1 D + b_2)f(t) \tag{9.12}$$

The $b_0 D^2 f(t)$ term is eliminated by letting $c(t) = x_1 + b_0 f(t)$. Thus,

$$\ddot{x}_1 + a_1\dot{x}_1 + a_2 x_1 = (b_1 - a_1 b_0)f'(t) + (b_2 - a_2 b_0)f(t) \tag{9.13}$$

Let it now be desired to transform this into the form

$$\begin{bmatrix}\dot{x}_1\\ \dot{x}_2\end{bmatrix} = \begin{bmatrix}0 & 1\\ -a_2 & -a_1\end{bmatrix}\begin{bmatrix}x_1\\ x_2\end{bmatrix} + \begin{bmatrix}h_1\\ h_2\end{bmatrix} f(t) \tag{9.14}$$

The corresponding matrix relationships are

$$\dot{x}_1 = x_2 + h_1 f(t)$$
$$\dot{x}_2 = -a_2 x_1 - a_1 x_2 + h_2 f(t)$$

Solving the first matrix relationship for x_2 shows that

$$x_2 = \dot{x}_1 - h_1 f(t)$$

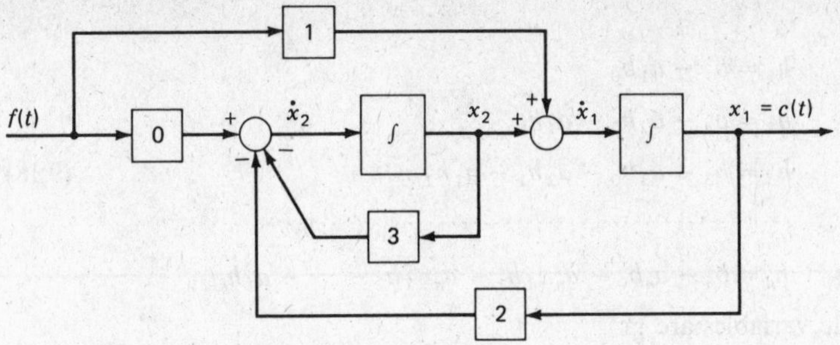

Figure 9.4 Computer diagram by general programming.

Differentiation gives

$$\dot{x}_2 = \ddot{x}_1 - h_1 f'(t)$$

Substitution of the preceding results for x_2 and $\dot{x}_2$ into the second matrix relationship yields

$$\ddot{x}_1 - h_1 f'(t) = -a_2 x_1 - a_1[\dot{x}_1 - h_1 f(t)] + h_2 f(t)$$

or

$$\ddot{x}_1 + a_1 \dot{x}_1 + a_2 x_1 = h_1 f'(t) + [h_2 + a_1 h_1] f(t)$$

This has the same form as Eq. (9.13). Equating coefficients of the $f'(t)$ and $f(t)$ terms shows that

$$h_1 = b_1 - a_1 b_0$$

$$h_2 = b_2 - a_2 b_0 - a_1 h_1$$

For the case of the differential equation given by Eq. (9.1), $a_1 = 3$, $a_2 = 2$, $b_0 = 0$, $b_1 = 1$, and $b_2 = 3$. Hence, $h_1 = 1$ and $h_2 = 0$. The resulting state-space representation is

$$\begin{bmatrix} \dot{x}_1 \\ \dot{x}_2 \end{bmatrix} = \begin{bmatrix} 0 & 1 \\ -2 & -3 \end{bmatrix} \begin{bmatrix} x_1 \\ x_2 \end{bmatrix} + \begin{bmatrix} 1 \\ 0 \end{bmatrix} f(t) \tag{9.15}$$

where $c(t) = x_1 - b_0 f(t) = x_1$. The block-diagram representation is shown in Fig. 9.4.

In general, the differential equation

$$(D^n + a_1 D^{n-1} + \cdots + a_{n-1} D + a_n) c(t)$$
$$= (b_0 D^n + b_1 D^{n-1} + \cdots + b_{n-1} D + b_n) f(t) \tag{9.16}$$

is transformed into the form

$$\begin{bmatrix} \dot{x}_1 \\ \dot{x}_2 \\ \vdots \\ \dot{x}_n \end{bmatrix} = \begin{bmatrix} 0 & 1 & 0 & \cdots & 0 \\ 0 & 0 & 1 & \cdots & 0 \\ \vdots & \vdots & \vdots & & \vdots \\ -a_n & -a_{n-1} & -a_{n-2} & \cdots & -a_1 \end{bmatrix} \begin{bmatrix} x_1 \\ x_2 \\ \vdots \\ x_n \end{bmatrix} + \begin{bmatrix} h_1 \\ h_2 \\ \vdots \\ h_n \end{bmatrix} f(t) \tag{9.17}$$

where

$$\begin{aligned} h_1 &= b_1 - a_1 b_0 \\ h_2 &= b_2 - a_2 b_0 - a_1 h_1 \\ h_3 &= b_3 - a_3 b_0 - a_2 h_1 - a_1 h_2 \\ &\cdots\cdots\cdots\cdots\cdots\cdots \\ h_n &= b_n - a_n b_0 - a_{n-1} h_1 - a_{n-2} h_2 - \cdots - a_1 h_{n-1} \end{aligned} \tag{9.18}$$

and the state variables are

$$\begin{aligned} x_1 &= c(t) - b_0 f(t) \\ x_2 &= \dot{x}_1 - h_1 f(t) \\ x_3 &= \dot{x}_2 - h_2 f(t) \\ &\cdots\cdots\cdots\cdots \\ x_n &= \dot{x}_{n-1} - h_{n-1} f(t) \end{aligned} \tag{9.19}$$

In this method, the state-space representation is obtained by substituting the coefficients of the differential equation into a general form, Eq. (9.17).

There is no unique state-space representation for a system. Comparison of Eqs. (9.4), (9.8), (9.11), and (9.15) shows that any system whose operation is described by a linear differential equation may be written in the general matrix form

$$\dot{\mathbf{x}} = A\mathbf{x} + \mathbf{b}f(t) \tag{9.20}$$

$$c = \mathbf{d}^T\mathbf{x} \tag{9.21}$$

In the following section, it is shown that the preceding matrix form is also applicable to closed-loop systems.

Closed-Loop Systems

The state-space representation may be obtained directly from the block diagram for a system. For the system shown in Fig. 9.5, the input is u and the output is $c(t)$. One state variable $x_1, x_2, \ldots$ is assigned for each order of D in the denominator.

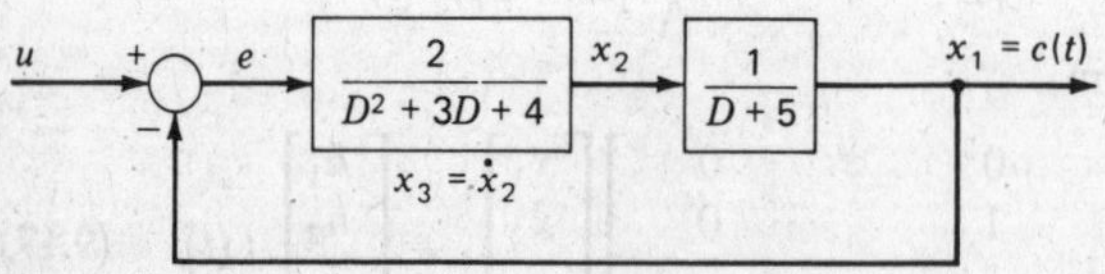

Figure 9.5 Closed-loop system.

For the $1/(D+5)$ term, the state variable is x_1. For the $2/(D^2+3D+4)$ term, the state variables are x_2 and x_3, where $x_3 = \dot{x}_2$. The equation for each block is

$$\frac{x_1}{x_2} = \frac{1}{D+5} \qquad \frac{x_2}{e} = \frac{2}{D^2+3D+4}$$

Thus,

$$\dot{x}_1 = -5x_1 + x_2$$
$$\dot{x}_2 = x_3$$
$$\dot{x}_3 = \ddot{x}_2 = -3\dot{x}_2 - 4x_2 + 2e$$

The equation for e is

$$e = u - c = u - x_1$$

The resulting state-space representation for this system is

$$\begin{bmatrix} \dot{x}_1 \\ \dot{x}_2 \\ \dot{x}_3 \end{bmatrix} = \begin{bmatrix} -5 & 1 & 0 \\ 0 & 0 & 1 \\ -2 & -4 & -3 \end{bmatrix} \begin{bmatrix} x_1 \\ x_2 \\ x_3 \end{bmatrix} + \begin{bmatrix} 0 \\ 0 \\ 2 \end{bmatrix} u$$

The output equation is

$$c = x_1$$

In Fig. 9.6*a* is shown a system which contains the numerator term $D + 2$. Numerator terms do not require additional state variables. To show this, the numerator term is displayed separately in Fig. 9.6*b*. The output z serves as a dummy variable. The equation for each block is

$$\frac{x_1}{z} = \frac{1}{D+5} \qquad \frac{x_2}{e} = \frac{1}{D^2+3D+4}$$

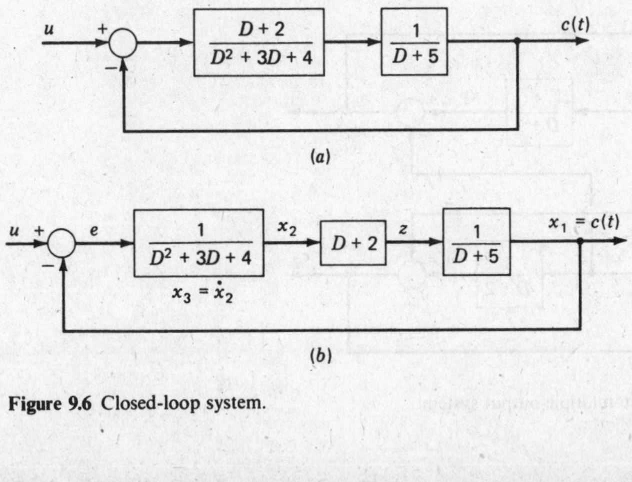

Figure 9.6 Closed-loop system.

Thus,

$$\dot{x}_1 = -5x_1 + z$$
$$\dot{x}_2 = x_3$$
$$\dot{x}_3 = \ddot{x}_2 = -3\dot{x}_2 - 4x_2 + e$$

Using the relationship $e = u - x_1$ to eliminate e and the relationship $z = \dot{x}_2 + 2x_2 = x_3 + 2x_2$ to eliminate z yields for the state-space representation for this system

$$\begin{bmatrix} \dot{x}_1 \\ \dot{x}_2 \\ \dot{x}_3 \end{bmatrix} = \begin{bmatrix} -5 & 2 & 1 \\ 0 & 0 & 1 \\ -1 & -4 & -3 \end{bmatrix} \begin{bmatrix} x_1 \\ x_2 \\ x_3 \end{bmatrix} + \begin{bmatrix} 0 \\ 0 \\ 1 \end{bmatrix} u$$

The output relationship is

$$c = x_1$$

Note that the preceding equations have the general form given by Eqs. (9.20) and (9.21).

A system which has one input u and one output c is referred to as a single-input–single-output system. A system with more than one input is a multiple-input system, and a system with more than one output is a multiple-output system. A system with more than one input and more than one output is a multiple-input–multiple-output system. Matrix methods lend themselves to the analysis of such systems. The system shown in Fig. 9.7 has two inputs and two outputs. The equation for each of the state variables is

$$\frac{x_1}{e_1} = \frac{1}{D+1} \qquad \frac{x_2}{x_3} = \frac{1}{D+2} \qquad \frac{x_3}{e_2} = \frac{1}{D}$$

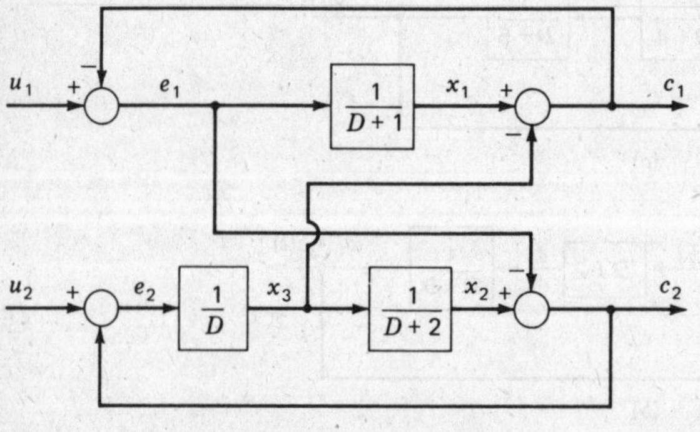

Figure 9.7 Multiple-input–multiple-output system.

Thus

$$\dot{x}_1 = -x_1 + e_1$$

$$\dot{x}_2 = -2x_2 + x_3$$

$$\dot{x}_3 = e_2$$

The equations for e_1 and e_2 are

$$e_1 = u_1 - c_1 = u_1 - (x_1 - x_3) = -x_1 + x_3 + u_1$$

$$\begin{aligned} e_2 &= u_2 - c_2 = u_2 - (x_2 - e_1) = u_2 - x_2 + (-x_1 + x_3 + u_1) \\ &= -x_1 - x_2 + x_3 + u_1 + u_2 \end{aligned}$$

Substituting e_1 and e_2 into the system equations and expressing the result in matrix form gives

$$\begin{bmatrix} \dot{x}_1 \\ \dot{x}_2 \\ \dot{x}_3 \end{bmatrix} = \begin{bmatrix} -2 & 0 & 1 \\ 0 & -2 & 1 \\ -1 & -1 & 1 \end{bmatrix} \begin{bmatrix} x_1 \\ x_2 \\ x_3 \end{bmatrix} + \begin{bmatrix} 1 & 0 \\ 0 & 0 \\ 1 & 1 \end{bmatrix} \begin{bmatrix} u_1 \\ u_2 \end{bmatrix}$$

The output relationships are

$$c_1 = x_1 - x_3$$

$$c_2 = x_2 - e_1 = -x_1 + x_2 + x_3 + u_1$$

The corresponding matrix form is

$$\begin{bmatrix} c_1 \\ c_2 \end{bmatrix} = \begin{bmatrix} 1 & 0 & -1 \\ -1 & 1 & 1 \end{bmatrix} \begin{bmatrix} x_1 \\ x_2 \\ x_3 \end{bmatrix} + \begin{bmatrix} 0 & 0 \\ 1 & 0 \end{bmatrix} \begin{bmatrix} u_1 \\ u_2 \end{bmatrix}$$

The general matrix representation for a multiple-input–multiple-output system is

$$\dot{\mathbf{x}} = A\mathbf{x} + B\mathbf{u} \tag{9.22}$$

The general output relationship is

$$\mathbf{c} = D\mathbf{x} + E\mathbf{u} \tag{9.23}$$

The block-diagram representation for these matrix relationships is shown in Fig. 9.8. The portion enclosed by the dashed box is the system equation. The remaining portion is the output relationship. The double-width arrows represent more than one variable. For the case of a single input u, B becomes the column matrix $\mathbf{b}$ and E becomes the column matrix $\mathbf{e}$. For the case of a single output c, D becomes $\mathbf{d}^T$. For the usual case in which there is no feedforward path from the input $\mathbf{u}$ to the output, the E term in Eq. (9.23) vanishes. Thus, most systems can be represented in the form given by Eqs. (9.20) and (9.21), in which $\mathbf{b}$ is replaced by B for multiple-input systems and $\mathbf{d}^T$ is replaced by D for multiple-output systems.

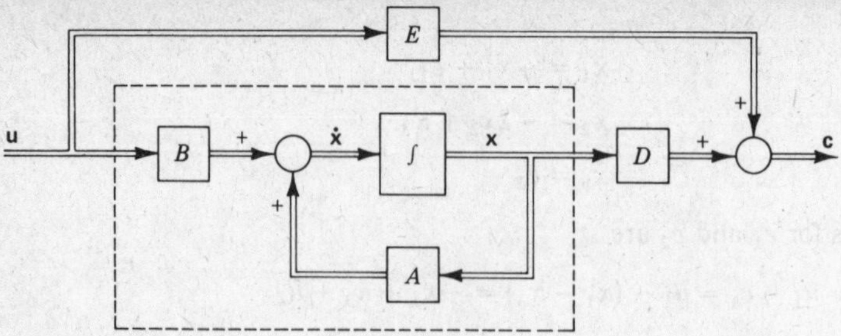

Figure 9.8 General state-space representation for a system.

9.2 SIGNAL FLOW GRAPHS

A signal flow graph is a diagram which may be used to represent a control system. The signal-flow-graph representation for a system appears to be quite similar to the block-diagram representation. However, there are important differences. For more complex systems, the signal flow graph is easier to construct than the block diagram. System equations are more readily obtained from the signal flow graph than from the block diagram.

The left side of Fig. 9.9 shows the block-diagram representation, and the right side shows the equivalent signal flow diagram. Each small circle in a signal flow diagram is called a node, which is a point that represents a variable or signal. The directed line segment joining two nodes is called a branch. The gain between two nodes is called the transmittance. In Fig. 9.9*a*, the variable x_1 is multiplied by the transmittance a to yield the output x_2 (i.e., $x_2 = ax_1$). In Fig. 9.9*b*, the output x_2 is the sum of ax_1 and bx_1 (i.e., $x_2 = ax_1 + bx_1$). In Fig. 9.9*c*, the signal x_3 is the sum of ax_1 and bx_2. In Fig. 9.9*d*, the signal x_2 is $ax_1 - cx_3$, and the signal x_3 is bx_2.

As is illustrated in Fig. 9.10*a*, the upper branch with a transmittance a and the lower branch with a transmittance b may be combined into one branch with a transmittance $a + b$ [note that $x_2 = ax_1 + bx_1 = (a + b)x_1$]. The equation for the left side of Fig. 9.10*b* is

$$x_3 = bx_2 = b(ax_1 - cx_3)$$

The equation for the equivalent signal flow graph shown in the middle of Fig. 9.10*b* is

$$x_3 = abx_1 - bcx_3$$

The basis for the signal flow representation shown on the right side of Fig. 9.10*b* is obtained by solving the preceding expression for x_3. That is,

$$x_3 = \frac{ab}{1 + bc} x_1$$

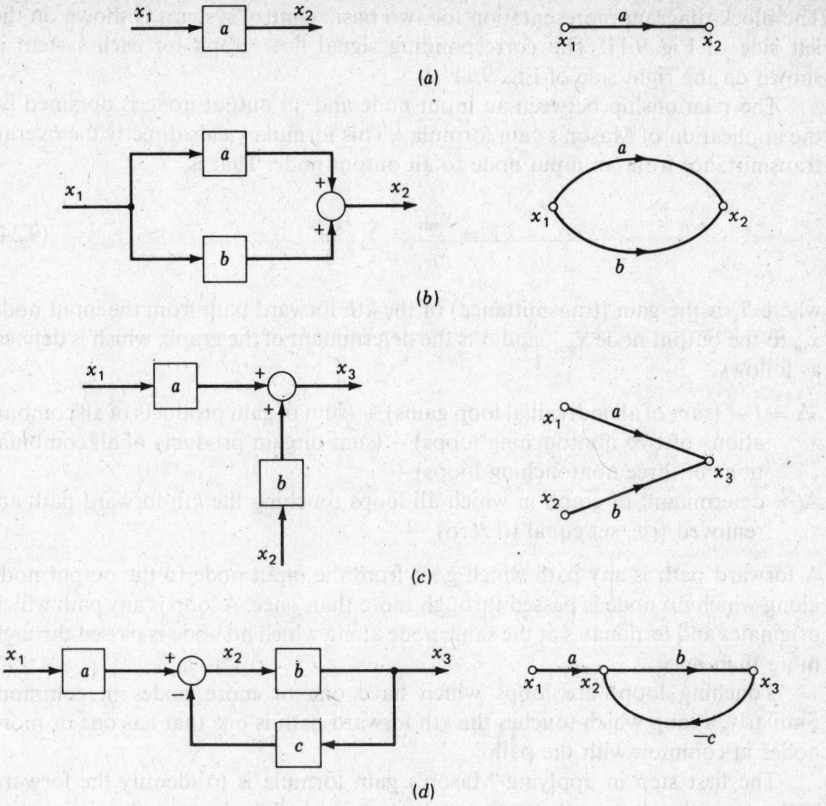

Figure 9.9 Block diagrams and corresponding signal flow graphs.

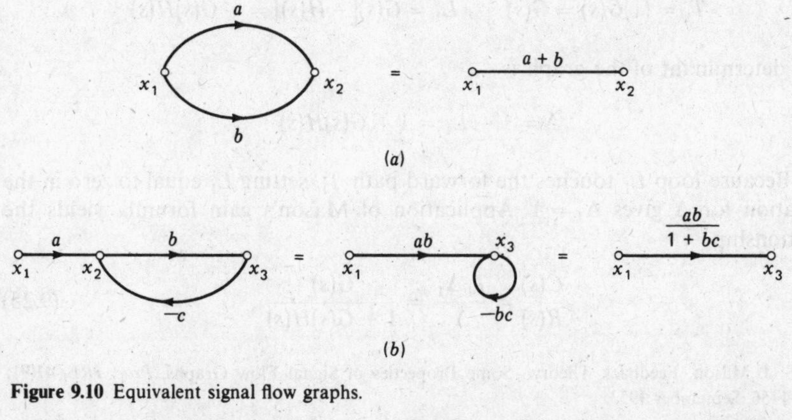

Figure 9.10 Equivalent signal flow graphs.

The block-diagram representation for two basic control systems is shown on the left side of Fig. 9.11. The corresponding signal flow graph for each system is shown on the right side of Fig. 9.11.

The relationship between an input node and an output node is obtained by the application of Mason's gain formula.[1] This formula yields directly the overall transmittance from an input node to an output node. That is,

$$T = \frac{x_{\text{out}}}{x_{\text{in}}} = \sum_k \frac{T_k \Delta_k}{\Delta} \tag{9.24}$$

where T_k is the gain (transmittance) of the kth forward path from the input node x_{in} to the output node x_{out}, and Δ is the determinant of the graph, which is defined as follows:

$\Delta = 1 -$ (sum of all individual loop gains) + (sum of gain products of all combinations of two nontouching loops) − (sum of gain products of all combinations of three nontouching loops) + $\cdots$

$\Delta_k =$ determinant of graph in which all loops touching the kth forward path are removed (i.e., set equal to zero)

A forward path is any path which goes from the input node to the output node along which no node is passed through more than once. A loop is any path which originates and terminates at the same node along which no node is passed through more than once.

Touching loops are loops which have one or more nodes in common. Similarly, a loop which touches the kth forward path is one that has one or more nodes in common with the path.

The first step in applying Mason's gain formula is to identify the forward paths, from the input node to the output node, and all the loops in the system. For the signal flow graph shown in Fig. 9.11a, there is one forward path from the input node $R(s)$ to the output node $C(s)$, and there is only one loop. Thus,

$$T_1 = (1)G(s) = G(s) \qquad L_1 = G(s)[-H(s)] = -G(s)H(s)$$

The determinant of the graph is

$$\Delta = 1 - L_1 = 1 + G(s)H(s)$$

Because loop L_1 touches the forward path T_1, setting L_1 equal to zero in the equation for Δ gives $\Delta_1 = 1$. Application of Mason's gain formula yields the relationship

$$\frac{C(s)}{R(s)} = \frac{T_1 \Delta_1}{\Delta} = \frac{G(s)}{1 + G(s)H(s)} \tag{9.25}$$

[1] S. J. Mason, Feedback Theory—Some Properties of Signal Flow Graphs, *Proc. IRE*, **41**(9): 1144–1156, September 1953.

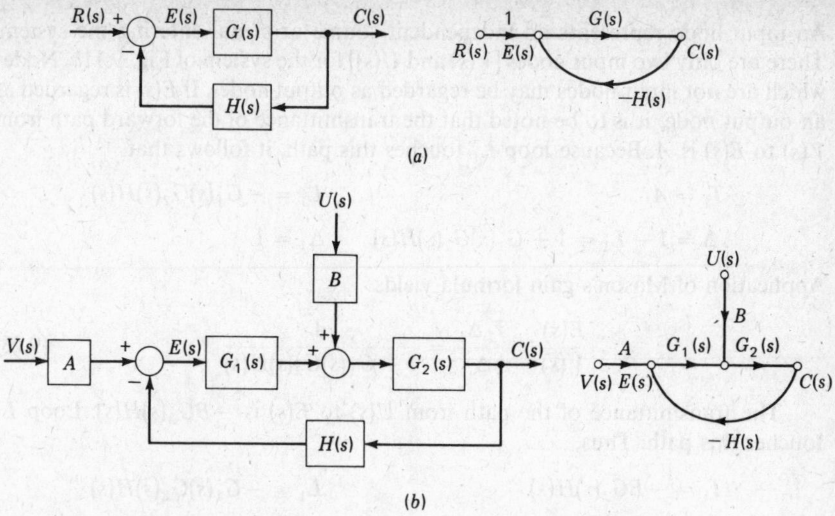

Figure 9.11 Basic systems.

For the signal flow graph of Fig. 9.11*b*, there is one forward path from the input node $V(s)$ to the output node $C(s)$, and there is only one loop. Thus,

$$T_1 = AG_1(s)G_2(s) \qquad L_1 = -G_1(s)G_2(s)H(s)$$

The determinant of the graph is

$$\Delta = 1 - L_1 = 1 + G_1(s)G_2(s)H(s)$$

Because loop L_1 touches the forward path T_1, setting L_1 equal to zero in the equation for Δ gives $\Delta_1 = 1$. Application of Mason's gain formula gives

$$\frac{C(s)}{V(s)} = \frac{T_1\Delta_1}{\Delta} = \frac{AG_1(s)G_2(s)}{1 + G_1(s)G_2(s)H(s)} \tag{9.26}$$

By regarding $U(s)$ as the input node in Fig. 9.11*b* and $C(s)$ as the output node, it follows that

$$T_1 = BG_2(s) \qquad L_1 = -G_1(s)G_2(s)H(s)$$

$$\Delta = 1 - L_1 = 1 + G_1(s)G_2(s)H(s)$$

Because the loop L_1 touches the forward path from $U(s)$ to $C(s)$, setting L_1 equal to zero in the expression for Δ yields $\Delta_1 = 1$. The overall relationship between $U(s)$ and $C(s)$ is

$$\frac{C(s)}{U(s)} = \frac{T_1\Delta_1}{\Delta} = \frac{BG_2(s)}{1 + G_1(s)G_2(s)H(s)} \tag{9.27}$$

An input node represents an independent source or signal entering the system. There are only two input nodes [$V(s)$ and $U(s)$] for the system of Fig. 9.11*b*. Nodes which are not input nodes may be regarded as output nodes. If $E(s)$ is regarded as an output node, it is to be noted that the transmittance of the forward path from $V(s)$ to $E(s)$ is A. Because loop L_1 touches this path, it follows that

$$T_1 = A \qquad L_1 = -G_1(s)G_2(s)H(s)$$

$$\Delta = 1 - L_1 = 1 + G_1(s)G_2(s)H(s) \qquad \Delta_1 = 1$$

Application of Mason's gain formula yields

$$\frac{E(s)}{V(s)} = \frac{T_1\Delta_1}{\Delta} = \frac{A}{1 + G_1(s)G_2(s)H(s)} \tag{9.28}$$

The transmittance of the path from $U(s)$ to $E(s)$ is $-BG_2(s)H(s)$. Loop L_1 touches this path. Thus,

$$T_1 = -BG_2(s)H(s) \qquad L_1 = -G_1(s)G_2(s)H(s)$$

$$\Delta = 1 - L_1 = 1 + G_1(s)G_2(s)H(s) \qquad \Delta_1 = 1$$

Application of Mason's gain formula gives

$$\frac{E(s)}{U(s)} = \frac{T_1\Delta_1}{\Delta} = -\frac{BG_2(s)H(s)}{1 + G_1(s)G_2(s)H(s)} \tag{9.29}$$

The block diagram and corresponding signal flow graph for a more complex system are shown in Fig. 9.12. There are two forward paths from the input $R(s)$ to the output $C(s)$.

$$T_1 = G_1G_2G_3G_5 \qquad T_2 = G_4G_5$$

The gains for the three loops in the system are

$$L_1 = -G_1G_2G_3G_5H_1 \qquad L_2 = -G_2H_2 \qquad L_3 = -G_4G_5H_1$$

The numbering of the forward paths and loops is arbitrary. Because L_2 and L_3 are nontouching loops,

$$\begin{aligned}\Delta &= 1 - (L_1 + L_2 + L_3) + (L_2L_3)\\ &= 1 + (G_1G_2G_3G_5H_1 + G_2H_2 + G_4G_5H_1) + G_2G_4G_5H_1H_2\end{aligned}$$

Because all three loops touch path T_1, setting $L_1 = L_2 = L_3 = 0$ in the preceding expression for Δ gives $\Delta_1 = 1$. Because loops L_1 and L_3 touch path T_2, setting $L_1 = L_3 = 0$ in the expression for Δ gives $\Delta_2 = 1 - L_2 = 1 + G_2H_2$. Substitution of these results into Mason's gain formula yields

$$\frac{C(s)}{R(s)} = \frac{T_1\Delta_1 + T_2\Delta_2}{\Delta} = \frac{(G_1G_2G_3G_5) + (G_4G_5)(1 + G_2H_2)}{1 + (G_1G_2G_3 + G_4 + G_2G_4H_2)G_5H_1 + G_2H_2} \tag{9.30}$$

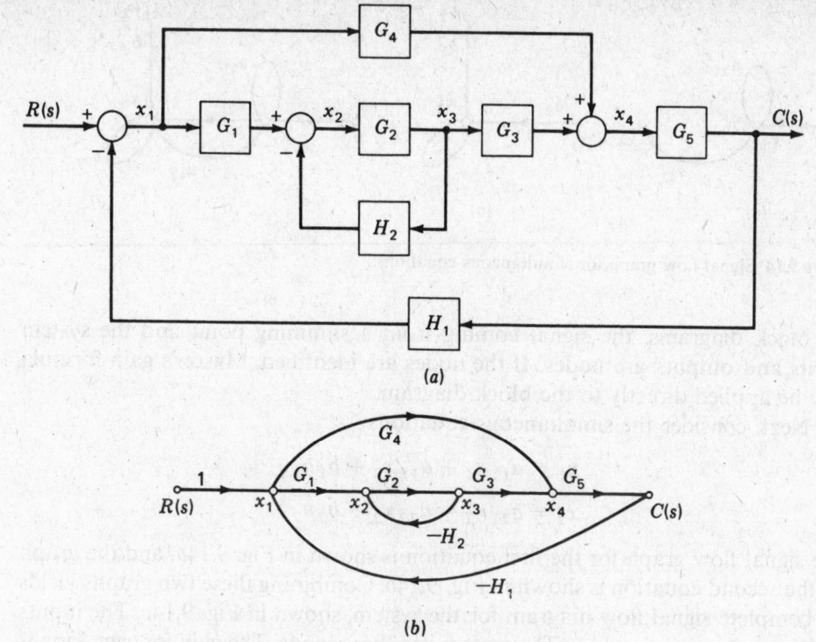

Figure 9.12 Block diagram and corresponding signal flow graph.

The signal flow graph corresponding to the block diagram of Fig. 9.3 is shown in Fig. 9.13. The symbol $D^{-1} = 1/D$ indicates integration. There are two loops, $L_1 = -3D^{-1}$ and $L_2 = -2D^{-2}$. Because there are no nontouching loops,

$$\Delta = 1 - (L_1 + L_2) = 1 + (3D^{-1} + 2D^{-2})$$

There are two forward paths from the input node $f(t)$ to the output node $c(t)$. The transmittance of the paths is $T_1 = D^{-1}$ and $T_2 = 3D^{-2}$, respectively. Each forward path touches both loops, so that $\Delta_1 = \Delta_2 = 1$. Application of Mason's gain formula gives

$$c(t) = \frac{T_1\Delta_1 + T_2\Delta_2}{\Delta} f(t) = \frac{D^{-1} + 3D^{-2}}{1 + 3D^{-1} + 2D^{-2}} f(t) = \frac{(D+3)}{D^2 + 3D + 2} f(t) \tag{9.1}$$

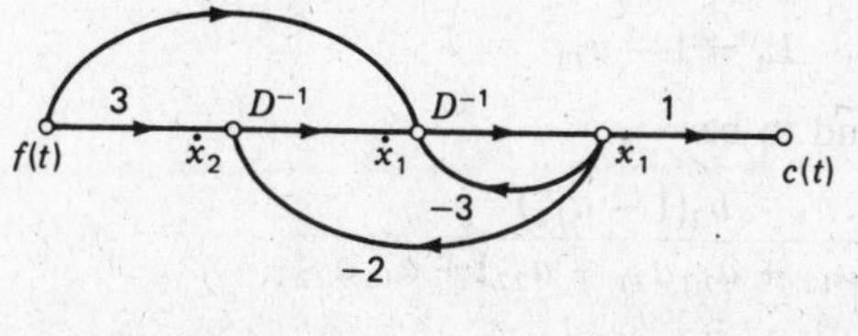

Figure 9.13 Signal flow graph.

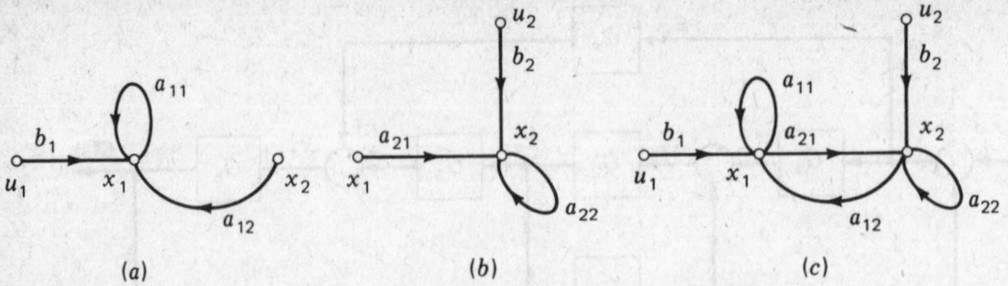

Figure 9.14 Signal flow graph for simultaneous equations.

On block diagrams, the signal coming from a summing point and the system inputs and outputs are nodes. If the nodes are identified, Mason's gain formula may be applied directly to the block diagram.

Next, consider the simultaneous equations

$$x_1 = a_{11}x_1 + a_{12}x_2 + b_1u_1$$

$$x_2 = a_{21}x_1 + a_{22}x_2 + b_2u_2$$

The signal flow graph for the first equation is shown in Fig. 9.14*a*, and the graph for the second equation is shown in Fig. 9.14*b*. Combining these two graphs yields the complete signal flow diagram for the system, shown in Fig. 9.14*c*. The inputs to the system are u_1 and u_2. The system has three loops. The gain for each loop is

$$L_1 = a_{11} \qquad L_2 = a_{12}a_{21} \qquad L_3 = a_{22}$$

To obtain the equation relating u_1 and x_2, first note that there is only one forward path from u_1 to x_2. The gain of this path is

$$T_1 = b_1a_{21}$$

The loops L_1 and L_3 are nontouching. Thus, the determinant for the system is

$$\Delta = 1 - (L_1 + L_2 + L_3) + (L_1L_3) = 1 - (a_{11} + a_{12}a_{21} + a_{22}) + a_{11}a_{22}$$

Because all three loops touch the forward path, $\Delta_1 = 1$. Application of Mason's gain formula yields

$$\frac{x_2}{u_1} = \frac{T_1\Delta_1}{\Delta} = \frac{b_1a_{21}}{1 - (a_{11} + a_{12}a_{21} + a_{22}) + a_{11}a_{22}}$$

To obtain the equation relating u_2 and x_2, first note that there is only one forward path from u_2 to x_2. The gain of this path is $T_1 = b_2$. Because loops L_2 and L_3 touch this path, setting $L_2 = L_3 = 0$ in the equation for Δ gives

$$\Delta_1 = 1 - L_1 = 1 - a_{11}$$

The overall relationship is now found to be

$$\frac{x_2}{u_2} = \frac{T_1\Delta_1}{\Delta} = \frac{b_2(1 - a_{11})}{1 - (a_{11} + a_{12}a_{21} + a_{22}) + a_{11}a_{22}}$$

The gain of the forward path from u_1 to x_1 is $T_1 = b_1$. Because loops L_1 and L_2 touch this path, setting $L_1 = L_2 = 0$ in the equation for Δ gives

$$\Delta_1 = 1 - L_3 = 1 - a_{22}$$

Application of Mason's gain formula shows that

$$\frac{x_1}{u_1} = \frac{T_1\Delta_1}{\Delta} = \frac{b_1(1 - a_{22})}{1 - (a_{11} + a_{12}a_{21} + a_{22}) + a_{11}a_{22}}$$

The gain of the forward path from u_2 to x_1 is $T_1 = a_{12}b_2$. Because all loops touch this forward path, $\Delta_1 = 1$. Thus it is found that

$$\frac{x_1}{u_2} = \frac{a_{12}b_2}{1 - (a_{11} + a_{12}a_{21} + a_{22}) + a_{11}a_{22}}$$

Signal flow graphs provide the basis for many powerful techniques employed in the design of control systems.

9.3 LINEAR ALGEBRA

One of the most powerful features of matrix methods is that they lend themselves to computer solution. To gain a deeper insight into the nature of matrix methods, it is necessary to investigate analytical techniques and procedures for solving differential equations in matrix form. Thus, consider the system of n first-order differential equations:

$$\begin{aligned}
\dot{x}_1 &= a_{11}x_1 + a_{12}x_2 + \cdots + a_{1n}x_n \\
\dot{x}_2 &= a_{21}x_1 + a_{22}x_2 + \cdots + a_{2n}x_n \\
&\cdots\cdots\cdots\cdots\cdots\cdots\cdots\cdots \\
\dot{x}_n &= a_{n1}x_1 + a_{n2}x_2 + \cdots + a_{nn}x_n
\end{aligned} \tag{9.31}$$

The corresponding matrix representation is

$$\dot{\mathbf{x}} = A\mathbf{x} \tag{9.32}$$

where $\mathbf{x} = \begin{bmatrix} x_1 \\ x_2 \\ \vdots \\ x_n \end{bmatrix} \qquad A = \begin{bmatrix} a_{11} & a_{12} & \cdots & a_{1n} \\ a_{21} & a_{22} & \cdots & a_{2n} \\ \cdots & \cdots & \cdots & \cdots \\ a_{n1} & a_{n2} & \cdots & a_{nn} \end{bmatrix}$

The solution of this system is simplified considerably if a matrix P can be determined such that the transformation $\mathbf{x} = P\mathbf{y}$ transforms the preceding system into the form

$$\begin{aligned}
\dot{y}_1 &= \lambda_1 y_1 + 0 + \cdots + 0 \\
\dot{y}_2 &= 0 + \lambda_2 y_2 + \cdots + 0 \\
&\cdots\cdots\cdots\cdots\cdots\cdots \\
\dot{y}_n &= 0 + 0 + \cdots + \lambda_n y_n
\end{aligned}$$

This is called the canonical, or normal, form. The corresponding matrix representation is

$$\dot{\mathbf{y}} = \Lambda \mathbf{y} \tag{9.33}$$

where

$$\mathbf{y} = \begin{bmatrix} y_1 \\ y_2 \\ \vdots \\ y_n \end{bmatrix} \qquad \Lambda = \begin{bmatrix} \lambda_1 & 0 & \cdots & 0 \\ 0 & \lambda_2 & \cdots & 0 \\ \cdots & \cdots & \cdots & \cdots \\ 0 & 0 & \cdots & \lambda_n \end{bmatrix}$$

The matrix Λ is called the lambda matrix. To determine P, first note that Eq. (9.31) is satisfied by

$$x_1 = c_1 e^{\lambda t}$$
$$x_2 = c_2 e^{\lambda t}$$
$$x_n = c_n e^{\lambda t}$$

Substituting these values for $x_1, x_2, \ldots, x_n$ into Eq. (9.31) yields

$$\begin{aligned} c_1 \lambda e^{\lambda t} &= a_{11} c_1 e^{\lambda t} + a_{12} c_2 e^{\lambda t} + \cdots + a_{1n} c_n e^{\lambda t} \\ c_2 \lambda e^{\lambda t} &= a_{21} c_1 e^{\lambda t} + a_{22} c_2 e^{\lambda t} + \cdots + a_{2n} c_n e^{\lambda t} \\ &\cdots\cdots\cdots\cdots \\ c_n \lambda e^{\lambda t} &= a_{n1} c_1 e^{\lambda t} + a_{n2} c_2 e^{\lambda t} + \cdots + a_{nn} c_n e^{\lambda t} \end{aligned}$$

Canceling the $e^{\lambda t}$ factor and rearranging gives

$$\begin{aligned} (a_{11} - \lambda) c_1 + a_{12} c_2 + \cdots + a_{1n} c_n &= 0 \\ a_{21} c_1 + (a_{22} - \lambda) c_2 + \cdots + a_{2n} c_n &= 0 \\ \cdots\cdots\cdots\cdots \\ a_{n1} c_1 + a_{n2} c_2 + \cdots + (a_{nn} - \lambda) c_n &= 0 \end{aligned}$$

Application of Cramer's rule to determine $c_1, c_2, \ldots, c_n$ reveals that nontrivial solutions occur if, and only if,

$$\begin{vmatrix} (a_{11} - \lambda) & a_{12} & \cdots & a_{1n} \\ a_{21} & (a_{22} - \lambda) & \cdots & a_{2n} \\ \cdots & \cdots & \cdots & \cdots \\ a_{n1} & a_{n2} & \cdots & (a_{nn} - \lambda) \end{vmatrix} = 0 \tag{9.34}$$

The matrix representation for the preceding determinant is

$$|A - \lambda I| = 0 \tag{9.35}$$

In evaluating this determinant, an nth-order polynomial in λ results. This polynomial is the characteristic equation for the system. The roots of the characteristic equation are the n values of λ for which the characteristic equation vanishes. These

n values, which are designated $(\lambda_1, \lambda_2, \ldots, \lambda_n)$, are called the eigenvalues for the system. For $\lambda = \lambda_i$, Eq. (9.34) becomes

$$\begin{vmatrix} (a_{11}-\lambda_i) & a_{12} & \cdots & a_{1n} \\ a_{21} & (a_{22}-\lambda_i) & \cdots & a_{2n} \\ \cdots & \cdots & \cdots & \cdots \\ a_{n1} & a_{n2} & \cdots & (a_{nn}-\lambda_i) \end{vmatrix} = 0$$

By designating the cofactors of the first row as $A_{1i}, A_{2i}, \ldots, A_{ni}$, the preceding determinant may be expressed in terms of its first-row expansion. That is,

$$(a_{11}-\lambda_i)A_{1i} + a_{12}A_{2i} + \cdots + a_{1n}A_{ni} = 0$$

or

$$a_{11}A_{1i} + a_{12}A_{2i} + \cdots + a_{1n}A_{ni} = \lambda_i A_{1i}$$

If the first row is replaced by the mth row (the first row is now identical to the mth row), the value of the determinant is still zero. The new first-row expansion is

$$a_{m1}A_{1i} + a_{m2}A_{2i} + \cdots + (a_{mm}-\lambda_i)A_{mi} + \cdots + a_{mn}A_{ni} = 0$$

or

$$a_{m1}A_{1i} + a_{m2}A_{2i} + \cdots + a_{mm}A_{mi} + \cdots + a_{mn}A_{ni} = \lambda_i A_{mi} \tag{9.36}$$

Application of the transformation $\mathbf{x} = P\mathbf{y}$ to Eq. (9.32) shows that

$$\dot{\mathbf{x}} = A\mathbf{x} = AP\mathbf{y}$$

If P is taken as the matrix

$$P = \begin{bmatrix} A_{11} & A_{12} & \cdots & A_{1n} \\ A_{21} & A_{22} & \cdots & A_{2n} \\ \cdots & \cdots & \cdots & \cdots \\ A_{n1} & A_{n2} & \cdots & A_{nn} \end{bmatrix} \tag{9.37}$$

then the product AP is

$$AP = \begin{bmatrix} a_{11} & a_{12} & \cdots & a_{1n} \\ \cdots & \cdots & \cdots & \cdots \\ a_{m1} & a_{m2} & \cdots & a_{mn} \\ \cdots & \cdots & \cdots & \cdots \\ a_{n1} & a_{n2} & \cdots & a_{nn} \end{bmatrix} \begin{bmatrix} A_{11} & \cdots & A_{1i} & \cdots & A_{1n} \\ A_{21} & \cdots & A_{2i} & \cdots & A_{2n} \\ \cdots & \cdots & \cdots & \cdots & \cdots \\ A_{n1} & \cdots & A_{ni} & \cdots & A_{nn} \end{bmatrix}$$

The product of the mth row of the A matrix and the ith column of the P matrix is the left side of Eq. (9.36), which is equal to $\lambda_i A_{mi}$. The resulting product AP may thus be written in the form

$$AP = \begin{bmatrix} \lambda_1 A_{11} & \cdots & \lambda_i A_{1i} & \cdots & \lambda_n A_{1n} \\ \cdots & \cdots & \cdots & \cdots & \cdots \\ \lambda_1 A_{m1} & \cdots & \lambda_i A_{mi} & \cdots & \lambda_n A_{mn} \\ \cdots & \cdots & \cdots & \cdots & \cdots \\ \lambda_1 A_{n1} & \cdots & \lambda_i A_{ni} & \cdots & \lambda_n A_{nn} \end{bmatrix} = \begin{bmatrix} \lambda_1 A_{11} & \lambda_2 A_{12} & \cdots & \lambda_n A_{1n} \\ \lambda_1 A_{21} & \lambda_2 A_{22} & \cdots & \lambda_n A_{2n} \\ \cdots & \cdots & \cdots & \cdots \\ \lambda_1 A_{n1} & \lambda_2 A_{n2} & \cdots & \lambda_n A_{nn} \end{bmatrix}$$

$$= \begin{bmatrix} A_{11} & A_{12} & \cdots & A_{1n} \\ A_{21} & A_{22} & \cdots & A_{2n} \\ \cdots & \cdots & \cdots & \cdots \\ A_{n1} & A_{n2} & \cdots & A_{nn} \end{bmatrix} \begin{bmatrix} \lambda_1 & 0 & \cdots & 0 \\ 0 & \lambda_2 & \cdots & 0 \\ \cdots & \cdots & \cdots & \cdots \\ 0 & 0 & \cdots & \lambda_n \end{bmatrix}$$

$$= \quad P\Lambda$$

Multiplying through by P^{-1} reveals that

$$P^{-1}AP = \Lambda \tag{9.38}$$

The substitution of $\mathbf{x} = P\mathbf{y}$ and $\dot{\mathbf{x}} = P\dot{\mathbf{y}}$ into Eq. (9.32) gives

$$P\dot{\mathbf{y}} = AP\mathbf{y}$$

Premultiplying by P^{-1} shows that

$$\dot{\mathbf{y}} = P^{-1}AP\mathbf{y} = \Lambda\mathbf{y} \tag{9.39}$$

Thus, the matrix P as given by Eq. (9.37) is the desired matrix which transforms Eq. (9.31) to the canonical form.

Illustrative example 1 Use direct programming to determine the solution of the following differential equation for the case in which $f(t) = 0$ and the initial conditions are $c_0 = 1$ and $\dot{c}_0 = 0$.

$$\ddot{c} + 5\dot{c} + 6c = f(t) \tag{9.40}$$

The solution when the right side is zero $[f(t) = 0]$ is called the force-free response. The next section shows that the methods used to obtain the force-free response can be readily extended to determine the response when $f(t)$ is not zero (i.e., the forced response).

SOLUTION For direct programming, $c = x_1$ and $\dot{c} = \dot{x}_1 = x_2$. The resulting state-space representation for the differential equation is

$$\dot{x}_1 = x_2$$

$$\dot{x}_2 = -6x_1 - 5x_2$$

The corresponding matrix representation is

$$\begin{bmatrix} \dot{x}_1 \\ \dot{x}_2 \end{bmatrix} = \begin{bmatrix} 0 & 1 \\ -6 & -5 \end{bmatrix} \begin{bmatrix} x_1 \\ x_2 \end{bmatrix}$$

The characteristic equation for this system is

$$|A - \lambda I| = \left|\begin{bmatrix} 0 & 1 \\ -6 & -5 \end{bmatrix} - \begin{bmatrix} \lambda & 0 \\ 0 & \lambda \end{bmatrix}\right| = \begin{vmatrix} -\lambda & 1 \\ -6 & -5-\lambda \end{vmatrix}$$

$$= \lambda^2 + 5\lambda + 6 = (\lambda + 2)(\lambda + 3) = 0$$

Thus, the eigenvalues for this system are $\lambda_1 = -2$ and $\lambda_2 = -3$. For $\lambda_1 = -2$, the determinant becomes

$$|A - \lambda_1 I| = \begin{vmatrix} 0+2 & 1 \\ -6 & -5+2 \end{vmatrix} = \begin{vmatrix} 2 & 1 \\ -6 & -3 \end{vmatrix}$$

The cofactors for the first row are $A_{11} = -3$ and $A_{21} = 6$. Similarly, for $\lambda_2 = -3$, it is found that $A_{12} = -2$ and $A_{22} = 6$. The P matrix corresponding to Eq. (9.37) is

$$P = \begin{bmatrix} -3 & -2 \\ 6 & 6 \end{bmatrix} \tag{9.41}$$

The inverse P^{-1} is

$$P^{-1} = \begin{bmatrix} -1 & -\frac{1}{3} \\ 1 & \frac{1}{2} \end{bmatrix} \tag{9.42}$$

Evaluation of $\Lambda = P^{-1}AP$ verifies that P is such that the eigenvalues are displayed on the diagonal. That is,

$$\Lambda = \begin{bmatrix} -2 & 0 \\ 0 & -3 \end{bmatrix}$$

The canonical form $\dot{\mathbf{y}} = \Lambda\mathbf{y}$ of the differential equation is

$$\begin{bmatrix} \dot{y}_1 \\ \dot{y}_2 \end{bmatrix} = \begin{bmatrix} -2 & 0 \\ 0 & -3 \end{bmatrix}\begin{bmatrix} y_1 \\ y_2 \end{bmatrix}$$

The corresponding differential equations are

$$\dot{y}_1 + 2y_1 = 0 \qquad \text{and} \qquad \dot{y}_2 + 3y_2 = 0$$

The general solution of these canonical differential equations is

$$y_1 = C_1 e^{-2t} \qquad \text{and} \qquad y_2 = C_2 e^{-3t}$$

To evaluate C_1 and C_2, it is necessary to know the initial conditions in terms of y_1 and y_2. Because $\mathbf{x} = P\mathbf{y}$, then $\mathbf{y} = P^{-1}\mathbf{x}$. Thus,

$$\begin{bmatrix} y_1 \\ y_2 \end{bmatrix} = \begin{bmatrix} -1 & -\frac{1}{3} \\ 1 & \frac{1}{2} \end{bmatrix}\begin{bmatrix} x_1 \\ x_2 \end{bmatrix}$$

Evaluation at time $t = 0$ gives

$$y_1(0) = -x_1(0) - \frac{x_2(0)}{3} = -1$$

$$y_2(0) = x_1(0) + \frac{x_2(0)}{2} = 1$$

where $x_1(0) = c_0 = 1$ and $x_2(0) = \dot{c}_0 = 0$. Evaluation of y_1 and y_2 at time $t = 0$ shows that $C_1 = -1$ and $C_2 = 1$. Thus

$$y_1 = -e^{-2t} \qquad \text{and} \qquad y_2 = e^{-3t}$$

The desired result is now obtained by using the relationship $\mathbf{x} = P\mathbf{y}$ to transform the solution from the canonical form back to the original form.

$$\begin{bmatrix} x_1 \\ x_2 \end{bmatrix} = \begin{bmatrix} -3 & -2 \\ 6 & 6 \end{bmatrix} \begin{bmatrix} y_1 \\ y_2 \end{bmatrix}$$

Thus,

$$\begin{aligned} c = x_1 &= -3y_1 - 2y_2 = 3e^{-2t} - 2e^{-3t} \\ \dot{c} = x_2 &= 6y_1 + 6y_2 = -6e^{-2t} + 6e^{-3t} \end{aligned} \tag{9.43}$$

It is to be noted that $\dot{c}$ could also have been obtained by differentiating c.

Forced Response

In the general form given by Eq. (9.31), there is no forcing function $f(t)$. This is referred to as the force-free case. The general state-space representation for a system excited by a forcing function $f(t)$ is

$$\begin{aligned} \dot{x}_1 &= a_{11}x_1 + a_{12}x_2 + \cdots + a_{1n}x_n + b_1 f(t) \\ \dot{x}_2 &= a_{21}x_1 + a_{22}x_2 + \cdots + a_{2n}x_n + b_2 f(t) \\ &\cdots\cdots\cdots\cdots\cdots\cdots\cdots\cdots\cdots\cdots \\ \dot{x}_n &= a_{n1}x_1 + a_{n2}x_2 + \cdots + a_{nn}x_n + b_n f(t) \end{aligned}$$

The corresponding matrix form is

$$\dot{\mathbf{x}} = A\mathbf{x} + \mathbf{b}f(t) \tag{9.20}$$

where

$$\mathbf{x} = \begin{bmatrix} x_1 \\ x_2 \\ \vdots \\ x_n \end{bmatrix} \qquad A = \begin{bmatrix} a_{11} & a_{12} & \cdots & a_{1n} \\ a_{21} & a_{22} & \cdots & a_{2n} \\ \vdots & \vdots & & \vdots \\ a_{n1} & a_{n2} & \cdots & a_{nn} \end{bmatrix} \qquad \mathbf{b} = \begin{bmatrix} b_1 \\ b_2 \\ \vdots \\ b_n \end{bmatrix}$$

The transformation $\mathbf{x} = P\mathbf{y}$ transforms this system into the form

$$P\dot{\mathbf{y}} = AP\mathbf{y} + \mathbf{b}f(t)$$

Premultiplying by the inverse P^{-1} shows that

$$\dot{\mathbf{y}} = P^{-1}AP\mathbf{y} + P^{-1}\mathbf{b}f(t) = \Lambda\mathbf{y} + P^{-1}\mathbf{b}f(t) \tag{9.44}$$

This is the desired canonical form.

Illustrative example 2 Use direct programming to determine the solution of the differential equation

$$\ddot{c} + 5\dot{c} + 6c = f(t) \tag{9.40}$$

The forcing function $f(t)$ is a step function of height $h = 6$, and all the initial conditions are zero.

SOLUTION For direct programming, $c = x_1$ and $\dot{c} = \dot{x}_1 = x_2$. The resulting state-space representation for the differential equation is

$$\begin{bmatrix} \dot{x}_1 \\ \dot{x}_2 \end{bmatrix} = \begin{bmatrix} 0 & 1 \\ -6 & -5 \end{bmatrix} \begin{bmatrix} x_1 \\ x_2 \end{bmatrix} + \begin{bmatrix} 0 \\ 1 \end{bmatrix} f(t)$$

The A matrix is the same as for Illustrative Example 1. Thus, the P and P^{-1} matrices for Illustrative Example 1, given by Eqs. (9.41) and (9.42), are also applicable here. The product $P^{-1}\mathbf{b}$ is

$$\begin{bmatrix} -1 & -\frac{1}{3} \\ 1 & \frac{1}{2} \end{bmatrix} \begin{bmatrix} 0 \\ 1 \end{bmatrix} = \begin{bmatrix} -\frac{1}{3} \\ \frac{1}{2} \end{bmatrix}$$

The canonical form $\dot{\mathbf{y}} = \Lambda\mathbf{y} + P^{-1}\mathbf{b}f(t)$ for this system is

$$\begin{bmatrix} \dot{y}_1 \\ \dot{y}_2 \end{bmatrix} = \begin{bmatrix} -2 & 0 \\ 0 & -3 \end{bmatrix} \begin{bmatrix} y_1 \\ y_2 \end{bmatrix} + \begin{bmatrix} -\frac{1}{3} \\ \frac{1}{2} \end{bmatrix} f(t)$$

The corresponding differential equations are

$$\dot{y}_1 + 2y_1 = -\tfrac{1}{3}f(t)$$

$$\dot{y}_2 + 3y_2 = \tfrac{1}{2}f(t)$$

The initial conditions in terms of $\mathbf{x}$ are $x_1(0) = c_0 = 0$ and $x_2(0) = \dot{c}_0 = 0$. Because the initial conditions in terms of $\mathbf{x}$ are zero, the initial conditions in terms of $\mathbf{y}$ ($\mathbf{y} = P^{-1}\mathbf{x}$) are also zero. For $f(t) = 6$, the general solution of the canonical differential equations is

$$y_1 = C_1e^{-2t} - 1$$

$$y_2 = C_2e^{-3t} + 1$$

Evaluation at $t = 0$, in which case $y_1(0) = y_2(0) = 0$, shows that $C_1 = 1$ and $C_2 = -1$. Thus,

$$y_1 = -(1 - e^{-2t})$$

$$y_2 = 1 - e^{-3t}$$

The desired solution is now obtained by transforming $\mathbf{x} = P\mathbf{y}$ back to the original state variables. Thus,

$$c = x_1 = -3y_1 - 2y_2 = 3(1 - e^{-2t}) - 2(1 - e^{-3t}) = 1 - 3e^{-2t} + 2e^{-3t}$$

$$\dot{c} = x_2 = 6y_1 + 6y_2 = -6(1 - e^{-2t}) + 6(1 - e^{-3t}) = 6e^{-2t} - 6e^{-3t} \qquad (9.45)$$

Alternative Forms of the P and P^{-1} Matrices

When each element of the ith column of a P matrix is multiplied by a constant and each element of the ith row of the inverse P^{-1} is divided by the same constant, the new P and P^{-1} matrices retain the property that $P^{-1}AP = \Lambda$. Any consistent set of P and P^{-1} matrices may be used in solving differential equations by matrix methods. The essential property is that the matrices be such that $P^{-1}AP = \Lambda$.

The P and P^{-1} matrices given by Eqs. (9.41) and (9.42) are

$$P = \begin{bmatrix} -3 & -2 \\ 6 & 6 \end{bmatrix} \qquad \text{and} \qquad P^{-1} = \begin{bmatrix} -1 & -\frac{1}{3} \\ 1 & \frac{1}{2} \end{bmatrix}$$

If the first column of P is multiplied by $-\frac{1}{3}$ and the second column is multiplied by $\frac{1}{2}$, then to retain a consistent set of matrices the first row of P^{-1} must be divided by $-\frac{1}{3}$ and the second row must be divided by $\frac{1}{2}$. The resulting matrices are

$$P = \begin{bmatrix} 1 & -1 \\ -2 & 3 \end{bmatrix} \qquad \text{and} \qquad P^{-1} = \begin{bmatrix} 3 & 1 \\ 2 & 1 \end{bmatrix}$$

For either set, $P^{-1}AP = \Lambda$.

Partial-Fraction Method

This is a simple algebraic procedure which yields directly a consistent set of P and P^{-1} matrices. To illustrate this technique, consider the differential equation of Illustrative Examples 1 and 2; that is

$$\ddot{c} + 5\dot{c} + 6c = (D^2 + 5D + 6)c = f(t) \qquad (9.40)$$

The general canonical form is $\mathbf{y} = \Lambda\mathbf{y} + P^{-1}\mathbf{b}f(t)$. For distinct roots, the Λ matrix displays the eigenvalues on the principal diagonal. In Sec. 9.8, it is proved that the eigenvalues are the roots of the characteristic equation. Because each row of P^{-1} may be multiplied by an arbitrary constant, it is convenient to select the $P^{-1}\mathbf{b}$ matrix such that each element is unity. The resulting canonical form for the preceding differential equation is

$$\begin{bmatrix} \dot{y}_1 \\ \dot{y}_2 \end{bmatrix} = \begin{bmatrix} -2 & 0 \\ 0 & -3 \end{bmatrix} \begin{bmatrix} y_1 \\ y_2 \end{bmatrix} + \begin{bmatrix} 1 \\ 1 \end{bmatrix} f(t) \qquad (9.46)$$

The corresponding differential equations are

$$\dot{y}_1 + 2y_1 = f(t)$$

$$\dot{y}_2 + 3y_2 = f(t)$$

The operator form of these differential equations is

$$y_1 = \frac{f(t)}{D+2} \qquad y_2 = \frac{f(t)}{D+3}$$

Illustrative Examples 1 and 2 employed direct programming for which $c(t) = x_1$ and $\dot{c}(t) = \dot{x}_1 = x_2$. To obtain the $\mathbf{x} = P\mathbf{y}$ relationship, first express x_1 in terms of its partial fraction expansion. That is,

$$x_1 = \frac{f(t)}{(D+2)(D+3)} = \left[\frac{1}{D+2} - \frac{1}{D+3}\right] f(t) = y_1 - y_2 \tag{9.47}$$

Application of the matrix relationship $x_2 = \dot{x}_1$ gives

$$x_2 = \dot{x}_1 = \dot{y}_1 - \dot{y}_2 = [f(t) - 2y_1] - [f(t) - 3y_2] = -2y_1 + 3y_2$$

The matrix form $\mathbf{x} = P\mathbf{y}$ for these relationships is

$$\begin{bmatrix} x_1 \\ x_2 \end{bmatrix} = \begin{bmatrix} 1 & -1 \\ -2 & 3 \end{bmatrix} \begin{bmatrix} y_1 \\ y_2 \end{bmatrix}$$

The first matrix on the right is the P matrix. To obtain the inverse P^{-1} matrix, replace $f(t)/(D+2)$ in Eq. (9.47) by y_1. Thus

$$x_1 = \frac{y_1}{D+3}$$

or
$$y_1 = (D+3)x_1 = \dot{x}_1 + 3x_1 = 3x_1 + x_2$$

Similarly, replacing $f(t)/(D+3)$ in Eq. (9.47) by y_2 gives

$$x_1 = \frac{y_2}{D+2}$$

or
$$y_2 = (D+2)x_1 = \dot{x}_1 + 2x_1 = 2x_1 + x_2$$

The matrix form $\mathbf{y} = P^{-1}\mathbf{x}$ of the preceding relationships is

$$\begin{bmatrix} y_1 \\ y_2 \end{bmatrix} = \begin{bmatrix} 3 & 1 \\ 2 & 1 \end{bmatrix} \begin{bmatrix} x_1 \\ x_2 \end{bmatrix}$$

The first matrix on the right is the inverse P^{-1} matrix. The $P^{-1}\mathbf{b}$ matrix [1, 1] obtained for the canonical form, Eq. (9.46), is different from that obtained in Illustrative Example 2 $[-\frac{1}{3}, \frac{1}{2}]$. Division of the first row of P^{-1} of Illustrative Example 2 by $-\frac{1}{3}$ and the second row by $\frac{1}{2}$ yields the P^{-1} matrix obtained by the partial-fraction method.

For the case of Illustrative Example 1, $x_1(0) = c_0 = 1$ and $x_2(0) = \dot{c}_0 = 0$. Application of $\mathbf{y}(0) = P^{-1}\mathbf{x}(0)$ shows that $y_1(0) = 3$ and $y_2(0) = 2$. For $f(t) = 0$, the canonical differential equations are $\dot{y}_1 + 2y_1 = 0$ and $\dot{y}_2 + 3y_2 = 0$. The solutions are $y_1 = C_1 e^{-2t}$ and $y_2 = C_2 e^{-3t}$. Evaluation at $t = 0$ shows that $C_1 = 3$ and

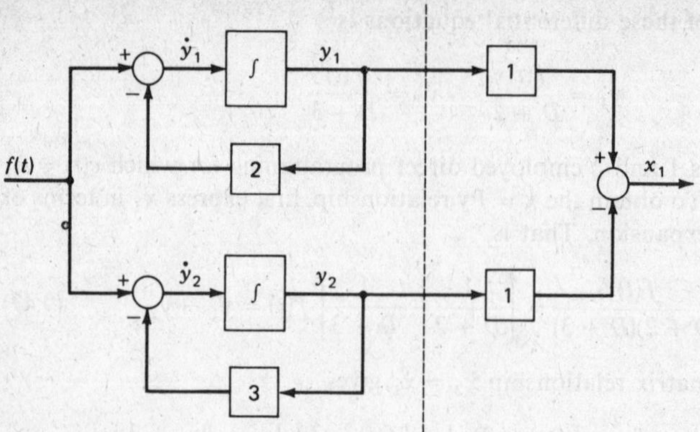

Figure 9.15 Computer flow diagram (distinct roots).

$C_2 = 2$. Transforming $\mathbf{x} = P\mathbf{y}$ back to the original state variables yields for the solution

$$c = x_1 = y_1 - y_2 = 3e^{-2t} - 2e^{-3t}$$

$$\dot{c} = x_2 = -2y_1 + 3y_2 = -6e^{-2t} + 6e^{-3t}$$

This verifies the result given by Eq. (9.43).

For the case of Illustrative Example 2, all initial conditions are zero and $f(t) = 6$. The canonical differential equations are $\dot{y}_1 + 2y_1 = 6$ and $\dot{y}_2 + 3y_2 = 6$. The general solutions are $y_1 = C_1 e^{-2t} + 3$ and $y_2 = C_2 e^{-3t} + 2$. For $y_1(0) = y_2(0) = 0$, evaluation at $t = 0$ shows that $C_1 = -3$ and $C_2 = -2$. Transforming back to the original state variables yields for the solution

$$c = x_1 = y_1 - y_2 = 3(1 - e^{-2t}) - 2(1 - e^{-3t}) = 1 - 3e^{-2t} + 2e^{-3t}$$

$$\dot{c} = x_2 = -2y_1 + 3y_2 = -2(3)(1 - e^{-2t}) + 3(2)(1 - e^{-3t}) = 6e^{-2t} - 6e^{-3t}$$

This verifies the result given by Eq. (9.45).

The computer flow diagram for generating the canonical variables y_1 and y_2 is shown in Fig. 9.15. This flow diagram automatically generates the response to any forcing function $f(t)$.

Illustrative example 3 Determine the solution of the differential equation

$$\ddot{c} + 5\dot{c} + 6c = f'(t) + 6f(t) \tag{9.48}$$

The forcing function $f(t)$ is a unit step function, and all the initial conditions are zero.

SOLUTION Any of the techniques explained in Sec. 9.1 may be used to convert the differential equation to the $\dot{\mathbf{x}} = A\mathbf{x} + \mathbf{b}f(t)$ form. Application of the general form given by Eq. (9.16) shows that $a_1 = 5$, $a_2 = 6$, $b_0 = 0$, $b_1 = 1$, and $b_2 = 6$. From Eq. (9.17), it follows that $h_1 = b_1 - a_1 b_0 = 1$, and $h_2 = b_2 - a_2 b_0 - a_1 h_1 = 6 - 0 - 5 = 1$. Thus

$$\begin{bmatrix} \dot{x}_1 \\ \dot{x}_2 \end{bmatrix} = \begin{bmatrix} 0 & 1 \\ -6 & -5 \end{bmatrix} \begin{bmatrix} x_1 \\ x_2 \end{bmatrix} + \begin{bmatrix} 1 \\ 1 \end{bmatrix} f(t)$$

where $x_1 = c - b_0 f(t) = c$. The corresponding equations are

$$\dot{x}_1 = x_2 + f(t)$$

$$\dot{x}_2 = -6x_1 - 5x_2 + f(t)$$

To prove that these equations are equivalent to the original differential equation, solve the first equation for x_2 $[x_2 = \dot{x}_1 - f(t)]$, differentiate to obtain $\dot{x}_2$ $[\dot{x}_2 = \ddot{x}_1 - f'(t)]$, and then substitute these results into the second equation. Thus

$$\ddot{x}_1 - f'(t) = -6x_1 - 5[\dot{x}_1 - f(t)] + f(t)$$

Rearranging gives

$$\ddot{x}_1 + 5\dot{x}_1 + 6x_1 = f'(t) + 6f(t)$$

or

$$x_1 = \frac{D + 6}{(D + 2)(D + 3)} f(t)$$

where $x_1 = c$.

Because the roots of the characteristic equation (-2 and -3) are the eigenvalues, the canonical form may be written directly. That is,

$$\begin{bmatrix} \dot{y}_1 \\ \dot{y}_2 \end{bmatrix} = \begin{bmatrix} -2 & 0 \\ 0 & -3 \end{bmatrix} \begin{bmatrix} y_1 \\ y_2 \end{bmatrix} + \begin{bmatrix} 1 \\ 1 \end{bmatrix} f(t) \tag{9.46}$$

The corresponding differential equations are

$$\dot{y}_1 = -2y_1 + f(t)$$

$$\dot{y}_2 = -3y_2 + f(t)$$

The operator form of these differential equations is

$$y_1 = \frac{f(t)}{D + 2} \qquad y_2 = \frac{f(t)}{D + 3}$$

To obtain the $\mathbf{x} = P\mathbf{y}$ relationship, first express x_1 in terms of its partial-fraction expansion. That is,

$$x_1 = \frac{D + 6}{(D + 2)(D + 3)} f(t) = \left(\frac{4}{D + 2} - \frac{3}{D + 3} \right) f(t) = 4y_1 - 3y_2$$

Application of the matrix relationship $x_2 = \dot{x}_1 - f(t)$ gives

$$\begin{aligned} x_2 &= 4\dot{y}_1 - 3\dot{y}_2 - f(t) \\ &= 4[-2y_1 + f(t)] - 3[-3y_2 + f(t)] - f(t) = -8y_1 + 9y_2 \end{aligned}$$

The matrix form ($\mathbf{x} = P\mathbf{y}$) of these relationships is

$$\begin{bmatrix} x_1 \\ x_2 \end{bmatrix} = \begin{bmatrix} 4 & -3 \\ -8 & 9 \end{bmatrix} \begin{bmatrix} y_1 \\ y_2 \end{bmatrix}$$

To obtain the inverse relationship, first substitute $y_1 = f(t)/(D+2)$ into the equation for x_1. Thus

$$x_1 = \frac{(D+6)f(t)}{(D+2)(D+3)} = \frac{(D+6)y_1}{D+3}$$

or

$$\dot{x}_1 + 3x_1 = \dot{y}_1 + 6y_1$$

The dot terms are eliminated by the relationships $\dot{x}_1 = x_2 + f(t)$ and $\dot{y}_1 = -2y_1 + f(t)$. Hence it is found that

$$y_1 = \frac{3x_1 + x_2}{4}$$

Next, substituting $y_2 = f(t)/(D+3)$ into the equation for x_1 gives

$$x_1 = \frac{(D+6)f(t)}{(D+2)(D+3)} = \frac{(D+6)y_2}{D+2}$$

or

$$\dot{x}_1 + 2x_1 = \dot{y}_2 + 6y_2$$

Substitution of $\dot{x}_1 = x_2 + f(t)$ and $\dot{y}_2 = -3y_2 + f(t)$ gives

$$y_2 = \frac{2x_1 + x_2}{3}$$

Thus, the inverse ($\mathbf{y} = P^{-1}\mathbf{x}$) matrix relationship is

$$\begin{bmatrix} y_1 \\ y_2 \end{bmatrix} = \frac{1}{12} \begin{bmatrix} 9 & 3 \\ 8 & 4 \end{bmatrix} \begin{bmatrix} x_1 \\ x_2 \end{bmatrix}$$

The general solution of the canonical differential equation for $f(t) = 1$ is $y_1 = \frac{1}{2} + C_1 e^{-2t}$ and $y_2 = \frac{1}{3} + C_2 e^{-3t}$. Evaluation at time $t = 0$, in which case $y_1(0) = y_2(0) = 0$, shows that $C_1 = -\frac{1}{2}$ and $C_2 = -\frac{1}{3}$. Thus,

$$y_1 = \frac{1 - e^{-2t}}{2} \qquad y_2 = \frac{1 - e^{-3t}}{3}$$

Applying the $\mathbf{x} = P\mathbf{y}$ transform and noting that $c = x_1$ yields for the solution

$$c = x_1 = 4y_1 - 3y_2 = 2(1 - e^{-2t}) - (1 - e^{-3t}) = 1 - 2e^{-2t} + e^{-3t}$$

$$\dot{c} = \dot{x}_1 = x_2 + f(t) = -8y_1 + 9y_2 + 1 = 4e^{-2t} - 3e^{-3t} \tag{9.49}$$

Any of the methods discussed in Sec. 9.1 may be used to transform a differential equation into the form $\dot{\mathbf{x}} = A\mathbf{x} + \mathbf{b}f(t)$. In general, different methods yield different A, P, P^{-1}, and $\mathbf{b}$ matrices, but the final answer is the same regardless of which method is used. This fact will now be demonstrated by solving Illustrative Example 3 by the method of direct programming. Thus, the differential equation is written in the form

$$c(t) = (D + 6)x_1$$

where

$$x_1 = \frac{f(t)}{D^2 + 5D + 6}$$

By letting $\dot{x}_1 = x_2$, the preceding equations become

$$\dot{x}_2 = -5\dot{x}_1 - 6x_1 + f(t) = -6x_1 - 5x_2 + f(t)$$

$$c(t) = \dot{x}_1 + 6x_1 = 6x_1 + x_2$$

Thus, the state-space form is

$$\begin{bmatrix} \dot{x}_1 \\ \dot{x}_2 \end{bmatrix} = \begin{bmatrix} 0 & 1 \\ -6 & -5 \end{bmatrix} \begin{bmatrix} x_1 \\ x_2 \end{bmatrix} + \begin{bmatrix} 0 \\ 1 \end{bmatrix} f(t)$$

$$c = 6x_1 + x_2$$

Because the roots of the characteristic equation are -2 and -3, the canonical form is given by Eq. (9.46). To obtain the $\mathbf{x} = P\mathbf{y}$ relationship, first express x_1 in terms of its partial fraction expansion. Thus

$$x_1 = \frac{f(t)}{(D + 2)(D + 3)} = \left[\frac{1}{D + 2} - \frac{1}{D + 3}\right] f(t) = y_1 - y_2$$

Application of the $x_2 = \dot{x}_1$ relationship gives

$$x_2 = \dot{x}_1 = \dot{y}_1 - \dot{y}_2 = [f(t) - 2y_1] - [f(t) - 3y_2] = -2y_1 + 3y_2$$

The resulting $\mathbf{x} = P\mathbf{y}$ relationship is

$$\begin{bmatrix} x_1 \\ x_2 \end{bmatrix} = \begin{bmatrix} 1 & -1 \\ -2 & 3 \end{bmatrix} \begin{bmatrix} y_1 \\ y_2 \end{bmatrix}$$

To obtain the inverse relationship, first substitute $y_1 = f(t)/(D + 2)$ into the x_1 relationship.

$$x_1 = \frac{f(t)}{(D + 2)(D + 3)} = \frac{y_1}{D + 3}$$

Hence

$$y_1 = \dot{x}_1 + 3x_1 = 3x_1 + x_2$$

Next, replacing $f(t)/(D+3)$ by y_2 gives

$$y_2 = \dot{x}_1 + 2x_1 = 2x_1 + x_2$$

Thus, the inverse relationship ($\mathbf{y} = P^{-1}\mathbf{x}$) is

$$\begin{bmatrix} y_1 \\ y_2 \end{bmatrix} = \begin{bmatrix} 3 & 1 \\ 2 & 1 \end{bmatrix} \begin{bmatrix} x_1 \\ x_2 \end{bmatrix}$$

The canonical equations are $\dot{y}_1 + 2y_1 = f(t)$ and $\dot{y}_2 + 3y_2 = f(t)$. The solution of these equations for $f(t) = 1$ when all initial conditions are zero is $y_1 = (1 - e^{-2t})/2$ and $y_2 = (1 - e^{-3t})/3$. Substitution of these results into the preceding $\mathbf{x} = P\mathbf{y}$ relationship gives

$$x_1 = \frac{1 - e^{-2t}}{2} - \frac{1 - e^{-3t}}{3} = \frac{1 - 3e^{-2t} + 2e^{-3t}}{6}$$

$$x_2 = -(1 - e^{-2t}) + (1 - e^{-3t}) = e^{-2t} - e^{-3t}$$

The desired solution is now found to be

$$c = 6x_1 + x_2 = (1 - 3e^{-2t} + 2e^{-3t}) + (e^{-2t} - e^{-3t}) = 1 - 2e^{-2t} + e^{-3t}$$

$$\dot{c} = 6\dot{x}_1 + \dot{x}_2 = 6x_2 - 6x_1 - 5x_2 + f(t) = -6x_1 + x_2 + 1$$

$$= 4e^{-2t} - 3e^{-3t}$$

This verifies the previously attained results given by Eq. (9.49).

To solve Illustrative Example 3 by parallel programming, first express $c(t)$ in terms of its partial fraction expansion. That is,

$$c(t) = \frac{D+6}{(D+2)(D+3)} f(t) = \left(\frac{4}{D+2} - \frac{3}{D+3}\right) f(t) = 4x_1 - 3x_2$$

where $x_1 = f(t)/(D+2) = y_1$ and $x_2 = f(t)/(D+3) = y_2$. Because $x_1 = y_1$ and $x_2 = y_2$, then $P = P^{-1} = I$ and $A = \Lambda$. In parallel programming, the state-space representation is the canonical form. The solution of the canonical differential equations is $x_1 = (1 - e^{-2t})/2$ and $x_2 = (1 - e^{-3t})/3$. Hence

$$c(t) = 4x_1 - 3x_2 = 2(1 - e^{-2t}) - (1 - e^{-3t}) = 1 - 2e^{-2t} + e^{-3t}$$

$$\dot{c}(t) = 4\dot{x}_1 - 3\dot{x}_2 = 4[f(t) - 2x_1] - 3[f(t) - 3x_2] = -8x_1 + 9x_2 + f(t)$$

$$= -4(1 - e^{-2t}) + 3(1 - e^{-3t}) + 1 = 4e^{-2t} - 3e^{-3t}$$

This verifies the result given in Eq. (9.49).

It is possible to solve Illustrative Example 3 by using a state-space representation which is not of the form $\dot{\mathbf{x}} = A\mathbf{x} + \mathbf{b}f(t)$. For example, letting $c = x_1$ and $\dot{c} = \dot{x}_1 = x_2$ in Eq. (9.48) yields the state-space representation

$$\begin{bmatrix} \dot{x}_1 \\ \dot{x}_2 \end{bmatrix} = \begin{bmatrix} 0 & 1 \\ -6 & -5 \end{bmatrix} \begin{bmatrix} x_1 \\ x_2 \end{bmatrix} + \begin{bmatrix} 0 \\ 1 \end{bmatrix} f'(t) + \begin{bmatrix} 0 \\ 1 \end{bmatrix} f(t)$$

This has the form $\dot{\mathbf{x}} = A\mathbf{x} + \mathbf{b}_1 f'(t) + \mathbf{b}_2 f(t)$. Letting $\mathbf{x} = P\mathbf{y} + \mathbf{b}_1 f(t)$ transforms this state-space representation into the canonical form $\dot{\mathbf{y}} = \Lambda\mathbf{y} + \mathbf{b}f(t)$ where $\mathbf{b} = A\mathbf{b}_1 + \mathbf{b}_2$. The canonical form for Illustrative Example 3 is given by Eq. (9.46). To obtain the $\mathbf{x} = P\mathbf{y} + \mathbf{b}_1 f(t)$ relationship, first express x_1 in terms of its partial fraction expansion and then apply the $x_2 = \dot{x}_1$ relationship. The resulting $\mathbf{x} = P\mathbf{y} + \mathbf{b}_1 f(t)$ relationship is

$$\begin{bmatrix} x_1 \\ x_2 \end{bmatrix} = \begin{bmatrix} 4 & -3 \\ -8 & 9 \end{bmatrix} \begin{bmatrix} x_1 \\ x_2 \end{bmatrix} + \begin{bmatrix} 0 \\ 1 \end{bmatrix} f(t)$$

To obtain the inverse relationship $\mathbf{y} = P^{-1}\mathbf{x} - P^{-1}\mathbf{b}_1 f(t)$, first replace $f(t)/(D+2)$ by y_1 in the expression for x_1. Similarly, replacing $f(t)/(D+3)$ by y_2 yields

$$\begin{bmatrix} y_1 \\ y_2 \end{bmatrix} = \begin{bmatrix} \frac{3}{4} & \frac{1}{4} \\ \frac{2}{3} & \frac{1}{3} \end{bmatrix} \begin{bmatrix} x_1 \\ x_2 \end{bmatrix} + \begin{bmatrix} -\frac{1}{4} \\ -\frac{1}{3} \end{bmatrix} f(t)$$

The solution of the canonical differential equations when all the initial conditions are zero and $f(t) = 1$ is $y_1 = (1 - e^{-2t})/2$ and $y_2 = (1 - e^{-3t})/3$. Application of the $\mathbf{x} = P\mathbf{y} + \mathbf{b}_1 f(t)$ transform yields

$$c = x_1 = 4y_1 - 3y_2 = 2(1 - e^{-2t}) - (1 - e^{-3t}) = 1 - 2e^{-2t} + e^{-3t}$$

$$\dot{c} = \dot{x}_1 = x_2 = -8y_1 + 9y_2 + f(t) = -4(1 - e^{-2t}) + 3(1 - e^{-3t}) + 1$$

$$= 4e^{-2t} - 3e^{-3t}$$

This is the same result given by Eq. (9.49). Although various state-space forms may be used, for standardization of notation and procedure it is customary to use the $\dot{\mathbf{x}} = A\mathbf{x} + \mathbf{b}f(t)$ form.

9.4 REPEATED EIGENVALUES

When two or more eigenvalues λ are equal, the matrix P is singular. A singular matrix does not have an inverse; hence, P^{-1} does not exist. Thus, for repeated eigenvalues a slightly different procedure must be followed. To illustrate this situation, consider the second-order system

$$\begin{bmatrix} \dot{x}_1 \\ \dot{x}_2 \end{bmatrix} = \begin{bmatrix} a & b \\ c & d \end{bmatrix} \begin{bmatrix} x_1 \\ x_2 \end{bmatrix}$$

It is initially assumed that the two eigenvalues, λ and $\lambda + \Delta\lambda$, are slightly different. To determine the P matrix, first form the $A - \lambda I$ and $A - (\lambda + \Delta\lambda)I$ determinants. That is,

$$\begin{vmatrix} a-\lambda & b \\ c & d-\lambda \end{vmatrix} \qquad \begin{vmatrix} a-(\lambda+\Delta\lambda) & b \\ c & d-(\lambda+\Delta\lambda) \end{vmatrix}$$

The left determinant shows that $A_{11} = d - \lambda$ and $A_{21} = -c$. Similarly, the determinant on the right shows that $A_{12} = d - (\lambda + \Delta\lambda)$ and $A_{22} = -c$. Thus, the P matrix is

$$P = \begin{bmatrix} d-\lambda & d-(\lambda+\Delta\lambda) \\ -c & -c \end{bmatrix}$$

Calculation of $P^{-1}AP$ shows that

$$P^{-1}AP = \begin{bmatrix} \lambda & 0 \\ 0 & \lambda+\Delta\lambda \end{bmatrix}$$

To obtain the desired form of the Λ matrix for repeated roots, it is necessary to make a second transformation $\mathbf{y} = Q\mathbf{z}$. The transformation $\mathbf{x} = P\mathbf{y}$ transforms the system $\dot{\mathbf{x}} = A\mathbf{x} + \mathbf{b}f(t)$ into the form $\dot{\mathbf{y}} = P^{-1}AP\mathbf{y} + P^{-1}\mathbf{b}f(t)$. The transformation $\mathbf{y} = Q\mathbf{z}$ further transforms the preceding into the form

$$\begin{aligned}\dot{\mathbf{z}} &= Q^{-1}P^{-1}APQ\mathbf{z} + Q^{-1}P^{-1}\mathbf{b}f(t) = R^{-1}AR\mathbf{z} + R^{-1}\mathbf{b}f(t) \\ &= \Lambda\mathbf{z} + R^{-1}\mathbf{b}f(t) \end{aligned} \tag{9.50}$$

where $R = PQ$ and $R^{-1} = (PQ)^{-1} = Q^{-1}P^{-1}$. The matrix $\Lambda = R^{-1}AR$ is the desired canonical form for repeated roots. By letting

$$Q = \lim_{\Delta\lambda\to 0}\begin{bmatrix} 0 & -1/\Delta\lambda \\ 1 & 1/\Delta\lambda \end{bmatrix} \qquad \text{then} \qquad Q^{-1} = \lim_{\Delta\lambda\to 0}\begin{bmatrix} 1 & 1 \\ -\Delta\lambda & 0 \end{bmatrix}$$

The resulting Λ matrix is

$$\Lambda = Q^{-1}(P^{-1}AP)Q = \begin{bmatrix} \lambda & 1 \\ 0 & \lambda \end{bmatrix}$$

Computation of the R matrix yields

$$R = PQ = \begin{bmatrix} A_{11} & A'_{11} \\ A_{21} & A'_{21} \end{bmatrix}$$

where $A'_{11} = (d/d\lambda)A_{11}$ and $A'_{21} = (d/d\lambda)A_{21}$. By proceeding in a similar manner, it is found that for three repeated roots,

$$\Lambda = \begin{bmatrix} \lambda & 1 & 0 \\ 0 & \lambda & 1 \\ 0 & 0 & \lambda \end{bmatrix} \qquad \text{and} \qquad R = \begin{bmatrix} A_{11} & A'_{11}/1! & A''_{11}/2! \\ A_{21} & A'_{21}/1! & A''_{21}/2! \\ A_{31} & A'_{31}/1! & A''_{31}/2! \end{bmatrix}$$

In summary, for repeated eigenvalues $\mathbf{x} = R\mathbf{z}$ transforms the state-space representation $\dot{\mathbf{x}} = A\mathbf{x} + \mathbf{b}f(t)$ into the canonical form $\dot{\mathbf{z}} = \Lambda\mathbf{z} + R^{-1}\mathbf{b}f(t)$.

Illustrative example Use direct programming to determine the solution of the following differential equation for the case in which $f(t) = 0$ and the initial conditions are $c_0 = 1$ and $\dot{c}_0 = 0$.

$$\ddot{c} + 10\dot{c} + 25c = f(t) \tag{9.51}$$

SOLUTION For direct programming $c = x_1$ and $\dot{c} = \dot{x}_1 = x_2$. The resulting state-space representation for this differential equation is

$$\dot{x}_1 = x_2$$

$$\dot{x}_2 = -25x_1 - 10x_2$$

The corresponding matrix form is

$$\begin{bmatrix} \dot{x}_1 \\ \dot{x}_2 \end{bmatrix} = \begin{bmatrix} 0 & 1 \\ -25 & -10 \end{bmatrix} \begin{bmatrix} x_1 \\ x_2 \end{bmatrix}$$

The characteristic equation for this system is

$$|A - \lambda I| = \left| \begin{bmatrix} 0 & 1 \\ -25 & -10 \end{bmatrix} - \begin{bmatrix} \lambda & 0 \\ 0 & \lambda \end{bmatrix} \right| = \begin{vmatrix} -\lambda & 1 \\ -25 & -\lambda - 10 \end{vmatrix}$$

$$= \lambda^2 + 10\lambda + 25 = (\lambda + 5)^2 = 0$$

The repeated eigenvalue is $\lambda = -5$. The cofactors of the first row are $A_{11} = -(\lambda + 10)$ and $A_{21} = 25$. The R matrix is

$$R = \begin{bmatrix} A_{11} & A'_{11} \\ A_{21} & A'_{21} \end{bmatrix} = \begin{bmatrix} -(\lambda + 10) & -1 \\ 25 & 0 \end{bmatrix} = \begin{bmatrix} -5 & -1 \\ 25 & 0 \end{bmatrix} \tag{9.52}$$

The inverse is

$$R^{-1} = \frac{\begin{bmatrix} 0 & 1 \\ -25 & -5 \end{bmatrix}}{25} \tag{9.53}$$

The canonical form is

$$\begin{bmatrix} \dot{z}_1 \\ \dot{z}_2 \end{bmatrix} = \begin{bmatrix} \lambda & 1 \\ 0 & \lambda \end{bmatrix} \begin{bmatrix} z_1 \\ z_2 \end{bmatrix} = \begin{bmatrix} -5 & 1 \\ 0 & -5 \end{bmatrix} \begin{bmatrix} z_1 \\ z_2 \end{bmatrix}$$

The corresponding differential equations are

$$\dot{z}_1 + 5z_1 = z_2$$

$$\dot{z}_2 + 5z_2 = 0$$

The general form of the solution of the latter equation is

$$z_2 = C_2 e^{-5t}$$

The first of the differential equations may now be written in the form

$$\dot{z}_1 + 5z_1 = C_2 e^{-5t}$$

The general form of the solution of this differential equation is

$$z_1 = (C_1 + C_2 t)e^{-5t}$$

Evaluation of these equations at time $t = 0$ shows that $C_1 = z_1(0)$ and $C_2 = z_2(0)$. Thus

$$\begin{aligned} z_1 &= [z_1(0) + z_2(0)t]e^{-5t} \\ z_2 &= z_2(0)e^{-5t} \end{aligned} \tag{9.54}$$

The $\mathbf{x} = P\mathbf{y} = PQ\mathbf{z} = R\mathbf{z}$ and $\mathbf{z} = R^{-1}\mathbf{x}$ matrix equations are

$$\begin{aligned} \begin{bmatrix} x_1 \\ x_2 \end{bmatrix} &= \begin{bmatrix} -5 & -1 \\ 25 & 0 \end{bmatrix} \begin{bmatrix} z_1 \\ z_2 \end{bmatrix} \\ \begin{bmatrix} z_1 \\ z_2 \end{bmatrix} &= \frac{\begin{bmatrix} 0 & 1 \\ -25 & -5 \end{bmatrix}}{25} \begin{bmatrix} x_1 \\ x_2 \end{bmatrix} \end{aligned} \tag{9.55}$$

For $c_0 = x_1(0) = 1$ and $\dot{c}_0 = x_2(0) = 0$, evaluation of the $\mathbf{z} = R^{-1}\mathbf{x}$ matrix at time $t = 0$ shows that $z_1(0) = 0$ and $z_2(0) = -1$. Thus

$$z_1 = -te^{-5t}$$

$$z_2 = -e^{-5t}$$

From the $\mathbf{x} = R\mathbf{z}$ matrix, the desired result is found to be

$$\begin{aligned} c = x_1 &= -5z_1 - z_2 = (1 + 5t)e^{-5t} \\ \dot{c} = x_2 &= 25z_1 = -25te^{-5t} \end{aligned} \tag{9.56}$$

The result for $\dot{c} = x_2$ is verified by differentiation of the $c = x_1$ equation.

Partial-Fraction Method

The canonical form for two repeated roots is

$$\begin{bmatrix} \dot{z}_1 \\ \dot{z}_2 \end{bmatrix} = \begin{bmatrix} \lambda & 1 \\ 0 & \lambda \end{bmatrix} \begin{bmatrix} z_1 \\ z_2 \end{bmatrix} + \begin{bmatrix} 0 \\ 1 \end{bmatrix} f(t)$$

The corresponding differential equations are

$$\dot{z}_1 = \lambda z_1 + z_2$$

$$\dot{z}_2 = \lambda z_2 + f(t)$$

The operator form of these differential equations is

$$z_2 = \frac{f(t)}{D - \lambda} \qquad z_1 = \frac{f(t)}{(D - \lambda)^2}$$

The computer diagram for generating the canonical variables is shown in Fig. 9.16.

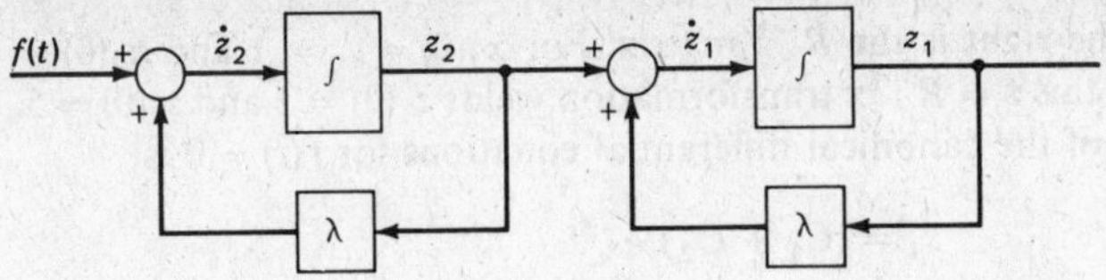

Figure 9.16 Computer flow diagram (repeated roots).

For the case of the illustrative example in this section, in which $\lambda = -5$, the canonical variables z_1 and z_2 are

$$z_2 = \frac{f(t)}{D+5} \qquad z_1 = \frac{f(t)}{(D+5)^2}$$

To obtain the $\mathbf{x} = R\mathbf{z}$ relationship, first express x_1 in terms of its partial-fraction expansion. That is,

$$x_1 = \frac{f(t)}{(D+5)^2} = z_1$$

Application of the $x_2 = \dot{x}_1$ relationship gives

$$x_2 = \dot{x}_1 = \dot{z}_1 = \lambda z_1 + z_2 = -5z_1 + z_2$$

The matrix form $\mathbf{x} = R\mathbf{z}$ of the two preceding equations is

$$\begin{bmatrix} x_1 \\ x_2 \end{bmatrix} = \begin{bmatrix} 1 & 0 \\ -5 & 1 \end{bmatrix} \begin{bmatrix} z_1 \\ z_2 \end{bmatrix}$$

The first matrix on the right is the R matrix. To obtain the inverse R^{-1} matrix, first substitute $z_1 = f(t)/(D+5)^2$ into the equation for x_1. That is,

$$x_1 = \frac{f(t)}{(D+5)^2} = z_1$$

or

$$z_1 = x_1$$

Substitution of $z_2 = f(t)/(D+5)$ into the equation for x_1 shows that

$$x_1 = \frac{1}{D+5}\frac{f(t)}{D+5} = \frac{z_2}{D+5}$$

or

$$z_2 = (D+5)x_1 = \dot{x}_1 + 5x_1 = 5x_1 + x_2$$

The matrix form $\mathbf{z} = R^{-1}\mathbf{x}$ of these relationships is

$$\begin{bmatrix} z_1 \\ z_2 \end{bmatrix} = \begin{bmatrix} 1 & 0 \\ 5 & 1 \end{bmatrix} \begin{bmatrix} x_1 \\ x_2 \end{bmatrix}$$

The first matrix on the right is the R^{-1} matrix. For $x_1(0) = c_0 = 1$ and $x_2(0) = \dot{c}_0 = 0$, application of this $\mathbf{z} = R^{-1}\mathbf{x}$ transformation yields $z_1(0) = 1$ and $z_2(0) = 5$. The general solution of the canonical differential equations for $f(t) = 0$ is

$$z_1 = (C_1 + C_2 t)e^{-5t}$$

$$z_2 = C_2 e^{-5t}$$

Evaluation at time $t = 0$ shows that $C_1 = 1$ and $C_2 = 5$. Thus,

$$z_1 = (1 + 5t)e^{-5t}$$

$$z_2 = 5e^{-5t}$$

Application of the $\mathbf{x} = R\mathbf{z}$ relationship to transform this solution back to the original state variables gives

$$c = x_1 = z_1 = (1 + 5t)e^{-5t}$$

$$\dot{c} = x_2 = -5z_1 + z_2 = -25te^{-5t}$$

This verifies the result given by Eq. (9.56).

In the preceding, matrix differential equations were solved by transforming them to the canonical form. To solve the canonical form, it is necessary to transform the initial conditions from the original system to the canonical system, $\mathbf{y}(0) = P^{-1}\mathbf{x}(0)$. The solution of the original system is then obtained by transforming the canonical solution back to the original state variables, $\mathbf{x} = P\mathbf{y}$. The P and P^{-1} matrices may be obtained by classical methods or by the partial-fraction-expansion method. In the following, a direct method for solving matrix differential equations which does not require solving the canonical differential equations is developed.

9.5 SOLUTION OF STATE-SPACE EQUATIONS

Consider the differential equation

$$\frac{dx}{dt} = ax \tag{9.57}$$

Integration yields

$$x(t) = x_0 + \int_0^t ax(\tau)\, d\tau \tag{9.58}$$

Replacing t by τ gives

$$x(\tau) = x_0 + \int_0^\tau ax(\tau)\, d\tau$$

Substituting this result into Eq. (9.58) shows that

$$x(t) = x_0 + \int_0^t a\left[x_0 + \int_0^\tau ax(\tau)\,d\tau\right]d\tau$$

$$= x_0 + x_0\int_0^t a\,d\tau + \int_0^t a\int_0^\tau ax(\tau)\,d\tau\,d\tau$$

Continuing this process of replacing t by τ and substituting the result into Eq. (9.58) yields

$$x(t) = x_0\left(1 + \int_0^t a\,d\tau + \int_0^t a\int_0^\tau a\,d\tau\,d\tau + \int_0^t a\int_0^\tau a\int_0^\tau a\,d\tau\,d\tau\,d\tau + \cdots\right)$$

The result of the preceding integrations is

$$\int_0^t a\,d\tau = at$$

$$\int_0^t a\int_0^\tau a\,d\tau\,d\tau = \int_0^t a(a\tau)\,d\tau = \frac{a^2t^2}{2!}$$

$$\int_0^t a\int_0^\tau a\int_0^\tau a\,d\tau\,d\tau\,d\tau = \int_0^t a\frac{a^2\tau^2}{2!}\,d\tau = \frac{a^3t^3}{3!}$$

Thus, the solution of the differential equation given by Eq. (9.57) is

$$x(t) = \left(1 + at + \frac{a^2t^2}{2!} + \frac{a^3t^3}{3!} + \cdots\right)x_0$$

$$= e^{at}x_0 \tag{9.59}$$

The solution of a system of differential equations is obtained in a similar manner. Thus, consider the system

$$\dot{\mathbf{x}}(t) = A\mathbf{x}(t) \qquad \mathbf{x}(0) = \mathbf{x}_0 \tag{9.60}$$

The corresponding differential equations are

$$\dot{x}_1 = a_{11}x_1 + a_{12}x_2 + \cdots + a_{1n}x_n$$

$$\dot{x}_2 = a_{21}x_1 + a_{22}x_2 + \cdots + a_{2n}x_n$$

$$\cdots\cdots\cdots\cdots\cdots\cdots\cdots\cdots\cdots\cdots\cdots\cdots$$

$$\dot{x}_n = a_{n1}x_1 + a_{n2}x_2 + \cdots + a_{nn}x_n$$

Integration of each equation gives

$$x_1 - x_1(0) = \int_0^t (a_{11}x_1 + a_{12}x_2 + \cdots + a_{1n}x_n)\,d\tau$$

$$x_2 - x_2(0) = \int_0^t (a_{21}x_1 + a_{22}x_2 + \cdots + a_{2n}x_n)\,d\tau$$

$$\cdots\cdots\cdots\cdots\cdots\cdots\cdots\cdots\cdots\cdots\cdots\cdots\cdots\cdots\cdots$$

$$x_n - x_n(0) = \int_0^t (a_{n1}x_1 + a_{n2}x_2 + \cdots + a_{nn}x_n)\,d\tau$$

The corresponding matrix representation is

$$\mathbf{x}(t) = \mathbf{x}(0) + \int_0^t A\mathbf{x}(\tau)\, d\tau$$

Replacing t by τ and substituting this result back into the preceding gives

$$\mathbf{x}(t) = \mathbf{x}(0) + \int_0^t A\left[\mathbf{x}(0) + \int_0^\tau A\mathbf{x}(\tau)\, d\tau\right] d\tau$$

$$= \mathbf{x}(0) + \mathbf{x}(0)\int_0^t A\, d\tau + \int_0^t A \int_0^\tau A\mathbf{x}(\tau)\, d\tau\, d\tau$$

Continuing this process,

$$\mathbf{x}(t) = \mathbf{x}(0)\left[I + \int_0^t A\, d\tau + \int_0^t A\int_0^\tau A\, d\tau + \int_0^t A\int_0^\tau A\int_0^\tau A\, d\tau\, d\tau\, d\tau + \cdots\right]$$

The result of each integration is

$$\int_0^t A\, d\tau = At$$

$$\int_0^t A\int_0^\tau A\, d\tau = \int_0^t A(A\tau)\, d\tau = \frac{A^2t^2}{2!}$$

$$\int_0^t A\int_0^\tau A\int_0^\tau A\, d\tau\, d\tau\, d\tau = \int_0^t A\left(\frac{A^2\tau^2}{2!}\right) d\tau = \frac{A^3t^3}{3!}$$

Thus, the solution of the system of differential equations represented by Eq. (9.60) is

$$\mathbf{x}(t) = \left[I + At + \frac{A^2t^2}{2!} + \frac{A^3t^3}{3!} + \cdots\right]\mathbf{x}(0) = e^{At}\mathbf{x}(0)$$

$$= \Phi(t)\mathbf{x}(0) \tag{9.61}$$

where

$$\Phi(t) = e^{At} = \left[I + At + \frac{A^2t^2}{2!} + \frac{A^3t^3}{3!} + \cdots\right] \tag{9.62}$$

The function $\Phi(t) = e^{At}$ is called the state-transition matrix. The state-transition matrix operates on the initial state of the system $\mathbf{x}(0)$ to yield the state of the system at any time t.

The exponential representation of the state-transition matrix ($e^{At} = I + At + A^2t^2/2! + \cdots$) has properties similar to its scalar analog ($e^{at} = 1 + at + a^2t^2/2! + \cdots$). An important property is revealed by differentiation of the preceding expression. That is,

$$\frac{d\Phi(t)}{dt} = Ae^{At} = A\left[I + At + \frac{A^2t^2}{2!} + \cdots\right] \tag{9.63}$$

When the initial state of the system is known at time t_0 rather than at time $t = 0$, carrying through the preceding analysis with t_0 as the lower limit of integration yields

$$\mathbf{x}(t) = \left(I + \int_{t_0}^{t} A\,d\tau + \int_{t_0}^{t} A \int_{t_0}^{\tau} A\,d\tau\,d\tau + \cdots\right)\mathbf{x}(t_0)$$

Evaluating the integrals shows that

$$\int_{t_0}^{t} A\,d\tau = A(t - t_0)$$

$$\int_{t_0}^{t} A \int_{t_0}^{\tau} A\,d\tau\,d\tau = \int_{t_0}^{t} A[A(\tau - t_0)]\,d\tau = A^2\frac{(t - t_0)^2}{2!}$$

Thus,

$$\mathbf{x}(t) = \left[I + A(t - t_0) + A^2\frac{(t - t_0)^2}{2!} + \cdots\right]\mathbf{x}(t_0) = e^{A(t-t_0)}\mathbf{x}(t_0)$$

$$= \Phi(t - t_0)\mathbf{x}(t_0) \tag{9.64}$$

Properties of the state-transition matrix are most readily obtained using the exponential representation. This is illustrated as follows:

$$\Phi(0) = e^{A0} = I$$

$$\Phi^{-1}(t) = (e^{At})^{-1} = e^{-At} = \Phi(-t)$$

$$\Phi^{k}(t) = (e^{At})^{k} = e^{A(kt)} = \Phi(kt) \tag{9.65}$$

$$\Phi(t_1 + t_2) = e^{A(t_1+t_2)} = e^{At_1}e^{At_2} = \Phi(t_1)\Phi(t_2) = \Phi(t_2)\Phi(t_1)$$

$$\Phi(t_2 - t_1)\Phi(t_1 - t_0) = e^{A(t_2-t_1)+A(t_1-t_0)} = \Phi(t_2 - t_0)$$

Such relationships can save considerable time and computational effort.

Illustrative example Determine the state-transition matrix for the system represented by Eq. (9.40).

SOLUTION From Illustrative Example 1 in Sec. 9.3, the solution of the canonical equations is

$$y_1 = C_1e^{-2t} = y_1(0)e^{-2t} = -\left[x_1(0) + \frac{x_2(0)}{3}\right]e^{-2t}$$

$$y_2 = C_2e^{-3t} = y_2(0)e^{-3t} = \left[x_1(0) + \frac{x_2(0)}{2}\right]e^{-3t}$$

From the $\mathbf{x} = P\mathbf{y}$ matrix, it follows that

$$x_1 = -3y_1 - 2y_2 = [3x_1(0) + x_2(0)]e^{-2t} - [2x_1(0) + x_2(0)]e^{-3t}$$

$$x_2 = 6y_1 + 6y_2 = [-6x_1(0) - 2x_2(0)]e^{-2t} + [6x_1(0) + 3x_2(0)]e^{-3t}$$

This result may now be expressed in the form

$$\begin{bmatrix} x_1 \\ x_2 \end{bmatrix} = \begin{bmatrix} (3e^{-2t} - 2e^{-3t}) & (e^{-2t} - e^{-3t}) \\ (-6e^{-2t} + 6e^{-3t}) & (-2e^{-2t} + 3e^{-3t}) \end{bmatrix} \begin{bmatrix} x_1(0) \\ x_2(0) \end{bmatrix}$$

Comparison with Eq. (9.61) reveals the desired result,

$$\Phi(t) = \begin{bmatrix} (3e^{-2t} - 2e^{-3t}) & (e^{-2t} - e^{-3t}) \\ (-6e^{-2t} + 6e^{-3t}) & (-2e^{-2t} + 3e^{-3t}) \end{bmatrix} \tag{9.66}$$

Application of Eq. (9.62) yields for $\Phi(t)$

$$\Phi(t) = \begin{bmatrix} 1 & 0 \\ 0 & 1 \end{bmatrix} + \begin{bmatrix} 0 & 1 \\ -6 & -5 \end{bmatrix} t + \begin{bmatrix} -6 & -5 \\ 30 & 19 \end{bmatrix} \frac{t^2}{2!} + \begin{bmatrix} 30 & 19 \\ -114 & -65 \end{bmatrix} \frac{t^3}{3!} + \cdots \tag{9.67}$$

Equation (9.66) is the exponential form for $\Phi(t)$, and Eq. (9.67) is the equivalent series form. This fact can be verified by expressing each term in Eq. (9.66) as a series. For the first term,

$$\begin{aligned} 3e^{-2t} - 2e^{-3t} &= 3\left(1 - 2t + \frac{(2t)^2}{2!} - \frac{(2t)^3}{3!} + \cdots\right) - 2\left(1 - 3t + \frac{(3t)^2}{2!} - \frac{(3t)^3}{3!} + \cdots\right) \\ &= 1 - 0t - \frac{6t^2}{2!} + \frac{30t^3}{3!} + \cdots \end{aligned}$$

9.6 METHODS OF COMPUTING $\Phi(t)$

A major problem in solving differential equations by the state-space method is the determination of the state-transition matrix. The infinite-series representation for $\Phi(t)$ involves lengthy computations and results in a very awkward form. Considerable simplification is afforded by taking advantage of diagonalization to utilize the canonical form.

Distinct Roots

Consider the differential equation

$$\dot{\mathbf{x}} = A\mathbf{x}$$

The transformation $\mathbf{x} = P\mathbf{y}$ transforms this to the canonical form:

$$\dot{\mathbf{y}} = P^{-1}AP\mathbf{y} = \Lambda\mathbf{y}$$

By analogy with Eqs. (9.60) and (9.61) the solution of this resulting canonical equation is

$$\mathbf{y}(t) = e^{\Lambda t}\mathbf{y}(0) \tag{9.68}$$

From Eq. (9.62), it follows that

$$e^{\Lambda t} = I + \Lambda t + \frac{\Lambda^2 t^2}{2!} + \frac{\Lambda^3 t^3}{3!} + \cdots$$

$$= \begin{bmatrix} 1 & 0 & \cdots & 0 \\ 0 & 1 & \cdots & 0 \\ \cdots & \cdots & \cdots & \cdots \\ 0 & 0 & \cdots & 1 \end{bmatrix} + \begin{bmatrix} \lambda_1 t & 0 & \cdots & 0 \\ 0 & \lambda_2 t & \cdots & 0 \\ \cdots & \cdots & \cdots & \cdots \\ 0 & 0 & \cdots & \lambda_n t \end{bmatrix} + \begin{bmatrix} \frac{\lambda_1^2 t^2}{2!} & 0 & \cdots & 0 \\ 0 & \frac{\lambda_2^2 t^2}{2!} & \cdots & 0 \\ \cdots & \cdots & \cdots & \cdots \\ 0 & 0 & \cdots & \frac{\lambda_n^2 t^2}{2!} \end{bmatrix} + \cdots$$

$$= \begin{bmatrix} e^{\lambda_1 t} & 0 & \cdots & 0 \\ 0 & e^{\lambda_2 t} & \cdots & 0 \\ \cdots & \cdots & \cdots & \cdots \\ 0 & 0 & \cdots & e^{\lambda_n t} \end{bmatrix} \tag{9.69}$$

Thus, $e^{\Lambda t}$ is ascertained directly from the eigenvalues. Substitution of $\mathbf{y} = P^{-1}\mathbf{x}$ into Eq. (9.68) gives

$$P^{-1}\mathbf{x}(t) = e^{\Lambda t} P^{-1}\mathbf{x}(0)$$

Hence,

$$\mathbf{x}(t) = P e^{\Lambda t} P^{-1}\mathbf{x}(0)$$

Comparison of this result with Eq. (9.61) shows that

$$\Phi(t) = e^{At} = P e^{\Lambda t} P^{-1} \tag{9.70}$$

For Illustrative Example 1 in Sec. 9.3, P is given by Eq. (9.41) and P^{-1} is given by Eq. (9.42). Application of Eq. (9.70) yields for the state-transition matrix

$$\Phi(t) = P e^{\Lambda t} P^{-1} = \begin{bmatrix} -3 & -2 \\ 6 & 6 \end{bmatrix} \begin{bmatrix} e^{-2t} & 0 \\ 0 & e^{-3t} \end{bmatrix} \begin{bmatrix} -1 & -\frac{1}{3} \\ 1 & \frac{1}{2} \end{bmatrix}$$

$$= \begin{bmatrix} (3e^{-2t} - 2e^{-3t}) & (e^{-2t} - e^{-3t}) \\ (-6e^{-2t} + 6e^{-3t}) & (-2e^{-2t} + 3e^{-3t}) \end{bmatrix}$$

This substantiates the result given by Eq. (9.66).

Repeated Roots

The series expansion for the matrix $e^{\Lambda t}$ is

$$e^{\Lambda t} = I + \Lambda t + \frac{\Lambda^2 t^2}{2!} + \cdots \tag{9.71}$$

For a root λ which is repeated twice

$$e^{\Lambda t} = \begin{bmatrix} 1 & 0 \\ 0 & 1 \end{bmatrix} + \begin{bmatrix} \lambda & 1 \\ 0 & \lambda \end{bmatrix} t + \begin{bmatrix} \lambda^2 & 2\lambda \\ 0 & \lambda^2 \end{bmatrix} \frac{t^2}{2!} + \cdots$$

$$= \begin{bmatrix} e^{\lambda t} & te^{\lambda t} \\ 0 & e^{\lambda t} \end{bmatrix}$$

The general form for a root λ which is repeated n times is

$$e^{\Lambda t} = \begin{bmatrix} e^{\lambda t} & te^{\lambda t} & \cdots & \dfrac{t^{n-1}}{(n-1)!} e^{\lambda t} \\ 0 & e^{\lambda t} & \cdots & \dfrac{t^{n-2}}{(n-2)!} e^{\lambda t} \\ \cdots & \cdots & \cdots & \cdots \\ 0 & 0 & \cdots & e^{\lambda t} \end{bmatrix} \tag{9.72}$$

Illustrative example 1 Determine the state-transition matrix for the system represented by Eq. (9.51) of the illustrative example in Sec. 9.4.

SOLUTION The $\mathbf{x} = R\mathbf{z}$ and $\mathbf{z} = R^{-1}\mathbf{x}$ matrix relationships are given by Eq. (9.55). The solution of the canonical equation is given by Eq. (9.54). Application of the $\mathbf{z} = R^{-1}\mathbf{x}$ matrix to express the initial conditions $z_1(0)$ and $z_2(0)$ in terms of $x_1(0)$ and $x_2(0)$ gives

$$\begin{aligned} z_1 &= [z_1(0) + z_2(0)t]e^{-5t} = -te^{-5t}x_1(0) + \frac{(1-5t)e^{-5t}}{25} x_2(0) \\ z_2 &= z_2(0)e^{-5t} = -e^{-5t}x_1(0) - \frac{e^{-5t}}{5} x_2(0) \end{aligned} \tag{9.54}$$

Application of the $\mathbf{x} = R\mathbf{z}$ matrix yields the desired form

$$\begin{bmatrix} x_1 \\ x_2 \end{bmatrix} = \begin{bmatrix} (1+5t)e^{-5t} & te^{-5t} \\ -25te^{-5t} & (1-5t)e^{-5t} \end{bmatrix} \begin{bmatrix} x_1(0) \\ x_2(0) \end{bmatrix} \tag{9.73}$$

The first matrix on the right is the state-transition matrix, $\Phi(t)$.

This result is obtained directly by the application of Eq. (9.70). That is,

$$\Phi(t) = Re^{\Lambda t}R^{-1} = \begin{bmatrix} 5 & -1 \\ 25 & 0 \end{bmatrix} \begin{bmatrix} e^{-5t} & te^{-5t} \\ 0 & e^{-5t} \end{bmatrix} \frac{\begin{bmatrix} 0 & 1 \\ -25 & -5 \end{bmatrix}}{25}$$

$$= \begin{bmatrix} (1+5t)e^{-5t} & te^{-5t} \\ -25te^{-5t} & (1-5t)e^{-5t} \end{bmatrix} \tag{9.74}$$

where the R and R^{-1} matrices are given by Eqs. (9.52) and (9.53), respectively.

Laplace Transform Method

Consider the system of equations

$$\dot{x}_1 = a_{11}x_1 + a_{12}x_2 + \cdots + a_{1n}x_n$$
$$\dot{x}_2 = a_{21}x_1 + a_{22}x_2 + \cdots + a_{2n}x_n$$
$$\cdots\cdots\cdots\cdots\cdots\cdots\cdots\cdots\cdots$$
$$\dot{x}_n = a_{n1}x_1 + a_{n2}x_2 + \cdots + a_{nn}x_n$$

The Laplace transform is

$$sX_1(s) - x_1(0) = a_{11}X_1(s) + a_{12}X_2(s) + \cdots + a_{1n}X_n(s)$$
$$sX_2(s) - x_2(0) = a_{21}X_1(s) + a_{22}X_2(s) + \cdots + a_{2n}X_n(s)$$
$$\cdots\cdots\cdots\cdots\cdots\cdots\cdots\cdots\cdots\cdots\cdots\cdots\cdots$$
$$sX_n(s) - x_n(0) = a_{n1}X_1(s) + a_{n2}X_2(s) + \cdots + a_{nn}X_n(s)$$

The matrix representation for each of the preceding systems of equations is

$$\dot{\mathbf{x}}(t) = A\mathbf{x}(t)$$

and

$$s\mathbf{X}(s) - \mathbf{x}(0) = A\mathbf{X}(s)$$

Note that matrix differential equations transform in the same manner as ordinary differential equations. The preceding expression may be written in the form

$$[sI - A]\mathbf{X}(s) = \mathbf{x}(0)$$

Premultiplying by the inverse matrix, $[sI - A]^{-1}$, yields

$$\mathbf{X}(s) = [sI - A]^{-1}\mathbf{x}(0)$$

Inverting yields for the desired solution

$$\mathbf{x}(t) = \mathscr{L}^{-1}[sI - A]^{-1}\mathbf{x}(0)$$

Comparison with Eq. (9.61) reveals that

$$\Phi(t) = \mathscr{L}^{-1}[sI - A]^{-1} \tag{9.75}$$

This provides an alternative, and in most cases simpler, method for obtaining the state-transition matrix. For the case of Illustrative Example 1 in Sec. 9.3, the $[sI - A]$ matrix is

$$[sI - A] = \begin{bmatrix} s & -1 \\ 6 & s+5 \end{bmatrix}$$

Thus

$$\Phi(s) = [sI - A]^{-1} = \frac{\begin{bmatrix} s+5 & 1 \\ -6 & s \end{bmatrix}}{s^2 + 5s + 6}$$

Writing each element in the form of a partial-fraction expansion shows that

$$\Phi(s) = \begin{bmatrix} \dfrac{3}{s+2} - \dfrac{2}{s+3} & \dfrac{1}{s+2} - \dfrac{1}{s+3} \\ \dfrac{-6}{s+2} + \dfrac{6}{s+3} & \dfrac{-2}{s+2} + \dfrac{3}{s+3} \end{bmatrix}$$

Inverting verifies the result given by Eq. (9.66).

For the case of the illustrative example in Sec. 9.4, the $[sI - A]$ matrix is

$$[sI - A] = \begin{bmatrix} s & -1 \\ 25 & s+10 \end{bmatrix}$$

Thus

$$\Phi(s) = [sI - A]^{-1} = \frac{\begin{bmatrix} s+10 & 1 \\ -25 & s \end{bmatrix}}{s^2 + 10s + 25}$$

Writing each element in the form of a partial-fraction expansion gives

$$\Phi(s) = \begin{bmatrix} \dfrac{1}{s+5} + \dfrac{5}{(s+5)^2} & \dfrac{1}{(s+5)^2} \\ \dfrac{-25}{(s+5)^2} & \dfrac{1}{s+5} - \dfrac{5}{(s+5)^2} \end{bmatrix}$$

Inverting yields the same result given by Eq. (9.74).

Signal-Flow-Graph Method

The use of signal flow graphs saves considerable computational effort in determining the state-transition matrix $\Phi(t)$. The general solution for the force-free case is

$$\mathbf{x}(t) = \Phi(t)\mathbf{x}(0)$$

The Laplace transform is

$$\mathbf{X}(s) = \Phi(s)\mathbf{x}(0)$$

For a second-order system, this relationship is

$$\begin{bmatrix} X_1(s) \\ X_2(s) \end{bmatrix} = \begin{bmatrix} \phi_{11}(s) & \phi_{12}(s) \\ \phi_{21}(s) & \phi_{22}(s) \end{bmatrix} \begin{bmatrix} x_1(0) \\ x_2(0) \end{bmatrix}$$

Inverting yields

$$\begin{bmatrix} x_1(t) \\ x_2(t) \end{bmatrix} = \begin{bmatrix} \phi_{11}(t) & \phi_{12}(t) \\ \phi_{21}(t) & \phi_{22}(t) \end{bmatrix} \begin{bmatrix} x_1(0) \\ x_2(0) \end{bmatrix}$$

For an nth order system, $\Phi(s)$ has the form

$$\Phi(s) = \begin{bmatrix} \phi_{11}(s) & \phi_{12}(s) & \cdots & \phi_{1n}(s) \\ \phi_{21}(s) & \phi_{22}(s) & \cdots & \phi_{2n}(s) \\ \cdots & \cdots & \cdots & \cdots \\ \phi_{n1}(s) & \phi_{n2}(s) & \cdots & \phi_{nn}(s) \end{bmatrix} \tag{9.76}$$

Inverting yields the state-transition matrix

$$\Phi(t) = \begin{bmatrix} \phi_{11}(t) & \phi_{12}(t) & \cdots & \phi_{1n}(t) \\ \phi_{21}(t) & \phi_{22}(t) & \cdots & \phi_{2n}(t) \\ \cdots & \cdots & \cdots & \cdots \\ \phi_{n1}(t) & \phi_{n2}(t) & \cdots & \phi_{nn}(t) \end{bmatrix} \tag{9.77}$$

Each element $\phi_{ij}(s)$ may be determined directly from the signal flow graph for the system.

Illustrative example 2 Use the signal-flow-graph method to determine the solution of Illustrative Example 1 in Sec. 9.3.

SOLUTION The matrix relationships are

$$\dot{x}_1 = x_2$$
$$\dot{x}_2 = -6x_1 - 5x_2$$

To construct the signal flow graph, first take the Laplace transform of these matrix relationships. Thus,

$$sX_1(s) - x_1(0) = X_2(s)$$
$$sX_2(s) - x_2(0) = -6X_1(s) - 5X_2(s)$$

Taking the initial-condition terms to the right side and dividing through by s gives

$$X_1(s) = s^{-1}X_2(s) + s^{-1}x_1(0)$$
$$X_2(s) = s^{-1}[-6X_1(s) - 5X_2(s)] + s^{-1}x_2(0)$$

The signal flow graph for the first relationship is shown in Fig. 9.17*a*, and the graph for the second relationship is shown in Fig. 9.17*b*. These two graphs are combined to yield the signal flow graph for the system, shown in Fig. 9.17*c*. This graph has two loops,

$$L_1 = \frac{-5}{s} \qquad L_2 = \frac{-6}{s^2}$$

Because there are no nontouching loops, the system determinant is

$$\Delta = 1 - (L_1 + L_2) = 1 + \left(\frac{5}{s} + \frac{6}{s^2}\right) = \frac{s^2 + 5s + 6}{s^2}$$

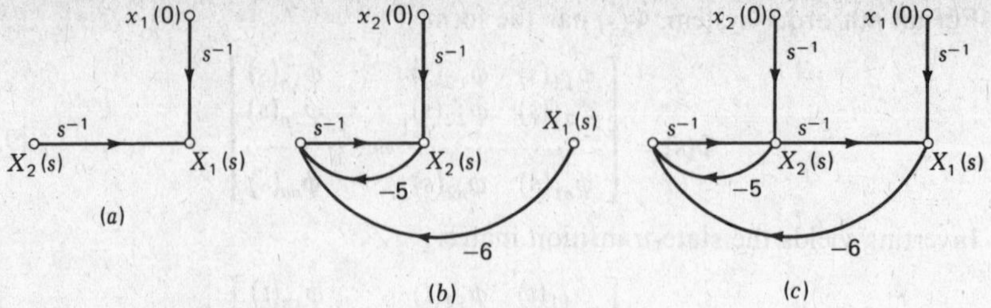

Figure 9.17 Signal flow graph.

The transfer function relating the input $x_1(0)$ to the output $X_1(s)$ is $\phi_{11}(s)$. The transmittance of the forward path from $x_1(0)$ to $X_1(s)$ is $T_1 = 1/s$. Because L_2 touches T_1, setting $L_2 = 0$ in the equation for Δ gives $\Delta_1 = 1 - L_1 = 1 + 5/s = (s + 5)/s$. The transfer function relating the input $x_2(0)$ to the output $X_1(s)$ is $\phi_{12}(s)$. The transmittance of the forward path from $x_2(0)$ to $X_1(s)$ is $T_2 = 1/s^2$. Because both L_1 and L_2 touch T_2, letting $L_1 = L_2 = 0$ in the equation for Δ gives $\Delta_2 = 1$. Thus, the equation for $X_1(s)$ is

$$X_1(s) = \phi_{11}(s)x_1(0) + \phi_{12}(s)x_2(0) = \frac{T_1\Delta_1}{\Delta}x_1(0) + \frac{T_2\Delta_2}{\Delta}x_2(0)$$

$$= \frac{s+5}{s^2+5s+6}x_1(0) + \frac{1}{s^2+5s+6}x_2(0)$$

The transfer function relating $x_1(0)$ to $X_2(s)$ is $\phi_{21}(s)$. The transmittance of this path is $T_3 = -6/s^2$. Because L_1 and L_2 touch this path, setting $L_1 = L_2 = 0$ in the equation for Δ gives $\Delta_3 = 1$. The transfer function relating $x_2(0)$ to $X_2(s)$ is $\phi_{22}(s)$. The transmittance of this path is $T_4 = 1/s$. Because L_1 and L_2 touch this path, $\Delta_4 = 1$. The resulting equation for $X_2(s)$ is

$$X_2(s) = \phi_{21}(s)x_1(0) + \phi_{22}(s)x_2(0) = \frac{T_3\Delta_3}{\Delta}x_1(0) + \frac{T_4\Delta_4}{\Delta}x_2(0)$$

$$= \frac{-6}{s^2+5s+6}x_1(0) + \frac{s}{s^2+5s+6}x_2(0)$$

The matrix form of the preceding relationships is

$$\begin{bmatrix} X_1(s) \\ X_2(s) \end{bmatrix} = \frac{\begin{bmatrix} s+5 & 1 \\ -6 & s \end{bmatrix}}{s^2+5s+6} \begin{bmatrix} x_1(0) \\ x_2(0) \end{bmatrix}$$

The first term on the right is the $\Phi(s) = [sI - A]^{-1}$ matrix. This is the same result attained by the Laplace transform method. Note that the signal-flow-graph method eliminates the need to obtain the matrix inverse.

Illustrative example 3 Use the signal-flow-graph method to determine the state-transition matrix for the illustrative example in Sec. 9.4.

SOLUTION The matrix relationships for this illustrative example are

$$\dot{x}_1 = x_2$$
$$\dot{x}_2 = -25x_1 - 10x_2$$

The Laplace transform of these relationships is

$$sX_1(s) - x_1(0) = X_2(s)$$
$$sX_2(s) - x_2(0) = -25X_1(s) - 10X_2(s)$$

Taking the initial conditions to the right side and dividing through by s gives

$$X_1(s) = s^{-1}X_2(s) + s^{-1}x_1(0)$$
$$X_2(s) = s^{-1}[-25X_1(s) - 10X_2(s)] + s^{-1}x_2(0)$$

The signal flow graph for the first relationship is shown in Fig. 9.18*a*, and the graph for the second relationship is shown in Fig. 9.18*b*. Combining these two graphs yields the signal flow graph for the system, which is shown in Fig. 9.18*c*. This system has two loops,

$$L_1 = \frac{-10}{s} \qquad L_2 = \frac{-25}{s^2}$$

The determinant for the system is

$$\Delta = 1 - (L_1 + L_2) = \frac{s^2 + 10s + 25}{s^2}$$

Application of Mason's gain formula yields the following equation for $X_1(s)$ and $X_2(s)$:

$$\begin{bmatrix} X_1(s) \\ X_2(s) \end{bmatrix} = \frac{\begin{bmatrix} s+10 & 1 \\ -25 & s \end{bmatrix}}{(s+5)^2} \begin{bmatrix} x_1(0) \\ x_2(0) \end{bmatrix}$$

The first matrix on the right is the $\Phi(s) = [sI - A]^{-1}$ matrix. This is the same result attained by the Laplace transform method.

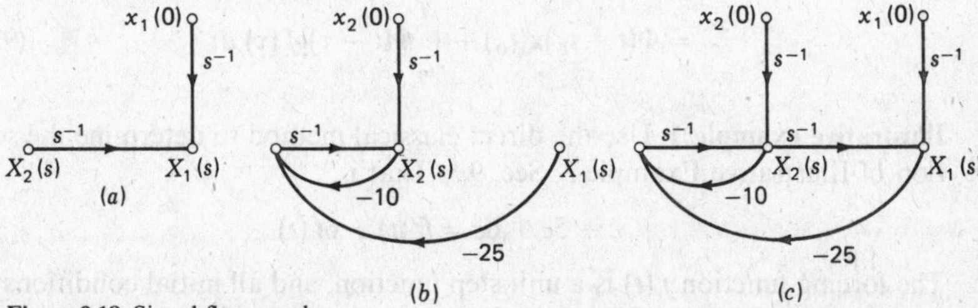

Figure 9.18 Signal flow graph.

9.7 FORCED RESPONSE

The general representation for a system of differential equations with a forcing function is

$$\dot{\mathbf{x}}(t) = A\mathbf{x}(t) + \mathbf{b}f(t) \qquad \mathbf{x}(0) = \mathbf{x}_0 \tag{9.78}$$

To solve this system, first rewrite it in the form

$$\dot{\mathbf{x}}(t) - A\mathbf{x}(t) = \mathbf{b}f(t)$$

Multiplying through by e^{-At} shows that

$$e^{-At}[\dot{\mathbf{x}}(t) - A\mathbf{x}(t)] = \frac{d}{dt}[e^{-At}\mathbf{x}(t)] = e^{-At}\mathbf{b}f(t)$$

Integration between the limits 0 and t of the two expressions on the right side of the preceding equation gives

$$e^{-At}\mathbf{x}(t) - \mathbf{x}(0) = \int_0^t e^{-A\tau}\mathbf{b}f(\tau)\,d\tau \tag{9.79}$$

Multiplying through by e^{At} yields the desired solution:

$$\mathbf{x}(t) = e^{At}\mathbf{x}(0) + \int_0^t e^{A(t-\tau)}\mathbf{b}f(\tau)\,d\tau \tag{9.80}$$

Replacing e^{At} by $\Phi(t)$ and $e^{A(t-\tau)}$ by $\Phi(t-\tau) = \Phi(t)\Phi(-\tau)$ yields the form

$$\mathbf{x}(t) = \Phi(t)\mathbf{x}(0) + \Phi(t)\int_0^t \Phi(-\tau)\mathbf{b}f(\tau)\,d\tau \tag{9.81}$$

For the case in which the initial state is known at time t_0 rather than at $t = 0$, Eq. (9.79) becomes

$$e^{-At}\mathbf{x}(t) - e^{-At_0}\mathbf{x}(t_0) = \int_{t_0}^t e^{-A\tau}\mathbf{b}f(\tau)\,d\tau$$

Multiplying through by e^{At} yields

$$\mathbf{x}(t) = e^{A(t-t_0)}\mathbf{x}(t_0) + \int_{t_0}^t e^{A(t-\tau)}\mathbf{b}f(\tau)\,d\tau$$

$$= \Phi(t-t_0)\mathbf{x}(t_0) + \int_{t_0}^t \Phi(t-\tau)\mathbf{b}f(\tau)\,d\tau \tag{9.82}$$

Illustrative example 1 Use the direct classical method to determine the solution of Illustrative Example 3, Sec. 9.3. That is,

$$\ddot{c} + 5\dot{c} + 6c = f'(t) + 6f(t)$$

The forcing function $f(t)$ is a unit step function, and all initial conditions are zero.

SOLUTION The state-space representation used in Illustrative Example 3, Sec. 9.3, was

$$\begin{bmatrix}\dot{x}_1\\ \dot{x}_2\end{bmatrix} = \begin{bmatrix}0 & 1\\ -6 & -5\end{bmatrix}\begin{bmatrix}x_1\\ x_2\end{bmatrix} + \begin{bmatrix}1\\ 1\end{bmatrix} f(t)$$

where $c = x_1$. The corresponding Λ, P, and P^{-1} matrices were

$$\Lambda = \begin{bmatrix}-2 & 0\\ 0 & -3\end{bmatrix} \qquad P = \begin{bmatrix}4 & -3\\ -8 & 9\end{bmatrix} \qquad P^{-1} = \frac{1}{12}\begin{bmatrix}9 & 3\\ 8 & 4\end{bmatrix}$$

The $e^{\Lambda t}$ matrix is

$$e^{\Lambda t} = \begin{bmatrix}e^{-2t} & 0\\ 0 & e^{-3t}\end{bmatrix}$$

Note that the arrangement of the $e^{\lambda t}$ terms is the same as the arrangement of the λ terms in the Λ matrix. Although it makes no difference which eigenvalue is taken first (-2 or -3), the order must be retained because it determines the order in which the rows are obtained in the P matrix and the order in which the columns are obtained in the P^{-1} matrix. From the preceding values of P, $e^{\Lambda t}$, and P^{-1}, the state-transition matrix $\Phi(t)$ is found to be

$$\Phi(t) = Pe^{\Lambda t}P^{-1} = \begin{bmatrix}(3e^{-2t} - 2e^{-3t}) & (e^{-2t} - e^{-3t})\\ (-6e^{-2t} + 6e^{-3t}) & (-2e^{-2t} + 3e^{-3t})\end{bmatrix} \tag{9.83}$$

Replacing t by $-\tau$ and then multiplying by $\mathbf{b}$ gives

$$\Phi(-\tau)\mathbf{b} = \begin{bmatrix}4e^{2\tau} - 3e^{3\tau}\\ -8e^{2\tau} + 9e^{3\tau}\end{bmatrix}$$

Calculation of $\int_0^t \Phi(-\tau)\mathbf{b}f(\tau)\,d\tau$ where $f(\tau) = 1$ gives

$$\begin{bmatrix}\int_0^t (4e^{2\tau} - 3e^{3\tau})\,d\tau\\ \int_0^t (-8e^{2\tau} + 9e^{3\tau})\,d\tau\end{bmatrix} = \begin{bmatrix}2e^{2t} - e^{3t} - 1\\ -4e^{2t} + 3e^{3t} + 1\end{bmatrix}$$

Because the initial conditions are all zero, the solution following Eq. (9.81) is $\mathbf{x}(t) = \Phi(t)\int_0^t \Phi(-\tau)\mathbf{b}f(\tau)\,d\tau$. The result of this computation is

$$\begin{bmatrix}x_1\\ x_2\end{bmatrix} = \begin{bmatrix}1 - 2e^{-2t} + e^{-3t}\\ -1 + 4e^{-2t} - 3e^{-3t}\end{bmatrix} \tag{9.84}$$

From Illustrative Example 3, $c = x_1$ and $\dot{c} = \dot{x}_1 = x_2 + f(t) = x_2 + 1$. Thus

$$c = 1 - 2e^{-2t} + e^{-3t}$$

$$\dot{c} = 4e^{-2t} - 3e^{-3t} \tag{9.49}$$

This verifies the previously attained result, given by Eq. (9.49).

Laplace Transform Method

The Laplace transform of Eq. (9.78) is

$$s\mathbf{X}(s) - \mathbf{x}(0) = A\mathbf{X}(s) + \mathbf{b}F(s)$$

This may be written in the form

$$[sI - A]\mathbf{X}(s) = \mathbf{x}(0) + \mathbf{b}F(s)$$

Premultiplying by the inverse $[sI - A]^{-1}$ gives

$$\mathbf{X}(s) = [sI - A]^{-1}\mathbf{x}(0) + [sI - A]^{-1}\mathbf{b}F(s)$$

Inverting yields for the solution

$$\mathbf{x}(t) = \mathscr{L}^{-1}[sI - A]^{-1}\mathbf{x}(0) + \mathscr{L}^{-1}[sI - A]^{-1}\mathbf{b}F(s)$$

Comparison with Eq. (9.81) shows that

$$\Phi(t) = \mathscr{L}^{-1}[sI - A]^{-1} \tag{9.75}$$

and

$$\Phi(t)\int_0^t \Phi(-\tau)\mathbf{b}f(\tau)\,d\tau = \mathscr{L}^{-1}[sI - A]^{-1}\mathbf{b}F(s) \tag{9.85}$$

The first result was previously established by Eq. (9.75).

Illustrative example 2 Use the Laplace transform method to determine the solution of Illustrative Example 3, Sec. 9.3.

SOLUTION From Illustrative Example 3, Sec. 9.3, the A and $\mathbf{b}$ matrices are

$$A = \begin{bmatrix} 0 & 1 \\ -6 & -5 \end{bmatrix} \qquad \mathbf{b} = \begin{bmatrix} 1 \\ 1 \end{bmatrix}$$

The $[sI - A]$ matrix is

$$[sI - A] = \begin{bmatrix} s & -1 \\ 6 & s+5 \end{bmatrix}$$

The inverse is

$$[sI - A]^{-1} = \frac{\begin{bmatrix} s+5 & 1 \\ -6 & s \end{bmatrix}}{s^2 + 5s + 6} = \begin{bmatrix} \dfrac{3}{s+2} - \dfrac{2}{s+3} & \dfrac{1}{s+2} - \dfrac{1}{s+3} \\[2ex] \dfrac{-6}{s+2} + \dfrac{6}{s+3} & \dfrac{-2}{s+2} + \dfrac{3}{s+3} \end{bmatrix} \tag{9.86}$$

Taking the inverse Laplace transform yields the same result for $\Phi(t)$ as was given by Eq. (9.83). Multiplication of $\mathbf{b}F(s)$ by the $[sI - A]^{-1}$ matrix gives

$$[sI - A]^{-1}\mathbf{b}F(s) = \begin{bmatrix} \frac{1}{s} - \frac{2}{s+2} + \frac{1}{s+3} \\ -\frac{1}{s} + \frac{4}{s+2} - \frac{3}{s+3} \end{bmatrix} \tag{9.87}$$

where $F(s) = 1/s$ for a unit step function. The inverse Laplace transform verifies the result for $\Phi(t) \int_0^t \Phi(-\tau)\mathbf{b}f(\tau)\,d\tau$ which is shown on the right side of Eq. (9.84).

Signal-Flow-Graph Method

To apply this method, first take the Laplace transform of the state-space equation, $\dot{\mathbf{x}} = A\mathbf{x} + \mathbf{b}f(t)$. That is,

$$s\mathbf{X}(s) - \mathbf{x}(0) = A\mathbf{X}(s) - \mathbf{b}f(t)$$

The signal flow graph is then constructed by writing this in the form

$$\mathbf{X}(s) = s^{-1}\mathbf{x}(0) + s^{-1}A\mathbf{X}(s) + s^{-1}\mathbf{b}F(s)$$

The input nodes for the resulting graph are the initial conditons $\mathbf{x}(0)$ and the transform of the input, $F(s)$. The output nodes are the transform of the state variables $\mathbf{X}(s)$. Application of Mason's gain formula yields directly the following matrix:

$$\begin{bmatrix} X_1(s) \\ X_2(s) \\ \vdots \\ X_n(s) \end{bmatrix} = \begin{bmatrix} \phi_{11}(s) & \phi_{12}(s) & \cdots & \phi_{1n}(s) \\ \phi_{21}(s) & \phi_{22}(s) & \cdots & \phi_{2n}(s) \\ \vdots & \vdots & & \vdots \\ \phi_{n1}(s) & \phi_{n2}(s) & \cdots & \phi_{nn}(s) \end{bmatrix} \begin{bmatrix} x_1(0) \\ x_2(0) \\ \vdots \\ x_n(0) \end{bmatrix} + \begin{bmatrix} \psi_1(s) \\ \psi_2(s) \\ \vdots \\ \psi_n(s) \end{bmatrix} F(s) \tag{9.88}$$

Inverting yields the desired solution. Note that each element $\phi_{ij}(s)$ and $\psi_i(s)$ is obtained individually from the signal flow graph.

Illustrative example 3 Use the signal-flow-graph method to determine the solution of Illustrative Example 3 in Sec. 9.3.

SOLUTION The Laplace transform of the state-space equation is

$$sX_1(s) - x_1(0) = X_2(s) + F(s)$$

$$sX_2(s) - x_2(0) = -6X_1(s) - 5X_2(s) + F(s)$$

Taking the initial conditions to the right side and dividing through by s gives

$$X_1(s) = s^{-1}x_1(0) + s^{-1}[X_2(s) + F(s)]$$

$$X_2(s) = s^{-1}x_2(0) + s^{-1}[-6X_1(s) - 5X_2(s) + F(s)]$$

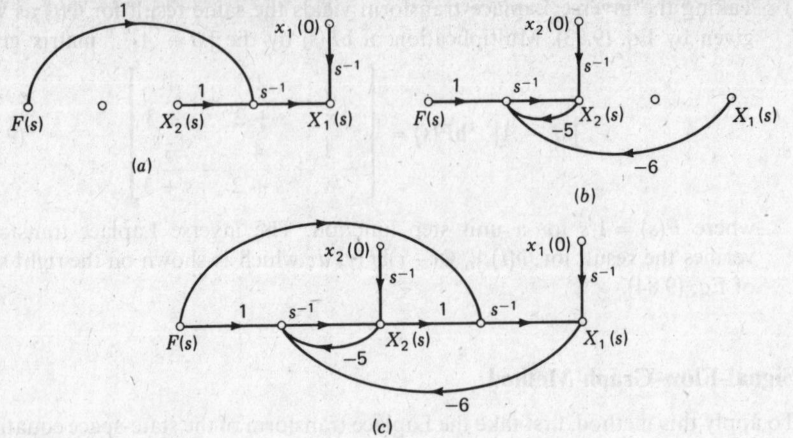

Figure 9.19 Signal flow graph.

The signal flow graph for the first equation is shown in Fig. 9.19*a*, and the graph for the second equation is shown in Fig. 9.19*b*. These graphs are combined to yield the resultant graph for the system, shown in Fig. 9.19*c*. Application of Mason's gain formula to this graph yields

$$\begin{bmatrix} X_1(s) \\ X_2(s) \end{bmatrix} = \begin{bmatrix} \dfrac{s+5}{s^2+5s+6} & \dfrac{1}{s^2+5s+6} \\ \dfrac{-6}{s^2+5s+6} & \dfrac{s}{s^2+5s+6} \end{bmatrix} \begin{bmatrix} x_1(0) \\ x_2(0) \end{bmatrix} + \begin{bmatrix} \dfrac{s+6}{s^2+5s+6} \\ \dfrac{s-6}{s^2+5s+6} \end{bmatrix} F(s)$$

The first matrix on the right side is the $[sI - A]^{-1}$ matrix, and the last matrix is the $[sI - A]^{-1}\mathbf{b}$ matrix. These are the same results as were obtained by the Laplace transform method, Eqs. (9.86) and (9.87). A major feature of the signal-flow-graph method is that it eliminates the need to obtain the matrix inverse.

Illustrative example 4 Use the signal-flow-graph method to determine the solution of the differential equation

$$\ddot{c} + 6\dot{c} + 25c = 100f(t)$$

The forcing function $f(t)$ is a unit step function, and all initial conditions are zero.

SOLUTION Letting $c = x_1$ and $\dot{c} = \dot{x}_1 = x_2$, the state-space representation is

$$\dot{x}_1 = x_2$$

$$\dot{x}_2 = -25x_1 - 6x_2 + 100f(t)$$

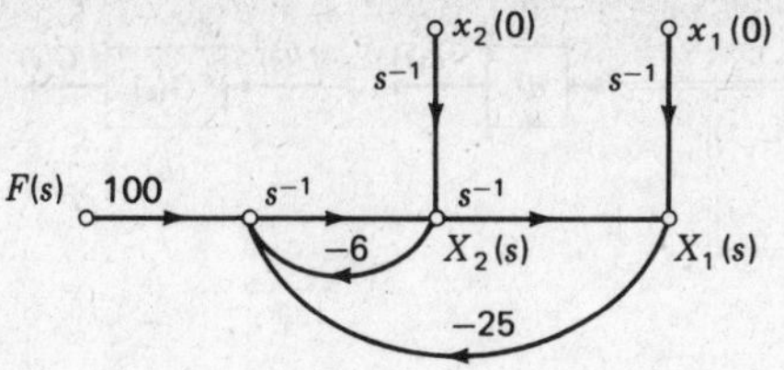

Figure 9.20 Signal flow graph.

Transforming gives

$$sX_1(s) - x_1(0) = X_2(s)$$
$$sX_2(s) - x_2(0) = -25X_1(s) - 6X_2(s) + 100F(s)$$

The form for constructing the signal flow graph is

$$X_1(s) = s^{-1}x_1(0) + s^{-1}X_2(s)$$
$$X_2(s) = s^{-1}x_2(0) + s^{-1}[-25X_1(s) - 6X_2(s) + 100F(s)]$$

The resulting signal flow graph is shown in Fig. 9.20.

Application of Mason's gain formula gives

$$\begin{bmatrix} X_1(s) \\ X_2(s) \end{bmatrix} = \frac{\begin{bmatrix} s+6 & 1 \\ -25 & s \end{bmatrix}\begin{bmatrix} x_1(0) \\ x_2(0) \end{bmatrix}}{s^2 + 6s + 25} + \begin{bmatrix} 100 \\ 100s \end{bmatrix} \frac{F(s)}{s^2 + 6s + 25}$$

For $x_1(0) = x_2(0) = 0$ and $F(s) = 1/s$, the inverse yields the desired result

$$c = x_1 = 4 + 5e^{-3t} \sin (4t - 126.9^\circ)$$
$$\dot{c} = x_2 = 25e^{-3t} \sin 4t$$

Note that no special considerations are needed in applying this method to complex conjugate roots.

9.8 TRANSFER FUNCTIONS

The state-space representation for a system to be controlled is shown in Fig. 9.21*a*. The system to be controlled is referred to as the plant. In state-space notation the characteristics of the plant are given by Eqs. (9.20) and (9.21):

$$\dot{\mathbf{x}} = A\mathbf{x} + \mathbf{b}u \tag{9.20}$$

$$c = \mathbf{d}^T\mathbf{x} \tag{9.21}$$

The corresponding transfer-function representation for the plant is shown in Fig. 9.21*b*. In Sec. 9.1, techniques for obtaining various state-space representations for a system were illustrated. It is now shown how the transfer function may

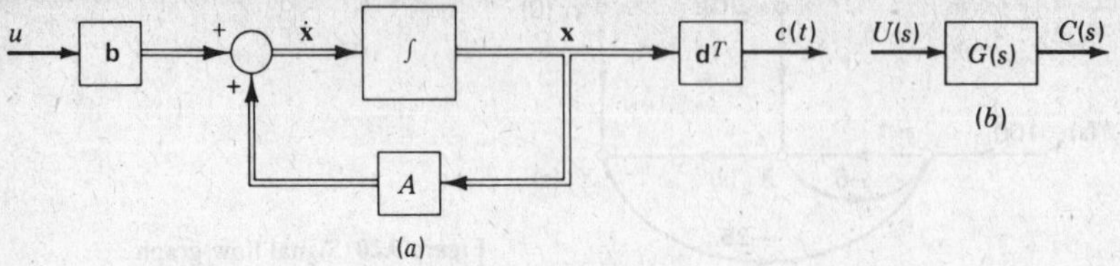

Figure 9.21 State-space representation and corresponding transfer function.

be obtained from the state-space representation. The Laplace transform of the preceding matrix equations is

$$s\mathbf{X}(s) - \mathbf{x}(0) = A\mathbf{X}(s) + \mathbf{b}U(s)$$

$$C(s) = \mathbf{d}^T\mathbf{X}(s)$$

In obtaining the transfer function, the initial conditions are ignored. Thus, the first relationship becomes

$$(sI - A)\mathbf{X}(s) = \mathbf{b}U(s)$$

Hence

$$\mathbf{X}(s) = (sI - A)^{-1}\mathbf{b}U(s) = \Phi(s)\mathbf{b}U(s)$$

where $\Phi(s) = (sI - A)^{-1}$ is the state-transition matrix for the plant. Substitution of this result into the second transformed equation gives

$$C(s) = \mathbf{d}^T\Phi(s)\mathbf{b}U(s) = G(s)U(s)$$

Hence

$$G(s) = \mathbf{d}^T\Phi(s)\mathbf{b} \tag{9.89}$$

Because $\Phi(s) = \text{adj }(sI - A)/|sI - A|$, the preceding may be written in the form

$$G(s) = \frac{C(s)}{U(s)} = \frac{\mathbf{d}^T[\text{adj }(sI - A)]\mathbf{b}}{|sI - A|}$$

The numerator polynomial for $G(s)$ is $\mathbf{d}^T[\text{adj }(sI - A)]\mathbf{b}$. The denominator, which is the characteristic function, is $|sI - A|$. The roots of the characteristic equation $|sI - A| = 0$ are the roots of $|\lambda I - A| = 0$ which are the eigenvalues for the system.

For a given plant $G(s)$, there are an infinite number of state-space representations. The transformation $\mathbf{x} = P\mathbf{y}$ transforms Eqs. (9.20) and (9.21) into the form

$$\dot{\mathbf{y}} = P^{-1}AP\mathbf{y} + P^{-1}\mathbf{b}u$$

$$c = \mathbf{d}^T P\mathbf{y}$$

This new state-space representation for the plant may be written in the form

$$\dot{\mathbf{y}} = A^*\mathbf{y} + \mathbf{b}^*u$$

$$c = \mathbf{d}^{*T}\mathbf{y}$$

where $A^* = P^{-1}AP$, $\mathbf{b}^* = P^{-1}\mathbf{b}$, and $\mathbf{d}^* = P^T\mathbf{d}$. Note that these equations have the same form as Eqs. (9.20) and (9.21) but are different matrix representations for the same plant. In this analysis, P is any matrix, not necessarily the one that transforms the system to the canonical form.

The characteristic equation for the plant transfer function $G(s)$ is $|sI - A|$. Because the characteristic equation is a unique property of the system and does not depend on the particular matrix representation, it follows that

$$|sI - A| = |sI - A^*|$$

To prove the preceding relationship, note that

$$\begin{aligned}|sI - A^*| &= |sI - P^{-1}AP| = |sIP^{-1}P - P^{-1}AP| \\ &= |P^{-1}(sI - A)P|\end{aligned}$$

Because the determinant of a product is equal to the product of the determinants,

$$\begin{aligned}|sI - A^*| &= |P^{-1}|\,|sI - A|\,|P| = |P^{-1}|\,|P|\,|sI - A| \\ &= |P^{-1}P|\,|sI - A| = |sI - A|\end{aligned}$$

Similarly, the transfer function for the plant $G(s) = \mathbf{d}^T(sI - A)^{-1}\mathbf{b}$ is unaffected by the particular matrix representation for the plant. Thus,

$$\mathbf{d}^T(sI - A)^{-1}\mathbf{b} = \mathbf{d}^{*T}(sI - A^*)^{-1}\mathbf{b}^*$$

The preceding relationship is proved as follows:

$$\begin{aligned}\mathbf{d}^{*T}(sI - A^*)^{-1}\mathbf{b}^* &= \mathbf{d}^T P(sI - P^{-1}AP)^{-1}P^{-1}\mathbf{b} = \mathbf{d}^T[P(sI - P^{-1}AP)P^{-1}]^{-1}\mathbf{b} \\ &= \mathbf{d}^T(sPP^{-1} - A)^{-1}\mathbf{b} = \mathbf{d}^T(sI - A)^{-1}\mathbf{b} = G(s)\end{aligned}$$

For the case of Illustrative Example 3, in Sec. 9.3,

$$\mathbf{d}^T = \begin{bmatrix}1\\0\end{bmatrix} \qquad A = \begin{bmatrix}0 & 1\\ -6 & -5\end{bmatrix} \qquad \mathbf{b} = \begin{bmatrix}1\\1\end{bmatrix}$$

Thus

$$(sI - A) = \begin{bmatrix}s & -1\\ 6 & s+5\end{bmatrix} \qquad \operatorname{adj}\,(sI - A) = \begin{bmatrix}s+5 & 1\\ -6 & s\end{bmatrix}$$

$$|sI - A| = \begin{vmatrix}s & -1\\ 6 & s+5\end{vmatrix} = s^2 + 5s + 6$$

Application of Eq. (9.89) yields

$$G(s) = \frac{[1 \quad 0]\begin{bmatrix}s+5 & 1\\ -6 & s\end{bmatrix}\begin{bmatrix}1\\1\end{bmatrix}}{s^2 + 5s + 6} = \frac{s+6}{s^2 + 5s + 6}$$

The differential equation for this system, Eq. (9.48), may be written in the operator form:

$$c(t) = \frac{D+6}{D^2 + 5D + 6} f(t)$$

Replacing the operator D by s verifies the result obtained for $G(s)$. When Illustrative Example 3 in Sec. 9.3 was solved by direct programming, the $\mathbf{d}^T$, A, and $\mathbf{b}$ matrices were

$$\mathbf{d}^T = \begin{bmatrix} 6 \\ 1 \end{bmatrix} \qquad A = \begin{bmatrix} 0 & 1 \\ -6 & -5 \end{bmatrix} \qquad \mathbf{b} = \begin{bmatrix} 0 \\ 1 \end{bmatrix}$$

Application of Eq. (9.89) yields the same result for $G(s)$. That is,

$$G(s) = \frac{[6 \quad 1]\begin{bmatrix} s+5 & 1 \\ -6 & s \end{bmatrix}\begin{bmatrix} 0 \\ 1 \end{bmatrix}}{\begin{vmatrix} s & -1 \\ 6 & s+5 \end{vmatrix}} = \frac{s+6}{s^2 + 5s + 6}$$

Closed-Loop Systems

A general block-diagram representation for a closed-loop system with linear state-variable feedback is shown in Fig. 9.22*a*. The corresponding state-space representation is shown in Fig. 9.22*b*. For linear state-variable feedback, the control input u is the difference between the reference input r and a weighted sum of the state variables. That is,

$$u = K[r - (k_1 x_1 + k_2 x_2 + \cdots + k_n x_n)]$$

In matrix notation, this relationship is

$$u = K(r - \mathbf{k}^T \mathbf{x})$$

To obtain the transfer function for the closed-loop system, first substitute u into Eq. (9.20). Thus,

$$\dot{\mathbf{x}} = (A - K\mathbf{b}\mathbf{k}^T)\mathbf{x} + K\mathbf{b}r$$
$$c = \mathbf{d}^T\mathbf{x}$$

Transforming each expression, then solving the first for $\mathbf{X}(s)$ and substituting this result into the second gives

$$C(s) = \mathbf{d}^T\mathbf{X}(s) = K\mathbf{d}^T[sI - (A - K\mathbf{b}\mathbf{k}^T)]^{-1}\mathbf{b}R(s)$$

The closed-loop transfer function $C(s)/R(s)$ may be written in the form

$$\frac{C(s)}{R(s)} = K\mathbf{d}^T(sI - A_c)^{-1}\mathbf{b} = K\mathbf{d}^T\Phi_c(s)\mathbf{b} \tag{9.90}$$

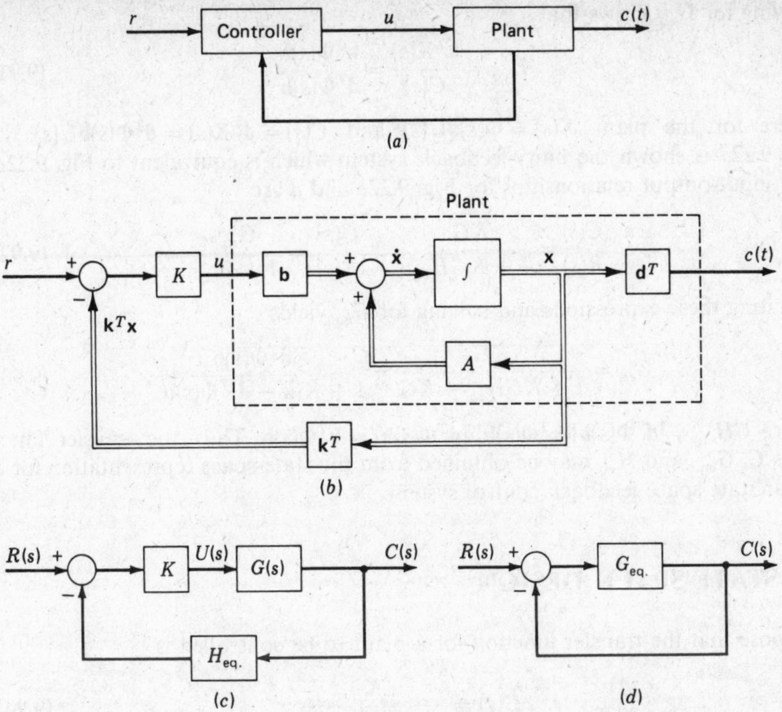

Figure 9.22 Closed-loop system with linear state-variable feedback.

where $A_c = (A - K\mathbf{b}\mathbf{k}^T)$ and $\Phi_c(s) = (sI - A_c)^{-1}$ is the state-transition matrix for the closed-loop system. Note that the state-transition matrix for the closed-loop system is the same as that for the plant except that A is replaced by $A_c = (A - K\mathbf{b}\mathbf{k}^T)$. The closed-loop transfer function may be written in the form

$$G_c(s) = \frac{C(s)}{R(s)} = \frac{K\mathbf{d}^T[\text{adj}\,(sI - A_c)]\mathbf{b}}{|sI - A_c|}$$

This shows that the denominator which is the characteristic equation for the closed-loop system is $|sI - A_c|$.

In Fig. 9.22c is shown an equivalent block-diagram representation for the system of Fig. 9.22b. The feedforward elements are the same for both cases. The feedback signal which goes to the comparator in Fig. 9.22b is $\mathbf{k}^T\mathbf{x}$. The Laplace transform for this signal is $\mathbf{k}^T\mathbf{X}(s)$. For the equivalent system the signal going to the comparator is $H_{eq}C(s)$. Thus

$$H_{eq}C(s) = \mathbf{k}^T\mathbf{X}(s)$$

Solving for H_{eq} shows that

$$H_{eq} = \frac{\mathbf{k}^T\mathbf{X}(s)}{C(s)} = \frac{\mathbf{k}^T\Phi(s)\mathbf{b}}{\mathbf{d}^T\Phi(s)\mathbf{b}} \tag{9.91}$$

where for the plant $\mathbf{X}(s) = \Phi(s)\mathbf{b}U(s)$ and $C(s) = \mathbf{d}^T\mathbf{X}(s) = \mathbf{d}^T\Phi(s)\mathbf{b}U(s)$. In Fig. 9.22*d* is shown the unity-feedback system which is equivalent to Fig. 9.22*c*. The input-output relationships for Fig. 9.22*c* and *d* are

$$\frac{C(s)}{R(s)} = \frac{KG}{1 + KGH_{eq}} \qquad \frac{C(s)}{R(s)} = \frac{G_{eq}}{1 + G_{eq}} \tag{9.92}$$

Equating these expressions and solving for G_{eq} yields

$$G_{eq} = \frac{KG}{1 + KGH_{eq} - KG} = \frac{K\mathbf{d}^T\Phi(s)\mathbf{b}}{1 + K(\mathbf{k} - \mathbf{d})^T\Phi(s)\mathbf{b}} \tag{9.93}$$

where $GH_{eq} = [\mathbf{d}^T\Phi(s)\mathbf{b}][\mathbf{k}^T\Phi(s)\mathbf{b}]/[\mathbf{d}^T\Phi(s)\mathbf{b}] = \mathbf{k}^T\Phi(s)\mathbf{b}$. Thus, the transfer functions G, G_{eq}, and H_{eq} may be obtained from the state-space representation for a linear state-space feedback control system.

9.9 STATE-SPACE DESIGN[1]

Suppose that the transfer function for a plant to be controlled is

$$G(s) = \frac{K}{s(s+1)(s+2)} \tag{9.94}$$

The state-variable representation of a closed-loop system for controlling this plant is shown in Fig. 9.23*a*. It is assumed that each of the state variables x_1, x_2, and x_3 is a real physical variable that may be employed in the system. By block-diagram algebra, the system of Fig. 9.23*a* may be represented as shown in Fig. 9.23*b*. The resulting closed-loop transfer function is

$$\frac{C(s)}{R(s)} = \frac{K}{s(s+1)(s+2) + K[k_3 s^2 + (k_2 + k_3)s + k_1]}$$
$$= \frac{K}{s^3 + (3 + Kk_3)s^2 + [2 + K(k_2 + k_3)]s + Kk_1} \tag{9.95}$$

The variables k_1, k_2, k_3, and K may now be selected to obtain any closed-loop transfer function which has the same form as Eq. (9.95). For example, let it be desired to have the following closed-loop transfer function:

$$\frac{C(s)}{R(s)} = \frac{50}{(s+2)(s^2 + 6s + 25)} = \frac{50}{s^3 + 8s^2 + 37s + 50} \tag{9.96}$$

[1] J. L. Melsa and D. G. Schultz, "Linear Control Systems," McGraw-Hill Book Company, New York, 1969.

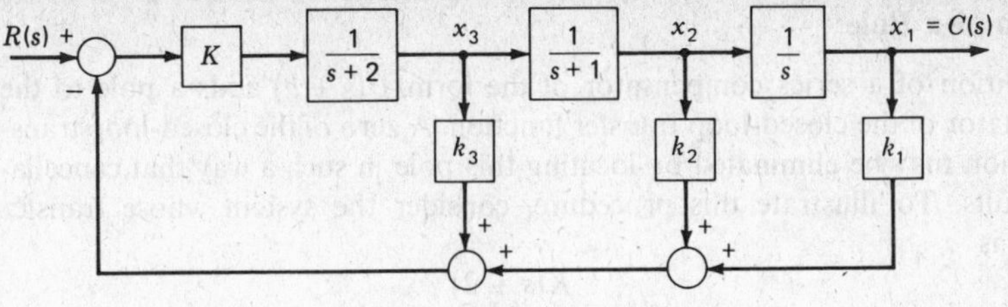

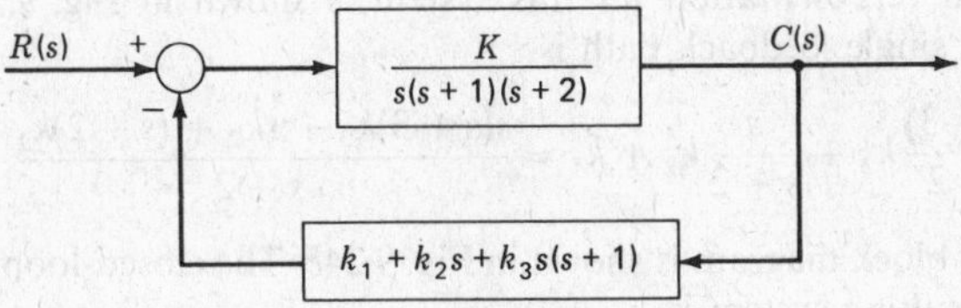

Figure 9.23 System with linear state-variable feedback.

Comparison of corresponding terms in Eqs. (9.95) and (9.96) shows that

$$K = 50$$

$$Kk_1 = 50$$

$$(3 + Kk_3) = 8$$

$$[2 + K(k_2 + k_3)] = 37$$

Thus, it is found that $k_1 = 1$, $k_2 = 0.6$, and $k_3 = 0.1$. The resulting feedback function H is

$$H = k_3 s(s + 1) + k_2 s + k_1 = 0.1(s^2 + 7s + 10) = 0.1(s + 2)(s + 5)$$

Using this numerical value for H in Fig. 9.23b yields the following closed-loop transfer function:

$$\frac{C(s)}{R(s)} = \frac{K}{s(s + 1)(s + 2) + 0.1K(s + 2)(s + 5)} = \frac{K}{(s + 2)[s(s + 1) + 0.1K(s + 5)]}$$

For $K = 50$, the term in brackets may be written in the form $s^2 + 6s + 25$. This result is verified by noting that for $K = 50$, then $s(s + 1) + 0.1K(s + 5) = s^2 + s + 5(s + 5) = s^2 + 6s + 25$. Thus, the parameters $K = 50$, $k_1 = 1$, $k_2 = 0.6$, and $k_3 = 0.1$ yield the desired closed-loop transfer function given by Eq. (9.96).

Addition of a Pole

The addition of a series compensator of the form $1/(s+b)$ adds a pole to the denominator of the closed-loop transfer function. A zero of the closed-loop transfer function may be eliminated by locating this pole in such a way that cancellation results. To illustrate this procedure, consider the system whose transfer function is

$$G(s) = \frac{K(s+2)}{s(s+3)}$$

The block-diagram representation for this system is shown in Fig. 9.24*a*. The equivalent H for a single feedback path is

$$H = \frac{s(s+3)}{s+2}k_3 + \frac{s}{s+2}k_2 + k_1 = \frac{s(s+3)k_3 + sk_2 + (s+2)k_1}{s+2}$$

The corresponding block diagram is shown in Fig. 9.24*b*. The closed-loop transfer function for the resulting system is

$$\frac{C(s)}{R(s)} = \frac{K(s+2)}{s(s+3)(s+b) + K[k_3 s^2 + (3k_3 + k_2 + k_1)s + 2k_1]}$$

$$= \frac{K(s+2)}{s^3 + (3 + b + Kk_3)s^2 + [3b + K(3k_3 + k_2 + k_1)]s + 2k_1 K} \qquad (9.97)$$

Let it be desired that the resulting closed-loop transfer function have the form

$$\frac{C(s)}{R(s)} = \frac{50}{s^2 + 6s + 25} = \frac{50(s+2)}{(s+2)(s^2 + 6s + 25)} = \frac{50(s+2)}{s^3 + 8s^2 + 37s + 50} \qquad (9.98)$$

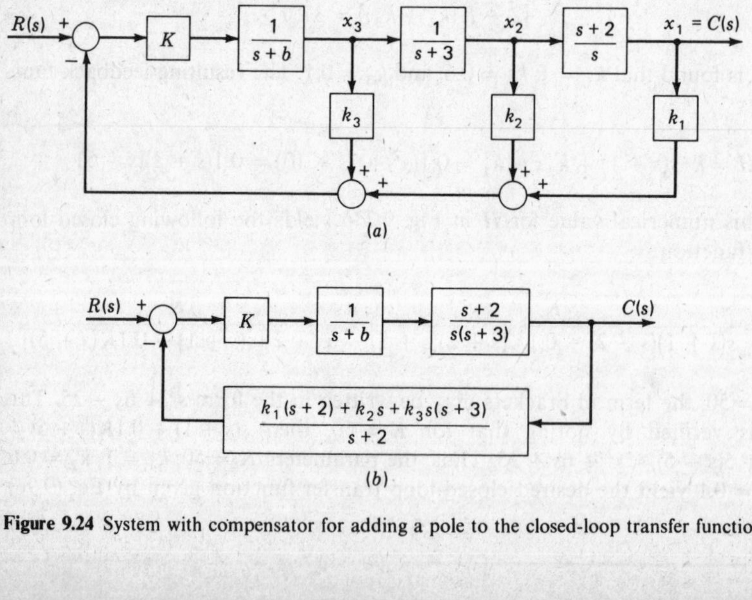

Figure 9.24 System with compensator for adding a pole to the closed-loop transfer function.

Comparison of corresponding terms in Eqs. (9.97) and (9.98) shows that

$$K = 50$$

$$2k_1 K = 50 \qquad \text{or} \qquad k_1 = 0.5$$

$$3 + (b + Kk_3) = 8 \qquad \text{or} \qquad b + Kk_3 = 5$$

$$K(k_1 + k_2) + 3(b + Kk_3) = 37 \qquad \text{or} \qquad k_1 + k_2 = \tfrac{22}{50} = 0.44 \qquad k_2 = -0.06$$

The values of k_3 and b may be selected arbitrarily so that $b + Kk_3 = 5$. The extreme cases are ($k_3 = 0$, $b = 5$) and ($b = 0$, $k_3 = 0.1$). Good proportioning is obtained by selecting as b the negative of the location of the pole which it is desired to introduce into the closed-loop transfer function. To cancel the zero located at -2, the pole is also located at -2, in which case $b = 2$ and $k_3 = (5 - 2)/K = 0.06$.

For the case in which $k_3 = 0$ and $b = 5$, the feedback function H is

$$H = \frac{k_3 s^2 + (3k_3 + k_2 + k_1)s + 2k_1}{s + 2} = \frac{0.44(s + 2.27)}{s + 2}$$

For this value of H it follows from Fig. 9.24*b* that the closed-loop transfer function is

$$\frac{C(s)}{R(s)} = \frac{K(s + 2)}{s(s + 3)(s + 5) + 0.44K(s + 2.27)}$$

The characteristic equation is the denominator of $C(s)/R(s)$. For $K = 50$, the factored form of the characteristic equation is $(s + 2)(s^2 + 6s + 25)$. Thus, the parameters $k_1 = 0.5$, $k_2 = -0.06$, $k_3 = 0$, $b = 5$, and $K = 50$ yield the desired form, given by Eq. (9.98).

For the case in which $k_3 = 0.06$ and $b = 2$, the feedback function H is

$$H = \frac{0.06s^2 + 0.62s + 1}{s + 2} = \frac{0.06(s^2 + \frac{31}{3}s + \frac{50}{3})}{(s + 2)}$$

$$= \frac{0.06(s + 2)(s + \frac{25}{3})}{(s + 2)} = 0.06\left(s + \frac{25}{3}\right)$$

The corresponding closed-loop transfer function is

$$\frac{C(s)}{R(s)} = \frac{K(s + 2)}{(s + 2)[s(s + 3) + 0.06K(s + \frac{25}{3})]}$$

For $K = 50$, the factored form of the characteristic equation is $s(s + 3) + 0.06K(s + \frac{25}{3}) = s^2 + 6s + 25$. Thus, the parameters $k_1 = 0.5$, $k_2 = -0.06$, $k_3 = 0.06$, $b = 2$, and $K = 50$ also yield the desired result.

For the case in which $k_3 = 0.1$ and $b = 0$, the feedback function H is

$$H = \frac{0.1s^2 + 0.74s + 1}{s + 2} = \frac{0.1(s^2 + 7.4s + 10)}{s + 2}$$

$$= \frac{0.1(s + 1.78)(s + 5.62)}{(s + 2)}$$

The corresponding closed-loop transfer function is

$$\frac{C(s)}{R(s)} = \frac{K(s+2)}{s^2(s+3) + 0.1K(s+1.78)(s+5.62)}$$

For $K = 50$, the factored form of the characteristic equation is $(s+2) \times (s^2 + 6s + 25)$. Thus the desired result is also obtained with the parameters $k_1 = 0.5$, $k_2 = -0.06$, $k_3 = 0.1$, $b = 0$, and $K = 50$.

Addition of a Pole and a Zero

The versatility of the preceding compensator is greatly enhanced by replacing the series block $1/(s+b)$ with $(a-b)/(s+b)$ and adding the feedforward loop, as shown in Fig. 9.25*a*. Whereas the preceding compensator was capable of adding a pole to the closed-loop transfer function, the new compensator adds both a pole and a zero. With the aid of block-diagram algebra, the desired representation for this compensator is obtained as shown in Fig. 9.25*b*.

To illustrate the application of this compensator, let it be desired that the term $s+2$ in the numerator of the closed-loop transfer function for the preceding problem be replaced by $s+5$. In effect, the location of the pole introduced by the compensator is such as to cancel the zero at -2, and in addition the zero introduced by the compensator is located at -5. The block diagram showing the individual feedback path is shown in Fig. 9.26*a*. The equivalent H for a single feedback path is

$$H = \frac{a-b}{s+a}\frac{s(s+3)}{s+2}k_3 + \frac{s}{s+2}k_2 + k_1$$

$$= \frac{s(s+3)(a-b)k_3 + s(s+a)k_2 + (s+a)(s+2)k_1}{(s+a)(s+2)}$$

$$= \frac{[(a-b)k_3 + k_2 + k_1]s^2 + [3(a-b)k_3 + ak_2 + (a+2)k_1]s + 2ak_1}{(s+a)(s+2)}$$

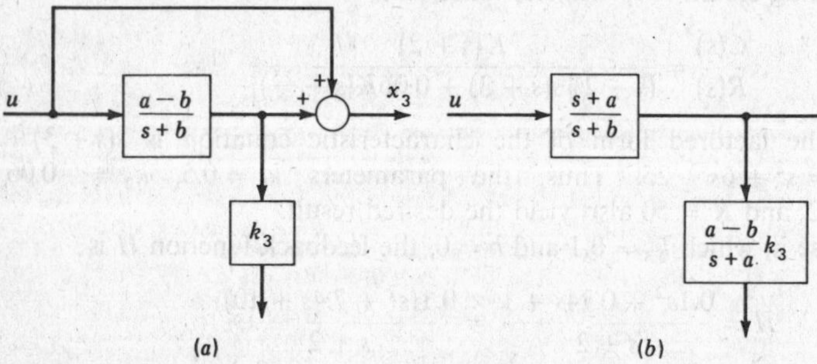

Figure 9.25 Compensator for adding a pole and a zero.

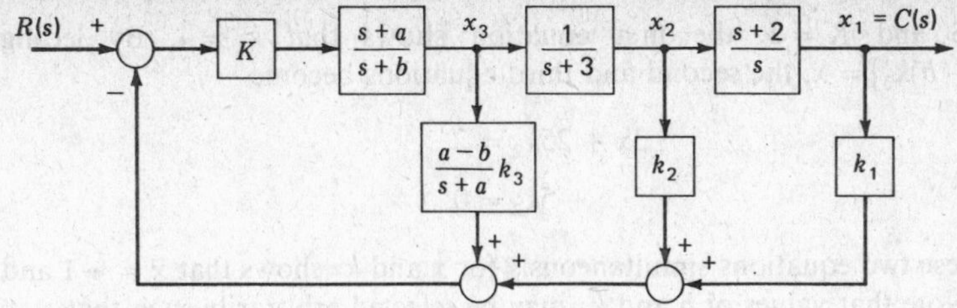

(a)

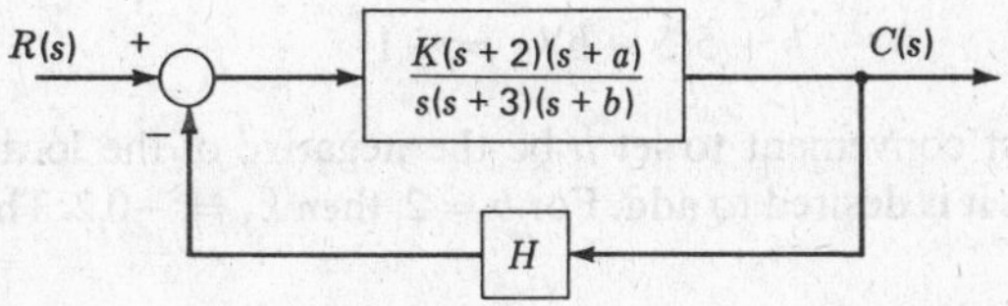

(b)

Figure 9.26 System with compensator for adding a pole and a zero to the closed-loop transfer function.

The corresponding block diagram is shown in Fig. 9.26*b*. The closed-loop transfer function is

$$\frac{C(s)}{R(s)} = \frac{K(s+2)(s+a)}{s(s+3)(s+b) + K\{[(a-b)k_3 + k_2 + k_1]s^2 + [3(a-b)k_3 + ak_2 + (a+2)k_1]s + 2ak_1\}} \tag{9.99}$$

Let the desired form of the closed-loop transfer function be

$$\begin{aligned}\frac{C(s)}{R(s)} &= \frac{5(s+5)}{s^2+6s+25} = \frac{5(s+2)(s+5)}{(s+2)(s^2+6s+25)} \\ &= \frac{5(s+2)(s+5)}{s^3+8s^2+37s+50}\end{aligned} \tag{9.100}$$

Comparison of the numerators of Eqs. (9.99) and (9.100) shows that $K = 5$ and $a = 5$. The value of a is the negative of the location of the zero introduced in the closed-loop transfer function. Equating coefficients of the same powers of s in the denominators of Eqs. (9.99) and (9.100) shows that

$$\begin{aligned} 2ak_1K &= 50 \\ 3[b + K(a-b)k_3] + ak_2K + (a+2)k_1K &= 37 \\ 3 + [b + K(a-b)k_3] + k_2K + k_1K &= 8 \end{aligned}$$

For $a = 5$ and $K = 5$, the first equation shows that $k_1 = 1$. By letting $[b + K(a - b)k_3] = x$, the second and third equations become

$$3x + 25k_2 = 2$$

$$x + 5k_2 = 0$$

Solving these two equations simultaneously for x and k_2 shows that $x = -1$ and $k_2 = 0.2$. Note that values of b and k_3 may be selected arbitrarily such that

$$b + K(a - b)k_3 = x = -1$$

or

$$b + 5(5 - b)k_3 = -1$$

Ordinarily, it is most convenient to let b be the negative of the location of the closed-loop pole that it is desired to add. For $b = 2$, then $k_3 = -0.2$. The resulting H is

$$H = \frac{3[s^2 + \frac{31}{3}s + \frac{50}{3}]}{5(s + 2)(s + 5)} = \frac{3(s + 2)(s + \frac{25}{3})}{5(s + 2)(s + 5)} = \frac{0.6(s + \frac{25}{3})}{s + 5}$$

The substitution of $a = 5$, $b = 2$, and the preceding value of H in Fig. 9.26b yields the following closed-loop transfer function:

$$\frac{C(s)}{R(s)} = \frac{K(s + 5)}{s(s + 3) + 0.6K(s + \frac{25}{3})}$$

For $K = 5$, the characteristic equation is $s(s + 3) + 3(s + \frac{25}{3}) = s^2 + 6s + 25$. Thus, the parameters $K = 5$, $a = 5$, $b = 2$, $k_1 = 1$, $k_2 = 0.2$, and $k_3 = -0.2$ yield the desired result. Numerous other applications of state-space methods are illustrated in the following chapters.

PROBLEMS

9.1 For the differential equation

$$y(t) = \frac{1}{(D + 2)(D + 3)} f(t)$$

determine the computer diagram and state-space representation by

(*a*) Direct programming
(*b*) Parallel programming
(*c*) Series programming
(*d*) General programming

9.2 For the differential equation

$$c(t) = \frac{2(D + 5)}{(D + 2)(D + 3)} f(t)$$

determine the computer diagram and state-space representation by
(*a*) Direct programming
(*b*) Parallel programming
(*c*) Series programming
(*d*) General programming

9.3 For the differential equation

$$c(t) = \frac{2(D + 5)}{(D + 2)(D + 3)(D + 4)} f(t)$$

determine the computer diagram and state-space representation by
(*a*) Direct programming
(*b*) Parallel programming
(*c*) Series programming
(*d*) General programming

9.4 For the system of Prob. 9.1, construct the signal flow graph corresponding to the computer diagram obtained by
(*a*) Direct programming
(*b*) Parallel programming
(*c*) Series programming
(*d*) General programming

Apply Mason's gain formula to verify that the signal flow graph represents the differential equation.

9.5 For the system of Prob. 9.2, construct the signal flow graph corresponding to the computer diagram obtained by
(*a*) Direct programming
(*b*) Parallel programming
(*c*) Series programming
(*d*) General programming

Apply Mason's gain formula to verify that the signal flow graph represents the differential equation.

9.6 For the system of Prob. 9.3, construct the signal flow graph corresponding to the computer diagram obtained by
(*a*) Direct programming
(*b*) Parallel programming
(*c*) Series programming
(*d*) General programming

Apply Mason's gain formula to verify that the signal flow graph represents the differential equation.

9.7 Construct the signal flow graph corresponding to the block diagram shown in Fig. P9.7. Use Mason's gain formula to determine the equation relating
(*a*) $c(t)$ and $r(t)$
(*b*) $c(t)$ and $d(t)$

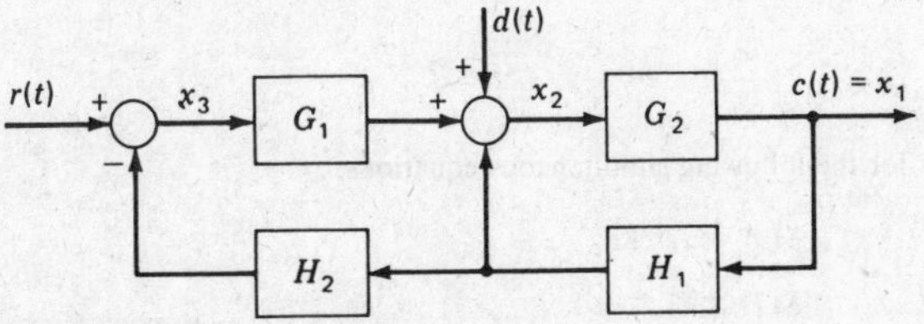

Figure P9.7

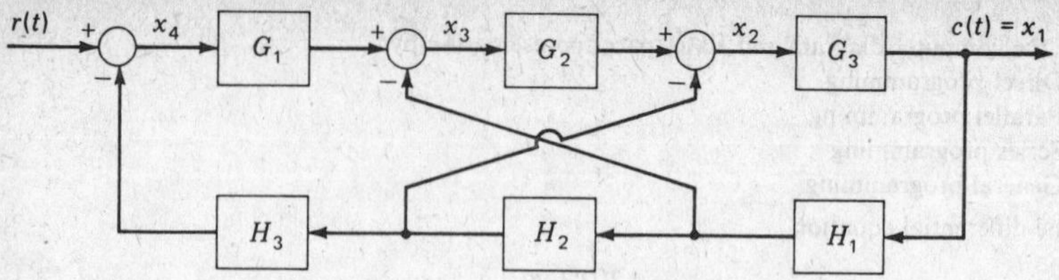

Figure P9.8

9.8 Construct the signal flow graph corresponding to the block diagram shown in Fig. P9.8. Use Mason's gain formula to determine the equation relating $c(t)$ and $r(t)$.

9.9 Determine the signal flow graph corresponding to the block diagram shown in Fig. P9.9. Use Mason's gain formula to determine the equation relating $c(t)$ and $r(t)$.

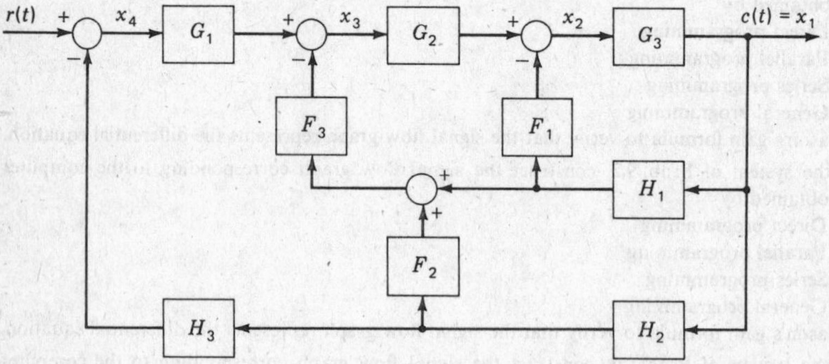

Figure P9.9

9.10 Determine the signal flow graph corresponding to the block diagram shown in
  (*a*) Fig. 9.1*b*
  (*b*) Fig. 9.2*b*
  (*c*) Fig. 9.4

Use Mason's gain formula to determine the equation relating $c(t)$ and $r(t)$.

9.11 Obtain the signal flow graph for the following simultaneous equations:

$$x_1 = 4x_2$$

$$x_2 = -x_1 + f(t)$$

Determine the equation relating
  (*a*) x_1 and $f(t)$
  (*b*) x_2 and $f(t)$

9.12 Obtain the signal flow graph for the following simultaneous equations:

$$x_1 = 4x_2 + u_1$$

$$x_2 = -x_1 + u_2$$

Determine the equation relating
  (*a*) x_1 to u_1 and u_2
  (*b*) x_2 to u_1 and u_2

9.13 Consider the differential equation

$$\ddot{c} + 3\dot{c} + 2c = f(t)$$

Use direct programming and the classical method to find the P, P^{-1}, and Λ matrices, and then determine the solution when $f(t) = 0$ and the initial conditions are

(a) $c_0 = 2$ and $\dot{c}_0 = 0$
(b) $c_0 = 0$ and $\dot{c}_0 = 2$
(c) $c_0 = 2$ and $\dot{c}_0 = 2$

9.14 Consider the differential equation

$$\ddot{c} + 7\dot{c} + 10c = f(t)$$

Use direct programming and the classical method to find the P, P^{-1}, and Λ matrices, and then determine the solution when $f(t) = 0$ and the initial conditions are

(a) $c_0 = 3$ and $\dot{c}_0 = 0$
(b) $c_0 = 0$ and $\dot{c}_0 = 3$
(c) $c_0 = 3$ and $\dot{c}_0 = 3$

9.15 Use the classical method to determine the solution of Prob. 9.13 for the case in which all the initial conditions are zero and $f(t) = 2$ for $t > 0$.

9.16 Use the classical method to determine the solution of Prob. 9.14 for the case in which all initial conditions are zero and $f(t) = 30$ for $t > 0$.

9.17 Use the partial-fraction method to determine the solution of

(a) Prob. 9.13
(b) Prob. 9.15

9.18 Use the partial-fraction method to determine the solution of

(a) Prob. 9.14
(b) Prob. 9.16

9.19 Verify the solution of Illustrative Example 3, Sec. 9.3, by series programming.

9.20 Consider the differential equation

$$(D + 1)(D + 2)(D + 5)c(t) = f(t)$$

Determine the solution when $f(t) = 0$ and the initial conditions are $c_0 = 6$ and $\dot{c}_0 = \ddot{c}_0 = 0$.

9.21 Determine the solution of Prob. 9.20 for the case in which all the initial conditions are zero and $f(t) = 60$ for $t > 0$.

9.22 Consider the differential equation

$$(D^2 + 5D + 6)c(t) = 2(D + 5)f(t)$$

Determine the solution when all the initial conditions are zero and $f(t) = 6$ for $t > 0$.

9.23 Consider the differential equation

$$(D^2 + 5D + 6)c(t) = (D^2 + 10D + 24)f(t)$$

Determine the solution when all the initial conditions are zero and $f(t) = 1$ for $t > 0$.

9.24 Consider the differential equation

$$(D + 3)(D + 4)(D + 5)c(t) = (D + 2)f(t)$$

Determine the solution when all initial conditions are zero and $f(t) = 30$ for $t > 0$.

9.25 Consider the differential equation

$$\ddot{c} + 6\dot{c} + 9c = f(t)$$

Determine the solution when $f(t) = 0$ and the initial conditions are $c_0 = 1$ and $\dot{c}_0 = 0$.

9.26 Determine the solution of Prob. 9.25 when all the initial conditions are zero and $f(t) = 9$ for $t > 0$.

9.27 Consider the differential equation

$$(D + 2)(D + 3)^2 c(t) = f(t)$$

Determine the solution when $f(t) = 0$ and the initial conditions are $c_0 = 1$ and $\dot{c}_0 = \ddot{c}_0 = 0$.

9.28 Determine the solution of Prob. 9.27 when all the initial conditions are zero and $f(t) = 18$ for $t > 0$.

9.29 Determine the state-transition matrix $\Phi(t)$ for Prob. 9.14 by:

(*a*) The classical method $\Phi(t) = Pe^{\Lambda t}P^{-1}$
(*b*) The Laplace transformation method $\Phi(t) = \mathcal{L}^{-1}[sI - A]^{-1}$
(*c*) The signal-flow-graph method

9.30 Determine the state-transition matrix $\Phi(t)$ for Prob. 9.25 by:

(*a*) The classical method, $\Phi(t) = Re^{\Lambda t}R^{-1}$
(*b*) The Laplace transformation method $\Phi(t) = \mathcal{L}^{-1}[sI - A]^{-1}$
(*c*) The signal-flow-graph method

9.31 Consider the differential equation

$$\ddot{c} + 4\dot{c} + 5c = f(t)$$

Use the signal-flow-graph method to determine the solution when $f(t) = 0$ and the initial conditions are $c_0 = 1$ and $\dot{c}_0 = 0$.

9.32 Determine the solution of Prob. 9.31 for the case in which all the initial conditions are zero and $f(t)$ is a unit step function.

9.33 Consider the differential equation

$$(D + 2)(D^2 + 4D + 5)c(t) = f(t)$$

Use the signal-flow-graph method to determine the solution when $f(t) = 0$ and the initial conditions are $c_0 = 1$ and $\dot{c}_0 = \ddot{c}_0 = 0$.

9.34 Determine the solution of Prob. 9.33 for the case in which all the initial conditions are zero and $f(t) = 10$ for $t > 0$.

9.35 For the system shown in Fig. 9.22*b*, $K = 2$, $\mathbf{d}^T = \mathbf{k}^T = [1, 0]$,

$$A = \begin{bmatrix} 0 & 1 \\ -2 & -3 \end{bmatrix} \qquad \mathbf{b} = \begin{bmatrix} 0 \\ 1 \end{bmatrix}$$

Determine the transfer function $G(s)$ for the plant, H_{eq}, and the closed-loop transfer function $G_c(s)$ for the system.

9.36 For the control system shown in Fig. P9.36, determine k_1, k_2, and K such that the closed-loop system has the transfer function

$$\frac{C(s)}{R(s)} = \frac{6}{(s + 2)(s + 3)}$$

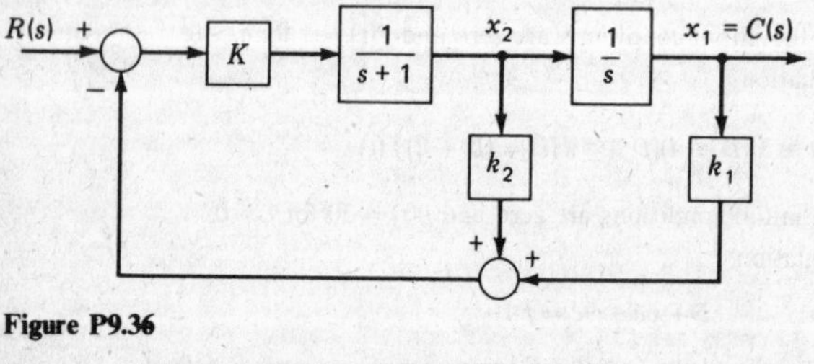

Figure P9.36

9.37 For the control system shown in Fig. P9.36, determine k_1, k_2, and K such that the closed-loop system has the transfer function

$$\frac{C(s)}{R(s)} = \frac{5}{s^2 + 4s + 5}$$

9.38 For the control system shown in Fig. P9.38, determine k_1, k_2, k_3, and K such that the closed-loop transfer function is

$$\frac{C(s)}{R(s)} = \frac{40}{(s + 4)(s^2 + 6s + 10)}$$

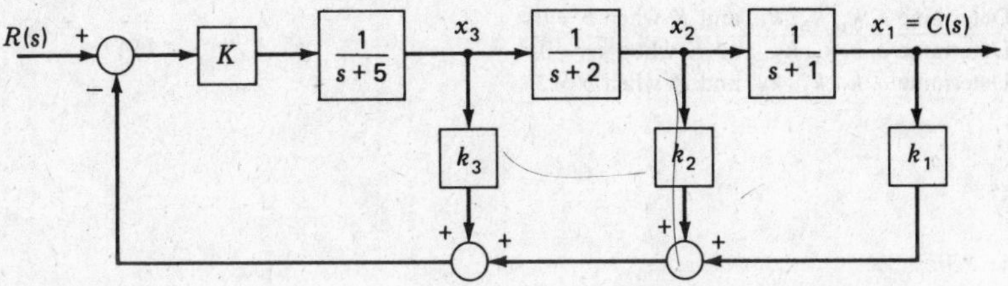

Figure P9.38

9.39 For the control system shown in Fig. P9.39, it is desired that the closed-loop transfer function be

$$\frac{C(s)}{R(s)} = \frac{10}{(s + 2)(s^2 + 4s + 5)}$$

(*a*) Determine k_1, k_2, k_3, and K when $b = 0$.
(*b*) Determine b, k_1, k_2, and K when $k_3 = 0$.
(*c*) Determine k_1, k_2, k_3, and K when $b = 2$.

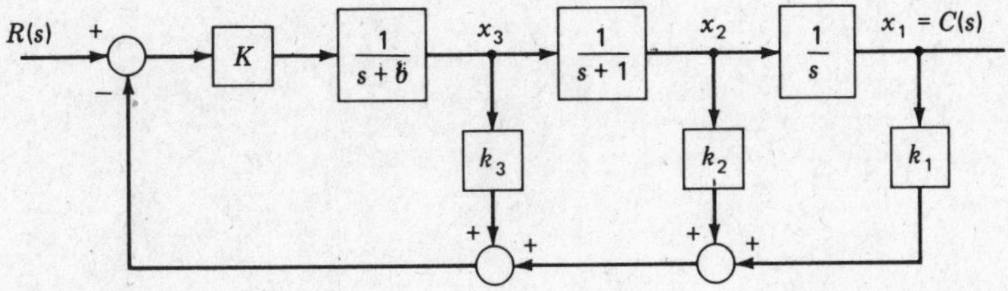

Figure P9.39

9.40 For the control system shown in Fig. P9.40, it is desired that the closed-loop transfer function be

$$\frac{C(s)}{R(s)} = \frac{s + 10}{(s + 2)(s^2 + 4s + 5)}$$

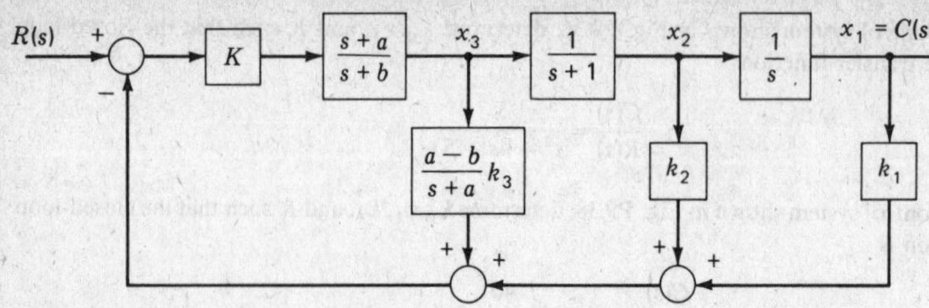

Figure P9.40

(*a*) Determine a, k_1, k_2, k_3, and K when $b = 0$.
(*b*) Determine a, b, k_1, k_2, and K when $k_3 = 0$.
(*c*) Determine a, k_1, k_2, k_3, and K when $b = 2$.

CHAPTER
TEN
DIGITAL-CONTROL SYSTEMS

Recently, numerous systems have been devised which utilize digital computers as control elements. Such systems are generally sampled-data systems. That is, the information fed into a digital computer is the value (sample) of the corresponding signal at some instant of time. The computed output remains unchanged until new information (another sample) is fed into the digital computer.

Another well-known application of the sampled-data process is the time sharing of telemetered information from spacecraft. Instead of temperature at five different places in the vehicle and pressure at three different places being telemetered back on eight different channels, each signal uses the same channel for one second out of eight. A similar application occurs in the control of industrial processes in which system variables such as temperature, pressure, and flow are sampled periodically in order to make more effective use of the expensive control equipment, especially the digital computer. Another example is a guidance system that utilizes radar scanning in which a given sector, or region, is scanned once every revolution. Thus, in any given direction the signal is sampled at a rate equal to the scan rate of the radar. Sampling is inherent in some applications (e.g., radar scanning), it is necessary in other applications (e.g., to enter data into digital computers), and finally, it is desirable for still other applications (e.g., time sharing).

10.1 SAMPLED-DATA SYSTEMS

A schematic representation of a sampler switch is shown in Fig. 10.1*a*. The switch closes every T seconds to admit the input signal. A typical input signal is represented by the continuous function $f(t)$ shown in Fig. 10.1*b*. The shaded pulses

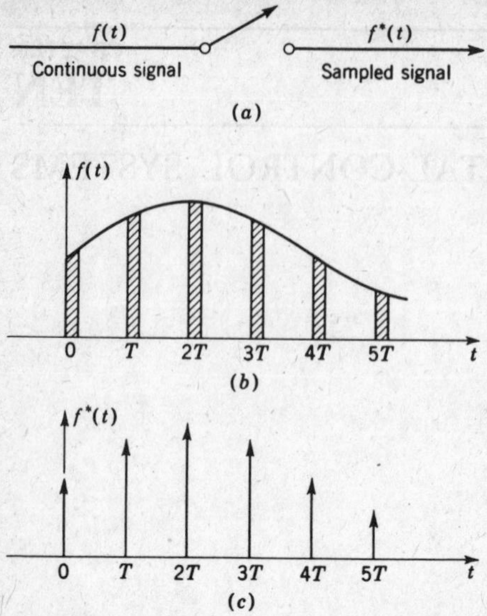

Figure 10.1 (*a*) Sampler switch; (*b*) continuous input $f(t)$ and output at switch (shaded pulses); (*c*) impulse approximation of switch output $f^*(t)$.

represent the signal at the output of the sampler. When the pulse duration is much shorter than the system time constants, the output of the sampler may be approximated by the train of impulses $f^*(t)$, as is illustrated in Fig. 10.1*c*. The term $f^*(t)$ is read *f* star of *t*.

The area of each impulse is equal to the value of the input signal at the time $t = nT$ of the particular impulse. Thus, the area of the *n*th impulse which occurs at time $t = nT$ is $f(nT)$. The equation for the entire train of impulses is

$$f^*(t) = f(0)u_1(t) + f(T)u_1(t - T) + f(2T)u_1(t - 2T) + \cdots$$

$$= \sum_{n=0}^{\infty} f(nT)u_1(t - nT) \tag{10.1}$$

where $u_1(t)$ is a unit impulse at $t = 0$ and $u_1(t - nT)$ is a unit impulse at $t = nT$.

The Laplace transform of the sampled signal is

$$F^*(s) = \mathscr{L}[f^*(t)] = f(0) + f(T)e^{-Ts} + f(2T)e^{-2Ts} + \cdots$$

$$= \sum_{n=0}^{\infty} f(nT)e^{-nTs} \tag{10.2}$$

To illustrate the preceding concepts, consider the continuous input

$$f(t) = e^{-at}$$

The corresponding sampled signal $f^*(t)$ is

$$f^*(t) = u_1(t) + e^{-aT}u_1(t - T) + e^{-2aT}u_1(t - 2T) + \cdots$$

$$= \sum_{n=0}^{\infty} e^{-anT}u_1(t - nT)$$

The Laplace transform of the input $f(t)$ is

$$F(s) = \mathscr{L}[f(t)] = \frac{1}{s+a}$$

The Laplace transform of the sampled signal $f^*(t)$ is

$$\begin{aligned} F^*(s) = \mathscr{L}[f^*(t)] &= 1 + e^{-aT}e^{-sT} + e^{-2aT}e^{-2sT} + \cdots \\ &= 1 + e^{-(s+a)T} + e^{-2(s+a)T} + \cdots \\ &= \sum_{n=0}^{\infty} e^{-n(s+a)T} \end{aligned}$$

The Laplace transform of a sampled signal is an infinite series. In the following, it is seen that the z transform greatly simplifies the analysis of such systems.

10.2 THE z TRANSFORM

The simple substitution

$$z = e^{Ts}$$

converts the Laplace transform to the z transform. Making this substitution in Eq. (10.2) gives

$$\begin{aligned} Z[f^*(t)] = F(z) = f(0) + \frac{f(T)}{z} + \frac{f(2T)}{z^2} + \cdots \\ = \sum_{n=0}^{\infty} f(nT)z^{-n} \end{aligned} \tag{10.3}$$

where $F(z)$ designates the z transform of $f^*(t)$. Because only values of the signal at the sampling instants are considered, the z transform of $f(t)$ is the same as that of $f^*(t)$.

Illustrative example 1 Determine the z transform for a unit step function. For this function $f(nT) = 1$ for $n = 0, 1, 2, \ldots$; thus application of Eq. (10.3) gives

$$Z[u^*(t)] = 1 + \frac{1}{z} + \frac{1}{z^2} + \cdots = \frac{z}{z-1} \tag{10.4}$$

This series is convergent for $|z| > 1$. In solving problems by z transforms, the term z acts as a dummy operator. There is no need to specify the values of z over which $F(z)$ is convergent. It suffices to know that such values exist.

Illustrative example 2 Determine the z transform of the exponential e^{-at}. For this function $f(nT) = e^{-anT}$; thus

$$Z(e^{-at}) = 1 + \frac{e^{-aT}}{z} + \left(\frac{e^{-aT}}{z}\right)^2 + \cdots = \frac{z}{z - e^{-aT}} \tag{10.5}$$

Table 10.1 *z* **transforms**

Time function	Laplace transform	*z* transform
$u_1(t)$	1	1
$u(t)$	$\frac{1}{s}$	$\frac{z}{z-1}$
t	$\frac{1}{s^2}$	$\frac{zT}{(z-1)^2}$
$\frac{t^2}{2}$	$\frac{1}{s^3}$	$\frac{z(z+1)T^2}{2(z-1)^3}$
e^{-at}	$\frac{1}{s+a}$	$\frac{z}{z-e^{-aT}}$
te^{-at}	$\frac{1}{(s+a)^2}$	$\frac{zTe^{-aT}}{(z-e^{-aT})^2}$
$a^{t/T}$	$\frac{1}{s-(1/T)\ln a}$	$\frac{z}{z-a}$ $(a>0)$
$\sin \omega t$	$\frac{\omega}{s^2+\omega^2}$	$\frac{z \sin \omega T}{z^2 - 2z\cos \omega T + 1}$
$\cos \omega t$	$\frac{s}{s^2+\omega^2}$	$\frac{z^2 - z\cos \omega T}{z^2 - 2z\cos \omega T + 1}$

In Table 10.1 is given a partial listing of Laplace transforms and corresponding z transforms for commonly encountered functions.

When the Laplace transform of a function is known, the corresponding z transform may be obtained by the partial-fraction method.

Illustrative example 3 Determine the z transform for the function whose Laplace transform is

$$F(s) = \frac{1}{s(s+1)} = \frac{1}{s} - \frac{1}{s+1}$$

From Table 10.1, the z transform corresponding to $1/s$ is $z/(z-1)$ and that corresponding to $1/(s+1)$ is $z/(z-e^{-T})$. Thus,

$$F(z) = \frac{z}{z-1} - \frac{z}{z-e^{-T}} = \frac{z(1-e^{-T})}{(z-1)(z-e^{-T})} \tag{10.6}$$

Illustrative example 4 Determine the z transform of $\cos \omega t$. It is known that the Laplace transform is $s/(s^2+\omega^2)$. Performing a partial-fraction expansion gives

$$\mathcal{L}(\cos \omega t) = \frac{s}{s^2 + \omega^2} = \frac{\frac{1}{2}}{s + j\omega} + \frac{\frac{1}{2}}{s - j\omega}$$

The corresponding z transform is

$$Z(\cos \omega t) = \frac{1}{2}\left[\frac{z}{z - e^{-j\omega T}} + \frac{z}{z - e^{j\omega T}}\right] = \frac{z^2 - z(e^{j\omega T} + e^{-j\omega T})/2}{z^2 - z(e^{j\omega T} + e^{-j\omega T}) + 1}$$

$$= \frac{z^2 - z \cos \omega T}{z^2 - 2z \cos \omega T + 1} \tag{10.7}$$

The Residue Method

This is a powerful technique for obtaining z transforms. The z transform of $f^*(t)$ may be expressed in the form

$$F(z) = Z[f^*(t)] = \sum \text{residues of } F(s)\frac{z}{z - e^{sT}} \text{ at poles of } F(s) \tag{10.8}$$

When the denominator of $F(s)$ contains a linear factor of the form $s - r$ such that $F(s)$ has a first-order pole at $s = r$, the corresponding residue R is

$$R = \lim_{s \to r} (s - r)\left[F(s)\frac{z}{z - e^{sT}}\right] \tag{10.9}$$

When $F(s)$ contains a repeated pole of order q, the residue is

$$R = \frac{1}{(q-1)!} \lim_{s \to r} \frac{d^{q-1}}{ds^{q-1}}\left[(s - r)^q F(s)\frac{z}{z - e^{sT}}\right] \tag{10.10}$$

As is illustrated by the following examples, the determination of residues is similar to evaluating the constants in a partial-fraction expansion.

Illustrative example 5 Determine the z transform of a unit step function. For $F(s) = 1/s$, there is but one pole at $s = 0$. The corresponding residue is

$$R = \lim_{s \to 0} s\left(\frac{1}{s}\frac{z}{z - e^{sT}}\right) = \frac{z}{z - 1}$$

This verifies the result of Eq. (10.4).

Illustrative example 6 Determine the z transform of e^{-at}. For this function, $F(s) = 1/(s + a)$, which has but one pole at $s = -a$. Thus,

$$R = \lim_{s \to -a} (s + a)\left[\frac{1}{(s + a)}\frac{z}{z - e^{sT}}\right] = \frac{z}{z - e^{-aT}}$$

This verifies the result of Eq. (10.5).

Illustrative example 7 Determine the z transform for the function whose Laplace transform is

$$F(s) = \frac{1}{s(s+1)}$$

The poles of $F(s)$ occur at $s = 0$ and $s = -1$. The residue due to the pole at $s = 0$ is

$$R_1 = \lim_{s \to 0} s\left[\frac{1}{s(s+1)} \frac{z}{z - e^{sT}}\right] = \frac{z}{z-1}$$

The residue due to the pole at $s = -1$ is

$$R_2 = \lim_{s \to -1} (s+1)\left[\frac{1}{s(s+1)} \frac{z}{z - e^{sT}}\right] = -\frac{z}{z - e^{-T}}$$

Adding these two residues verifies the result given by Eq. (10.6).

Illustrative example 8 Determine the z transform of $\cos \omega t$. The Laplace transform is

$$F(s) = \frac{s}{s^2 + \omega^2} = \frac{s}{(s - j\omega)(s + j\omega)}$$

The poles are at $s = j\omega$ and at $s = -j\omega$. Thus,

$$R_1 = \left(\frac{s}{s + j\omega} \frac{z}{z - e^{sT}}\right)_{s = j\omega} = \frac{1}{2} \frac{z}{z - e^{j\omega T}}$$

$$R_2 = \left(\frac{s}{s - j\omega} \frac{z}{z - e^{sT}}\right)_{s = -j\omega} = \frac{1}{2} \frac{z}{z - e^{-j\omega T}}$$

Adding these two residues verifies the result given by Eq. (10.7).

Illustrative example 9 Determine the z transform corresponding to the function $f(t) = t$. The Laplace transform is

$$F(s) = \frac{1}{s^2}$$

This has a second-order pole at $s = 0$. Application of Eq. (10.10) gives

$$R = \frac{d}{ds}\left(\frac{z}{z - e^{sT}}\right)_{s=0} = \left(\frac{zTe^{sT}}{(z - e^{sT})^2}\right)_{s=0} = \frac{Tz}{(z-1)^2}$$

Theorems

The following basic theorems extend the usefulness of the z transform method. In addition, these theorems help one to obtain a better understanding of z transformations.

Multiplication by e^{-at}. The z transform of $e^{-at}f(t)$ is

$$Z[e^{-at}f(t)] = F(ze^{aT}) \tag{10.11}$$

Thus, replacing z in $F(z)$ by ze^{aT} yields the transform for $e^{-at}f(t)$. It is recalled that the Laplace transform of $e^{-at}f(t)$ is equal to $F(s+a)$. That is, replacing s by $s+a$ gives the effect of multiplying by e^{-at}.

To prove this theorem, note from Eq. (10.3) that

$$Z[e^{-at}f(t)] = \sum_{n=0}^{\infty} f(nT)e^{-anT}z^{-n} = \sum_{n=0}^{\infty} f(nT)(ze^{aT})^{-n}$$

The right side is $F(z)$ with z replaced by (ze^{aT}).

Multiplication by t. The z transform of $tf(t)$ is

$$Z[tf(t)] = -zT\frac{d}{dz}F(z) \tag{10.12}$$

To prove this theorem, note that

$$-zT\frac{d}{dz}F(z) = -zT\frac{d}{dz}\left[f(0) + \frac{f(T)}{z} + \frac{f(2T)}{z^2} + \frac{f(3T)}{z^3} + \cdots\right]$$

$$= T\frac{f(T)}{z} + 2T\frac{f(2T)}{z^2} + 3T\frac{f(3T)}{z^3} + \cdots$$

The right side is the z transform of $tf(t)$.

To illustrate this theorem, consider the function $f(t) = e^{-at}$, for which $F(z) = z/(z - e^{-aT})$. Application of Eq. (10.12) shows that

$$Z[te^{-at}] = -zT\frac{d}{dz}\frac{z}{z - e^{-aT}} = \frac{zTe^{-aT}}{(z - e^{-aT})^2}$$

Multiplication by $a^{t/T}$. The z transform of $a^{t/T}f(t)$ is

$$Z[a^{t/T}f(t)] = F\left(\frac{z}{a}\right) \tag{10.13}$$

To prove this theorem, replace z by z/a in the expression for $F(z)$. Thus

$$F\left(\frac{z}{a}\right) = f(0) + a\frac{f(T)}{z} + a^2\frac{f(2T)}{z^2} + \cdots$$

The right side is the z transform of $a^{t/T}f(t)$.

Partial differentiation This theorem states that

$$Z\left[\frac{\partial}{\partial a}[f(t, a)]\right] = \frac{\partial}{\partial a}[F(z, a)] \tag{10.14}$$

This theorem is useful for ascertaining additional z transforms. For example, it is known that the z transform of e^{at} is $z/(z - e^{aT})$. Thus

$$Z\left[\frac{\partial}{\partial a} e^{at}\right] = Z[te^{at}] = \frac{\partial}{\partial a} \frac{z}{z - e^{aT}} = \frac{Tze^{aT}}{(z - e^{aT})^2}$$

For the case in which $a = 0$,

$$Z[t] = \frac{Tz}{(z-1)^2}$$

By proceeding in a similar manner, the z transforms for t^2, t^3, etc., are also obtained.

Initial-value theorem The area of the first impulse $f(0)$ of the sampled function $f^*(t)$ is

$$f(0) = \lim_{z \to \infty} F(z) \tag{10.15}$$

This theorem is verified directly by taking the limit as z approaches infinity in Eq. (10.3).

Final-value theorem The area of the impulse $f(nT)$ as n becomes infinite is

$$f(\infty) = \lim_{z \to 1} \frac{z-1}{z} F(z) \tag{10.16}$$

PROOF Consider the following sums S_n and S_{n-1}.

$$S_n = f(0) + \frac{f(T)}{z} + \cdots + \frac{f[(n-1)T]}{z^{n-1}} + \frac{f(nT)}{z^n}$$

$$S_{n-1} = f(0) + \frac{f(T)}{z} + \cdots + \frac{f[(n-1)T]}{z^{n-1}}$$

Dividing the second series by z and then subtracting the second from the first gives

$$\left(S_n - \frac{1}{z} S_{n-1}\right) = \left(1 - \frac{1}{z}\right) f(0) + \cdots + \left(1 - \frac{1}{z}\right) \frac{f[(n-1)T]}{z^{n-1}} + \frac{f(nT)}{z^n}$$

Taking the limit as z approaches 1 gives

$$\lim_{z \to 1} \left(S_n - \frac{1}{z} S_{n-1}\right) = f(nT)$$

When n is very large, $S_{n-1} \approx S_n \approx F(z)$. Thus, the final-value theorem given by Eq. (10.16) is verified.

Real translation The solid curve shown in Fig. 10.2a is the continuous function $f(t)$. The value at time $t = 0$ is $f(0)$, the value at $t = T$ is $f(T)$, etc. When the function is shifted to the right (delayed) by a time nT, as shown in Fig. 10.2b, the

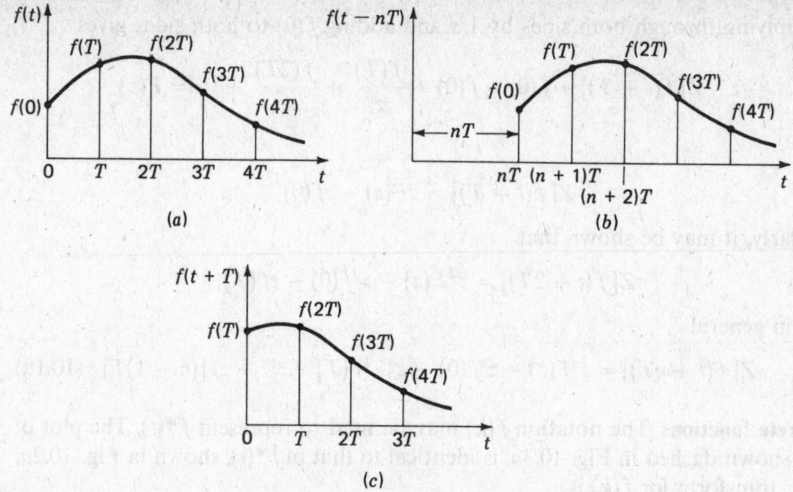

Figure 10.2 Translation of a continuous function $f(t)$.

function $f(t - nT)$ results. The value of $f(t - nT)$ at time $t = nT$ is $f(0)$, the value at $t = (n + 1)T$ is $f(T)$, etc. The z transform for $f(t)$ is

$$Z[f(t)] = f(0) + \frac{f(T)}{z} + \frac{f(2T)}{z^2} + \cdots$$

The z transform for $f(t - nT)$ is

$$\begin{aligned} Z[f(t - nT)] &= \frac{f(0)}{z^n} + \frac{f(T)}{z^{n+1}} + \frac{f(2T)}{z^{n+2}} + \cdots \\ &= \frac{1}{z^n}\left[f(0) + \frac{f(T)}{z} + \frac{f(2T)}{z^2} + \cdots\right] \\ &= z^{-n}F(z) \end{aligned} \tag{10.17}$$

Thus, multiplying a z transform by z^{-n} has the effect of delaying the function by a time nT. For Laplace transforms, multiplication by e^{-as} has the effect of delaying the function by a time a.

When the function of Fig. 10.2a is shifted to the left one period T, the function $f(t + T)$ shown in Fig. 10.2c results. The value of $f(t + T)$ at time $t = 0$ is $f(T)$, the value at $t = T$ is $f(2T)$, etc. The z transform for $f(t + T)$ is

$$Z[f(t + T)] = f(T) + \frac{f(2T)}{z} + \frac{f(3T)}{z^2} + \cdots$$

Multiplying through both sides by $1/z$ and adding $f(0)$ to both sides gives

$$z^{-1}Z[f(t+T)]+f(0)=f(0)+\frac{f(T)}{z}+\frac{f(2T)}{z^2}+\cdots=F(z)$$

Thus

$$Z[f(t+T)]=zF(z)-zf(0)$$

Similarly, it may be shown that

$$Z[f(t+2T)]=z^2F(z)-z^2f(0)-zf(T)$$

and, in general

$$Z[f(t+nT)]=z^nF(z)-z^nf(0)-z^{n-1}f(T)-\cdots-zf[(n-1)T] \qquad (10.18)$$

Discrete functions The notation $f(k)$ may be used to represent $f^*(t)$. The plot of $f(k)$, shown dashed in Fig. 10.3*a*, is identical to that of $f^*(t)$, shown in Fig. 10.2*a*. The z transform for $f(k)$ is

$$Z[f(k)]=f(0)+\frac{f(1)}{z}+\frac{f(2)}{z^2}+\frac{f(3)}{z^3}+\cdots=F(z) \qquad (10.19)$$

When $f(k)$ is delayed n sampling instants, the function $f(k-n)$ shown in Fig. 10.3*b* results. The value of $f(k-n)$ when $k=n$ is $f(0)$, the value when $k=n+1$ is $f(1)$, etc. The z transform of $f(k-n)$ is

$$Z[f(k-n)]=\frac{f(0)}{z^n}+\frac{f(1)}{z^{n+1}}+\frac{f(2)}{z^{n+2}}+\cdots$$

$$=\frac{1}{z^n}\left[f(0)+\frac{f(1)}{z}+\frac{f(2)}{z^2}+\cdots\right]$$

$$=z^{-n}F(z) \qquad (10.20)$$

When the function $f(k)$ of Fig. 10.3*a* is shifted one sampling period to the left, the function $f(k+1)$ shown in Fig. 10.3*c* results. The value of $f(k+1)$ when $k=0$ is $f(1)$, the value when $k=1$ is $f(2)$, etc. The z transform of $f(k+1)$ is

$$Z[f(k+1)]=f(1)+\frac{f(2)}{z}+\frac{f(3)}{z^2}+\cdots$$

Multiplying through both sides by $1/z$ and adding $f(0)$ to both sides gives

$$z^{-1}Z[f(k+1)]+f(0)=f(0)+\frac{f(1)}{z}+\frac{f(2)}{z^2}+\cdots=F(z)$$

Thus,

$$Z[f(k+1)]=zF(z)-zf(0)$$

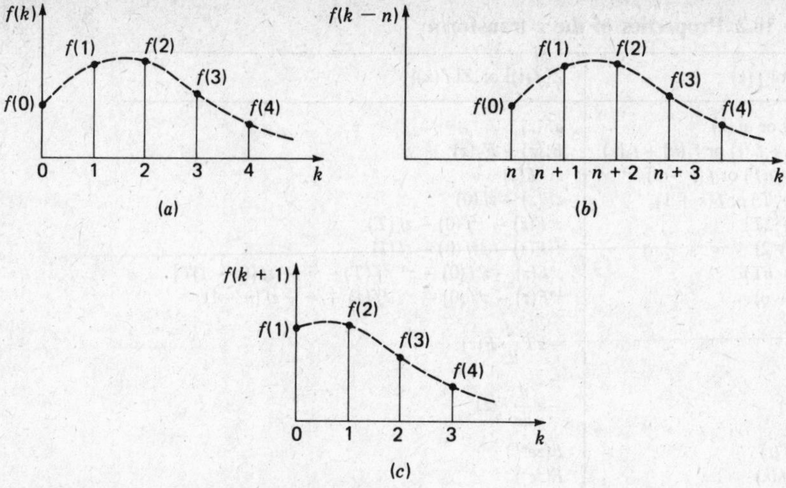

Figure 10.3 Translation of a discrete function $f(k)$.

Similarly, it follows that

$$Z[f(k+2)] = z^2F(z) - z^2f(0) - zf(1)$$

In general,

$$Z[f(k+n)] = z^nF(z) - z^nf(0) - z^{n-1}f(1) - \cdots - zf(n-1) \tag{10.21}$$

As shown in the following, z transform theorems for $f(k)$ are quite similar to those for $f(t)$.

Multiplication by a^k The z transform of $a^kf(k)$ is

$$Z[a^kf(k)] = F\left(\frac{z}{a}\right) \tag{10.22}$$

This theorem is readily proved by replacing z by z/a in Eq. (10.19). Thus

$$F\left(\frac{z}{a}\right) = f(0) + \frac{af(1)}{z} + \frac{a^2f(2)}{z^2} + \cdots$$

The right side is the z transform of $a^kf(k)$.

For a unit step function, $f(k) = 1$, and $F(z) = 1 + 1/z + 1/z^2 + \cdots = z/(z-1)$. Application of Eq. (10.22) shows that

$$Z[a^k] = F\left(\frac{z}{a}\right) = \frac{z/a}{(z/a)-1} = \frac{z}{z-a} \tag{10.23}$$

Table 10.2 Properties of the z transform

$f(t)$ or $f(k)$	$Z[f(t)]$ or $Z[f(k)]$
$af(t)$ or $af(k)$	$aF(z)$
$f_1(t)+f_2(t)$ or $f_1(k)+f_2(k)$	$F_1(z)+F_2(z)$
$f(t-nT)$ or $f(k-n)$	$z^{-n}F(z)$
$f(t+T)$ or $f(k+1)$	$zF(z)-zf(0)$
$f(t+2T)$	$z^2F(z)-z^2f(0)-zf(T)$
$f(k+2)$	$z^2F(z)-z^2f(0)-zf(1)$
$f(t+nT)$	$z^nF(z)-z^nf(0)-z^{n-1}f(T)-\cdots-zf[(n-1)T]$
$f(k+n)$	$z^nF(z)-z^nf(0)-z^{n-1}f(1)-\cdots-zf(n-1)$
$tf(t)$	$-zT\dfrac{d}{dz}F(z)$
$kf(k)$	$-z\dfrac{d}{dz}F(z)$
$e^{-at}f(t)$	$F(ze^{aT})$
$e^{-ak}f(k)$	$F(ze^{a})$
$a^{t/T}f(t)$ or $a^kf(k)$	$F(z/a)$
$\dfrac{\partial}{\partial a}f(t,a)$	$\dfrac{\partial}{\partial a}F(z,a)$

Multiplication by k The z transform of $kf(k)$ is

$$Z[kf(k)] = -z\frac{d}{dz}F(z) \tag{10.24}$$

To verify this theorem, note that

$$-z\frac{d}{dz}F(z) = -z\frac{d}{dz}\left[f(0)+\frac{f(1)}{z}+\frac{f(2)}{z^2}+\frac{f(3)}{z^3}+\cdots\right]$$

$$=\frac{f(1)}{z}+\frac{2f(2)}{z^2}+\frac{3f(3)}{z^3}+\cdots$$

This result is the z transform of $kf(k)$.

To illustrate this theorem, consider the function $f(k)=a^k$ for which $F(z)=z/(z-a)$. Application of Eq. (10.24) gives

$$Z[ka^k] = -z\frac{d}{dz}\frac{z}{z-a} = \frac{az}{(z-a)^2} \tag{10.25}$$

A listing of z transform theorems and properties is given in Table 10.2.

10.3 INVERSE z TRANSFORMS

Inspection of Table 10.1 shows that z transforms tend to be more complicated than corresponding Laplace transforms. Fortunately, there are some relatively simple techniques for obtaining inverse z transforms.

Partial-Fraction Method

To illustrate this method, let it be desired to obtain the inverse z transform for the function

$$F(z) = \frac{(1 - e^{-T})z}{(z-1)(z - e^{-T})} \tag{10.26}$$

Performing a partial-fraction expansion gives

$$F(z) = \left[\frac{1 - e^{-T}}{(z-1)(z-e^{-T})}\right]z = \left[\frac{K_1}{z-1} + \frac{K_2}{z - e^{-T}}\right]z$$

$$= \frac{z}{z-1} - \frac{z}{z - e^{-T}}$$

From Table 10.1 the corresponding time function is

$$f(t) = 1 - e^{-t}$$

Thus, the inverse $f^*(t)$ is

$$f^*(t) = \sum_{n=0}^{\infty} (1 - e^{-nT})u_1(t - nT) \tag{10.27}$$

Division Method

Dividing the numerator of $F(z)$ by the denominator yields a power series of the form

$$F(z) = C_0 + C_1 z^{-1} + C_2 z^{-2} + \cdots \tag{10.28}$$

The corresponding inverse is

$$f^*(t) = \sum_{n=0}^{\infty} C_n u_1(t - nT)$$

To obtain the inverse of Eq. (10.26) by the division method, divide the numerator by the denominator. This yields

$$F(z) = 0 + (1 - e^{-T})z^{-1} + (1 - e^{-2T})z^{-2} + (1 - e^{-3T})z^{-3} + \cdots$$

Inverting verifies the result given by Eq. (10.27).

Residue Method

To develop this method, first write the basic relationship for $F(z)$ in the form

$$F(z) = f(0) + \frac{f(T)}{z} + \cdots + \frac{f[(n-1)T]}{z^{n-1}} + \frac{f(nT)}{z^n} + \frac{f[(n+1)T]}{z^{n+1}} + \cdots$$

Multiplication by z^{n-1} gives

$$F(z)z^{n-1} = f(0)z^{n-1} + \cdots + f[(n-1)T] + \frac{f(nT)}{z} + \frac{f[(n+1)T]}{z^2} + \cdots \tag{10.29}$$

From complex variable theory it is known that the coefficient $f(nT)$ of the $1/z$ term of the preceding Laurent expansion is

$$\begin{aligned} f(nT) &= \frac{1}{2\pi j}\int_C F(z)z^{n-1}\,dz \\ &= \sum \text{residues of } F(z)z^{n-1} \text{ at poles of } F(z)z^{n-1} \end{aligned} \tag{10.30}$$

The contour C is any closed path which encloses all the poles of $F(z)z^{n-1}$.

Replacing the function $F(s)z/(z - e^{-sT})$ in Eqs. (10.9) and (10.10) by $F(z)z^{n-1}$ yields the following equations for determining the residues in Eq. (10.30). In particular, the residue due to a first-order pole at $z = r$ is

$$R = \lim_{z \to r} (z - r)[F(z)z^{n-1}] \tag{10.31}$$

Similarly, the residue due to a repeated pole of order q is

$$R = \frac{1}{(q-1)!} \lim_{z \to r} \frac{d^{q-1}}{dz^{q-1}} [(z - r)^q F(z)z^{n-1}] \tag{10.32}$$

Application of the residue method to determine the inverse of Eq. (10.26) gives

$$R_1 = \left[\frac{(1 - e^{-T})z^n}{z - e^{-T}}\right]_{z=1} = 1$$

$$R_2 = \left[\frac{(1 - e^{-T})z^n}{z - 1}\right]_{z=e^{-T}} = -e^{-nT}$$

Adding these residues gives $f(nT) = 1 - e^{-nT}$, which verifies the result given by Eq. (10.27).

As another example, determine the inverse z transform for the function

$$F(z) = \frac{Tz}{(z-1)^2}$$

This function has a second-order pole at $z = 1$; thus

$$R = \lim_{z \to 1} \frac{d}{dz} Tz^n = (nTz^{n-1})_{z=1} = nT$$

For $f(nT) = nT$, the corresponding time function is $f(t) = t$.

10.4 BLOCK-DIAGRAM ALGEBRA

In writing the transfer function for feedback control systems with sampling switches, one encounters some terms which are starred and some which are not. Thus, it is necessary to develop some mathematical techniques for handling such mixed terms. In Fig. 10.4*a* is shown a sampling switch followed by a linear element whose transfer function is $G(s)$. The transformed equation for the output $Y(s)$ is

$$Y(s) = F^*(s)G(s) \tag{10.33}$$

For $0 < t < T$, the response $y(t)$ is that due to the first impulse at $t = 0$ of area $f(0)$. Thus, for this interval

$$y(t) = \mathscr{L}^{-1}[f(0)G(s)] = f(0)\mathscr{L}^{-1}[G(s)] = f(0)g(t) \tag{10.34}$$

where $g(t) = \mathscr{L}^{-1}[G(s)]$ is the response of the linear element to a unit impulse which occurs at $t = 0$.

For $T < t < 2T$, the response $y(t)$ is that due to the impulse at $t = 0$ plus that at $t = T$. For this interval, $F^*(s) = f(0) + f(T)e^{-Ts}$. Thus,

$$Y(s) = [f(0) + f(T)e^{-Ts}]G(s)$$

Inverting gives

$$y(t) = f(0)g(t) + f(T)g(t - T) \tag{10.35}$$

where $g(t - T) = \mathscr{L}^{-1}[G(s)e^{-Ts}]$ is the response of the linear element to a unit impulse which occurs at time $t = T$. The response $y(t)$ for the interval $2T < t < 3T$ is

$$y(t) = f(0)g(t) + f(T)g(t - T) + f(2T)g(t - 2T)$$

In general, the response $y(t)$ is

$$y(t) = \sum_{n=0}^{\infty} f(nT)g(t - nT) \tag{10.36}$$

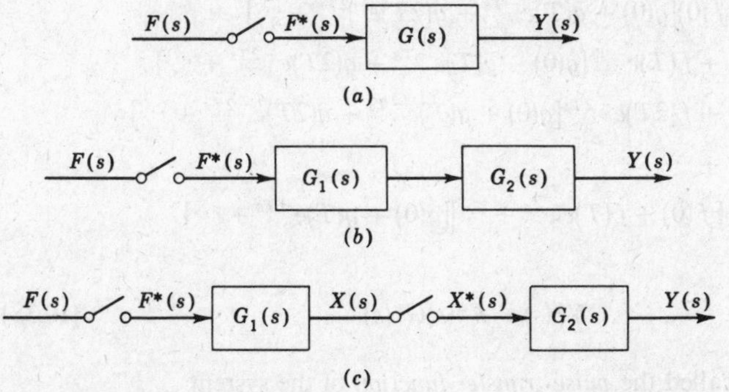

Figure 10.4 Sampler configurations.

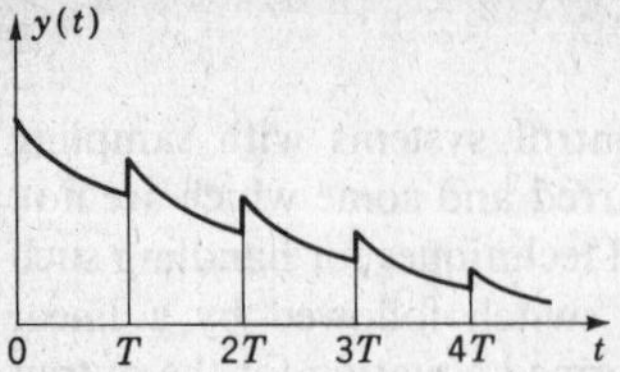

Figure 10.5 Response function which is discontinuous at the sampling instants.

When n is such that $nT > t$, then $g(t - nT)$ is zero. That is, the impulse response is zero for negative time.

Taking the limit as t approaches 0 in Eq. (10.34), and the limit as t approaches T in Eq. (10.35), etc., yields the value of $y(nT)$ at the sampling instants.

$$\begin{aligned} y(0) &= f(0)g(0) \\ y(T) &= f(0)g(T) + f(T)g(0) \\ y(2T) &= f(0)g(2T) + f(T)g(T) + f(2T)g(0) \\ &\cdots\cdots\cdots\cdots\cdots\cdots\cdots \\ y(nT) &= f(0)g(nT) + f(T)g[(n-1)T] + \cdots \end{aligned} \tag{10.37}$$

In Fig. 10.5 is shown a response function $y(t)$ which is discontinuous at the sampling instants. This occurs when the order of the denominator of $G(s)$ exceeds the order of the numerator by only one. When the order of the denominator exceeds the order of the numerator by two or more, $y(t)$ is continuous. When $y(t)$ is continuous, Eq. (10.37) yields the values at the sampling instants. When $y(t)$ is discontinuous, Eq. (10.37) yields the values immediately after the sampling instants [that is, $y(0+)$, $y(T+)$, $y(2T+)\cdots$]. Figure 10.1 shows that the values in Eq. (10.2) would also be the values immediately following the sampling instants if the function were discontinuous. Replacing f by y in Eq. (10.2) gives

$$Y^*(s) = y(0) + y(T)e^{-Ts} + y(2T)e^{-2Ts} + \cdots$$

Substitution of the values from Eq. (10.37) into the preceding expression gives

$$\begin{aligned} Y^*(s) &= f(0)[g(0) + g(T)e^{-Ts} + g(2T)e^{-2Ts} + \cdots] \\ &\quad + f(T)e^{-Ts}[g(0) + g(T)e^{-Ts} + g(2T)e^{-2Ts} + \cdots] \\ &\quad + f(2T)e^{-2Ts}[g(0) + g(T)e^{-Ts} + g(2T)e^{-2Ts} + \cdots] \\ &\quad + \cdots \\ &= [f(0) + f(T)e^{-Ts} + \cdots][g(0) + g(T)e^{-Ts} + \cdots] \end{aligned}$$

Thus,

$$Y^*(s) = F^*(s)G^*(s) \tag{10.38}$$

The term $G^*(s)$ is called the *pulse-transfer function* of the system.

Comparison of Eqs. (10.33) and (10.38) reveals a basic mathematical relationship for starring quantities. That is, starring both sides of Eq. (10.33) gives

$$[Y(s)]^* = Y^*(s)$$

$$[F^*(s)G(s)]^* = F^*(s)[G(s)]^* = F^*(s)G^*(s)$$

Letting $z = e^{sT}$ in Eq. (10.38) yields the z transform relationship

$$Y(z) = F(z)G(z) \tag{10.39}$$

For the sampler configuration of Fig. 10.4*b*, the Laplace transform relationship is

$$Y(s) = F^*(s)G_1(s)G_2(s)$$

Starring gives

$$Y^*(s) = F^*(s)[G_1(s)G_2(s)]^* = F^*(s)G_1G_2^*(s)$$

where $\quad G_1G_2^*(s) = [G_1(s)G_2(s)]^*$

The corresponding z transform is

$$Y(z) = F(z)G_1G_2(z) \tag{10.40}$$

Illustrative example 1 Determine the z transform for Fig. 10.4*b*, when $G_1(s) = 1/s$ and $G_2(s) = 1/(s+1)$. The product $G_1(s)G_2(s)$ is

$$G_1(s)G_2(s) = \frac{1}{s(s+1)}$$

The z transform for this function is given by Eq. (10.6). That is,

$$G_1G_2(z) = \frac{z(1-e^{-T})}{(z-1)(z-e^{-T})} \tag{10.41}$$

For the sampler configuration shown in Fig. 10.4*c*, the Laplace relationships are

$$X(s) = F^*(s)G_1(s)$$

$$Y(s) = X^*(s)G_2(s)$$

Starring the first equation and then substituting this result for $X^*(s)$ into the second equation gives

$$Y(s) = F^*(s)G_1^*(s)G_2(s)$$

Starring gives

$$Y^*(s) = F^*(s)G_1^*(s)G_2^*(s)$$

The corresponding z transform is

$$Y(z) = F(z)G_1(z)G_2(z) \tag{10.42}$$

Illustrative example 2 Determine the z transform for Fig. 10.4*c*, when $G_1(s) = 1/s$ and $G_2(s) = 1/(s + 1)$. From Eqs. (10.4) and (10.5), it follows that

$$G_1(z) = \frac{z}{z-1}$$

and

$$G_2(z) = \frac{z}{z-e^{-T}}$$

Thus

$$G_1(z)G_2(z) = \frac{z^2}{(z-1)(z-e^{-T})} \tag{10.43}$$

From the preceding two examples it is to be noted that

$$G_1G_2(z) \neq G_1(z)G_2(z) \tag{10.44}$$

The function $G_1G_2(z)$ is the z transform corresponding to the product $G_1(s)G_2(s)$, whereas the function $G_1(z)G_2(z)$ is the product of the z transform for $G_1(s)$ and the z transform for $G_2(s)$.

Two sampled-data feedback control systems are shown in Fig. 10.6. The general procedure for determining the transformed equation for a sampled-data system is

1. In addition to the actual system input R, regard all switch outputs (starred quantities) as inputs.
2. In addition to the system output C, regard all switch inputs as outputs.
3. Write equations for each output in terms of its inputs.
4. Star quantities as necessary in order to determine $C(z)$.

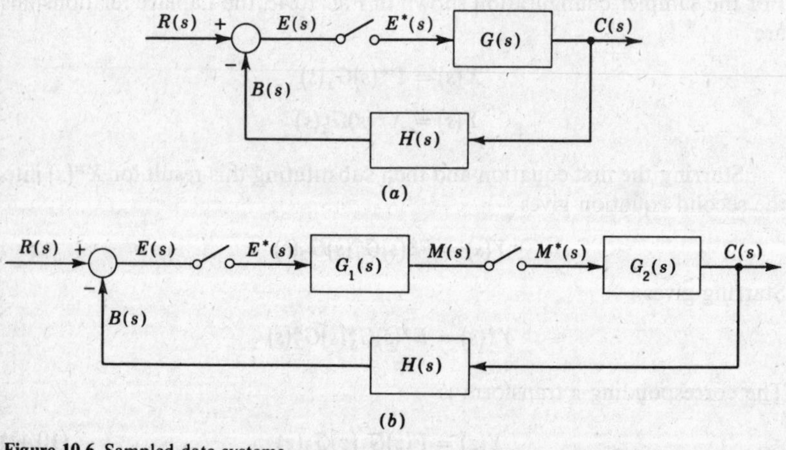

Figure 10.6 Sampled-data systems.

Application of this method to the system shown in Fig. 10.6*a* gives

$$C(s) = E^*(s)G(s)$$

$$E(s) = R(s) - E^*(s)G(s)H(s)$$

Starring gives

$$C^*(s) = E^*(s)G^*(s)$$

$$E^*(s) = R^*(s) - E^*(s)GH^*(s)$$

Solving the last equation for $E^*(s)$ and substituting into the first gives

$$C^*(s) = \frac{G^*(s)}{1 + GH^*(s)} R^*(s)$$

The corresponding z transform is

$$C(z) = \frac{G(z)}{1 + GH(z)} R(z) \tag{10.45}$$

The equations relating the inputs and outputs of Fig. 10.6*b* are

$$C(s) = M^*(s)G_2(s)$$

$$M(s) = E^*(s)G_1(s)$$

$$E(s) = R(s) - M^*(s)G_2(s)H(s)$$

Starring all equations, then solving for $C^*(s)$ gives

$$C^*(s) = \frac{G_1^*(s)G_2^*(s)}{1 + G_1^*(s)G_2H^*(s)} R^*(s)$$

The corresponding z transform is

$$C(z) = \frac{G_1(z)G_2(z)}{1 + G_1(z)G_2H(z)} R(z) \tag{10.46}$$

10.5 TRANSIENT RESPONSE

For continuous systems, it was found that a system is unstable if any root of the characteristic equation is in the right half of the s plane. This right half plane may be designated by $\sigma + j\omega$ in which $\sigma > 0$. The corresponding portion of the z plane is

$$z = e^{sT} = e^{\sigma T}e^{j\omega T}$$

The magnitude is

$$|z| = e^{\sigma T}$$

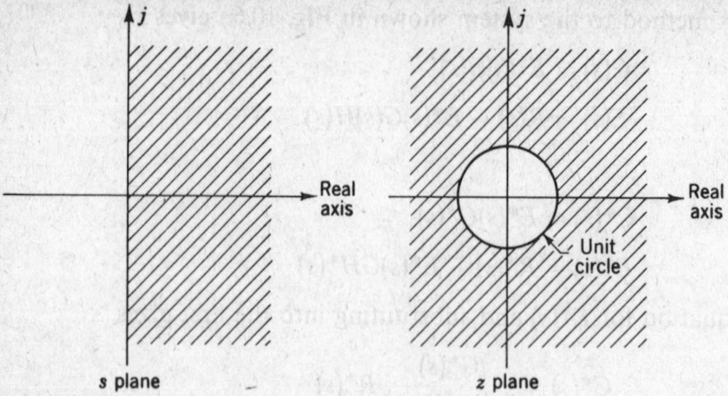

Figure 10.7 Stability regions for s plane and z plane.

For $\sigma > 0$, then $|z| > 1$. As is illustrated in Fig. 10.7, the right half of the s plane corresponds to the outside of the unit circle of the z plane. Thus, for stability, all the roots of the z-transformed characteristic equation must lie within the unit circle.

Consider now the sampled-data system shown in Fig. 10.8. The z transform for the output $C(z)$ is

$$C(z) = \frac{G(z)}{1 + G(z)} R(z) = \frac{N_{G(z)}}{D_{G(z)} + N_{G(z)}} R(z) \tag{10.47}$$

where $G(z) = N_{G(z)}/D_{G(z)}$ in which $N_{G(z)}$ is the numerator of $G(z)$ and $D_{G(z)}$ is the denominator of $G(z)$. The z-transformed characteristic equation is

$$N_{G(z)} + D_{G(z)} = 0 \tag{10.48}$$

The partial-fraction expansion for $G(s)$ is

$$G(s) = \frac{K}{4}\left(\frac{1}{s} - \frac{1}{s+4}\right)$$

The corresponding z transform is

$$G(z) = \frac{K}{4}\left(\frac{z}{z-1} - \frac{z}{z - e^{-4T}}\right) = \frac{z(1 - e^{-4T})K/4}{(z-1)(z - e^{-4T})} \tag{10.49}$$

Thus, the characteristic equation for this system is

$$(z-1)(z - e^{-4T}) + z(1 - e^{-4T})K/4 = 0 \tag{10.50}$$

Figure 10.8 Sampled-data system.

Routh's Criterion

To apply this criterion, it is necessary to transform the unit circle of the z plane to the vertical imaginary axis of the λ plane. This is accomplished by the transformation

$$\lambda = \frac{z+1}{z-1}$$

Solving for z gives

$$z = \frac{\lambda+1}{\lambda-1} \tag{10.51}$$

When the characteristic equation is expressed in terms of λ, then Routh's criterion may be applied in the same manner as for continuous systems.

Illustrative example 1 For a sampling period $T = \frac{1}{4}$ s, determine the value of K such that the system shown in Fig. 10.8 becomes unstable. That is, roots of the characteristic equation lie on the unit circle of the z plane (i.e., the imaginary axis of the λ plane).

SOLUTION For $T = \frac{1}{4}$, Eq. (10.50) becomes

$$(z-1)(z-0.368) + 0.158Kz = 0 \tag{10.52}$$

Using Eq. (10.51) to transform from the z plane to the λ plane gives

$$\frac{0.158K\lambda^2 + 1.264\lambda + (2.736 - 0.158K)}{(\lambda-1)^2} = 0 \tag{10.53}$$

The Routh array for the numerator is

$$\begin{array}{ll} 0.158K & (2.736 - 0.158K) \quad 0 \\ 1.264 & 0 \\ (2.736 - 0.158K) & 0 \end{array}$$

Thus, this system is unstable for

$$K \geq \frac{2.736}{0.158} = 17.3$$

In Fig. 7.1 is shown the root-locus plot for the continuous system corresponding to Fig. 10.8. The continuous system is stable for all values of K.

If, in the preceding example, the sampling rate is increased from 4 samples per second ($T = \frac{1}{4}$) to 10 samples per second ($T = \frac{1}{10}$), then the system would be unstable for $K \geq 42$. In general, making the sampling time shorter tends to make the system behave more like the corresponding continuous system. Usually, stability is improved as the sampling rate is increased.

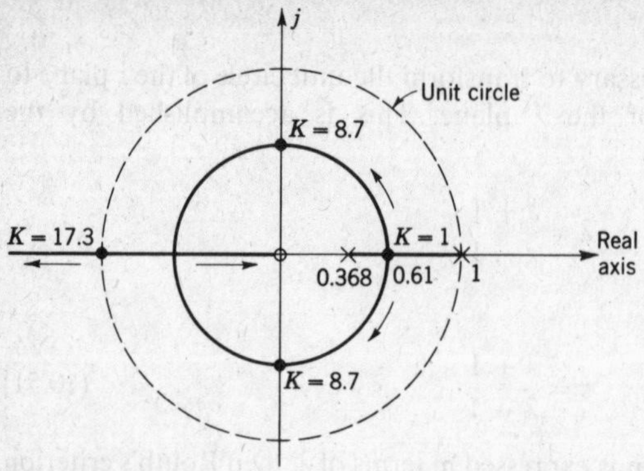

Figure 10.9 Root-locus plot for $(z-1)(z-0.368)+0.158Kz=0$.

Root Locus

All the techniques for constructing root-locus plots for continuous systems (in the s plane) apply equally well to sampled-data systems (in the z plane). For example, for $T=\frac{1}{4}$ the characteristic equation given by Eq. (10.50) becomes Eq. (10.52). This characteristic equation has an $\times$ at $z=1$ and at $z=0.368$. There is a $\odot$ at $z=0$. The complete root-locus plot may now be constructed as shown in Fig. 10.9. This root-locus plot crosses the unit circle at $z=-1$. The value of the gain $(0.158K)$ at any point on a root-locus plot is the product of the distance from this point to each $\times$ divided by the distance from this point to each $\odot$. Thus, the value of $0.158K$ at which the system becomes unstable is $0.158K=(1.368)(2)/(1)$, or

$$K=\frac{2.736}{0.158}=17.3$$

This verifies the result ascertained by Routh's criterion.

Two horizontal lines of constant b are shown in the s plane of Fig. 10.10a. The corresponding paths in the z plane are radial straight lines.

$$z=e^{sT}=e^{(a\pm jb)T}=e^{aT}e^{\pm jbT}$$

The angle of inclination of these radial lines is $\theta=\pm bT$.

Two vertical lines of constant a are shown in the s plane of Fig. 10.10b. The corresponding paths in the z plane are circles of radius e^{aT}. For negative values of a the circles are inside the unit circle of the z plane. For positive values of a the circles lie outside the unit circle of the z plane.

Radial lines of constant damping ratio $\zeta=\cos\beta$ are shown in Fig. 10.10c. In polar coordinates, $s=a\pm jb=-\zeta\omega_n\pm j\omega_n\sqrt{1-\zeta^2}$. Thus

$$z=e^{-\zeta\omega_n T}e^{\pm j\omega_n\sqrt{1-\zeta^2}\,T}$$

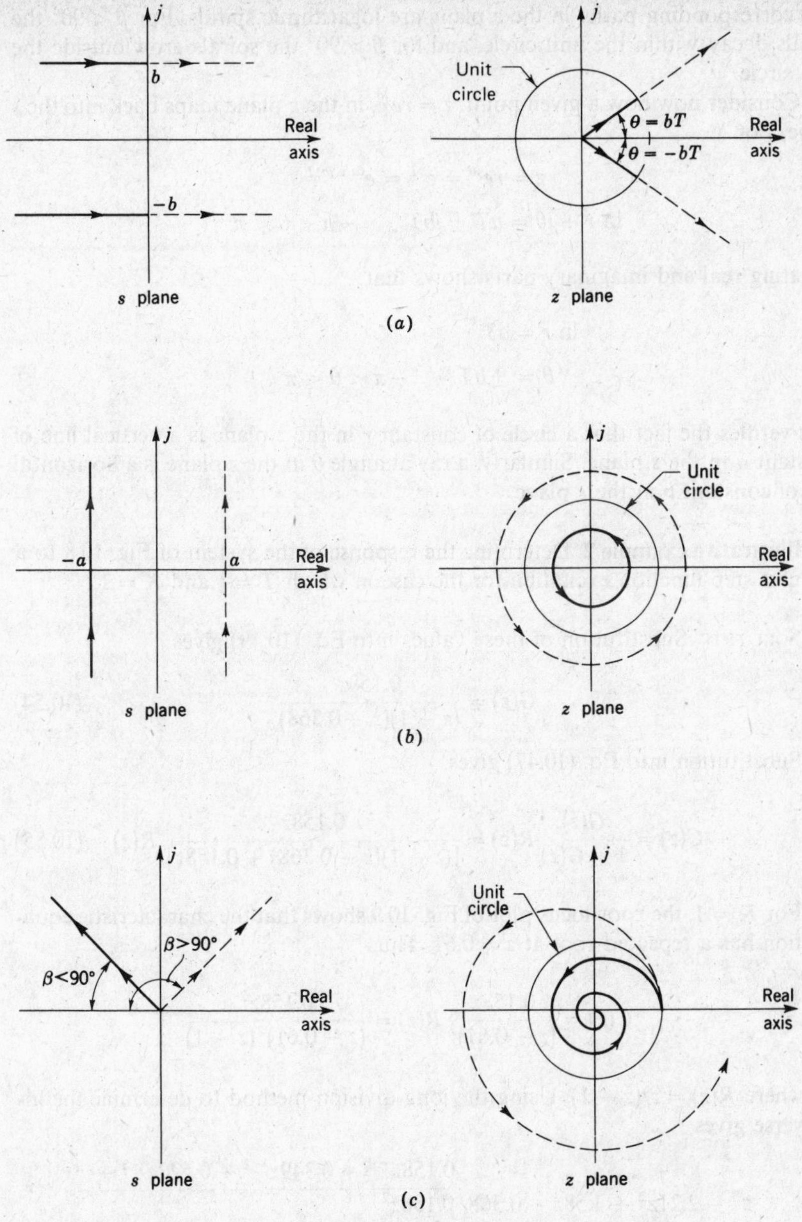

Figure 10.10 Corresponding paths in the s plane and z plane.

The corresponding paths in the z plane are logarithmic spirals. For $\beta < 90°$ the spirals decay within the unit circle, and for $\beta > 90°$ the spirals grow outside the unit circle.

Consider now how a given point, $z = re^{j\theta}$, in the z plane maps back into the s plane. For

$$z = re^{j\theta} = e^{sT} = e^{(a \pm jb)T}$$

$$\ln r + j\theta = aT \pm jbT \qquad -\pi < \theta < \pi$$

Equating real and imaginary parts shows that

$$\ln r = aT$$

$$\theta = \pm bT \qquad -\pi < \theta < \pi$$

This verifies the fact that a circle of constant r in the z plane is a vertical line of constant a in the s plane. Similarly, a ray at angle θ in the z plane is a horizontal line of constant b in the s plane.

Illustrative example 2 Determine the response of the system of Fig. 10.8 to a unit step-function excitation for the case in which $T = \frac{1}{4}$ and $K = 1$.

SOLUTION Substitution of these values into Eq. (10.49) gives

$$G(z) = \frac{0.158z}{(z - 1)(z - 0.368)} \tag{10.54}$$

Substitution into Eq. (10.47) gives

$$C(z) = \frac{G(z)}{1 + G(z)} R(z) = \frac{0.158z}{[(z - 1)(z - 0.368) + 0.158z]} R(z) \tag{10.55}$$

For $K = 1$, the root-locus plot of Fig. 10.9 shows that the characteristic equation has a repeated root at $z = 0.61$. Thus

$$C(z) = \frac{0.158z}{(z - 0.61)^2} R(z) = \frac{0.158z^2}{(z - 0.61)^2(z - 1)}$$

where $R(z) = z/(z - 1)$. Using the long-division method to determine the inverse gives

$$z^3 - 2.21z^2 + 1.58z - 0.368 \overline{\big)\, 0.158z^2} \quad \text{quotient: } 0.158z^{-1} + 0.349z^{-2} + 0.522z^{-3} + \cdots$$

Because

$$C(z) = c(0) + c(T)z^{-1} + c(2T)z^{-2} + c(3T)z^{-3} + \cdots$$

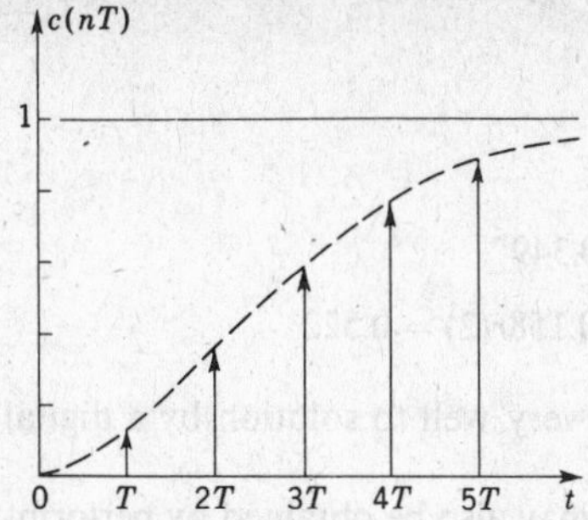

Figure 10.11 Response at sampling instants.

then

$$c(0) = 0$$
$$c(T) = 0.158$$
$$c(2T) = 0.349 \tag{10.56}$$
$$c(3T) = 0.522$$

A plot of the response $c(nT)$ at the sampling instants is shown in Fig. 10.11.

The long division method becomes quite cumbersome for computing $c(nT)$ for larger values of n. A more convenient procedure results from expressing the solution in the form of a difference equation.

Difference Equations

To determine the inverse z transform by this method, write the equation for $C(z)$, Eq. (10.55), in the form

$$C(z) = \frac{0.158z}{[(z-1)(z-0.368)+0.158z]} R(z) = \frac{0.158z}{z^2 - 1.21z + 0.368} R(z)$$

Thus

$$C(z) - 1.21z^{-1}C(z) + 0.368z^{-2}C(z) = 0.158z^{-1}R(z)$$

Application of Eq. (10.20) to invert the preceding expression yields directly the difference equation

$$c(k) = 1.21c(k-1) - 0.368c(k-2) + 0.158r(k-1) \tag{10.57}$$

This difference equation gives the value $c(k)$ at the kth sampling instant in terms of values at preceding sampling instants. Application of this result to obtain the values at the sampling instants gives

$$c(0) = 0$$
$$c(1) = 0.158r(0) = 0.158$$
$$c(2) = 1.21c(1) + 0.158r(1) = 0.349$$
$$c(3) = 1.21c(2) - 0.368c(1) + 0.158r(2) = 0.522$$

Such recurrence relationships lend themselves very well to solution by a digital computer.

The response $c(k)$ at the sampling instants may also be obtained by performing a partial-fraction expansion and then inverting. Thus

$$C(z) = z\left[\frac{0.158z}{(z-1)(z-0.61)^2}\right] = z\left[\frac{K_1}{z-1} + \frac{C_1}{(z-0.61)^2} + \frac{C_2}{z-0.61}\right]$$

The partial-fraction-expansion constants are $K_1 = 1.0$, $C_1 = -0.24 = -(0.39) \times (0.61)$, and $C_2 = -1.0$. Thus, $C(z)$ becomes

$$C(z) = \frac{z}{z-1} - \frac{z}{z-0.61} - 0.39\frac{0.61z}{(z-0.61)^2}$$

By noting that

$$Z^{-1}\left[\frac{z}{z-1}\right] = 1 \qquad Z^{-1}\left[\frac{z}{z-a}\right] = a^k \qquad Z^{-1}\left[\frac{az}{(z-a)^2}\right] = ka^k$$

the inverse is found to be

$$c(k) = 1.0 - (1.0 + 0.39k)(0.61)^k$$

With this method, the value of $c(k)$ at any sampling instant k may be calculated directly without the need to compute the value at all the preceding instants.

In summary, by the application of Eq. (10.20) a z-transformed expression may be inverted directly into the form of a difference equation in which values for $c(k)$ must be computed in succession. Alternatively, by performing a partial-fraction expansion and then inverting, an equation for $c(k)$ which does not depend on preceding values is obtained.

10.6 FILTERS

Sampled-data systems usually incorporate a filter, as illustrated in Fig. 10.12. A perfect filter would convert the sampled signal $f^*(t)$ back to the continuous input $f(t)$. That is, the output $y(t)$ of the filter would equal $f(t)$. If such a perfect filter were possible, then the sampled-data system would behave the same as the continuous system.

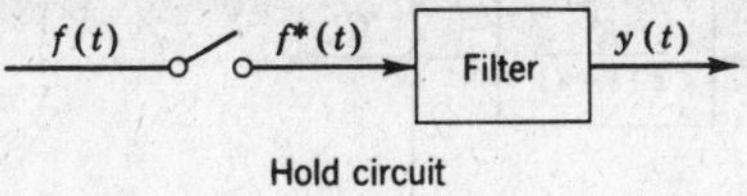

Figure 10.12 Schematic representation of sampler and filter.

Zero-Order Hold

The most commonly used filter is that in which the value of the last sample is retained until the next sample is taken. This type of filter is called a zero-order hold, or boxcar generator. The dashed curve in Fig. 10.13 represents the continuous function $f(t)$. The vertical arrows at the sampling instants are the impulses which represent the sampled signal $f^*(t)$. Because the zero-order hold retains the value of $f(t)$ at each sampling instant, $y(t)$ is the series of steps shown in Fig. 10.13. The equation for this series of steps (i.e., pulse functions) is

$$y(t) = f(0)[u(t) - u(t-T)] + f(T)[u(t-T) - u(t-2T)] + f(2T)[u(t-2T) - u(t-3T)] + \cdots$$

The Laplace transform is

$$\begin{aligned} Y(s) &= f(0)\left(\frac{1-e^{-Ts}}{s}\right) + f(T)\left(\frac{e^{-Ts}-e^{-2Ts}}{s}\right) \\ &\quad + f(2T)\left(\frac{e^{-2Ts}-e^{-3Ts}}{s}\right) + \cdots \\ &= \left(\frac{1-e^{-Ts}}{s}\right)[f(0) + f(T)e^{-Ts} + f(2T)e^{-2Ts} + \cdots] \\ &= \frac{1-e^{-Ts}}{s}F^*(s) \end{aligned}$$

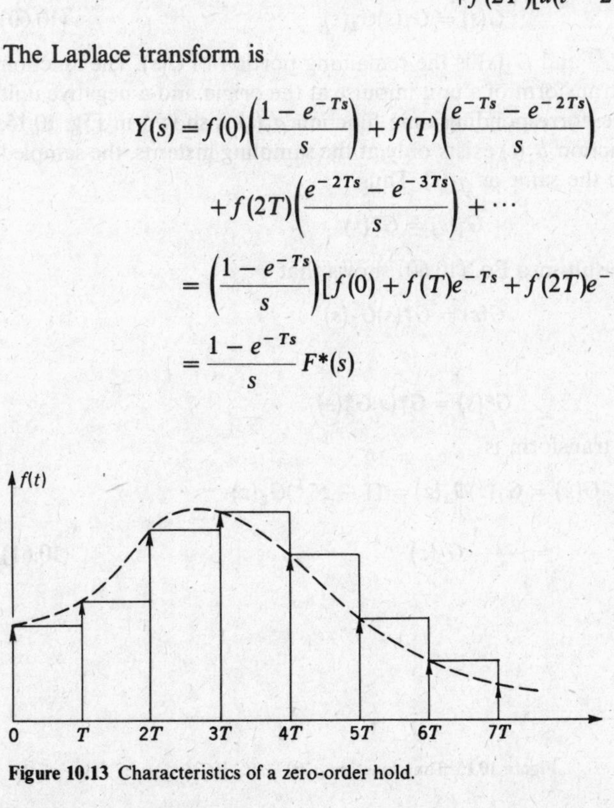

Figure 10.13 Characteristics of a zero-order hold.

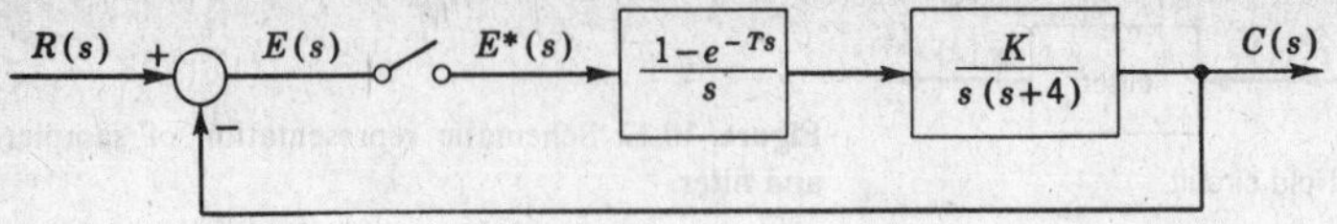

Figure 10.14 Sampled-data system with a zero-order hold.

This result shows that the Laplace transform for a zero-order hold is

$$\frac{1 - e^{-Ts}}{s} \tag{10.58}$$

Suppose that a zero-order hold is added to the system of Fig. 10.8. The new block diagram for this system is shown in Fig. 10.14. The transfer function for the hold is included in the overall transfer function $G(s)$. Thus,

$$G(s) = (1 - e^{-Ts})\frac{K}{s^2(s+4)} \tag{10.59}$$

To determine $G(z)$ when $G(s)$ contains a $(1 - e^{-Ts})$ factor, first write Eq. (10.59) in the form

$$G(s) = G_1(s)G_2(s) \tag{10.60}$$

where $G_1(s) = 1 - e^{-Ts}$ and $G_2(s)$ is the remaining portion of $G(s)$. The function $G_1(s)$ is the Laplace transform of a unit impulse at the origin and a negative unit impulse at $t = T$. The corresponding time function $g_1(t)$ is shown in Fig. 10.15. Because this time function $g_1(t)$ exists only at the sampling instants, the sampled function $g_1^*(t)$, will be the same as $g_1(t)$. Thus,

$$G_1(s) = G_1^*(s)$$

Substitution of this result into Eq. (10.60) shows that

$$G(s) = G_1^*(s)G_2(s)$$

Starring gives

$$G^*(s) = G_1^*(s)G_2^*(s)$$

The corresponding z transform is

$$G(z) = G_1(z)G_2(z) = (1 - z^{-1})G_2(z)$$

$$= \frac{z-1}{z}G_2(z) \tag{10.61}$$

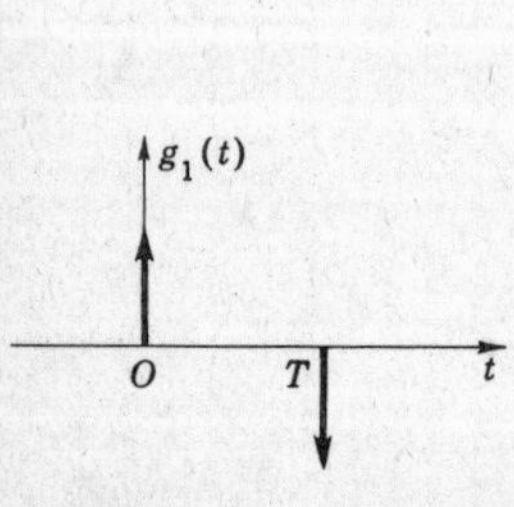

Figure 10.15 Time function $g_1(t) = \mathscr{L}^{-1}[G_1(s)] = \mathscr{L}^{-1}(1 - e^{-Ts})$.

For the case of Eq. (10.59),

$$G_2(s) = \frac{K}{s^2(s+4)} = \frac{K}{16}\left(\frac{4}{s^2} - \frac{1}{s} + \frac{1}{s+4}\right)$$

Thus,

$$G_2(z) = \frac{K}{16}\left(\frac{4Tz}{(z-1)^2} - \frac{z}{z-1} + \frac{z}{z-e^{-4T}}\right)$$

Substitution of this result into Eq. (10.61) gives

$$G(z) = \frac{K}{16}\left(\frac{4T}{z-1} - 1 + \frac{z-1}{z-e^{-4T}}\right) = \frac{K}{16}\left(\frac{4T}{z-1} + \frac{e^{-4T}-1}{z-e^{-4T}}\right)$$

For $T = \frac{1}{4}$, then $G(z)$ becomes

$$G(z) = \frac{0.368K(z+0.717)}{16(z-1)(z-0.368)} \tag{10.62}$$

The corresponding characteristic equation for this sampled-data system is

$$D_{G(z)} + N_{G(z)} = (z-1)(z-0.368) + 0.023K(z+0.717) = 0 \tag{10.63}$$

Replacing z by $(\lambda+1)/(\lambda-1)$ so that Routh's criterion may be applied gives

$$0.0395K\lambda^2 + (1.264 - 0.033K)\lambda + (2.736 - 0.0065K) = 0$$

The Routh array is

$$\begin{array}{cc} 0.0395K & (2.736 - 0.0065K) \\ (1.264 - 0.033K) & 0 \\ (2.736 - 0.0065K) & 0 \end{array}$$

Thus, the system becomes unstable for

$$K \geq \frac{1.264}{0.033} = 38.3$$

Without the zero-order hold, this system becomes unstable for $K \geq 17.3$.

From the characteristic equation, Eq. (10.63), the root-locus plot may be constructed as shown in Fig. 10.16. The root-locus plot crosses the unit circle at $K = 38.3$. Repeated roots, $z = 0.65$, occur at $K = 3.1$.

Let it now be desired to determine the response of this system to a unit step function for the case in which $K = 4$. From Eq. (10.62), it follows that

$$G(z) = \frac{4(0.368)(z+0.717)}{16(z-1)(z-0.368)} = \frac{0.092(z+0.717)}{z^2 - 1.368z + 0.368}$$

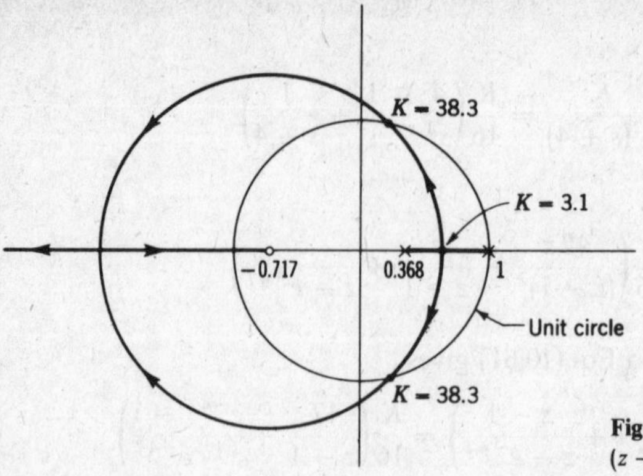

Figure 10.16 Root-locus plot for $(z-1)(z-0.368)+0.023K(z-0.717)$.

The z transform for the output is

$$C(z) = \frac{G(z)}{1+G(z)} R(z)$$

$$= \frac{N_{G(z)}}{D_{G(z)} + N_{G(z)}} R(z) = \frac{0.092(z+0.717)R(z)}{(z^2-1.368z+0.368)+0.092(z+0.717)}$$

Thus,

$$C(z) - 1.276z^{-1}C(z) + 0.434z^{-2}C(z) = 0.092z^{-1}R(z) + 0.066z^{-2}R(z)$$

Application of Eq. (10.20) yields the desired computational form

$$c(k) = 1.276c(k-1) - 0.434c(k-2) + 0.092r(k-1) + 0.066r(k-2)$$

The substitution of $c(k) = r(k) = 0$ for $k < 0$ and $r(k) = 1$ for $k \geq 0$ yields the following values for $c(k)$ at the sampling instants:

$$c(0) = 0$$

$$c(1) = 0.092r(0) = 0.092$$

$$c(2) = 1.276c(1) - 0.434c(0) + 0.092r(1) + 0.066r(0) = 0.275 \qquad (10.64)$$

$$c(3) = 1.276c(2) - 0.434c(1) + 0.092r(2) + 0.066r(1) = 0.469$$

The time at the kth sampling instant is $t = kT$. Replacing $c(k)$ by $c(kT)$ yields values in terms of time. For $T = \frac{1}{4}$, the values in terms of time are $c(0) = 0$, $c(0.25) = 0.092$, $c(0.50) = 0.275$, etc.

First-Order Hold

The characteristics of a first-order hold are illustrated in Fig. 10.17a. For the region $nT < t < (n+1)T$ the output is the straight line that is the extrapolation of the two preceding sampled values. That is,

$$f(t) = f(nT) + f'(nT)(t - nT) \qquad nT < t < (n+1)T$$

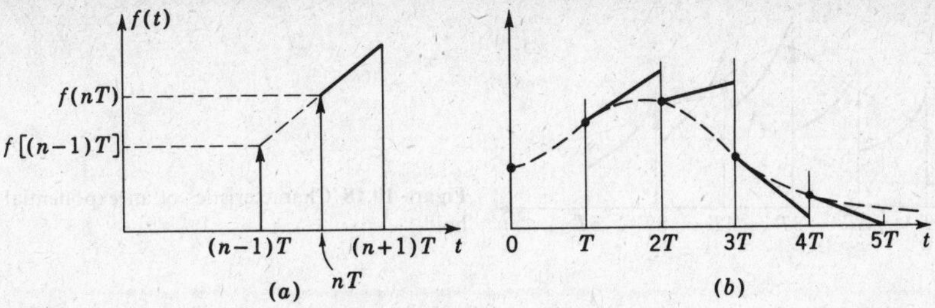

Figure 10.17 Characteristics and behavior of a first-order hold.

where the slope $f'(nT)$ is

$$f'(nT) = \frac{f(nT) - f[(n-1)T]}{T}$$

The behavior of a first-order hold is illustrated in Fig. 10.17*b*. The dashed curve is the continuous function $f(t)$. The output of the first-order hold is the series of straight-line segments. For a first-order hold the Laplace transform is

$$\left(\frac{1}{s} + \frac{1}{Ts^2}\right)(1 - e^{-Ts})$$

The entire class of higher-order hold circuits is revealed by writing the power-series approximation for $f(t)$ between the sampling instants $nT < t < (n+1)T$. Thus

$$f(t) = f(nT) + f'(nT)(t - nT) + \frac{f''(nT)}{2!}(t - nT) + \cdots$$

A zero-order hold approximates $f(t)$ by the first term, a first-order hold approximates $f(t)$ by the first two terms, a second-order hold approximates $f(t)$ by the first three terms, etc. Because of practical considerations, first-order and higher-order holds are seldom used. By far, the zero-order hold is the most commonly used circuit.

Exponential Hold

One of the simplest filters is the exponential hold. The transfer function for an exponential hold is

$$G(s) = \frac{T}{1 + Ts}$$

Many components have this transfer function, and thus may be used as exponential hold filters. The output from an exponential hold is an exponential decay between the sampling periods, as is illustrated in Fig. 10.18. At each sampling

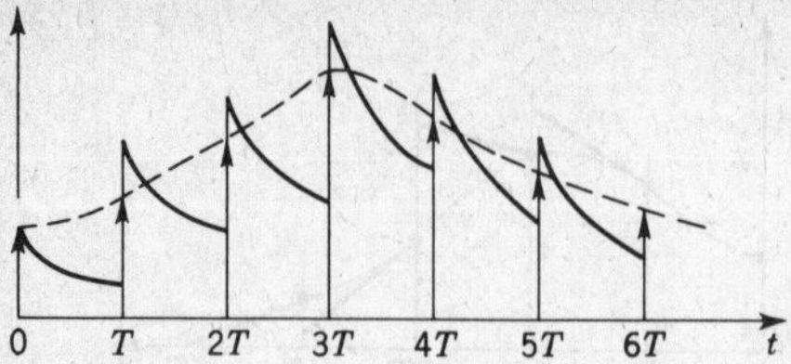

Figure 10.18 Characteristics of an exponential hold.

instant, there is a step change or discontinuity between successive exponential decays. The amount of the step change at each sampling instant is equal to the value (area) of the impulse at the particular sampling instant.

10.7 RESPONSE BETWEEN SAMPLING INSTANTS

Two different time functions which have the same sampled values are illustrated in Fig. 10.19. The inverse z transform $Z^{-1}[F(z)] = f^*(t)$ yields the value of the function at the sampling instants. The behavior between sampling instants may be determined by Linvill's[1–2] synthetic-sampler method.

Synthetic-Sampler Method

The dotted box in Fig. 10.20 represents a fictitious, or synthetic, sampler which is inserted in series with the actual sampler. The sampling rate of the fictitious sampler is m times that of the actual sampler ($m = 2, 3, \ldots$). The corresponding period is T/m. At submultiples of the sampling period T/m, when the fictitious sampler is closed, the actual sampler is open. Thus, the fictitious sampler does not affect the operation of the system. The fictitious sampler does not actually exist, but is merely employed as an aid for understanding the following analysis.

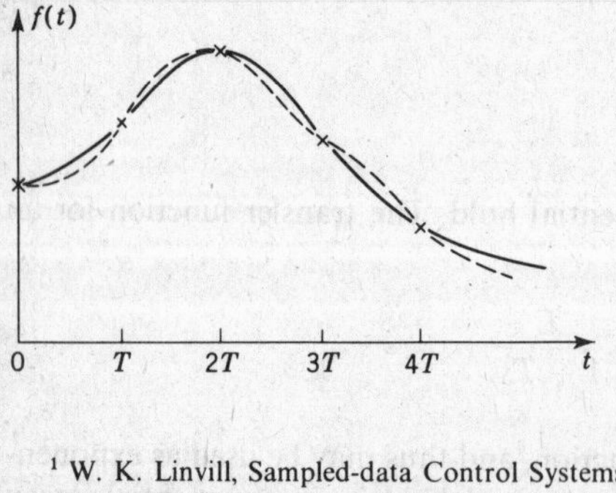

Figure 10.19 Two functions with the same values at the sampling instants.

[1] W. K. Linvill, Sampled-data Control Systems Studied through Comparison of Sampling with Amplitude Modulation, *Trans. AIEE*, *70:* 1779–1788 (1951).

[2] W. K. Linvill and R. W. Sittler, *IRE Convention Record* (1), 99–104 (1953).

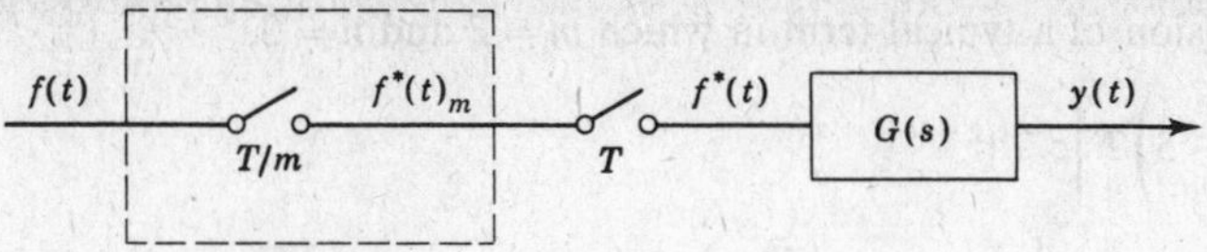

Figure 10.20 Fictitious sampler.

From Eq. (10.36) the continuous output $y(t)$ is

$$y(t) = \sum_{n=0}^{\infty} f(nT)g(t - nT)$$

Submultiples of the sampling period are represented by the term kT/m where $k = 0, 1, 2, \ldots$. For example, if $m = 3$, the successive intervals kT/m are 0, $T/3$, $2T/3$, T, $4T/3$, ... The value of the output at the submultiple intervals is obtained by letting $t = kT/m$ in the preceding equation.

$$y\left(\frac{kT}{m}\right) = \sum_{n=0}^{\infty} f(nT)g\left(\frac{kT}{m} - nT\right) \tag{10.65}$$

The output at the submultiple sampling instants $y(kT/m) = y^*(t)_m$ may also be expressed as an impulse train. That is,

$$y^*(t)_m = \sum_{k=0}^{\infty} y\left(\frac{kT}{m}\right)u_1\left(t - \frac{kT}{m}\right)$$

The Laplace transform is

$$Y^*(s)_m = \sum_{k=0}^{\infty} y\left(\frac{kT}{m}\right)e^{-kTs/m}$$

The corresponding z transform is

$$Y(z)_m = \sum_{k=0}^{\infty} y\left(\frac{kT}{m}\right)z^{-k/m}$$

Substituting $y(kT/m)$ from Eq. (10.65) into the preceding expression gives

$$\begin{aligned} Y(z)_m &= \sum_{k=0}^{\infty} \sum_{n=0}^{\infty} f(nT)g\left[\left(\frac{k}{m} - n\right)T\right]z^{-k/m} \\ &= \sum_{k=0}^{\infty} \sum_{n=0}^{\infty} f(nT)z^{-n}g\left[\left(\frac{k}{m} - n\right)T\right]z^{-(k/m-n)} \end{aligned} \tag{10.66}$$

Consider the expansion of a typical term in which $m = 2$ and $n = 3$,

$$\sum_{k=0}^{\infty} f(3T)z^{-3} g\left[\left(\frac{k}{2} - 3\right)T\right] z^{-(k/2-3)}$$

$$= f(3T)z^{-3}\left[g(0)z^0 + g\left(\frac{T}{2}\right)z^{-1/2} + g(T)z^{-1} + g\left(\frac{3T}{2}\right)z^{-3/2} + \cdots\right]$$

$$= f(3T)z^{-3}\sum_{l=0}^{\infty} g\left(\frac{lT}{m}\right)z^{-l/m}$$

For a physically realizable system the impulse response $g(t)$ is zero for negative time. Thus, the first term to appear in brackets is for $k = 6$, in which case $g[(k/2 - 3)T] = g(0)$. From the preceding result, the general form of Eq. (10.66) is

$$Y(z)_m = \sum_{n=0}^{\infty} f(nT)z^{-n} \sum_{l=0}^{\infty} g\left(\frac{lT}{m}\right)z^{-l/m}$$

$$= F(z)G(z)_m \tag{10.67}$$

where

$$G(z)_m = [G(z)]_{\substack{z = z^{1/m} \\ T = T/m}}$$

Thus, $G(z)_m$ is obtained by substituting $z^{1/m}$ for z and T/m for T in $G(z)$. The result given in Eq. (10.67) may also be obtained by letting $k/m - n = l/m$ where $l = 0, 1, 2, \ldots$, in Eq. (10.66).

The equation for $C(z)_m$ for the system of Fig. 10.21 is obtained as follows:

$$C(z)_m = E(z)G(z)_m$$

$$E(s) = R(s) - E^*(s)G(s)H(s)$$

Starring gives

$$E^*(s) = R^*(s) - E^*(s)GH^*(s)$$

Thus,

$$E(z) = R(z) - E(z)GH(z)$$

Solving this last equation for $E(z)$ and then substituting $E(z)$ into the first equation gives the desired result.

$$C(z)_m = \frac{G(z)_m}{1 + HG(z)} R(z) \tag{10.68}$$

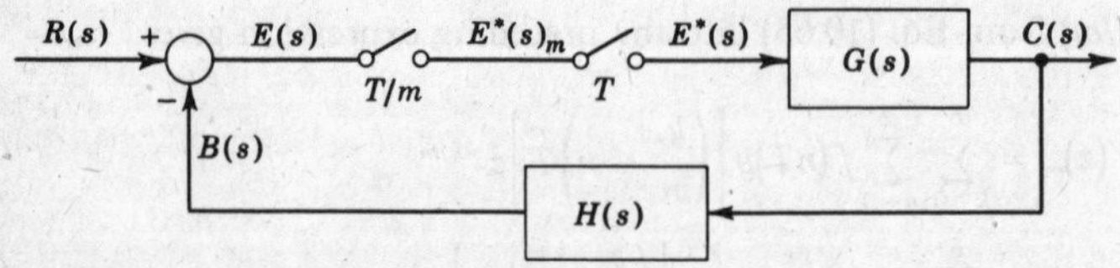

Figure 10.21 Sampled-data system with a fictitious sampler.

To illustrate the preceding concepts, let it be desired to determine the response midway between the sampling instants for the system of Fig. 10.8 to a unit step-function excitation. For $K = 1$ and $T = \frac{1}{4}$, the response at the sampling instants is shown in Fig. 10.11.

For this system, $HG(z) = G(z)$ is given by Eq. (10.49). Replacing T by $T/m = T/2$ and z by $z^{1/m} = z^{1/2}$ gives

$$G(z)_m = \frac{z^{1/2}(1 - e^{-2T})K/4}{(z^{1/2} - 1)(z^{1/2} - e^{-2T})}$$

For $K = 1$ and $T = \frac{1}{4}$, this becomes

$$G(z)_m = \frac{0.098z^{1/2}}{(z^{1/2} - 1)(z^{1/2} - 0.607)}$$

For $K = 1$ and $T = \frac{1}{4}$, the function $G(z)$ is given by Eq. (10.54). Substitution of these results into Eq. (10.68) gives

$$C(z)_m = \frac{0.098z^{1/2}}{(z^{1/2} - 1)(z^{1/2} - 0.607)} \frac{(z - 1)(z - 0.368)}{[(z - 1)(z - 0.368) + 0.158z]} R(z)$$

To eliminate fractional powers of z, let $w = z^{1/2}$. Thus,

$$C(w)_m = \frac{0.098w(w^4 - 1.368w^2 + 0.368)}{(w - 1)(w - 0.607)(w^4 - 1.21w^2 + 0.368)} R(w)$$

Cross-multiplying yields

$$(w^6 - 1.61w^5 - 0.60w^4 + 1.95w^3 - 0.37w^2 - 0.59w + 0.22)C(w)_m$$
$$= (0.098w^5 - 0.134w^3 + 0.036w)R(w) \qquad (10.69)$$

The significance of replacing $z^{1/2}$ by w is seen by noting that because

$$C(z)_m = c(0) + c\left(\frac{T}{2}\right)z^{-1/2} + c(T)z^{-1} + c\left(\frac{3T}{2}\right)z^{-3/2} + c(2T)z^{-2} + \cdots$$

then

$$C(w)_m = c(0) + c\left(\frac{T}{2}\right)w^{-1} + c(T)w^{-2} + c\left(\frac{3T}{2}\right)w^{-3} + c(2T)w^{-4} + \cdots$$

Thus, the w sampling instants are the desired submultiple sampling instants.

The difference equation associated with Eq. (10.69) is

$$c(k) = 1.61c(k - 1) + 0.60c(k - 2) - 1.95c(k - 3) + 0.37c(k - 4) + 0.59c(k - 5)$$
$$- 0.22c(k - 6) + 0.098r(k - 1) - 0.134r(k - 3) + 0.036r(k - 5) \qquad (10.70)$$

Because

$$R(z) = r(0) + r(T)z^{-1} + r(2T)z^{-2} + \cdots$$

then replacing z^{-1} by w^{-2} gives

$$R(w) = r(0) + 0w^{-1} + r(T)w^{-2} + 0w^{-3} + r(2T)w^{-4} + \cdots$$

Thus, $r = 0$ at the 1, 3, 5, ... sampling instants of w.

Application of Eq. (10.70) to obtain the values at the submultiple sampling instants gives

$$\begin{aligned}
c(0) &= 0 \\
c(1) &= 0.098r(0) = 0.098 \\
c(2) &= 1.61c(1) = 0.158 \\
c(3) &= 1.61c(2) + 0.60c(1) + 0.098r(2) - 0.134r(0) = 0.277 \\
c(4) &= 1.61c(3) + 0.60c(2) - 1.95c(1) = 0.350 \\
c(5) &= 1.61c(4) + 0.60c(3) - 1.95c(2) + 0.37c(1) \\
&\quad + 0.098r(4) - 0.134r(2) + 0.036r(0) = 0.458 \\
&\cdots\cdots\cdots\cdots
\end{aligned} \tag{10.71}$$

Replacing k by $kT/2$ shows that the response at the sampling instants $c(0)$, $c(1)$, $c(2)$, $c(3)$, etc., corresponds to the response at time $c(0)$, $c(0.5T)$, $c(T)$, $c(1.5T)$, etc.

The inverse could also have been obtained by the long-division method. For $R(z) = z/(z-1)$, then $R(w) = w^2/(w^2 - 1)$. Thus, substituting this value of $R(w)$ into Eq. (10.69), and then dividing the numerator of $C(w)_m$ by the denominator yields the desired values as the coefficients of the answer.

10.8 DISCRETE DATA SYSTEMS

When a system deals strictly with discrete data, the system can be described by the following set of discrete state equations:

$$\mathbf{x}[(k+1)T] = A\mathbf{x}(kT) + \mathbf{b}f(kT) \tag{10.72}$$

For $k = 0, 1, 2, \ldots$, the system equations are

$$\begin{aligned}
\mathbf{x}(T) &= A\mathbf{x}(0) + \mathbf{b}f(0) \\
\mathbf{x}(2T) &= A\mathbf{x}(T) + \mathbf{b}f(T) \\
\mathbf{x}(3T) &= A\mathbf{x}(2T) + \mathbf{b}f(2T) \\
&\cdots\cdots\cdots\cdots \\
\mathbf{x}(kT) &= A\mathbf{x}[(k-1)T] + \mathbf{b}f[(k-1)T]
\end{aligned}$$

Substitution of $\mathbf{x}(T)$ from the first into the second, and the resulting $\mathbf{x}(2T)$ from the second into the third, etc., yields

$$\mathbf{x}(kT) = A^k\mathbf{x}(0) + \sum_{i=0}^{k-1} A^{k-i-1}\mathbf{b}f(iT) \tag{10.73}$$

The Laplace transform method saves considerable time and effort in solving the state-transition equation for continuous systems. Similarly, the z transform method saves much computational effort in obtaining the solution of the state-transition equation for a discrete data system. The z transform of Eq. (10.72), which is the discrete time representation for a system, is

$$z\mathbf{X}(z) - z\mathbf{x}(0) = A\mathbf{X}(z) + \mathbf{b}F(z)$$

or

$$[zI - A]\mathbf{X}(z) = z\mathbf{x}(0) + \mathbf{b}F(z)$$

Premultiplying both sides by $[zI - A]^{-1}$ gives

$$\mathbf{X}(z) = [zI - A]^{-1}z\mathbf{x}(0) + [zI - A]^{-1}\mathbf{b}F(z) \tag{10.74}$$

Inverting yields

$$\mathbf{x}(kT) = Z^{-1}\{[zI - A]^{-1}z\}\mathbf{x}(0) + Z^{-1}\{[zI - A]^{-1}\mathbf{b}F(z)\} \tag{10.75}$$

Comparison with Eq. (10.73) shows that

$$A^k = Z^{-1}\{[zI - A]^{-1}z\}$$

and

$$\sum_{i=0}^{k-1} A^{k-i-1}\mathbf{b}f(iT) = Z^{-1}\{[zI - A]^{-1}\mathbf{b}F(z)\}$$

For computational purposes, it is usually more convenient to express Eq. (10.75) in the form

$$\mathbf{x}(kT) = Z^{-1}\{[zI - A]^{-1}[z\mathbf{x}(0) + \mathbf{b}F(z)]\} \tag{10.76}$$

Difference Equations

Any of the methods discussed in Sec. 9.1 may be used to obtain the state-space representation for a difference equation. For illustrative purposes, the method of general programming is described in the following. The general representation for an nth-order differential equation is given by Eq. (9.16). The corresponding state-space representation is given by Eqs. (9.17) and (9.18). Replacing $c(t)$ by $c(kT)$, $Dc(t)$ by $c[(k+1)T]$, $D^2c(t)$ by $c[(k+2)T]$, etc., yields the following general form for a difference equation:

$$\begin{aligned} c[(k+n)T] + a_1 c[(k+n-1)T] + \cdots + a_{n-1} c[(k+1)T] + a_n c(kT) \\ = b_0 f[(k+n)T] + b_1 f[(k+n-1)T] + \cdots + b_{n-1} f[(k+1)T] + b_n f(kT) \end{aligned} \tag{10.77}$$

The corresponding state-space representation is

$$\begin{bmatrix} x_1[(k+1)T] \\ x_2[(k+1)T] \\ \vdots \\ x_n[(k+1)T] \end{bmatrix} = \begin{bmatrix} 0 & 1 & 0 & \cdots & 0 \\ 0 & 0 & 1 & \cdots & 0 \\ \cdots & \cdots & \cdots & \cdots & \cdots \\ -a_n & -a_{n-1} & -a_{n-2} & \cdots & -a_1 \end{bmatrix} \begin{bmatrix} x_1(kT) \\ x_2(kT) \\ \vdots \\ x_n(kT) \end{bmatrix} + \begin{bmatrix} h_1 \\ h_2 \\ \vdots \\ h_n \end{bmatrix} f(kT) \tag{10.78}$$

where

$$\begin{aligned} x_1(kT) &= c(kT) - b_0 f(kT) \\ x_2(kT) &= x_1[(k+1)T] - h_1 f(kT) \\ &\cdots\cdots\cdots\cdots \\ x_n(kT) &= x_{n-1}[(k+1)T] - h_{n-1} f(kT) \end{aligned}$$

and

$$\begin{aligned} h_1 &= b_1 - a_1 b_0 \\ h_2 &= b_2 - a_2 b_0 - a_1 h_1 \\ &\cdots\cdots\cdots\cdots \\ h_n &= b_n - a_n b_0 - a_{n-1} h_1 - \cdots - a_2 h_{n-2} - a_1 h_{n-1} \end{aligned}$$

The preceding equations express values in terms of time kT at the sampling instants. Replacing kT by k, $(k+1)T$ by $(k+1)$, $(k+n)T$ by $(k+n)$, etc., yields the corresponding equations for values at the kth sampling instant.

Illustrative example 1 Obtain a state-space representation for the difference equation

$$c(k+2) + 0.7c(k+1) + 0.1c(k) = 2f(k+1) + f(k)$$

Solve for the response of this system for the case in which $c(k) = 0$ for $k \le 0$, $f(k) = 0$ for $k < 0$, and $f(k) = 1$ for $k \ge 0$.

SOLUTION This difference equation has the form of Eq. (10.77). For $a_1 = 0.7$, $a_2 = 0.1$, $b_0 = 0$, $b_1 = 2$, and $b_2 = 1$, it follows that $h_1 = b_1 - a_1 b_0 = 2$ and $h_2 = b_2 - a_2 b_0 - a_1 h_1 = 1 - 1.4 = -0.4$. The matrix form is now obtained from Eq. (10.78). Thus,

$$\begin{bmatrix} x_1(k+1) \\ x_2(k+1) \end{bmatrix} = \begin{bmatrix} 0 & 1.0 \\ -0.1 & -0.7 \end{bmatrix} \begin{bmatrix} x_1(k) \\ x_2(k) \end{bmatrix} + \begin{bmatrix} 2.0 \\ -0.4 \end{bmatrix} f(k)$$

where $x_1(k) = c(k)$. The algebraic form of the preceding matrix equations is

$$\begin{aligned} x_1(k+1) &= x_2(k) + 2f(k) \\ x_2(k+1) &= -0.1x_1(k) - 0.7x_2(k) - 0.4f(k) \end{aligned} \tag{10.79}$$

To prove that these relationships yield the original difference equation, solve the first expression for $x_2(k) = x_1(k+1) - 2f(k)$ and then replace k by

$k + 1$ to obtain $x_2(k + 1) = x_1(k + 2) - 2f(k + 1)$. Substitution of these results for $x_2(k)$ and $x_2(k + 1)$ into the second expression gives

$$x_1(k + 2) - 2f(k + 1) = -0.1x_1(k) - 0.7[x_1(k + 1) - 2f(k)] - 0.4f(k)$$

Rearranging yields the original difference equation, with $x_1(k) = c(k)$.

Letting $k = -1$ in the original difference equation yields $c(1) + 0.7c(0) + 0.1c(-1) = 2f(0) + f(-1)$. If $c(0) = c(-1) = f(-1) = 0$ and $f(0) = 1$, then $c(1) = 2$. The resulting initial conditions are $x_1(0) = c_1(0) = 0$ and $x_2(0) = x_1(1) - 2f(0) = 2 - 2 = 0$, where $x_1(1) = c(1) = 2$. For $F(z) = z/(z - 1)$,

$$[z\mathbf{x}(0) + \mathbf{b}F(z)] = \frac{z}{z-1}\begin{bmatrix} 2.0 \\ -0.4 \end{bmatrix}$$

The $[zI - A]^{-1}$ matrix is

$$[zI - A]^{-1} = \begin{bmatrix} z & -1.0 \\ 0.1 & z + 0.7 \end{bmatrix}^{-1} = \frac{\begin{bmatrix} z + 0.7 & 1.0 \\ -0.1 & z \end{bmatrix}}{(z + 0.2)(z + 0.5)}$$

From Eq. (10.75), it follows that

$$\begin{bmatrix} X_1(z) \\ X_2(z) \end{bmatrix} = z\frac{\begin{bmatrix} z + 0.7 & 1.0 \\ -0.1 & z \end{bmatrix}\begin{bmatrix} 2.0 \\ -0.4 \end{bmatrix}}{(z - 1)(z + 0.2)(z + 0.5)} = \frac{z\begin{bmatrix} 2.0 \\ -0.4 \end{bmatrix}}{(z - 1)(z + 0.2)}$$

The partial-fraction expansion is

$$\begin{bmatrix} X_1(z) \\ X_2(z) \end{bmatrix} = \begin{bmatrix} \dfrac{5}{3}\left(\dfrac{z}{z-1} - \dfrac{z}{z+0.2}\right) \\ -\dfrac{1}{3}\left(\dfrac{z}{z-1} - \dfrac{z}{z+0.2}\right) \end{bmatrix}$$

Inverting gives

$$x_1(k) = \frac{5}{3}[1 - (-0.2)^k]$$

$$x_2(k) = -\frac{1}{3}[1 - (-0.2)^k]$$

where $c(k) = x_1(k)$.

As illustrated in this example, in the z transform method it is necessary to obtain the matrix inverse $[zI - A]^{-1}$. For higher-order systems this can become a very time-consuming process. As in the case of continuous systems, the use of the signal flow graph results in the most direct method of solution.

Signal-Flow-Graph Method

The z transform of the discrete-data state equation, Eq. (10.72), is

$$z\mathbf{X}(z) - z\mathbf{x}(0) = A\mathbf{X}(z) + \mathbf{b}F(z)$$

To construct the signal flow graph, express the preceding in the form

$$\mathbf{X}(z) = \mathbf{x}(0) + z^{-1}[A\mathbf{X}(z) + \mathbf{b}F(z)]$$

The inputs for this signal flow graph are the initial conditions $\mathbf{x}(0)$ and the transform of the forcing function $F(z)$. The output nodes are the transform of the state variables $\mathbf{X}(z)$. The following matrix form is obtained directly from the signal flow graph.

$$\begin{bmatrix} X_1(z) \\ X_2(z) \\ \vdots \\ X_n(z) \end{bmatrix} = \begin{bmatrix} A_{11}(z) & A_{12}(z) \cdots & A_{1n}(z) \\ A_{21}(z) & A_{22}(z) \cdots & A_{2n}(z) \\ \cdots & \cdots & \cdots \\ A_{n1}(z) & A_{n2}(z) \cdots & A_{nn}(z) \end{bmatrix} \begin{bmatrix} x_1(0) \\ x_2(0) \\ \vdots \\ x_n(0) \end{bmatrix} + \begin{bmatrix} \psi_1(z) \\ \psi_2(z) \\ \vdots \\ \psi_n(z) \end{bmatrix} F(z)$$

Inverting yields the desired result. Note by comparison with Eq. (10.74) that the first matrix on the right is $[zI - A]^{-1}z$ and the last matrix is $[zI - A]^{-1}\mathbf{b}$.

Illustrative example 2 Use the signal-flow-graph method to determine the solution of Illustrative Example 1.

SOLUTION The z transform of Eqs. (10.79) is

$$zX_1(z) - zx_1(0) = X_2(z) + 2F(z)$$
$$zX_2(z) - zx_2(0) = -0.1X_1(z) - 0.7X_2(z) - 0.4F(z)$$

To construct the signal flow graph, first express these equations in the form

$$X_1(z) = x_1(0) + z^{-1}[X_2(z) + 2F(z)]$$

$$X_2(z) = x_2(0) + z^{-1}[-0.1X_1(z) - 0.7X_2(z) - 0.4F(z)]$$

The resulting signal flow graph is shown in Fig. 10.22. Application of Mason's

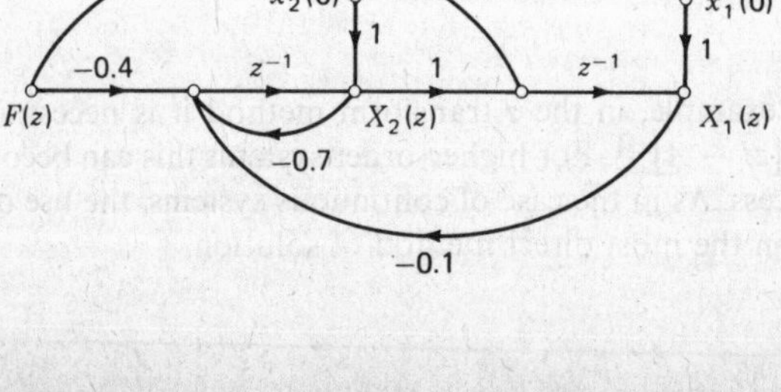

Figure 10.22 Signal flow graph.

gain formula to this signal flow graph gives

$$\begin{bmatrix} X_1(z) \\ X_2(z) \end{bmatrix} = \frac{\begin{bmatrix} z(z+0.7) & z \\ -0.1z & z^2 \end{bmatrix}}{(z+0.2)(z+0.5)} \begin{bmatrix} x_1(0) \\ x_2(0) \end{bmatrix} + \begin{bmatrix} \dfrac{2}{z+0.2} \\ \dfrac{-0.4}{z+0.2} \end{bmatrix} F(z)$$

For $x_1(0) = x_2(0) = 0$ and $F(z) = z/(z-1)$, the preceding reduces to the same transformed equation obtained in Illustrative Example 1. Thus, the same result follows.

Discrete Data Representation for Continuous Systems

The state-space representation for a continuous system is

$$\dot{\mathbf{x}} = A\mathbf{x} + \mathbf{b}f(t)$$

The solution referred to time $t = 0$ is given by Eq. (9.80). That is,

$$\mathbf{x}(t) = e^{At}\mathbf{x}(0) + \int_0^t e^{A(t-\tau)}\mathbf{b}f(\tau)\,d\tau \tag{9.80}$$

This is the state-transition equation for a continuous system. The solution referred to time t_0 is given by Eq. (9.82). That is

$$\mathbf{x}(t) = e^{A(t-t_0)}\mathbf{x}(t_0) + \int_{t_0}^t e^{A(t-\tau)}\mathbf{b}f(\tau)\,d\tau \tag{9.82}$$

For $t_0 = kT$ and $t = (k+1)T$, the preceding becomes

$$\mathbf{x}[(k+1)T] = e^{AT}\mathbf{x}(kT) + \int_{kT}^{(k+1)T} e^{A[(k+1)T-\tau]}\mathbf{b}f(\tau)\,d\tau$$

Assuming that $f(\tau)$ remains constant over the interval $kT < t < (k+1)T$, then $f(\tau)$ may be replaced by $f(kT)$. Letting $\lambda = (k+1)T - \tau$, in which case $d\tau = -d\lambda$, then

$$\mathbf{x}[(k+1)T] = e^{AT}\mathbf{x}(kT) + \int_0^T e^{A\lambda}\,d\lambda\,\mathbf{b}f(kT)$$

This result may be expressed in the form

$$\mathbf{x}[(k+1)T] = \Phi(T)\mathbf{x}(kT) + G(T)f(kT) \tag{10.80}$$

where

$$\Phi(T) = e^{AT} \qquad \text{and} \qquad G(T) = \left[\int_0^T e^{A\lambda}\,d\lambda\right]\mathbf{b}$$

This is the discrete-data representation for the continuous system $\dot{\mathbf{x}} = A\mathbf{x} + \mathbf{b}f(t)$. Note that it has the same form as Eq. (10.72), in which $\Phi(T)$ corresponds to A and $G(T)$ corresponds to $\mathbf{b}$.

Illustrative example 3 Obtain the discrete time state-space representation for the differential equation

$$\ddot{c} + 3\dot{c} + 2c = f(t)$$

Evaluate the resulting discrete time representation for a sampling period $T = 0.2$ s.

SOLUTION Letting $c = x_1$ and $\dot{c} = \dot{x}_1 = x_2$ yields the state-space representation

$$\begin{bmatrix} \dot{x}_1 \\ \dot{x}_2 \end{bmatrix} = \begin{bmatrix} 0 & 1 \\ -2 & -3 \end{bmatrix} \begin{bmatrix} x_1 \\ x_2 \end{bmatrix} + \begin{bmatrix} 0 \\ 1 \end{bmatrix} f(t)$$

The $\Phi(t) = e^{At}$ matrix is

$$\Phi(t) = \mathscr{L}^{-1}[sI - A]^{-1} = \mathscr{L}^{-1}\begin{bmatrix} s & -1 \\ 2 & s+3 \end{bmatrix}^{-1} = \mathscr{L}^{-1}\frac{\begin{bmatrix} s+3 & 1 \\ -2 & s \end{bmatrix}}{s^2 + 3s + 2}$$

$$= \begin{bmatrix} (2e^{-t} - e^{-2t}) & (e^{-t} - e^{-2t}) \\ (-2e^{-t} + 2e^{-2t}) & (-e^{-t} + 2e^{-2t}) \end{bmatrix}$$

Replacing t by T yields the matrix $\Phi(T)$. The $G(T)$ matrix is obtained as follows:

$$G(T) = \begin{bmatrix} \int_0^T (2e^{-\lambda} - e^{-2\lambda})\, d\lambda & \int_0^T (e^{-\lambda} - e^{-2\lambda})\, d\lambda \\ \int_0^T (-2e^{-\lambda} + 2e^{-2\lambda})\, d\lambda & \int_0^T (-e^{-\lambda} + 2e^{-2\lambda})\, d\lambda \end{bmatrix} \begin{bmatrix} 0 \\ 1 \end{bmatrix}$$

$$= \begin{bmatrix} \dfrac{(1 - 2e^{-T} + e^{-2T})}{2} \\ (e^{-T} - e^{-2T}) \end{bmatrix}$$

The substitution of these results into Eq. (10.80) yields

$$\begin{bmatrix} x_1[(k+1)T] \\ x_2[(k+1)T] \end{bmatrix} = \begin{bmatrix} (2e^{-T} - e^{-2T}) & (e^{-T} - e^{-2T}) \\ (-2e^{-T} + 2e^{-2T}) & (-e^{-T} + 2e^{-2T}) \end{bmatrix} \begin{bmatrix} x_1(kT) \\ x_2(kT) \end{bmatrix}$$

$$+ \begin{bmatrix} \dfrac{(1 - 2e^{-T} + e^{-2T})}{2} \\ (e^{-T} - e^{-2T}) \end{bmatrix} f(kT) \tag{10.81}$$

Evaluation at $T = 0.2$ gives

$$\begin{bmatrix} x_1[(k+1)T] \\ x_2[(k+1)T] \end{bmatrix} = \begin{bmatrix} 0.968 & 0.149 \\ -0.298 & 0.521 \end{bmatrix} \begin{bmatrix} x_1(kT) \\ x_2(kT) \end{bmatrix} + \begin{bmatrix} 0.016 \\ 0.149 \end{bmatrix} f(kT)$$

Note that the form of this result is identical to Eq. (10.72), in which the first matrix on the right is the A matrix and the last matrix is the **b** matrix.

Response between Sampling Instants

An important feature of the state-variable method is that it can be modified easily to determine the output between sampling instants. Thus, letting $t_0 = kT$ and $t = (k + \Delta)T$, where $0 \le \Delta < 1$, in Eq. (9.82) gives

$$\mathbf{x}[(k+\Delta)T] = e^{A\,\Delta T}\mathbf{x}(kT) + \int_{kT}^{(k+1)T} e^{A[(k+\Delta)T-\tau]}\mathbf{b}f(\tau)\,d\tau$$

Replacing $(k + \Delta)T - \tau$ by λ and noting that $d\tau = -d\lambda$ gives

$$\begin{aligned}\mathbf{x}[(k+\Delta)T] &= e^{A\,\Delta T}\mathbf{x}(kT) + \int_0^{\Delta T} e^{A\lambda}\,d\lambda\,\mathbf{b}f(kT)\\ &= \Phi(\Delta T)\mathbf{x}(kT) + G(\Delta T)f(kT) \qquad (10.82)\end{aligned}$$

where

$$\Phi(\Delta T) = e^{A\,\Delta T} \qquad \text{and} \qquad G(\Delta T) = \left[\int_0^{\Delta T} e^{A\lambda}\,d\lambda\right]\mathbf{b}$$

The function $\Phi(\Delta T)$ is obtained by replacing T by ΔT in the function $\Phi(T)$. Similarly, $G(\Delta T)$ is obtained by replacing T by ΔT in the $G(T)$ function.

Illustrative example 4 For the system of Illustrative Example 3, determine the discrete data representation for the response halfway between the sampling instants.

SOLUTION Replacing T by ΔT in the $\Phi(T)$ and $G(T)$ matrices of Eq. (10.81) yields the $\Phi(\Delta T)$ and $G(\Delta T)$ matrices. Application of Eq. (10.82) yields

$$\begin{bmatrix} x_1[(k+\Delta)T] \\ x_2[(k+\Delta)T] \end{bmatrix} = \begin{bmatrix} (2e^{-\Delta T} - e^{-2\,\Delta T}) & (e^{-\Delta T} - e^{-2\,\Delta T}) \\ (-2e^{-\Delta T} + 2e^{-2\,\Delta T}) & (-e^{-\Delta T} + 2e^{-2\,\Delta T}) \end{bmatrix} \begin{bmatrix} x_1(kT) \\ x_2(kT) \end{bmatrix} + \begin{bmatrix} \dfrac{1 - 2e^{-\Delta T} + e^{-2\,\Delta T}}{2} \\ (e^{-\Delta T} - e^{-2\,\Delta T}) \end{bmatrix} f(kT)$$

For $\Delta = 0.5$ and $T = 0.2$, then $\Delta T = 0.1$. Thus

$$\begin{bmatrix} x_1[(k+0.5)T] \\ x_2[(k+0.5)T] \end{bmatrix} = \begin{bmatrix} 0.991 & 0.086 \\ -0.172 & 0.733 \end{bmatrix} \begin{bmatrix} x_1(kT) \\ x_2(kT) \end{bmatrix} + \begin{bmatrix} 0.009 \\ 0.086 \end{bmatrix} f(kT)$$

Note that to obtain the response between the sampling instants, it is necessary to use Eq. (10.81) to obtain the values $\mathbf{x}(kT)$ used in the preceding expression.

Response at Sampling Instants

As is shown in Fig. 10.23, the continuous signal $f(t)$ is sampled every T seconds. The signal $f^*(t)$ which enters the system is a train of impulses. The following

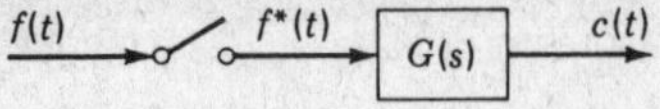

Figure 10.23 Train of impulses $f^*(t)$ entering system.

example points out important differences between the z transform and the state-space method of solution.

Illustrative example 5 For the system shown in Fig. 10.23, the transfer function is $G(s) = 1/(s + 1)$, the input signal $f(t)$ is a unit step function, and the sampling period is $T = 1$ s. Use the z transform method to determine the response at the sampling instants, and then use the state-space method to determine the equation $\mathbf{x}[(k + \Delta)T]$ for the response between sampling instants. Evaluate the response just before and just after the first two sampling instants.

SOLUTION From Fig. 10.23, it follows that $C(s) = G(s)F^*(s)$, where $G(s) = 1/(s + 1)$. The resulting z transform is

$$C(z) = G(z)F(z) = \frac{z}{z - e^{-T}} \frac{z}{z - 1} = z\left[\frac{z}{(z - 1)(z - 0.368)}\right]$$

$$= 1.58\left(\frac{z}{z - 1} - \frac{0.368z}{z - 0.368}\right)$$

Inverting yields for the response at the sampling instants

$$c(k) = 1.58[1 - 0.368(0.368)^k] = 1.58[1 - (0.368)^{k+1}]$$

Thus, it is found that $c(0) = 1.0$, $c(1) = 1.368$, $c(2) = 1.503$, etc.

To solve this problem by the state-space method, note that during the kth sampling period $kT \le t < (k + 1)T$, the input is

$$f^*(t) = f(kT)u_1(t - kT)$$

where $u_1(t - kT)$ is a unit impulse which is delayed for the time $t_0 = kT$. The differential equation of operation for the system is

$$c(t) = \frac{1}{D + 1} f^*(t)$$

or

$$\dot{c} + c = f^*(t)$$

Letting $c = x$ and $\dot{c} = \dot{x}$, the state-space representation is

$$\dot{x} = -x + f^*(t)$$

The Laplace transform is

$$sX(s) - x(kT) = -X(s) + F^*(s)$$

where $F^*(s) = \mathscr{L}[f^*(t)] = f(kT)$. Because of the time delay, each term in the transform should be multiplied by $e^{-t_0 s}$ where $t_0 = kT$. Simplicity of notation is afforded by solving this problem as though there were no time delay, then replacing t by $t - kT$ in the resulting inverse transform. Solving for the transform $X(s)$ gives

$$X(s) = \frac{1}{s+1}x(kT) + \frac{1}{s+1}F^*(s) = \frac{1}{s+1}x(kT) + \frac{1}{s+1}f(kT)$$

Inverting and replacing t by $t - kT$ gives

$$x(t) = e^{-(t-kT)}x(kT) + e^{-(t-kT)}f(kT)$$

$$= e^{-t^*}x(kT) + e^{-t^*}f(kT) \qquad kT \le t < (k+1)T$$

where $t^* = t - kT$. For $t = (k + \Delta)T$, then $t^* = \Delta T$. Thus

$$x[(k+\Delta)T] = e^{-\Delta T}x(kT) + e^{-\Delta T}f(kT)$$

For a unit step function, $f(kT) = 0$ for $k < 0$ and $f(kT) = 1$ for $k \ge 0$. For zero initial conditions, $c(0) = x(0) = 0$. The response just before each sampling instant is obtained by letting Δ approach 1. For $T = 1$ and $\Delta = 1$, then $e^{-\Delta T} = e^{-1} = 0.368$. Thus

$$x[(k+1)T] = 0.368x(kT) + 0.368f(kT)$$

Evaluation for $k = 0$, 1, and 2 gives

$$x(1) = 0 + 0.368(1) = 0.368$$

$$x(2) = 0.368(0.368) + 0.368(1) = 0.503$$

$$x(3) = 0.368(0.503) + 0.368(1) = 0.553$$

The values $x(1)$, $x(2)$, and $x(3)$ are the values just before the first, second, and third sampling instants.

The response just after each sampling instant is obtained by letting Δ approach zero. For this case, $e^{-\Delta T} \approx 1$. Thus

$$x[(k+0)T] = x(kT) + f(kT)$$

Evaluation for $k = 0$, 1, and 2 gives

$$x(0+) = 0 + 1.0 = 1.0$$

$$x(1+) = 0.368 + 1.0 = 1.368$$

$$x(2+) = 0.503 + 1.0 = 1.503$$

These are the values obtained by inverting $C(z)$. As stated in Sec. 10.4, the z transform method yields values immediately after each sampling instant. This example shows that the values $f(kT)$ are the values of the sampled signal at the sampling instants, the values $x[(k+1)T]$ are the values just before the $k+1$ sampling instant, and the values $x(kT)$ are the values just before the k sampling instant. As is illustrated by this example, when the input is an impulse

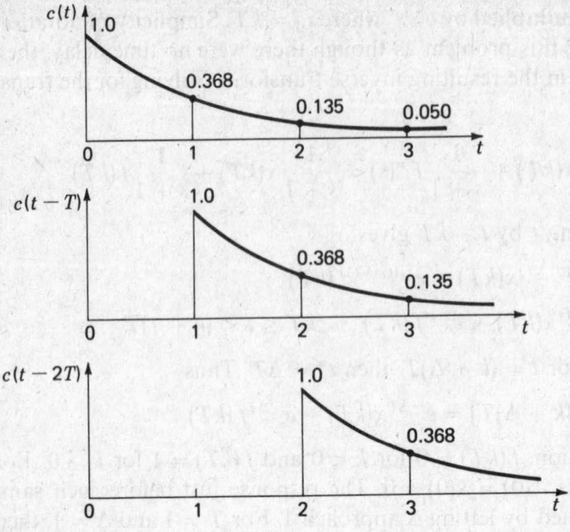

Figure 10.24 Response of system due to impulse at (*a*) $t = 0$; (*b*) $t = T = 1$; and (*c*) $t = 2T = 2$.

and when the order of the denominator exceeds the numerator by 1 [e.g., $G(s) = 1/(s + 1)$], there is a discontinuity in the response function at the sampling instants. When the order of the denominator exceeds the numerator by 2 or more, the response function is continuous.

The following analysis yields additional insight into the behavior of the response at the sampling instants. The function $f^*(t)$ is a train of unit impulses occurring every $T = 1$ seconds. For $G(s) = 1/(s + 1)$, the unit impulse response is $c(t) = e^{-t}$. The top graph of Fig. 10.24 shows the response due to the impulse which occurs at $t = 0$. The value at $t = 0+$ is $c(0+) = 1$, and the value just before the next sampling instant is $c(1-) = 0.368$. The contribution to the response due to the impulse which occurs at $t = T = 1$ is shown in the middle graph of Fig. 10.24. For $1 \le t < 2$, the response $c(t)$ is the sum of the response due to the impulse which occurs at $t = 0$ plus that due to the impulse at $t = 1$. For t slightly greater than 1, the sum is $c(1+) = 1.0 + 0.368 = 1.368$. For t slightly less than 2, the sum is $c(2-) = 0.368 + 0.135 = 0.503$. The contribution to the response due to the impulse which occurs at $t = 2T = 2$ is shown in the bottom graph of Fig. 10.24. For $2 \le t < 3$, the response $c(t)$ is the sum of that due to the impulse at $t = 0$ plus that due to the impulse at $t = 1$ plus that due to the impulse at $t = 2$. For t slightly greater than 2, the sum is $c(2+) = 0.135 + 0.368 + 1.0 = 1.503$. For t slightly less than 3, the sum is $c(3-) = 0.050 + 0.135 + 0.368 = 0.553$.

Sampled-Data Control Systems

For the system shown in Fig. 10.25*a*, the output of the sampler is $e^*(t)$. For the interval $kT \le t < (k + 1)T$, the output of the sampler is the unit impulse $e(kT)$.

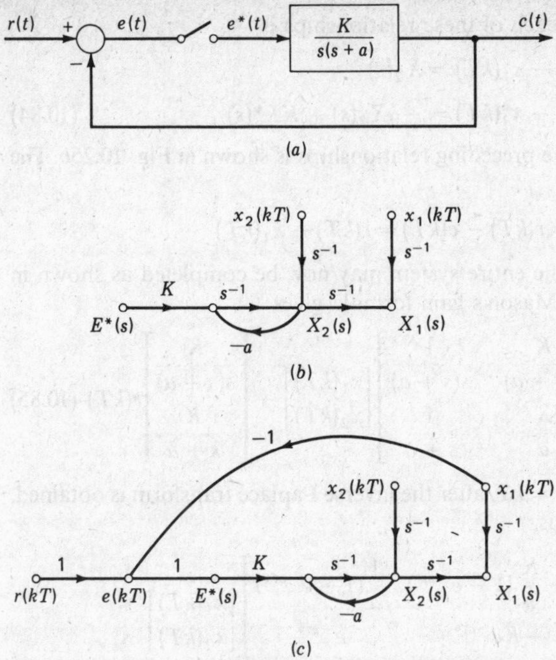

Figure 10.25 Sampled-data system and state-space representation.

That is,

$$e^*(t) = e(kT)u_1(t - kT) \qquad kT \le t < (k+1)T$$

The Laplace transform is

$$E^*(s) = e(kT)$$

The effect of the time delay $t_0 = kT$ will be accounted for later in the analysis by replacing t by $t - kT$ in the inverse Laplace transform.

The differential equation for the continuous portion of the system is

$$c(t) = \frac{Ke^*(t)}{D(D + a)}$$

or

$$\ddot{c} + a\dot{c} = Ke^*(t)$$

Letting $c = x_1$ and $\dot{c} = \dot{x}_1 = x_2$, the state-space representation is

$$\begin{bmatrix} \dot{x}_1 \\ \dot{x}_2 \end{bmatrix} = \begin{bmatrix} 0 & 1 \\ 0 & -a \end{bmatrix} \begin{bmatrix} x_1 \\ x_2 \end{bmatrix} + \begin{bmatrix} 0 \\ K \end{bmatrix} e^*(t) \qquad (10.83)$$

The Laplace transform for each of these relationships is

$$sX_1(s) - x_1(kT) = X_2(s)$$

$$sX_2(s) - x_2(kT) = -aX_2(s) + KE^*(s) \tag{10.84}$$

The signal flow graph for the preceding relationships is shown in Fig. 10.25*b*. The error signal at time kT is

$$e(kT) = r(kT) - c(kT) = r(kT) - x_1(kT)$$

The signal flow graph for the entire system may now be completed as shown in Fig. 10.25*c*. Application of Mason's gain formula gives

$$\begin{bmatrix} X_1(s) \\ X_2(s) \end{bmatrix} = \begin{bmatrix} \dfrac{1}{s} - \dfrac{K}{s(s+a)} & \dfrac{1}{s(s+a)} \\ \dfrac{-K}{s+a} & \dfrac{1}{s+a} \end{bmatrix} \begin{bmatrix} x_1(kT) \\ x_2(kT) \end{bmatrix} + \begin{bmatrix} \dfrac{K}{s(s+a)} \\ \dfrac{K}{s+a} \end{bmatrix} r(kT) \tag{10.85}$$

Because of the time delay $t_0 = kT$, after the inverse Laplace transform is obtained, t is replaced by $t - kT$. Thus,

$$\begin{bmatrix} x_1(t) \\ x_2(t) \end{bmatrix} = \begin{bmatrix} 1 - \dfrac{K}{a}(1 - e^{-at^*}) & \dfrac{1}{a}(1 - e^{-at^*}) \\ -Ke^{-at^*} & e^{-at^*} \end{bmatrix} \begin{bmatrix} x_1(kT) \\ x_2(kT) \end{bmatrix} + \begin{bmatrix} \dfrac{K}{a}(1 - e^{-at^*}) \\ Ke^{-at^*} \end{bmatrix} r(kT) \tag{10.86}$$

where $t^* = t - kT$. The value of the output at the sampling instants is obtained by letting $t = (k+1)T$, in which case $t^* = t - kT = (k+1)T - kT = T$. For $K = 1$ and $a = 4$, the preceding becomes

$$\begin{bmatrix} x_1[(k+1)T] \\ x_2[(k+1)T] \end{bmatrix} = \begin{bmatrix} 1 - \frac{1}{4}(1 - e^{-4T}) & \frac{1}{4}(1 - e^{-4T}) \\ -e^{-4T} & e^{-4T} \end{bmatrix} \begin{bmatrix} x_1(kT) \\ x_2(kT) \end{bmatrix} + \begin{bmatrix} \frac{1}{4}(1 - e^{-4T}) \\ e^{-4T} \end{bmatrix} r(kT) \tag{10.87}$$

For a sampling period $T = \frac{1}{4}$, these equations become

$$\begin{bmatrix} x_1[(k+1)T] \\ x_2[(k+1)T] \end{bmatrix} = \begin{bmatrix} 0.842 & 0.158 \\ -0.368 & 0.368 \end{bmatrix} \begin{bmatrix} x_1(kT) \\ x_2(kT) \end{bmatrix} + \begin{bmatrix} 0.158 \\ 0.368 \end{bmatrix} r(kT)$$

For $x_1(0) = c(0) = 0$, $x_2(0) = \dot{x}_1(0) = \dot{c}(0) = 0$, $r(kT) = 0$ for $k < 0$, and $r(kT) = 1$ for $k \geq 0$, this problem is the same as Illustrative Example 2 in Sec. 10.5. The preceding equation yields the values $x_1(0) = 0$, $x_1(T) = 0.158$, $x_1(2T) = 0.349$, and $x_1(3T) = 0.522$. These values correspond to the values $c(0)$, $c(T)$, $c(2T)$, and

$c(3T)$, respectively, of Eq. (10.56). To obtain the response between sampling instants, let $t = (k + \Delta)T$, in which case $t^* = t - kT = \Delta T$. Thus,

$$\begin{bmatrix} x_1[(k+\Delta)T] \\ x_2[(k+\Delta)T] \end{bmatrix} = \begin{bmatrix} 1 - \frac{1}{4}(1 - e^{-4\,\Delta T}) & \frac{1}{4}(1 - e^{-4\,\Delta T}) \\ -e^{-4\,\Delta T} & e^{-4\,\Delta T} \end{bmatrix} \begin{bmatrix} x_1(kT) \\ x_2(kT) \end{bmatrix} + \begin{bmatrix} \frac{1}{4}(1 - e^{-4\,\Delta T}) \\ e^{-4\,\Delta T} \end{bmatrix} r(kT)$$

The response at the midpoint is obtained by letting $\Delta = 0.5$. Thus

$$\begin{bmatrix} x_1[(k+0.5)T] \\ x_2[(k+0.5)T] \end{bmatrix} = \begin{bmatrix} 0.902 & 0.098 \\ -0.606 & 0.606 \end{bmatrix} \begin{bmatrix} x_1(kT) \\ x_2(kT) \end{bmatrix} + \begin{bmatrix} 0.098 \\ 0.606 \end{bmatrix} r(kT)$$

Values midway between the sampling instants are $x_1(0.5T) = 0.098$, $x_1(1.5T) = 0.277$, $x_1(2.5T) = 0.458$, etc. This is the same problem that was worked by the synthetic sampler method. The values $x_1(0.5T)$, $x_1(1.5T)$, and $x_1(2.5T)$ correspond to $c(1)$, $c(3)$, and $c(5)$, respectively, of Eq. (10.71).

Zero-Order Hold

The system shown in Fig. 10.26*a* is the same as that of Fig. 10.25*a* except that a zero-order hold has been added after the sampler. The output $h(t)$ of the zero-order hold is constant between sampling instants. That is,

$$h(t) = e(kT) \qquad kT \le t < (k+1)T$$

The Laplace transform is

$$H(s) = \frac{e(kT)}{s} \tag{10.88}$$

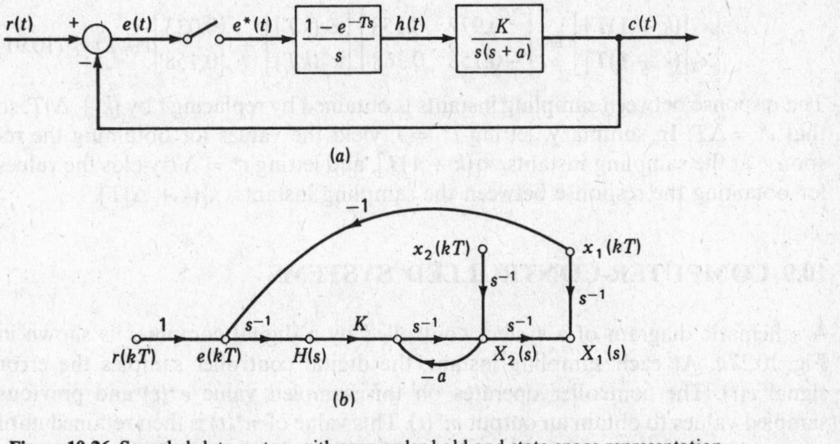

Figure 10.26 Sampled-data system with zero-order hold and state-space representation.

The effect of the time delay $t_0 = kT$ will be accounted for later by replacing t by $t - kT$. The error signal at time kT is

$$e(kT) = r(kT) - c(kT) = r(kT) - x_1(kT) \tag{10.89}$$

The signal flow graph for the plant is the same as that shown in Fig. 10.25*b* except that $E^*(s)$ is replaced by $H(s)$. Incorporation of the signal flow representation for Eqs. (10.88) and (10.89) with that for the plant yields the system graph shown in Fig. 10.26*b*. Application of Mason's gain formula to this signal flow graph yields

$$\begin{bmatrix} X_1(s) \\ X_2(s) \end{bmatrix} = \begin{bmatrix} \dfrac{1}{s} - \dfrac{K}{s^2(s+a)} & \dfrac{1}{s(s+a)} \\ \dfrac{-K}{s(s+a)} & \dfrac{1}{s+a} \end{bmatrix} \begin{bmatrix} x_1(kT) \\ x_2(kT) \end{bmatrix} + \begin{bmatrix} \dfrac{K}{s^2(s+a)} \\ \dfrac{K}{s(s+a)} \end{bmatrix} r(kT) \tag{10.90}$$

Because of the time delay $t_0 = kT$, after the inverse Laplace transform has been obtained, t is replaced by $t - kT$. The resulting inverses for some basic terms in the preceding matrix are

$$\mathscr{L}^{-1}\left[\frac{1}{s+a}\right] = e^{-at^*}$$

$$\mathscr{L}^{-1}\left[\frac{1}{s(s+a)}\right] = \frac{1}{a}(1 - e^{-at^*})$$

$$\mathscr{L}^{-1}\left[\frac{1}{s^2(s+a)}\right] = \frac{1}{a^2}[at^* - (1 - e^{-at^*})]$$

where $t^* = t - kT$. The value of the output at the sampling instants is obtained by letting $t = (k+1)T$, in which case $t^* = t - kT = (k+1)T - kT = T$. For $K = 1$, $a = 4$, and $T = \frac{1}{4}$, the response at the sampling instants is

$$\begin{bmatrix} x_1[(k+1)T] \\ x_2[(k+1)T] \end{bmatrix} = \begin{bmatrix} 0.977 & 0.158 \\ -0.158 & 0.368 \end{bmatrix} \begin{bmatrix} x_1(kT) \\ x_2(kT) \end{bmatrix} + \begin{bmatrix} 0.023 \\ 0.158 \end{bmatrix} r(kT) \tag{10.91}$$

The response between sampling instants is obtained by replacing t by $(k + \Delta)T$, so that $t^* = \Delta T$. In summary, letting $t^* = T$ yield the values for obtaining the response at the sampling instants, $\mathbf{x}[(k+1)T]$, and letting $t^* = \Delta T$ yields the values for obtaining the response between the sampling instants, $\mathbf{x}[(k+\Delta)T]$.

10.9 COMPUTER-CONTROLLED SYSTEMS

A schematic diagram of a system controlled by a digital computer is shown in Fig. 10.27*a*. At each sampling instant, the digital controller samples the error signal $e(t)$. The controller operates on this sampled value $e^*(t)$ and previous sampled values to obtain an output $m^*(t)$. This value of $m^*(t)$ is then retained until a new value is computed at the next sampling instant.

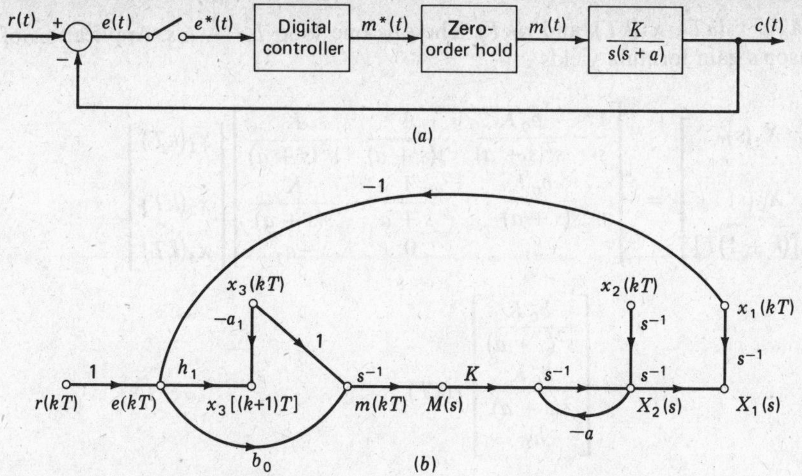

Figure 10.27 System with digital controller and state-space representation.

For the system shown, suppose that

$$m[(k+1)T] + a_1 m(kT) = b_0 e[(k+1)T] + b_1 e(kT)$$

This difference equation has the same form as Eq. (10.77) in which $m(kT)$ corresponds to $c(kT)$ and $e(kT)$ corresponds to $f(kT)$. Application of the general form given by Eq. (10.78) to the preceding yields the equivalent form

$$x_3[(k+1)T] = -a_1 x_3(kT) + h_1 e(kT) \tag{10.92}$$

where $h_1 = b_1 - a_1 b_0$. The state variable $x_3(kT)$ is

$$x_3(kT) = m(kT) - b_0 e(kT)$$

or

$$m(kT) = x_3(kT) + b_0 e(kT) \tag{10.93}$$

Because x_1 and x_2 are reserved as state variables for the plant, the symbol x_3 is used in the preceding. The output from the controller remains constant between sampling instants. That is,

$$m(t) = m(kT) \qquad kT \le t < (k+1)T$$

The Laplace transform is

$$M(s) = \frac{m(kT)}{s} \qquad kT \le t < (k+1)T \tag{10.94}$$

The signal flow graph for the plant is the same as that shown in Fig. 10.25*b*. Incorporation of the signal flow representation for Eqs. (10.92), (10.93), and (10.94), with that for the plant yields the system shown in Fig. 10.27*b*. The output nodes for this system are $X_1(s)$, $X_2(s)$, and $x_3[(k+1)T]$. The input nodes are

$x_1(kT)$, $x_2(kT)$, $x_3(kT)$, and $r(kT)$. There is one loop $L = -a/s$. Application of Mason's gain formula yields

$$\begin{bmatrix} X_1(s) \\ X_2(s) \\ x_3[(k+1)T] \end{bmatrix} = \begin{bmatrix} \dfrac{1}{s} - \dfrac{b_0 K}{s^2(s+a)} & \dfrac{1}{s(s+a)} & \dfrac{K}{s^2(s+a)} \\ \dfrac{-b_0 K}{s(s+a)} & \dfrac{1}{s+a} & \dfrac{K}{s(s+a)} \\ -h_1 & 0 & -a_1 \end{bmatrix} \begin{bmatrix} x_1(kT) \\ x_2(kT) \\ x_3(kT) \end{bmatrix} + \begin{bmatrix} \dfrac{b_0 K}{s^2(s+a)} \\ \dfrac{b_0 K}{s(s+a)} \\ h_1 \end{bmatrix} r(kT)$$

After inverting $X_1(s)$ and $X_2(s)$, the time delay $t_0 = kT$ is effected by replacing t by $t - kT$. The resulting inverses for some basic terms in the preceding matrix are $\mathcal{L}^{-1}[1/s(s+a)] = (1 - e^{-at^*})/a$ and $\mathcal{L}^{-1}[1/s^2(s+a)] = [at^* - (1 - e^{-at^*})]/a^2$ where $t^* = t - kT$. At the sampling instants, $t^* = T$. For $K = 1$, $a = 4$, and $T = \frac{1}{4}$, the inverse of the preceding matrix evaluated at the sampling instants is

$$\begin{bmatrix} x_1[(k+1)T] \\ x_2[(k+1)T] \\ x_3[(k+1)T] \end{bmatrix} = \begin{bmatrix} 1 - 0.023b_0 & 0.158 & 0.023 \\ 0.158b_0 & 0.368 & 0.158 \\ -h_1 & 0 & -a_1 \end{bmatrix} \begin{bmatrix} x_1(kT) \\ x_2(kT) \\ x_3(kT) \end{bmatrix} + \begin{bmatrix} 0.023b_0 \\ 0.158b_0 \\ h_1 \end{bmatrix} r(kT)$$

The value of x_1 and x_2 between sampling instants $x_1[(k+\Delta)T]$ and $x_2[(k+\Delta)T]$ is obtained by replacing t^* by ΔT rather than by T. The signal x_3 remains the same throughout each sampling interval.

Process Controllers

A typical digital process control loop is shown in Fig. 10.28. The characteristics of the digital controller are indicated by $D(z)$. The z transform for the output is

$$C(z) = \frac{G(z)D(z)R(z)}{1 + G(z)D(z)}$$

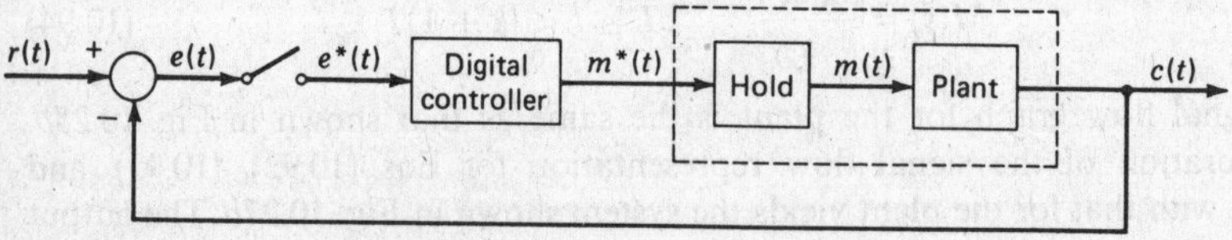

Figure 10.28 Typical digital process controller.

Solving for the z transform of the controller gives

$$D(z) = \frac{C(z)}{G(z)[R(z) - C(z)]} = \frac{1}{G(z)} \frac{C(z)/R(z)}{1 - C(z)/R(z)} \tag{10.95}$$

This result shows that the controller characteristics $D(z)$ may be obtained by knowing the plant and hold characteristics $G(z)$ and the desired response $C(z)$ to a given input $R(z)$.

Illustrative example 1 Determine the characteristics $D(z)$ of a digital controller such that the response of the system to a unit step function will be $c(t) = 1 - e^{-0.5t}$. The transfer function for the plant is $1/(1 + 5s)$, and the sampling period is $T = 1.0$ s.

SOLUTION For the plant and zero-order hold,

$$G(s) = G_1(s)G_2(s) = (1 - e^{-Ts})\frac{1}{s(1 + 5s)}$$

where $G_1(s) = (1 - e^{-Ts})$ and $G_2(s) = 1/s(1 + 5s) = [1/s - 1/(s + 0.2)]$. Application of Eq. (10.61) yields

$$G(z) = \frac{z-1}{z} G_2(z) = \frac{z-1}{z}\left[\frac{z}{z-1} - \frac{z}{z - e^{-0.2}}\right] = \frac{0.18}{z - 0.82}$$

For $R(s) = 1/s$ and $C(s) = 1/s(1 + 2s)$, then $R(z) = z/(z - 1)$, $C(z) = 0.39z/(z - 1)(z - 0.61)$, and $C(z)/R(z) = 0.39/(z - 0.61)$. Substitution of the preceding result into Eq. (10.95) gives

$$D(z) = \frac{z - 0.82}{0.18} \frac{0.39}{z - 1} = \frac{2.2(z - 0.82)}{z - 1}$$

or

$$D(z) = \frac{M(z)}{E(z)} = \frac{2.2 - 1.8z^{-1}}{1 - z^{-1}}$$

The discrete form of this z transform yields the desired controller characteristic

$$m(k) = 2.2e(k) - 1.8e(k - 1) + m(k - 1) \tag{10.96}$$

Discrete Equivalent of Analog Controllers

One of the most versatile and widely used controllers for continuous systems is the one which provides proportional plus integral action. The equation of operation for this controller is

$$m(t) = \left(K_1 + K_2 \frac{1}{D}\right) e(t)$$

The contribution of the various actions is adjusted by varying the constants K_1 and K_2. The discrete equivalent of this controller is commonly employed as the digital controller for process control systems. Using the trapezoidal method to approximate the integration yields for the discrete form

$$m(k) = K_1 e(k) + K_2 T \sum_{n=1}^{k} e(n) + m(0)$$

Generally it is more accurate and more convenient to work with the change in m in going from one sampling period to the next. Thus replacing k by $k - 1$ in the preceding and subtracting yields

$$\Delta m(k) = m(k) - m(k-1) = K_1[e(k) - e(k-1)] + K_2 Te(k)$$

Note that the preceding equation eliminates the need to know the initial value $m(0)$. The z transform of this equation is

$$M(z) - z^{-1}M(z) = K_1[E(z) - z^{-1}E(z)] + K_2 TE(z)$$

or

$$D(z) = \frac{M(z)}{E(z)} = K_1 + \frac{K_2 T}{1 - z^{-1}}$$

The Laplace transform for the continuous controller is

$$D(s) = \frac{M(s)}{E(s)} = K_1 + \frac{K_2 T}{s}$$

Note that the $1 - z^{-1}$ term in the denominator for the discrete controller corresponds to integration in the equivalent continuous controller (i.e., the $1/s$ term).

Optimum Response

It is now shown how the characteristics of a controller may be selected to yield optimum response. Any one of numerous optimum-performance criterion may be used. In the following, the method developed by Kalman[1] for obtaining the controller characteristics to yield a desired transient behavior is described. In Fig. 10.28 is shown a schematic diagram of the overall system. For illustrative purposes assume that the transfer function of the plant is $ab/(s + a)(s + b)$. The transient behavior is considered optimum when the system responds to a step function in minimum time with no overshoot. In addition, there should be no steady-state error.

In Fig. 10.29, the optimum response $c(t)$ is indicated by the heavy line. The unit step input is $r(t) = 1$. During the first interval $0 \leq t < T$, the input to the plant $m(t) = q_0$ is large so as to accelerate the system rapidly toward its final value.

[1] R. E. Kalman (discussion of) "Sampled-data Processing Techniques for Feedback Control Systems," Bergon and J. R. Ragazzini, *Trans. AIEE*, **73** (2): 245–246 (1954).

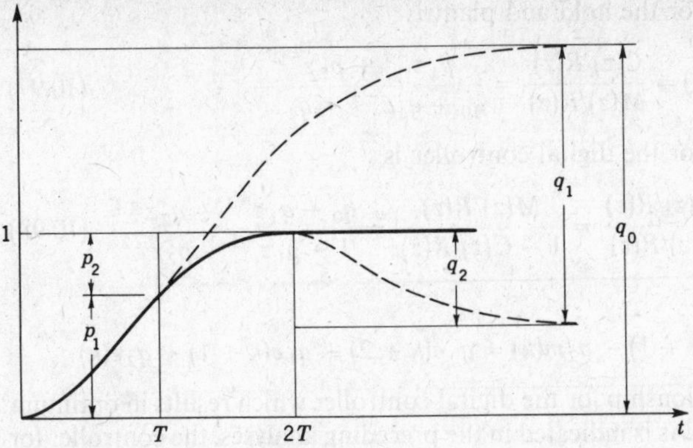

Figure 10.29 Optimum response.

The first dotted extension in Fig. 10.29 shows the subsequent response if the plant input is not changed after the first sampling period. Thus, at time $t = T$, it is necessary to begin to decelerate the response so as to achieve the desired final value $c(t) = r(t) = 1$. During the second interval $T \le t < 2T$, the plant input is changed by an amount q_1, so that $m(t) = q_0 + q_1$. As drawn in Fig. 10.29, the term q_1 is a negative constant. The response $c(t)$ reaches the final value at the end of the second interval $t = 2T$. The second dotted extension shows the path of the response if the plant input is not changed after the second interval. Thus for the third and subsequent intervals, the plant input is $q_0 + q_1 + q_2 = c(t) = r(t) = 1$.

A desirable feature of this performance criterion is that the error is reduced exactly to zero after two periods. The error then remains zero not only at the sampling points but also in between. This criterion thus eliminates the possibility of ripple (i.e., undesirable oscillations between sampling instants).

Because $m(t)$ is the output of a zero-order hold, it follows that the z transform of the sampled input $m^*(t)$ is

$$M(z) = q_0 + (q_0 + q_1)z^{-1} + (q_0 + q_1 + q_2)(z^{-2} + z^{-3} + \cdots)$$

Dividing $M(z)$ by the z transform of the unit step input $[R(z) = 1 + z^{-1} + z^{-2} + \cdots]$ gives

$$\frac{M(z)}{R(z)} = q_0 + q_1 z^{-1} + q_2 z^{-2}$$

Similarly, from Fig. 10.29 the z transform of the response at the sampling instants is

$$C(z) = p_1 z^{-1} + (p_1 + p_2)(z^{-2} + z^{-3} + z^{-4} + \cdots)$$

Dividing by $R(z)$ shows that

$$\frac{C(z)}{R(z)} = p_1 z^{-1} + p_2 z^{-2}$$

The pulsed transform for the hold and plant is

$$G(z) = \frac{C(z)/R(z)}{M(z)/R(z)} = \frac{p_1 z^{-1} + p_2 z^{-2}}{q_0 + q_1 z^{-1} + q_2 z^{-2}} \tag{10.97}$$

The pulsed transform for the digital controller is

$$D(z) = \frac{M(z)}{E(z)} = \frac{M(z)/R(z)}{E(z)/R(z)} = \frac{M(z)/R(z)}{1 - C(z)/R(z)} = \frac{q_0 + q_1 z^{-1} + q_2 z^{-2}}{1 - p_1 z^{-1} - p_2 z^{-2}} \tag{10.98}$$

Inverting yields

$$m(k+2) - p_1 m(k+1) - p_2 m(k) = q_0 e(k+2) + q_1 e(k+1) + q_2 e(k)$$

This is the desired relationship for the digital controller which results in optimum response for the system. As is indicated in the preceding analyses, the controller for a digital control system is programmed to yield a desired behavior. Because of the flexibility of programming, a digital controller is more versatile than a controller for a continuous system, which is limited to some action described by a differential operator.

Illustrative example 2 For the computer-controlled system shown in Fig. 10.28, the transfer function for the plant is $2/(s+1)(s+2)$. Determine the difference equation for the digital controller to yield optimum response, then obtain the signal flow graph for the resulting system when $T = 1$ s.

SOLUTION By letting $G_2(s) = 2/s(s+1)(s+2)$, it follows from Eq. (10.61) that the z transform for the hold and plant is

$$G(z) = \frac{z-1}{z} G_2(z) = \frac{0.40z^{-1} + 0.15z^{-2}}{1 - 0.50z^{-1} + 0.05z^{-2}} = \frac{0.73z^{-1} + 0.27z^{-2}}{1.82 - 0.91z^{-1} + 0.09z^{-2}}$$

In order that $p_1 + p_2 = 1$ and $q_0 + q_1 + q_2 = 1$, both numerator and denominator are multiplied by 1.82. From Eq. (10.97), it follows that the resulting coefficients are $p_1 = 0.73$, $p_2 = 0.27$, $q_0 = 1.82$, $q_1 = -0.91$, and $q_2 = 0.09$. The difference equation for the digital controller is

$$m(k+2) - 0.73m(k+1) - 0.27m(k) = 1.82e(k+2) - 0.91e(k+1) + 0.09e(k)$$

To obtain the signal flow graph, first write the equation for the plant in the form

$$c(t) = \frac{2}{(D+1)(D+2)} m(t)$$

or

$$\ddot{c} + 3\dot{c} + 2c = 2m(t)$$

Letting $c(t) = x_1$ and $\dot{c}(t) = \dot{x}_1 = x_2$ yields the state-space form

$$\begin{bmatrix} \dot{x}_1 \\ \dot{x}_2 \end{bmatrix} = \begin{bmatrix} 0 & 1 \\ -2 & -3 \end{bmatrix} \begin{bmatrix} x_1 \\ x_2 \end{bmatrix} + \begin{bmatrix} 0 \\ 2 \end{bmatrix} m(t)$$

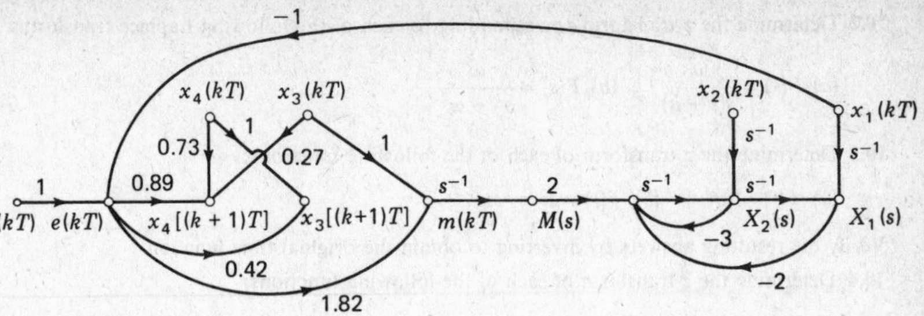

Figure 10.30 Signal flow graph.

The Laplace transform yields

$$X_1(s) = s^{-1}x_1(kT) + s^{-1}X_2(s)$$
$$X_2(s) = s^{-1}x_2(kT) + s^{-1}[-2X_1(s) - 3X_2(s) + 2M(s)]$$

The error signal at time kT is

$$e(kT) = r(kT) - c(kT) = r(kT) - x_1(kT)$$

Application of the general form given by Eqs. (10.77) and (10.78) to the difference equation for the controller yields the state-space form

$$\begin{bmatrix} x_3[(k+1)T] \\ x_4[(k+1)T] \end{bmatrix} = \begin{bmatrix} 0 & 1 \\ 0.27 & 0.73 \end{bmatrix} \begin{bmatrix} x_3(kT) \\ x_4(kT) \end{bmatrix} + \begin{bmatrix} 0.42 \\ 0.89 \end{bmatrix} e(kT)$$

where

$$x_3(kT) = m(kT) - 1.82e(kT)$$

or

$$m(kT) = x_3(kT) + 1.82e(kT)$$

The constants are $a_1 = -0.73$, $a_2 = -0.27$, $b_0 = 1.82$, $b_1 = -0.91$, $b_2 = 0.09$, $h_1 = b_1 - a_1b_0 = 0.42$, and $h_2 = b_2 - a_2 b_0 - a_1h_1 = 0.89$. The resulting signal flow graph for this system is shown in Fig. 10.30. The input nodes are $x_1(kT)$, $x_2(kT)$, $x_3(kT)$, $x_4(kT)$, and $r(kT)$. The output nodes are $X_1(s)$, $X_2(s)$, $x_3[(k+1)T]$, and $x_4[(k+1)T]$. Applying Mason's gain formula, inverting, and evaluating at $T = 1$ yields for the response at the sampling instants

$$\begin{bmatrix} x_1(k+1) \\ x_2(k+1) \\ x_3(k+1) \\ x_4(k+1) \end{bmatrix} = \begin{bmatrix} -0.128 & 0.233 & 0.400 & 0 \\ -1.314 & -0.098 & 0.466 & 0 \\ -0.42 & 0 & 0 & 1 \\ -0.89 & 0 & 0.27 & 0.73 \end{bmatrix} \begin{bmatrix} x_1(k) \\ x_2(k) \\ x_3(k) \\ x_4(k) \end{bmatrix} + \begin{bmatrix} 0.728 \\ 0.848 \\ 0.42 \\ 0.89 \end{bmatrix} r(k)$$

PROBLEMS

10.1 Determine the z transform of each of the following functions:

(a) $f(t) = 1 - e^{-at}$ (b) $f(t) = a^{t/T}$

10.2 Determine the z transform corresponding to each of the following Laplace transforms:

$$(a)\ F(s) = \frac{a}{s(s+a)} \qquad (b)\ F(s) = \frac{\omega}{s^2 - \omega^2}$$

10.3 Determine the z transform of each of the following functions:

$(a)\ f(t) = te^{at} \qquad (b)\ f(t) = t^2$

Verify the resulting answers by inverting to obtain the original time function.

10.4 Determine the z transform of each of the following functions:

(a) $\sin \omega t \qquad (b)$ $e^{at} \sin \omega t$

Verify the resulting answers by inverting to obtain the original time functions.

10.5 Use block-diagram algebra to determine $C(z)$ for each of the systems shown in Fig. P10.5.

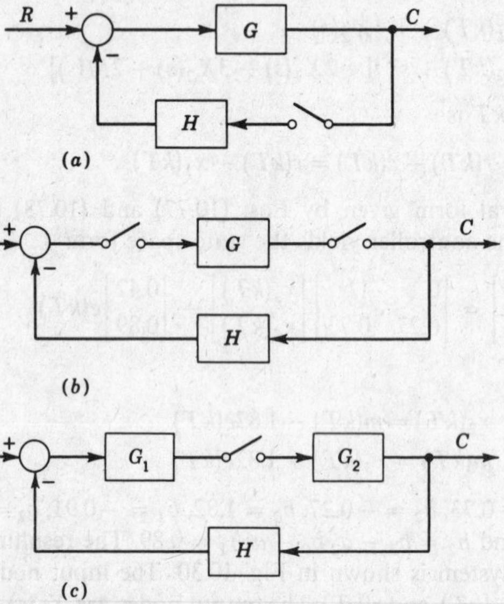

Figure P10.5

10.6 In Fig. P10.6 is shown a sampled-data system whose sampling rate is $T = 1$.

(a) Apply Routh's criterion to determine whether or not the system becomes unstable.

(b) Construct the root-locus plot for the system.

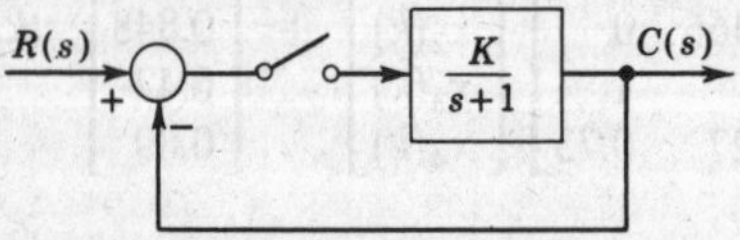

Figure P10.6

10.7 Determine the unit step-function response for the system of Prob. 10.6 for the case in which $K = 1$.

10.8 For the system shown in Fig. 10.8 in the text, it is desired to use a sampling rate $T = 1$ rather than $T = \frac{1}{4}$. Determine the value of K at which the system becomes unstable.

10.9 In Fig. 10.9 is shown the root-locus plot for the system of Fig. 10.8 when $T = \frac{1}{4}$. Determine the unit step-function response when $K = 8.7$.

10.10 In Fig. P10.10 is shown a sampled-data system whose sampling rate is $T = 1$.

(*a*) Apply Routh's criterion to determine whether or not the system becomes unstable.
(*b*) Construct the root-locus plot for the system.

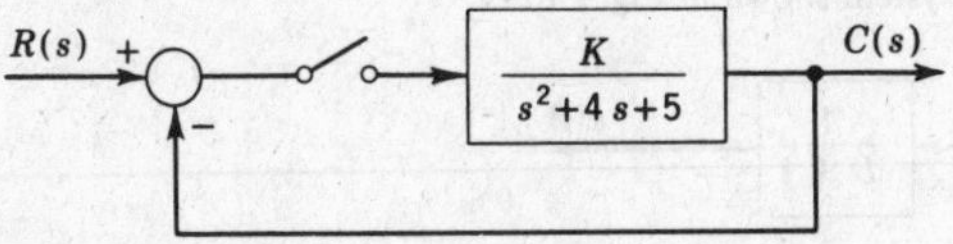

Figure P10.10

10.11 For the system shown in Fig. P10.10, it is desired to use a sampling rate $T = 2$. Determine the value of K at which the system becomes unstable.

10.12 The system shown in Fig. P10.12 is the same as that shown in Fig. P10.6 except that a zero-order hold has been added. Determine the value of the gain K at which the system with the zero-order hold becomes unstable. The sampling rate is $T = 1$ s.

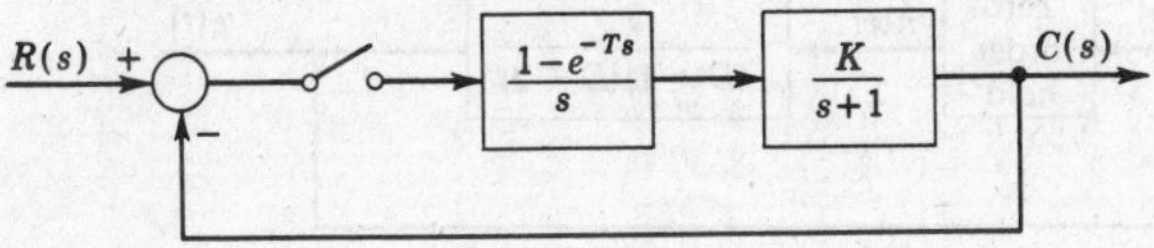

Figure P10.12

10.13 Same as Prob. 10.12, except use an exponential hold rather than a zero-order hold.

10.14 Determine the unit step-function response for the system of Prob. 10.13 for each of the following cases:

(*a*) $K = 4.0$
(*b*) $K = 5.08$

10.15 Verify the solution of Illustrative Example 1 in Sec. 10.8 by (*a*) direct programming and (*b*) series programming.

10.16 Determine the discrete time state-space representation for the response at the sampling instants and for the response midway between the sampling instants for $T = 0.2$ s for each of the following continuous systems

(*a*) $\dot{c} + c = f(t)$
(*b*) $\ddot{c} + 2\dot{c} + c = f(t)$

Evaluate the response at $t = 0.1$, 0.2, 0.3, and 0.4 s, when $f(t)$ is a unit step function and all the initial conditions are zero.

10.17 For the system shown in Fig. P10.17, the input $f(t)$ is a unit step function and $T = 1$ s. Use the z transform method to determine the response at each of the first two sampling instants. Use the

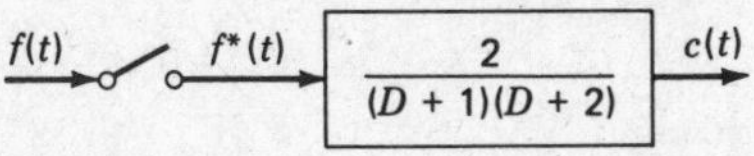

Figure P10.17

state-space method to determine the response just before and just after each of the first two sampling instants.

10.18 Same as Prob. 10.17 except for the system shown in Fig. P10.18.

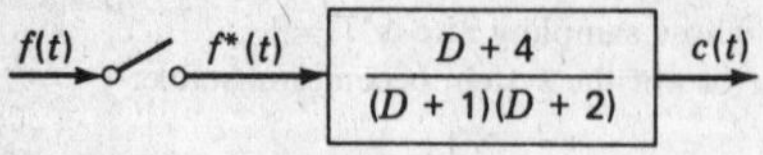

Figure P10.18

10.19 Same as Prob. 10.17 except for the system shown in Fig. P10.19.

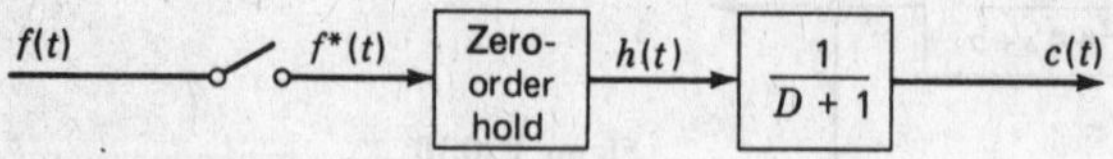

Figure P10.19

10.20 For the system shown in Fig. P10.20, the input $r(t)$ is a unit step function and $T = 1$ s. Use the z transform method to determine the response at each of the first two sampling instants. Use the state-space method to determine the response just before and just after each of the first two sampling instants.

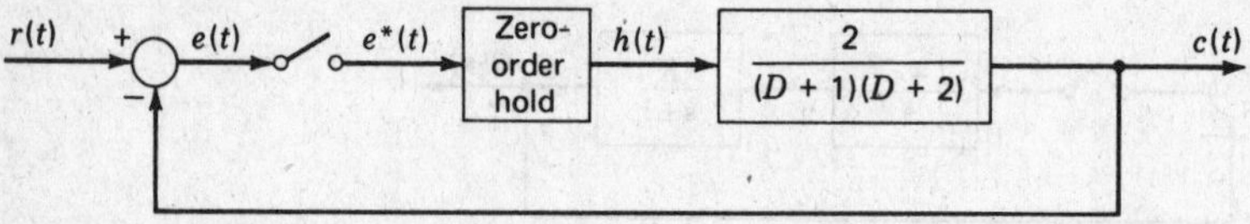

Figure P10.20

10.21 For the system shown in Fig. 10.28, the transfer function for the plant is $1/(s + 1)^2$ and the sampling period is $T = 1$ s. Determine the characteristics of the digital controller such that the response of the system to a unit step function will be $c(t) = 1 - e^{-2t}$.

10.22 Same as Prob. 10.21, except determine the characteristics of the digital controller such that the response will be optimum in accordance with the criterion developed by Kalman.

CHAPTER

ELEVEN

FREQUENCY-RESPONSE METHODS

Frequency-response methods provide a convenient means for investigating the dynamic behavior of control systems. By frequency response is meant the response of a system to a sinusoidal input $f = f_0 \sin \omega t$. A characteristic of linear systems is that after the effect of the initial transients has "died out," the response also becomes a sinusoid with the same angular velocity ω of the input. As is illustrated in Fig. 11.1, the response $y = y_0 \sin(\omega t + \phi)$ is displaced some phase angle ϕ from the input, and the amplitude y_0 is different from that of the input f_0. Both the phase angle ϕ and the amplitude ratio y_0/f_0 are functions of the angular velocity ω of the input signal. Graphs of ϕ versus ω and of amplitude ratio y_0/f_0 versus ω form the basis for frequency-response methods.

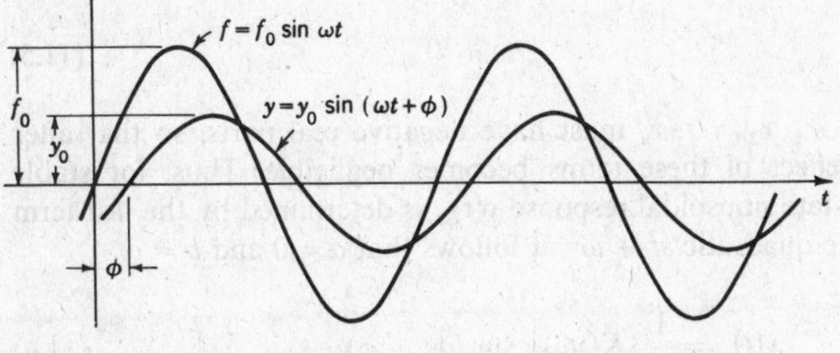

Figure 11.1 Sinusoidal response.

11.1 FREQUENCY RESPONSE

Because frequency-response methods are based on a knowledge of ϕ versus ω and y_0/f_0 versus ω, it is now shown how these quantities may be determined directly by substitution of $j\omega$ for D in the operational form of the differential equation for the system. The general operational form of a differential equation is

$$y(t) = \frac{(a_m D^m + a_{m-1} D^{m-1} + \cdots + a_1 D + a_0) f(t)}{D^n + b_{n-1} D^{n-1} + \cdots + b_1 D + b_0} = \frac{L_m(D) f(t)}{L_n(D)} \tag{11.1}$$

The transform of the preceding expression is

$$Y(s) = \frac{L_m(s)F(s) + I(s)}{L_n(s)} = \frac{L_m(s)N_{F(s)}}{L_n(s)D_{F(s)}} + \frac{I(s)}{L_n(s)} \tag{11.2}$$

The transform for the input is

$$F(s) = \mathscr{L}(f_0 \sin \omega t) = \frac{\omega f_0}{s^2 + \omega^2} = \frac{N_{F(s)}}{D_{F(s)}} \tag{11.3}$$

Expanding Eq. (11.2) in a partial-fraction expansion and noting that $D_{F(s)} = s^2 + \omega^2 = (s - j\omega)(s + j\omega)$ gives

$$Y(s) = \frac{K_1}{s - r_1} + \cdots + \frac{K_n}{s - r_n} + \frac{K_C}{s - j\omega} + \frac{K_{-C}}{s + j\omega} + \frac{I_1}{s - r_1} + \cdots + \frac{I_n}{s - r_n} \tag{11.4}$$

where $r_1, r_2, \ldots, r_n$ are the zeros of $L_n(s)$; and $K_1, K_2, \ldots, K_n$, K_C, and K_{-C} are the constants which arise from the partial-fraction expansion of $L_m(s)N_{F(s)}/L_n(s)D_{F(s)}$; and $I_1, I_2, \ldots, I_n$ are the constants which arise from the partial-fraction expansion of $I(s)/L_n(s)$. Inverting Eq. (11.4) gives

$$y(t) = (K_1 + I_1)e^{r_1 t} + \cdots + (K_n + I_n)e^{r_n t} + \frac{1}{b} \, |K(a + jb)| \, e^{at} \sin (bt + \phi) \tag{11.5}$$

For a stable system, $r_1, r_2, \ldots, r_n$ must have negative real parts, so that after sufficient time the effect of these terms becomes negligible. Thus, for stable systems, the steady-state sinusoidal response $y(t)_{ss}$ is determined by the last term of Eq. (11.5). For the quadratic $s^2 + \omega^2$, it follows that $a = 0$ and $b = \omega$.

Thus

$$y(t)_{ss} = \frac{1}{\omega} \, |K(j\omega)| \, \sin (\omega t + \phi) \tag{11.6}$$

The terms $|K(j\omega)|$ and $\phi = \measuredangle K(j\omega)$ are evaluated as follows:

$$K(j\omega) = \lim_{s \to j\omega} \left[(s^2 + \omega^2) \frac{L_m(s) N_{F(s)}}{L_n(s) D_{F(s)}} \right] \tag{11.7}$$

$$= \lim_{s \to j\omega} \left[\frac{(s^2 + \omega^2) L_m(s) \omega f_0}{L_n(s)(s^2 + \omega^2)} \right]$$

$$= \frac{L_m(j\omega)\omega f_0}{L_n(j\omega)} \tag{11.8}$$

The terms $L_m(j\omega)$ and $L_n(j\omega)$ are obtained by substituting $j\omega$ for D in $L_m(D)$ and $L_n(D)$. From Eq. (11.8) it follows that

$$|K(j\omega)| = \left| \frac{L_m(j\omega)}{L_n(j\omega)} \right| \omega f_0 \tag{11.9}$$

and

$$\phi = \measuredangle \left[\frac{L_m(j\omega)}{L_n(j\omega)} \right] \omega f_0 = \measuredangle \frac{L_m(j\omega)}{L_n(j\omega)} \tag{11.10}$$

Substitution of Eq. (11.9) into Eq. (11.6) yields

$$y(t)_{ss} = \left| \frac{L_m(j\omega)}{L_n(j\omega)} \right| f_0 \sin(\omega t + \phi) = y_0 \sin(\omega t + \phi) \tag{11.11}$$

From Eq. (11.11), the amplitude y_0 of the steady-state response $y(t)_{ss}$ is seen to be

$$y_0 = \left| \frac{L_m(j\omega)}{L_n(j\omega)} \right| f_0 \tag{11.12}$$

The amplitude ratio is

$$\frac{y_0}{f_0} = \left| \frac{L_m(j\omega)}{L_n(j\omega)} \right| \tag{11.13}$$

Illustrative example A system is described by the differential equation

$$\frac{dy}{dt} + y = f(t) \qquad \text{or} \qquad y = \frac{1}{D+1} f(t)$$

Determine the response $y(t)$ to the sinusoidal input $f(t) = f_0 \sin \omega t$.

SOLUTION The transform of the differential equation is

$$sY(s) - y(0) + Y(s) = F(s)$$

or

$$Y(s) = \frac{F(s)}{s+1} + \frac{y(0)}{s+1} = \frac{\omega f_0}{(s+1)(s^2+\omega^2)} + \frac{y(0)}{(s+1)}$$

The partial-fraction expansion is

$$Y(s) = \frac{K_1}{s+1} + \frac{K_c}{s-j\omega} + \frac{K_{-c}}{s+j\omega} + \frac{I_1}{s+1}$$

where $I_1 = y(0)$. Inverting yields

$$y(t) = (K_1 + I_1)e^{-t} + \frac{1}{\omega}\,|K(j\omega)|\,\sin(\omega t + \phi)$$

where

$$K_1 = \lim_{s\to -1}\left[\frac{(s+1)\omega f_0}{(s+1)(s^2+\omega^2)}\right] = \frac{\omega f_0}{\omega^2+1}$$

and

$$K(j\omega) = \lim_{s\to j\omega}\left[\frac{(s^2+\omega^2)\omega f_0}{(s+1)(s^2+\omega^2)}\right] = \frac{\omega f_0}{1+j\omega}$$

$$|K(j\omega)| = \frac{\omega f_0}{\sqrt{1+\omega^2}} \qquad \phi = \measuredangle K(j\omega) = -\tan^{-1}\omega$$

The resulting transient response is

$$y(t) = \left[\frac{\omega f_0}{\omega^2+1} + y(0)\right]e^{-t} + \frac{f_0}{\sqrt{1+\omega^2}}\sin(\omega t + \phi)$$

The first term is the initial transient which "dies out" because of the decaying exponential e^{-t}. The second term is the steady-state frequency response, $y(t)_{ss} = y_0 \sin(\omega t + \phi)$, where

$$y_0 = \frac{f_0}{\sqrt{1+\omega^2}} \qquad \text{and} \qquad \phi = -\tan^{-1}\omega$$

The amplitude ratio and phase shift may be verified directly by application of Eqs. (11.10) and (11.13). From the differential equation it follows that the differential operator is $1/(D+1)$. Replacing D by $j\omega$ shows that

$$\frac{y_0}{f_0} = \left|\frac{L_m(j\omega)}{L_n(j\omega)}\right| = \left|\frac{1}{j\omega+1}\right| = \frac{1}{\sqrt{1+\omega^2}}$$

$$\phi = \measuredangle\frac{L_m(j\omega)}{L_n(j\omega)} = \measuredangle\frac{1}{j\omega+1} = -\tan^{-1}\omega$$

It is now shown how to obtain plots of the amplitude ratio y_0/f_0 versus ω and also phase angle ϕ versus ω. Consider the first-order linear differential equation

$$y(t) = \frac{1}{1 + \tau D} f(t) \tag{11.14}$$

The substitution of $j\omega$ for D in the differential operator gives

$$\frac{L_m(j\omega)}{L_n(j\omega)} = \frac{1}{1 + j\tau\omega} \tag{11.15}$$

The ratio of the amplitude of the output to that of the input is

$$\frac{y_0}{f_0} = \left| \frac{L_m(j\omega)}{L_n(j\omega)} \right| = \frac{1}{\sqrt{1 + (\tau\omega)^2}} \tag{11.16}$$

The phase angle ϕ is

$$\phi = \measuredangle \frac{1}{1 + j\tau\omega} \tag{11.17}$$

The angle of the numerator is $\measuredangle(1 + j0) = \tan^{-1} 0 = 0$. Thus, subtracting the angle of the denominator from the angle of the numerator gives

$$\phi = 0 - \measuredangle(1 + j\tau\omega) = -\tan^{-1} \tau\omega \tag{11.18}$$

In Fig. 11.2 is shown a graph of the amplitude ratio y_0/f_0 versus ω and a graph of the phase angle ϕ as a function of the angular velocity ω of the forcing function. When ω is small, the amplitude of the output is almost equal to that of the input and the phase angle ϕ is quite small. The output cannot keep up with the

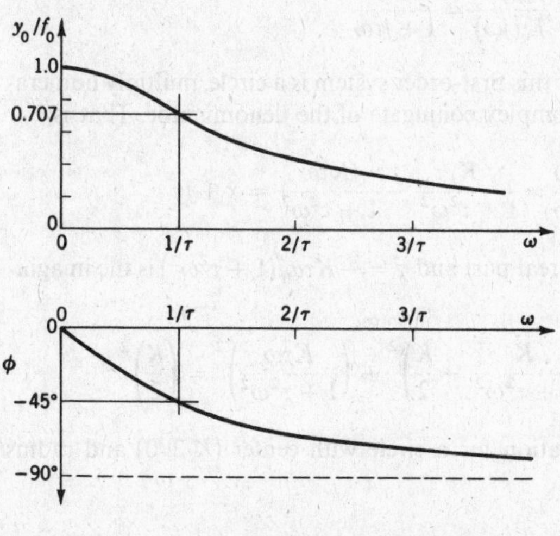

Figure 11.2 Response curves for the function $1/(1 + j\tau\omega)$.

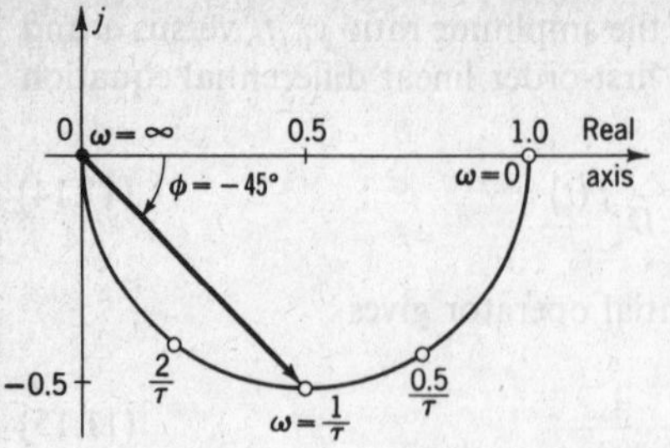

Figure 11.3 Polar plot for the function $1/(1 + j\tau\omega)$.

input at higher frequencies, and it begins to lag behind the input. For $\omega > 1/\tau$ this effect becomes very pronounced.

From Fig. 11.2, it is to be noticed that, for a given ω, the amplitude ratio has a given value, and also there is a certain phase angle ϕ between the input and the output. This amplitude ratio $|L_m(j\omega)/L_n(j\omega)|$ and phase angle $\measuredangle L_m(j\omega)/L_n(j\omega)$ determine a vector $L_m(j\omega)/L_n(j\omega)$. The path of the tip of this vector (vector loci) for values of ω from zero to ∞ is shown in Fig. 11.3. This is called a polar plot. The polar plot shown in Fig. 11.3 is seen to convey the same information as the two separate curves shown in Fig. 11.2. The polar plot for this first-order system is a semicircle, as shown in Fig. 11.3. At $\omega = 0$, the length of the vector is 1, and the phase angle is zero. At $\omega = 1/\tau$ the phase angle $\phi = -45°$, and the length of the vector is 0.707.

Consider the general first-order system

$$y(t) = \frac{K}{1 + \tau D} f(t)$$

Replacing D by $j\omega$ in the differential operator shows that

$$\frac{L_m(j\omega)}{L_n(j\omega)} = \frac{K}{1 + j\tau\omega}$$

To prove that the polar plot for this first-order system is a circle, multiply numerator and denominator by the complex conjugate of the denominator. That is,

$$\frac{K}{1 + j\tau\omega}\,\frac{1 - j\tau\omega}{1 - j\tau\omega} = \frac{K}{1 + \tau^2\omega^2} - \frac{jK\tau\omega}{1 + \tau^2\omega^2} = x + jy$$

where $x = K/(1 + \tau^2\omega^2)$ is the real part and $y = -K\tau\omega/(1 + \tau^2\omega^2)$ is the imaginary part. Now, note that

$$\left(x - \frac{K}{2}\right)^2 + y^2 = \left(\frac{K}{1 + \tau^2\omega^2} - \frac{K}{2}\right)^2 + \left(\frac{K\tau\omega}{1 + \tau^2\omega^2}\right)^2 = \left(\frac{K}{2}\right)^2$$

This is recognized as the equation for a circle with center $(K/2, 0)$ and radius $R = K/2$.

The operation of the feedforward part of a control system is given by the equation

$$c(t) = G(D)e(t) \tag{11.19}$$

When the actuating signal $e(t)$ is a sinusoid $[e(t) = e_0 \sin \omega t]$, then the controlled variable $c(t)$ is also a sinusoid $[c(t) = c_0 \sin (\omega t + \phi)]$. The amplitude ratio c_0/e_0 and the phase angle ϕ are

$$\frac{c_0}{e_0} = |G(j\omega)|$$

$$\phi = \measuredangle G(j\omega) \tag{11.20}$$

Thus $G(j\omega)$ completely describes the frequency response of the feedforward elements. Similarly, the response of the feedback elements is determined by $H(j\omega)$.

The transfer function is the same as the differential operator except that D is replaced by s. Thus either the substitution of $j\omega$ for D in the differential operator or the substitution of $j\omega$ for s in the transfer function gives the vector equation for evaluating the frequency response.

11.2 LOGARITHMIC REPRESENTATION

Frequency-response methods are based on the response $G(j\omega)$ of the feedforward elements and $H(j\omega)$ of the feedback elements. The transfer functions for these quantities are $G(s)$ and $H(s)$, respectively. These quantities are usually obtained in factored form and are composed of multiples or ratios of one or more of the following types of terms: s, $1 + \tau s$, $(s^2 + 2\zeta\omega_n s + \omega_n^2)/\omega_n^2$. The substitution of $j\omega$ for s means that $G(j\omega)$ or $H(j\omega)$ will be composed of terms such as $j\omega$, $1 + j\tau\omega$, or $(\omega_n^2 - \omega^2 + j2\zeta\omega_n\omega)/\omega_n^2$. To obtain the resulting frequency response, the multiplication of such terms is simplified by the use of logarithms. For example, let the value of $G(s)$ be given by the equation

$$G(s) = \frac{K}{s(1 + \tau s)} \tag{11.21}$$

Substituting $j\omega$ for s yields

$$G(j\omega) = \frac{K}{j\omega(1 + j\tau\omega)} \tag{11.22}$$

The magnitude is

$$|G(j\omega)| = \frac{K}{|j\omega|\,|1 + j\tau\omega|} = \frac{K}{\omega\sqrt{1 + \tau^2\omega^2}} \tag{11.23}$$

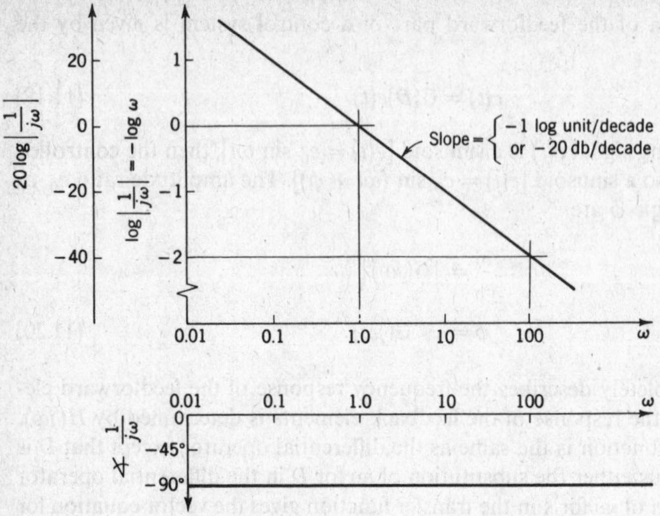

Figure 11.4 Log-magnitude plot for $1/j\omega$.

The logarithm of the preceding expression is

$$\log \left| \frac{G(j\omega)}{K} \right| = -\log \omega - \frac{1}{2}\log(1 + \tau^2\omega^2) \tag{11.24}$$

The angle ϕ is

$$\begin{aligned} \phi = \measuredangle G(j\omega) &= -\measuredangle j\omega - \measuredangle(1 + j\tau\omega) \\ &= -90^\circ - \tan^{-1} \tau\omega \end{aligned} \tag{11.25}$$

The contribution due to the $1/j\omega$ term is shown in Fig. 11.4. The equation for the amplitude is $\log |1/j\omega| = -\log \omega$. When ω is 1, the value of $-\log \omega$ is 0, and when ω changes by multiples of 10, the value of $-\log \omega$ changes in increments of 1. The slope of this straight-line logarithmic response shown in Fig. 11.4 is -1 log unit/decade. A decade is the horizontal distance on the frequency scale from any value of ω to ten times ω. Thus, the distance from $\omega = 1$ to $\omega = 10$ or from $\omega = 3$ to $\omega = 30$, etc., is a decade.

The vertical log-magnitude scale is sometimes expressed in decibel units. To convert the vertical log-magnitude scale of Fig. 11.4 to decibel units, it is necessary only to multiply by a factor of 20. Using decibel units, the slope is -20 dB/decade rather than -1 log unit/decade. In this text, the log-magnitude scale is expressed directly in logarithmic units rather than in decibels.

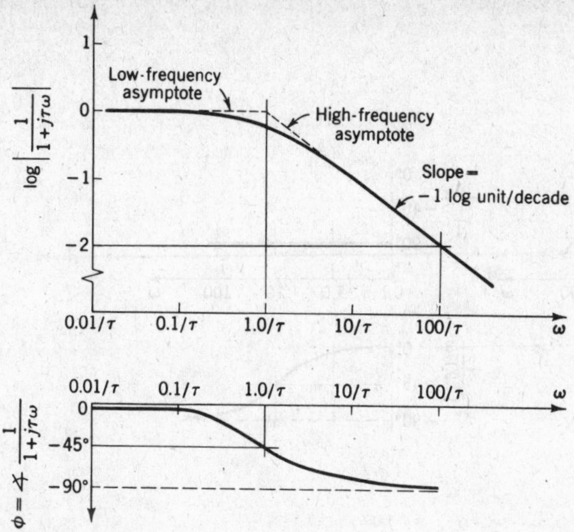

Figure 11.5 Log-magnitude plot for $1/(1 + j\tau\omega)$.

The contribution due to log $|1/(1 + j\tau\omega)|$ is shown in Fig. 11.5. For small values of ω such that $\omega \ll 1/\tau$,

$$-\tfrac{1}{2} \log (1 + \tau^2\omega^2) \approx -\tfrac{1}{2} \log 1 = 0 \tag{11.26}$$

This is the equation for the low-frequency asymptote to the exact curve, as is shown in Fig. 11.5. For $\omega \gg 1/\tau$,

$$-\tfrac{1}{2} \log (1 + \tau^2\omega^2) \approx -\tfrac{1}{2} \log \tau^2\omega^2 = -\log \tau\omega \tag{11.27}$$

This is the high-frequency asymptote. When $\omega = 1/\tau$, the value of $-\log \tau\omega$ is zero, and for $\omega = 10/\tau$, the value is -1, etc. The slope of this high-frequency asymptote is thus seen to be -1 log unit/decade, or -20 dB/decade. The break frequency ($\omega = 1/\tau$) is located directly under the intersection of the two asymptotes. For most preliminary design work, the asymptotes are sufficiently close to the exact curve so that the extra effort involved in using the exact curve is generally not warranted. The maximum error occurs at the "break frequency" and is $0 - \frac{1}{2}$ log $(1 + 1) = -0.303/2 = -0.1515$. It should be noticed that Fig. 11.5 is applicable for any value of τ.

The phase-angle curve is obtained by solving the equation

$$\phi = -\tan^{-1} \tau\omega \tag{11.28}$$

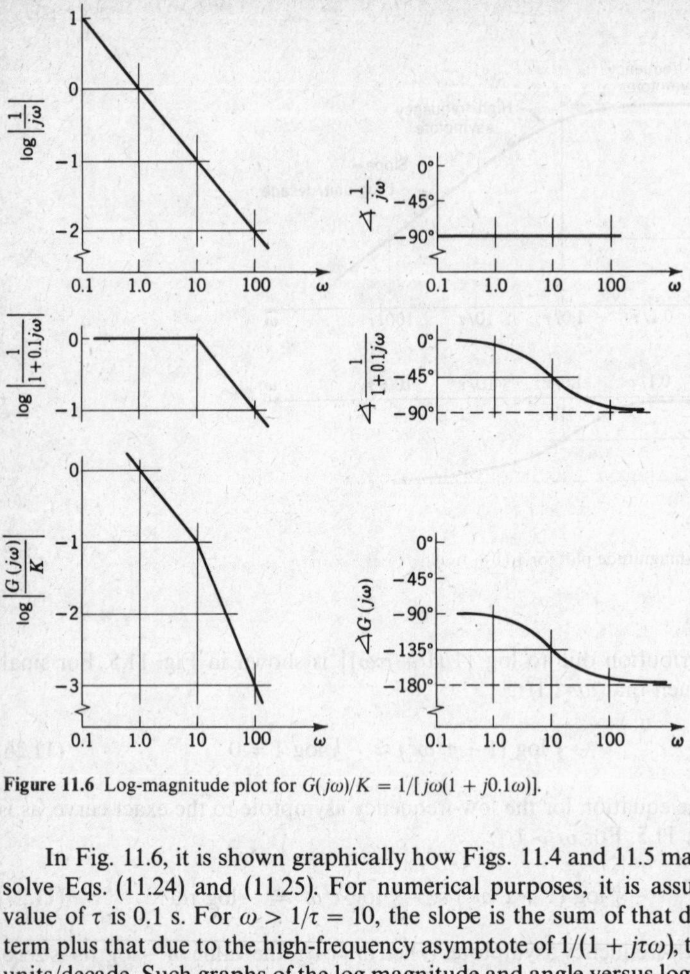

Figure 11.6 Log-magnitude plot for $G(j\omega)/K = 1/[j\omega(1 + j0.1\omega)]$.

In Fig. 11.6, it is shown graphically how Figs. 11.4 and 11.5 may be added to solve Eqs. (11.24) and (11.25). For numerical purposes, it is assumed that the value of τ is 0.1 s. For $\omega > 1/\tau = 10$, the slope is the sum of that due to the $1/j\omega$ term plus that due to the high-frequency asymptote of $1/(1 + j\tau\omega)$, that is, -2 log units/decade. Such graphs of the log magnitude and angle versus log frequency are called log-magnitude or Bode diagrams. H. W. Bode[1] made many contributions to the development of frequency-response techniques.

A feature of the logarithmic method is that, if the term appears in the numerator rather than the denominator, it is necessary merely to change the sign of the amplitude and phase-angle scales in tabulating the result. For example, if Eq. (11.22) were of the form

$$G(j\omega) = \frac{K(1 + j\tau\omega)}{j\omega}$$

[1] H. W. Bode, "Network Analysis and Feedback Amplifier Design," D. Van Nostrand Company, Inc., Princeton, N.J., 1945.

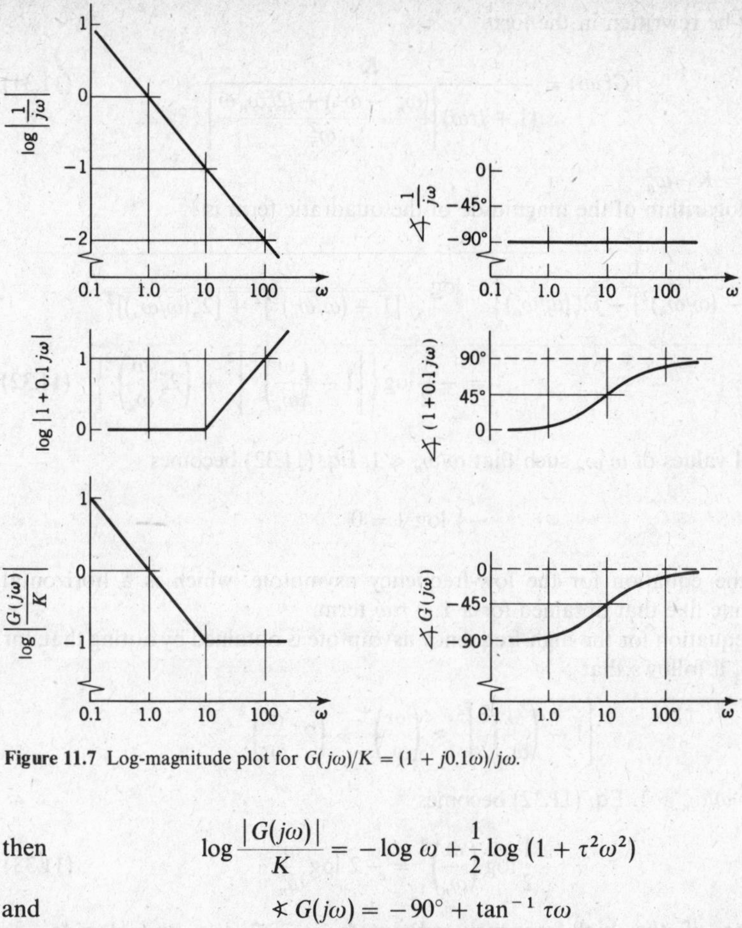

Figure 11.7 Log-magnitude plot for $G(j\omega)/K = (1 + j0.1\omega)/j\omega$.

then
$$\log \frac{|G(j\omega)|}{K} = -\log \omega + \frac{1}{2} \log (1 + \tau^2\omega^2) \tag{11.29}$$

and
$$\measuredangle G(j\omega) = -90^\circ + \tan^{-1} \tau\omega \tag{11.30}$$

By comparing Eqs. (11.29) and (11.30) with Eqs. (11.24) and (11.25), it is seen that only the sign of the term which went from the denominator to the numerator has changed. In Fig. 11.7 is shown the log-magnitude diagram for $G(j\omega)/K = (1 + j\tau\omega)/j\omega$, in which the value of τ is assumed to be 0.1 s. Comparison of the log-magnitude diagram for $1 + j\tau\omega$ of Fig. 11.7 with that for $1/(1 + j\tau\omega)$ of Fig. 11.6 shows that the sign of the logarithm of the amplitude ratio and the sign of the phase angle have been changed.

The third type of term which occurs is of the form $(\omega_n^2 - \omega^2 + j2\zeta\omega_n\omega)/\omega_n^2$. By using a generalized graph, this term may be treated in a manner analogous to that described for evaluating terms of the form $1 + j\tau\omega$. Consider the function

$$G(j\omega) = \frac{K_1}{(1 + j\tau\omega)(\omega_n^2 - \omega^2 + j2\zeta\omega_n\omega)}$$

This may be rewritten in the form

$$G(j\omega) = \frac{K}{(1 + j\tau\omega)\left[\dfrac{(\omega_n^2 - \omega^2) + j2\zeta\omega_n\omega}{\omega_n^2}\right]} \tag{11.31}$$

where $K = K_1/\omega_n^2$.

The logarithm of the magnitude of the quadratic term is

$$\log\left|\frac{1}{[1 - (\omega/\omega_n)^2] + j2\zeta(\omega/\omega_n)}\right| = \log\frac{1}{\sqrt{[1 - (\omega/\omega_n)^2]^2 + [2\zeta(\omega/\omega_n)]^2}}$$

$$= -\frac{1}{2}\log\left\{\left[1 - \left(\frac{\omega}{\omega_n}\right)^2\right]^2 + \left(2\zeta\frac{\omega}{\omega_n}\right)^2\right\} \tag{11.32}$$

For small values of ω/ω_n such that $\omega/\omega_n \ll 1$, Eq. (11.32) becomes

$$-\tfrac{1}{2}\log 1 = 0$$

This is the equation for the low-frequency asymptote, which is a horizontal straight line like that obtained for a $1 + j\tau\omega$ term.

The equation for the high-frequency asymptote is obtained by noting that, for $\omega/\omega_n \gg 1$, it follows that

$$\left[1 - \left(\frac{\omega}{\omega_n}\right)^2\right]^2 \approx \left(\frac{\omega}{\omega_n}\right)^4 \gg \left(2\zeta\frac{\omega}{\omega_n}\right)^2$$

Thus, for $\omega/\omega_n \gg 1$, Eq. (11.32) becomes

$$-\frac{1}{2}\log\left(\frac{\omega}{\omega_n}\right)^4 = -2\log\frac{\omega}{\omega_n} \tag{11.33}$$

The slope of the high-frequency asymptote is -2 log units/decade, or -40 dB/decade, and this asymptote intersects the low-frequency asymptote at $\omega/\omega_n = 1$.

The value of the phase angle is

$$\phi = -\tan^{-1}\frac{2\zeta(\omega/\omega_n)}{1 - (\omega/\omega_n)^2} \tag{11.34}$$

The nondimensional curves for the logarithm of the amplitude and the phase angle, as given by Eqs. (11.32) and (11.34), respectively, are shown in Fig. 11.8. The curves for the reciprocal of this function are obtained by merely changing the sign of the amplitude and phase-angle scales.

The magnitude plot of Fig. 11.8 shows that the amplitude ratio attains its maximum value in the vicinity of $\omega/\omega_n = 1$. The frequency ω at which this maxi-

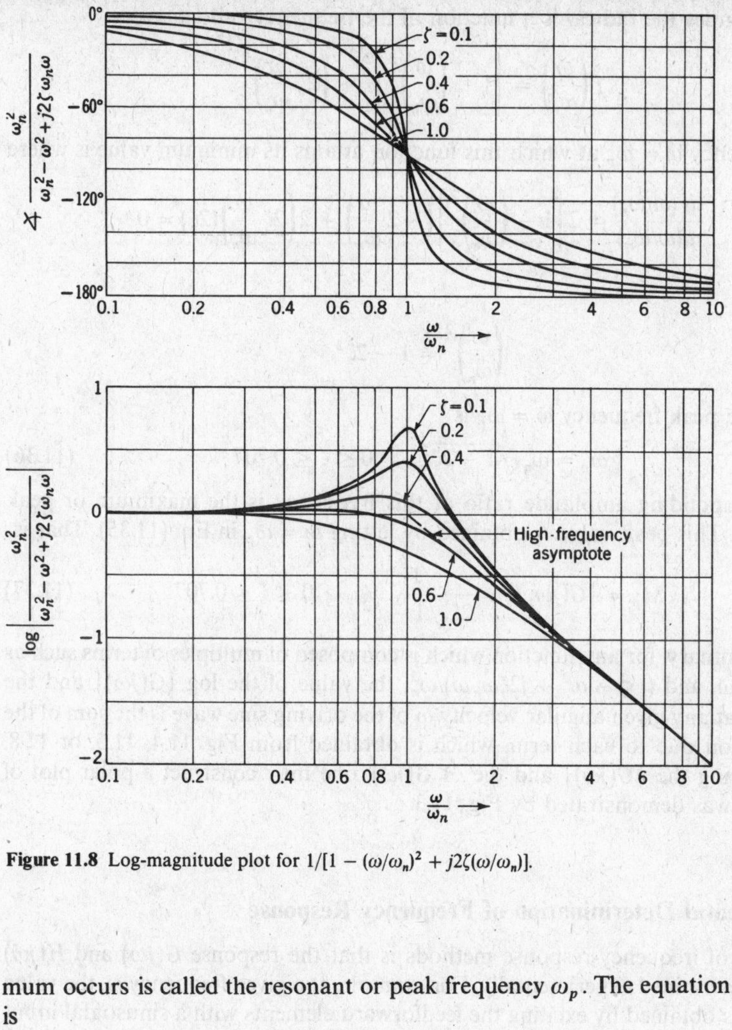

Figure 11.8 Log-magnitude plot for $1/[1 - (\omega/\omega_n)^2 + j2\zeta(\omega/\omega_n)]$.

mum occurs is called the resonant or peak frequency ω_p. The equation for $G(j\omega)$ is

$$G(j\omega) = \frac{1}{1 - (\omega/\omega_n)^2 + j2\zeta(\omega/\omega_n)}$$

The magnitude of $G(j\omega)$ is

$$|G(j\omega)| = \frac{1}{\sqrt{[1 - (\omega/\omega_n)^2]^2 + [2\zeta(\omega/\omega_n)]^2}} \tag{11.35}$$

The maximum value of $|G(j\omega)|$ occurs when the denominator is a minimum. The quantity under the radical is a function of the frequency ratio, ω/ω_n:

$$f\left(\frac{\omega}{\omega_n}\right) = \left[1 - \left(\frac{\omega}{\omega_n}\right)^2\right]^2 + \left(2\zeta\frac{\omega}{\omega_n}\right)^2$$

The frequency $\omega = \omega_p$ at which this function attains its minimum value is where

$$\frac{df(\omega/\omega_n)}{d(\omega/\omega_n)} = 2\left[1 - \left(\frac{\omega}{\omega_n}\right)^2\right]\left(-2\frac{\omega}{\omega_n}\right) + 2\left(2\zeta\frac{\omega}{\omega_n}\right)(2\zeta) = 0$$

or

$$\left(\frac{\omega}{\omega_n}\right)^2 = 1 - 2\zeta^2$$

Hence, the peak frequency $\omega = \omega_p$ is

$$\omega_p = \omega_n\sqrt{1 - 2\zeta^2} \qquad 0 \le \zeta \le 0.707 \tag{11.36}$$

The corresponding amplitude ratio at this frequency is the maximum or peak value M_p. This peak value is obtained by letting $\omega = \omega_p$ in Eq. (11.35). That is,

$$M_p = |G(j\omega_p)| = \frac{1}{2\zeta\sqrt{1 - \zeta^2}} \qquad 0 \le \zeta \le 0.707 \tag{11.37}$$

In summary, for any function which is composed of multiples of terms such as $j\omega$, $1 + j\tau\omega$, and $(\omega_n^2 - \omega^2 + j2\zeta\omega_n\omega)/\omega_n^2$, the value of the log $|G(j\omega)|$ and the $\measuredangle G(j\omega)$ at any given angular velocity ω of the driving sine wave is the sum of the contribution due to each term, which is obtained from Fig. 11.4, 11.5, or 11.8. Thus, having the $|G(j\omega)|$ and the $\measuredangle G(j\omega)$, one may construct a polar plot of $G(j\omega)$, as was demonstrated by Fig. 11.3.

Experimental Determination of Frequency Response

A feature of frequency-response methods is that the response $G(j\omega)$ and $H(j\omega)$ may be determined experimentally. For example, at a given frequency ω, the value of $G(j\omega)$ is obtained by exciting the feedforward elements with a sinusoidal input of angular velocity ω and then measuring the ratio of the amplitude of the output to that of the input and also measuring the phase angle ϕ. By repeating this process for a wide range of values of ω, the frequency response is obtained. The response $H(j\omega)$ is similarly obtained by sinusoidally exciting the feedback elements.

The asymptotes of an experimentally determined log-magnitude plot are shown in Fig. 11.9. Because of the change of slope at ω_1, there is a term $1/(1 + j\tau_1\omega)$, where $\tau_1 = 1/\omega_1$ in the frequency-response equation. At the angular velocity ω_2 there is a net increase of $+1$ log unit/decade, and thus the term $1 + j\tau_2\omega$, where $\tau_2 = 1/\omega_2$, appears in the numerator of the response expression. The change in

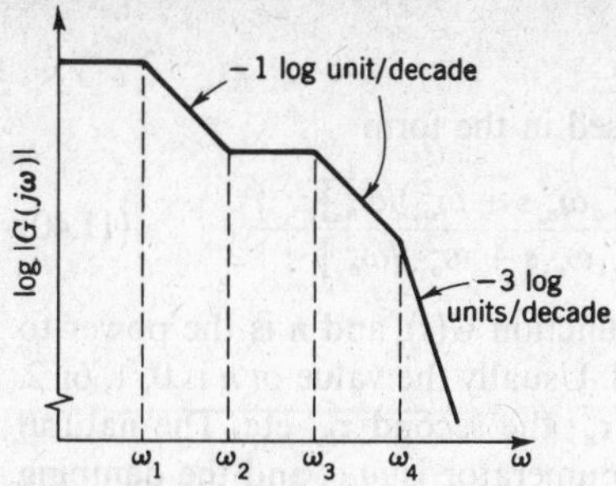

Figure 11.9 Experimentally determined log-magnitude plot.

slope at ω_3 is indicative of the term $1/(1 + j\tau_3 \omega)$, where $\tau_3 = 1/\omega_3$. Because the slope changes by -2 log units/decade at ω_4, there is a quadratic term in the denominator. The value of the break frequency ω_4 is equal to the natural frequency ω_n for the quadratic. That is, from Fig. 11.8, it follows that at the break point for a quadratic, $\omega/\omega_n = \omega_4/\omega_n = 1$ or $\omega_n = \omega_4$. To determine the damping ratio ζ, it is necessary to compare the exact response curve for the component which causes this quadratic term in $G(j\omega)$ to the general response curves of Fig. 11.8. From the preceding, it follows that the frequency response for $G(j\omega)$ is

$$G(j\omega) = \frac{K(1 + j\tau_2 \omega)}{(1 + j\tau_1 \omega)(1 + j\tau_3 \omega)[(\omega_4^2 - \omega^2 + j2\zeta\omega_4 \omega)/\omega_4^2]} \tag{11.38}$$

In the next section, it is shown how the value of K can be determined directly from the low-frequency portion of the log-magnitude diagram.

After the equation for the frequency response has been experimentally determined, it is a simple matter to substitute s for $j\omega$ to obtain the transfer function. The substitution of s for $j\omega$ in Eq. (11.38) gives

$$G(s) = \frac{K(1 + \tau_2 s)}{(1 + \tau_1 s)(1 + \tau_3 s)[(s^2 + 2\zeta\omega_4 s + \omega_4^2)/\omega_4^2]} \tag{11.39}$$

The substitution of D for s gives the differential equation of operation.

The magnitude of $1 + j\tau\omega$ is the same as that of $1 - j\tau\omega$. However, as the phase angle for $1 + j\tau\omega$ goes from 0 to $+90°$, the phase angle for $1 - j\tau\omega$ goes from 0 to $-90°$. Most systems are minimum-phase systems; i.e., all factors are of the form $j\omega$, $1 + j\tau\omega$, or $(\omega_n^2 - \omega^2 + j2\zeta\omega_n \omega)/\omega_n^2$. For minimum-phase systems, as ω becomes infinite, the phase angle is $\phi = -90°(n - m)$, where n is the order of the denominator and m that of the numerator. Non-minimum-phase systems may be detected from the phase-angle plot, because as ω becomes infinite, $\phi \neq -90°(n - m)$. For either minimum- or non-minimum-phase systems the slope of the log-magnitude diagram at high frequencies is $-(n - m)$ log units/decade. All the frequency-response techniques to be discussed in this text are equally valid for minimum- or non-minimum-phase systems.

11.3 EVALUATING THE GAIN K

In general, a transfer function may be expressed in the form

$$G(s) = \frac{K_n\{(1 + \tau_a s) \cdots [(s^2 + 2\zeta_a \omega_{n_a} s + \omega_{n_a}^2)/\omega_{n_a}^2] \cdots\}}{s^n\{(1 + \tau_1 s) \cdots [(s^2 + 2\zeta_1 \omega_{n_1} s + \omega_{n_1}^2)/\omega_{n_1}^2] \cdots\}} \tag{11.40}$$

where K_n is the overall gain of the transfer function $G(s)$, and n is the power to which the s term in the denominator is raised. Usually the value of n is 0, 1, or 2. The first time constant in the numerator is τ_a, the second τ_b, etc. The natural frequency for the first quadratic term in the numerator is ω_{n_a}, and the damping ratio is ζ_a. Similarly, τ_1 is the first time constant which appears in the denominator, τ_2 is the second, etc. The natural frequency for the first quadratic term in the denominator is ω_{n_1}, and its damping ratio is ζ_1.

The substitution of $j\omega$ for s in Eq. (11.40) gives

$$G(j\omega) = \frac{K_n\{(1 + j\tau_a \omega) \cdots [(\omega_{n_a}^2 - \omega^2 + j2\zeta_a \omega_{n_a} \omega)/\omega_{n_a}^2] \cdots\}}{(j\omega)^n\{(1 + j\tau_1 \omega) \cdots [(\omega_{n_1}^2 - \omega^2 + j2\zeta_1 \omega_{n_1} \omega)/\omega_{n_1}^2] \cdots\}} \tag{11.41}$$

For small values of ω all the terms inside the braces of the preceding expression approach 1, so that

$$G(j\omega) = \frac{K_n}{(j\omega)^n} \qquad \omega \approx 0 \tag{11.42}$$

As is indicated from the preceding expression, the gain K_n can be determined from the low-frequency portion of the log-magnitude plot. The techniques for evaluating K_n for $n = 0$, 1, or 2 are described in the following.

$n = 0$. When n is zero, there is no $j\omega$ term in $G(j\omega)$. Thus, Eq. (11.42) becomes

$$G(j\omega) = K_0 \qquad \omega \approx 0 \tag{11.43}$$

A typical log-magnitude plot for this case is shown in Fig. 11.10*a*. For small values of ω the low-frequency asymptote has a constant value $G(j\omega) = K_0$.

$n = 1$. For small values of ω and for n equal to 1, it follows from Eq. (11.42) that

$$G(j\omega) = \frac{K_1}{j\omega} \qquad \omega \approx 0 \tag{11.44}$$

The logarithm of the magnitude of $G(j\omega)$ is

$$\log |G(j\omega)| = \log K_1 - \log \omega \qquad \omega \approx 0 \tag{11.45}$$

From Eq. (11.45), it follows that, as ω changes by a factor of 10, $\log |G(j\omega)|$ changes by -1. Thus for $\omega \approx 0$ the slope of the curve of $\log |G(j\omega)|$ versus ω is -1 log unit/decade. A typical log-magnitude diagram for the case in which $n = 1$ is shown in Fig. 11.10*b*. It is to be noted that the low-frequency slope of -1 log unit/decade or its extension intersects the horizontal line through $\log |G(j\omega)| = 0$ at the point where $\omega = K_1$. This fact follows directly from Eq. (11.45) by noting that, when $\log |G(j\omega)| = 0$, then $\log \omega = \log K_1$ or simply $\omega = K_1$. In addition, for ω

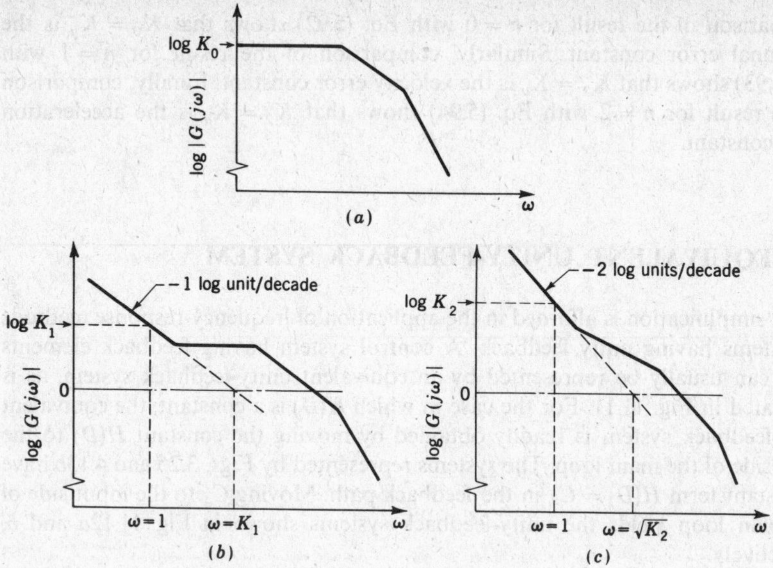

Figure 11.10 Log-magnitude plots: (a) $n = 0$; (b) $n = 1$; (c) $n = 2$.

equal to 1, Eq. (11.45) becomes $\log|G(j\omega)| = \log K_1$. Thus, as is shown in Fig. 11.10*b*, a vertical line through $\omega = 1$ intersects the low-frequency asymptote or its extension at the value $\log K_1$.

$n = 2$. The low-frequency equation for this case is

$$G(j\omega) = \frac{K_2}{(j\omega)^2} = -\frac{K_2}{\omega^2} \tag{11.46}$$

The logarithm of the magnitude of $G(j\omega)$ is

$$\log|G(j\omega)| = \log K_2 - 2\log\omega \tag{11.47}$$

A typical log-magnitude diagram for $n = 2$ is illustrated in Fig. 11.10*c*. The slope at low frequencies is -2 log units/decade. From Eq. (11.47), it follows that, when $\log|G(j\omega)| = 0$, then $\log\omega = \frac{1}{2}\log K_2$ or $\omega = \sqrt{K_2}$. Thus, the low-frequency asymptote or its extension intersects the horizontal line, $\log|G(j\omega)| = 0$, at the frequency $\omega = \sqrt{K_2}$. When $\omega = 1$, then Eq. (11.47) becomes $\log|G(j\omega)| = \log K_2$. Thus, a vertical line through $\omega = 1$ intersects the low-frequency asymptote or its extension at $\log K_2$.

Replacing $j\omega$ by s in Eq. (11.42) and solving for K_n shows that

$$K_n = \lim_{s\to 0} s^n G(s)$$

Comparison of the result for $n = 0$ with Eq. (5.92) shows that $K_0 = K_p$ is the positional error constant. Similarly, comparison of the result for $n = 1$ with Eq. (5.93) shows that $K_1 = K_v$ is the velocity error constant. Finally, comparison of the result for $n = 2$ with Eq. (5.94) shows that $K_2 = K_a$ is the acceleration error constant.

11.4 EQUIVALENT UNITY-FEEDBACK SYSTEM

Much simplification is afforded in the application of frequency-response methods to systems having unity feedback. A control system having feedback elements $H(D)$ can usually be represented by an equivalent unity-feedback system, as is illustrated in Fig. 11.11. For the case in which $H(D)$ is a constant, the equivalent unity-feedback system is readily obtained by moving the constant $H(D)$ to the input side of the main loop. The systems represented by Figs. 3.25 and 4.13*b* have a constant term $H(D) = C_4$ in the feedback path. Moving C_4 to the input side of the main loop yields the unity-feedback systems shown in Fig. 11.12*a* and *b*, respectively.

To obtain the equivalent unity-feedback system when $H(D)$ is not a constant, first write $H(D)$ in the form $H(D) = C[1 + H_1(D)]$. The constant C may now be taken out of the feedback path, and the remaining term $1 + H_1(D)$ may be represented as shown in Fig. 11.13 by two separate paths. The design of such systems in which there is an inner, or minor, feedback path is often facilitated by the use of inverse polar plots, as is discussed in Sec. 12.7.

In obtaining the equivalent unity-feedback system, only constant terms are to be taken outside the main loop. The fact that $r(t)$ is equal to some constant times the command signal does not affect the basic dynamic behavior of the system.

System Type

When a system is represented in its equivalent unity-feedback form, the value of n in $G(s)$ as indicated by Eq. (11.40) has a predominant effect upon the behavior of the system. When $n = 0$, the system is designated as a type 0 system. A type 1 system is one for which $n = 1$, a type 2 system is one for which $n = 2$, etc.

A type 0 system results when there is no integration, as in a proportional control. For an integral control in which there is one integrator in the feedforward elements, n is equal to 1. A type 2 system has two integrations in the feedforward elements, etc. The system shown in Fig. 11.12*a* is a type 0 system, and the system shown in Fig. 11.12*b* is a type 1 system.

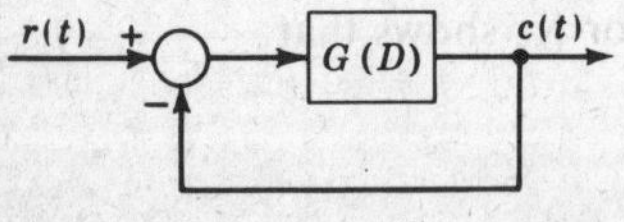

Figure 11.1 Unity-feedback system.

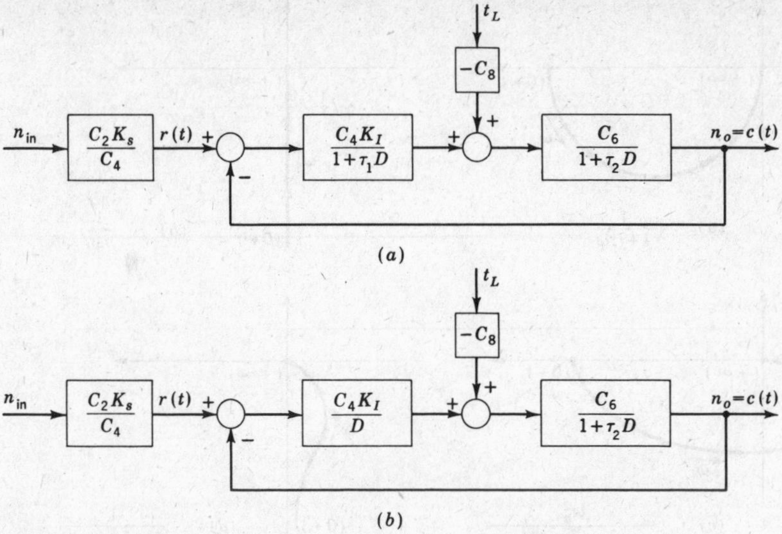

Figure 11.12 Equivalent unity-feedback systems when $H(D)$ is a constant.

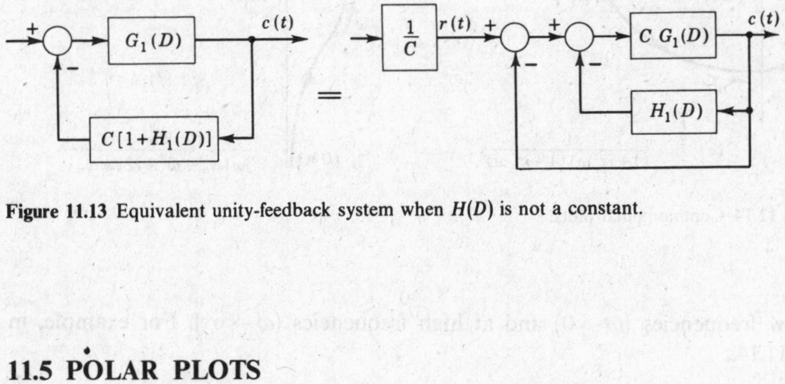

Figure 11.13 Equivalent unity-feedback system when $H(D)$ is not a constant.

11.5 POLAR PLOTS

Vector loci or polar plots are better suited for the solution of certain control problems than are log-magnitude diagrams, and vice versa. As is later explained, other methods of representing frequency-response information are the log-modulus, or Nichols, plot and the inverse polar plot. A control engineer must be familiar with all these means of plotting frequency-response data in order to be able to select the method which is best suited to a particular problem.

The polar plots for a number of commonly encountered functions are shown in Fig. 11.14. Polar plots may often be roughly sketched by knowing the location

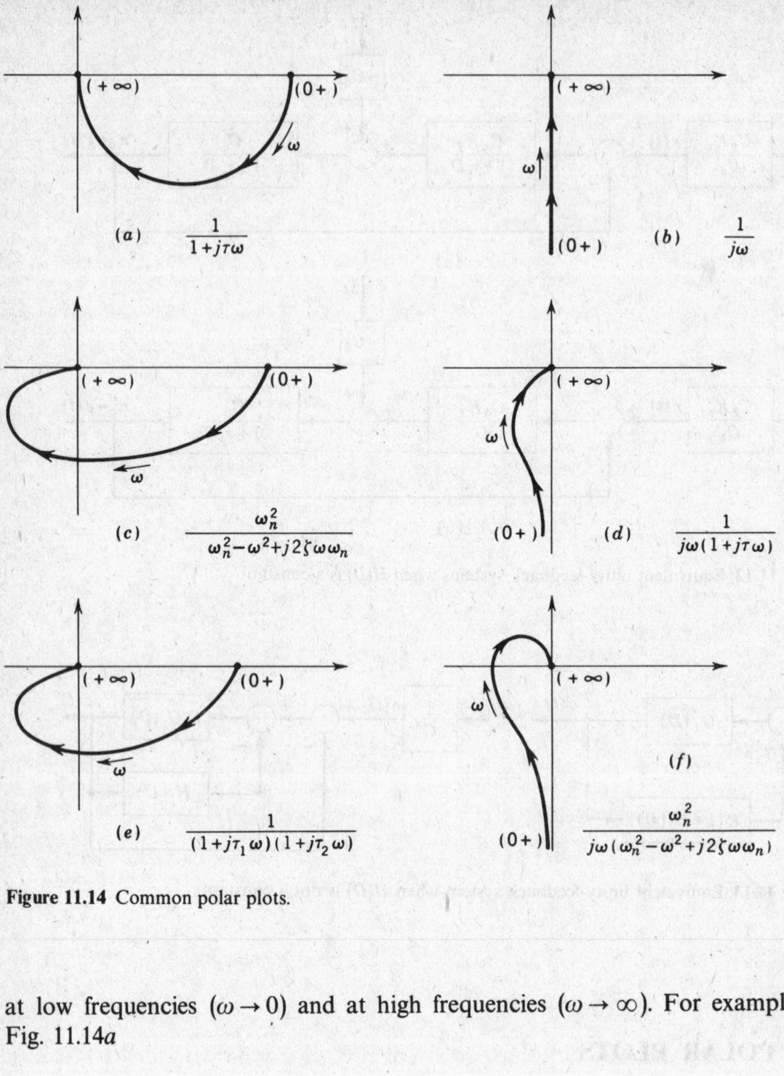

Figure 11.14 Common polar plots.

at low frequencies ($\omega \to 0$) and at high frequencies ($\omega \to \infty$). For example, in Fig. 11.14*a*

$$\left.\frac{1}{1+j\tau\omega}\right|_{\omega=0+} = 1$$

$$\left.\frac{1}{1+j\tau\omega}\right|_{\omega=+\infty} \approx \left.\frac{1}{j\tau\omega}\right|_{\omega=+\infty} = \left.\frac{e^{-j90^\circ}}{\tau\omega}\right|_{\omega=+\infty} = (0+)e^{-j90^\circ} \tag{11.48}$$

Thus, the locus of Fig. 11.14*a* begins at the $+1$ point on the positive real axis ($\theta = 0^\circ$), and as ω approaches ∞, the locus approaches 0 along the -90° axis. The low- and high-frequency values for Fig. 11.14*b* are

$$\left.\frac{1}{j\omega}\right|_{\omega=0+} = \left.\frac{1}{\omega}e^{-j90^\circ}\right|_{\omega=0+} = (+\infty)e^{-j90^\circ}$$

$$\left.\frac{1}{j\omega}\right|_{\omega=+\infty} = \left.\frac{1}{\omega}e^{-j90^\circ}\right|_{\omega=+\infty} = (0+)e^{-j90^\circ} \tag{11.49}$$

For Fig. 11.14*c*

$$\left.\frac{1}{1-(\omega/\omega_n)^2 + j2\zeta(\omega/\omega_n)}\right|_{\omega=0+} = 1$$

$$\left.\frac{1}{1-(\omega/\omega_n)^2 + j2\zeta(\omega/\omega_n)}\right|_{\omega=+\infty} \approx \left.\frac{1}{-(\omega/\omega_n)^2}\right|_{\omega=+\infty} = -\left.\left(\frac{\omega_n}{\omega}\right)^2\right|_{\omega=+\infty}$$

$$= (0+)e^{-j180^\circ} \tag{11.50}$$

The limiting value for a function composed of multiples of the preceding terms is equal to the product of the contribution of each term. For example, in Fig. 11.14*d*

$$\left.\frac{1}{j\omega(1+j\tau\omega)}\right|_{\omega=0+} = \left.\frac{1}{j\omega}\right|_{\omega=0+} \times \left.\frac{1}{1+j\tau\omega}\right|_{\omega=0+} = (+\infty)e^{-j90^\circ}$$

$$\left.\frac{1}{j\omega(1+j\tau\omega)}\right|_{\omega=+\infty} = \left.\frac{1}{j\omega}\right|_{\omega=+\infty} \times \left.\frac{1}{1+j\tau\omega}\right|_{\omega=+\infty} = (0+)e^{-j90^\circ}(0+)e^{-j90^\circ}$$

$$= (0+)e^{-j180^\circ} \tag{11.51}$$

Application of this technique will verify the results shown in Fig. 11.14*e* and *f*.

The low- and high-frequency locations are summarized in Table 11.1. The reciprocal of any term in Table 11.1 is obtained by changing the sign of the phase angle and taking the reciprocal of the magnitude. At low frequencies, there is a phase shift with the $1/j\omega$ term only. Thus, for a type 0 system, the polar plot originates on the positive real axis, where ϕ is zero. Typical polar plots for type 0,

Table 11.1

ω	$\dfrac{1}{j\omega}$	$\dfrac{1}{1+j\tau\omega}$	$\dfrac{\omega_n^2}{\omega_n^2-\omega^2+j2\zeta\omega\omega_n}$
0+	$\infty\angle-90^\circ$	$1\angle0^\circ$	$1\angle0^\circ$
$+\infty$	$0\angle-90^\circ$	$0\angle-90^\circ$	$0\angle-180^\circ$

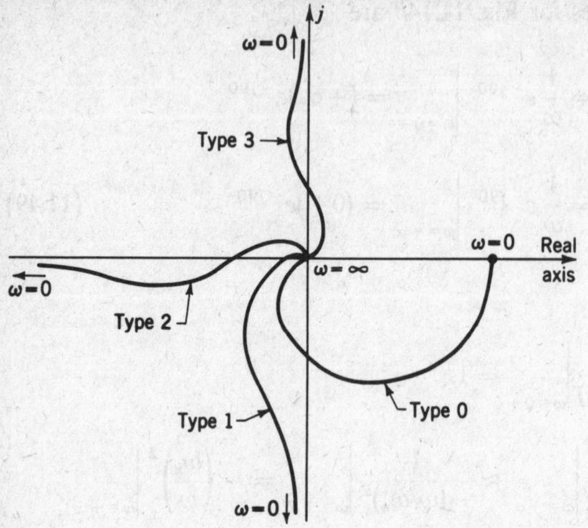

Figure 11.15 Polar plots for type 0, 1, 2, and 3 systems.

1, 2, and 3 systems are shown in Fig. 11.15. A type 1 system begins at infinity on the negative 90° axis, a type 2 system begins at infinity on the negative 180° axis, etc. For most systems, the polar plot terminates at the origin when $\omega = \infty$.

11.6 *M* AND α CIRCLES

Frequency-response methods make extensive use of the open-loop frequency response $G(j\omega)$. The open-loop response is the response that would be obtained if the feedback path were disconnected at the comparator (i.e., opened).

For unity-feedback systems, the closed-loop frequency response

$$C(j\omega)/R(j\omega)$$

is related to the open-loop response $G(j\omega)$ by the equation

$$\frac{C(j\omega)}{R(j\omega)} = \frac{G(j\omega)}{1 + G(j\omega)} \tag{11.52}$$

In Fig. 11.16 is shown a typical $G(j\omega)$ plot. The vector from the origin to a point on the curve is $G(j\omega)$, and the vector from the point $-1 + j0$ to the same point on this curve is $1 + G(j\omega)$. The ratio of these two vectors is the closed-loop frequency response for the value of ω at that point. This shows that every point on the $G(j\omega)$ plane corresponds to a certain value of $C(j\omega)/R(j\omega)$. The magnitude of the ratio of the amplitude of the output sinusoid to the input is designated by the symbol $M = |C(j\omega)/R(j\omega)|$.

In Fig. 11.17, it is to be seen that the locus of lines of constant M are circles on the $G(j\omega)$ plane. The proof of this follows: Consider any point $G(j\omega) = x + jy$ in

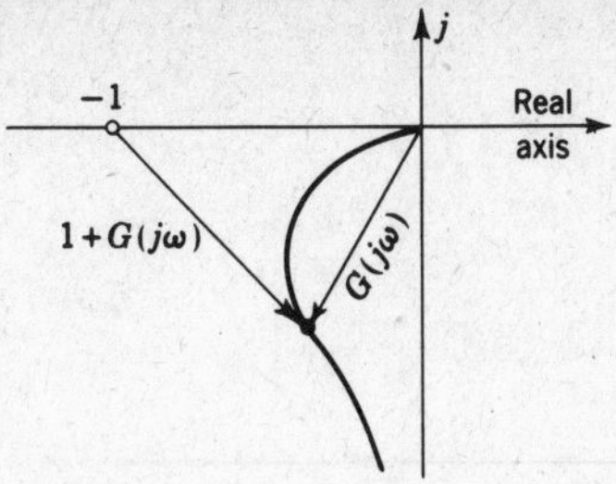

Figure 11.16 Determination of closed-loop frequency response from open-loop response.

the $G(j\omega)$ plane of Fig. 11.17. The closed-loop frequency response is

$$\frac{C(j\omega)}{R(j\omega)} = \frac{x + jy}{1 + x + jy} \tag{11.53}$$

The magnitude of the preceding equation is

$$M = \left| \frac{C(j\omega)}{R(j\omega)} \right| = \left(\frac{x^2 + y^2}{1 + 2x + x^2 + y^2} \right)^{1/2} \tag{11.54}$$

Squaring and cross-multiplying gives

$$x^2(M^2 - 1) + 2xM^2 + y^2(M^2 - 1) = -M^2 \tag{11.55}$$

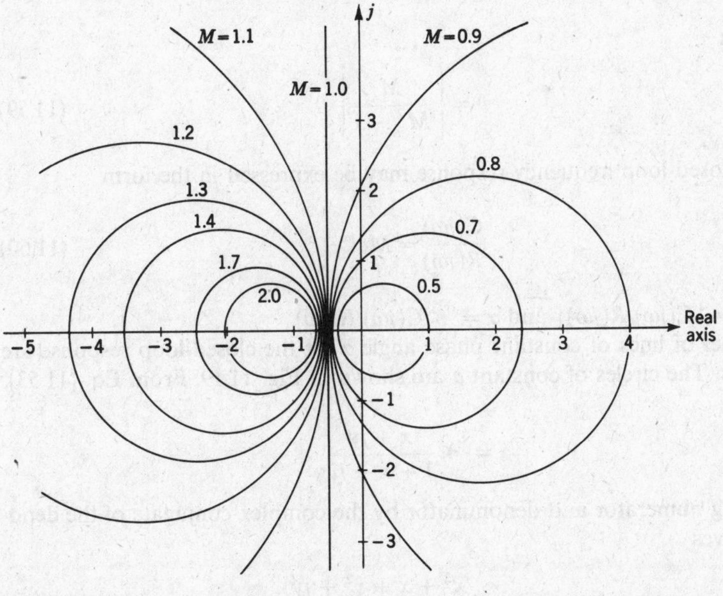

Figure 11.17 Constant M circles.

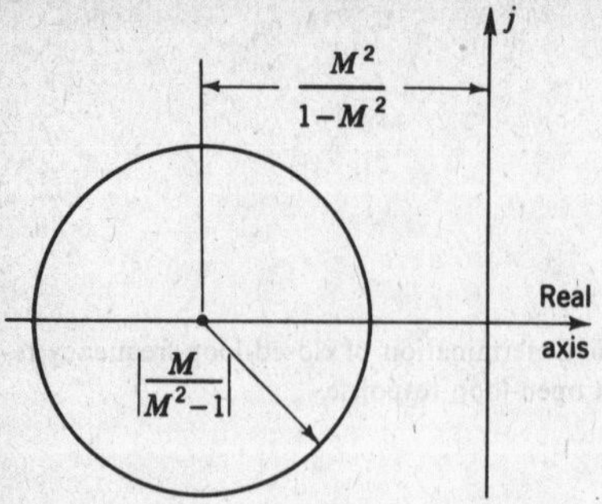

Figure 11.18 Typical M circle.

Dividing by $M^2 - 1$ and completing the square by adding $M^4/(M^2 - 1)^2$ to both sides yields

$$x^2 + \frac{2xM^2}{M^2 - 1} + \frac{M^4}{(M^2 - 1)^2} + y^2 = \frac{M^4}{(M^2 - 1)^2} - \frac{M^2}{M^2 - 1} \tag{11.56}$$

Thus,

$$\left(x + \frac{M^2}{M^2 - 1}\right)^2 + y^2 = \frac{M^2}{(M^2 - 1)^2} \tag{11.57}$$

Equation (11.57) is the equation of a circle, as shown in Fig. 11.18, with center at

$$x = \frac{M^2}{1 - M^2} \qquad y = 0 \tag{11.58}$$

and radius

$$r = \left| \frac{M}{M^2 - 1} \right| \tag{11.59}$$

The closed-loop frequency response may be expressed in the form

$$\frac{C(j\omega)}{R(j\omega)} = Me^{j\alpha} \tag{11.60}$$

where $M = |C(j\omega)/R(j\omega)|$ and $\alpha = \measuredangle\, C(j\omega)/R(j\omega)$.

The loci of lines of constant phase angle α for the closed-loop response are also circles. The circles of constant α are shown in Fig. 11.19. From Eq. (11.53),

$$\alpha = \measuredangle \frac{x + jy}{1 + x + jy}$$

Multiplying numerator and denominator by the complex conjugate of the denominator gives

$$\alpha = \measuredangle \frac{x^2 + x + y^2 + jy}{(1 + x)^2 + y^2}$$

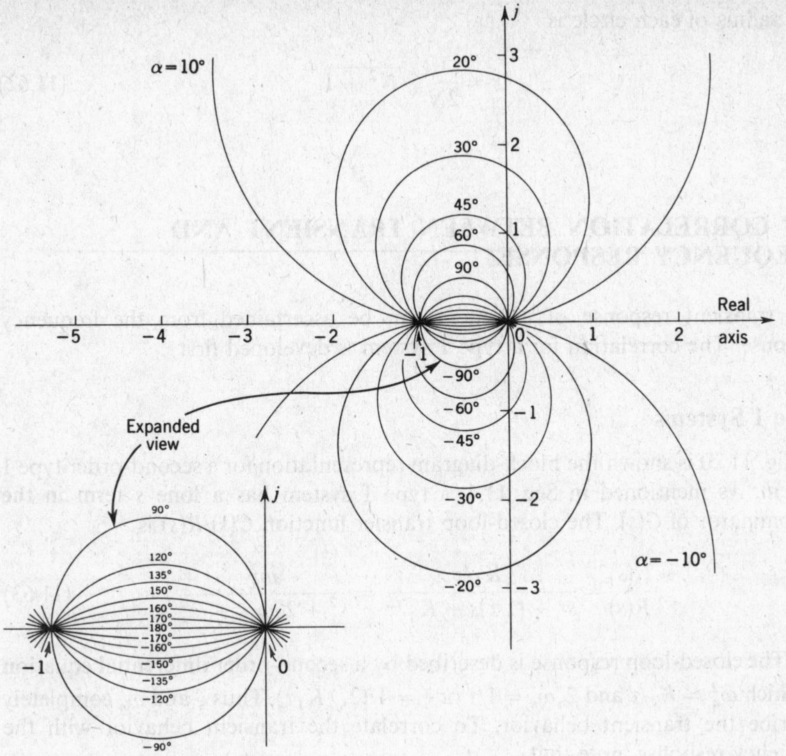

Figure 11.19 Constant-α circles.

Letting $N = \tan \alpha$, then

$$N = \tan \alpha = \frac{y}{x^2 + x + y^2}$$

This may be written in the form

$$x^2 + x + y^2 - \frac{y}{N} = 0$$

Completing the square gives

$$\left(x + \frac{1}{2}\right)^2 + \left(y - \frac{1}{2N}\right)^2 = \frac{N^2 + 1}{4N^2}$$

The centers of these circles are located at

$$x = -\tfrac{1}{2} \qquad \text{and} \qquad y = \tfrac{1}{2}N \tag{11.61}$$

The radius of each circle is

$$r = \frac{1}{2N}\sqrt{N^2 + 1} \tag{11.62}$$

11.7 CORRELATION BETWEEN TRANSIENT AND FREQUENCY RESPONSE

The transient response of a system can be ascertained from the frequency response. The correlation for a type 1 system is developed first.

Type 1 Systems

In Fig. 11.20 is shown the block-diagram representation for a second-order type 1 system. As mentioned in Sec. 11.4, a type 1 system has a lone s term in the denominator of $G(s)$. The closed-loop transfer function $C(s)/R(s)$ is

$$\frac{C(s)}{R(s)} = \frac{K_1/\tau}{s^2 + (1/\tau)s + K_1/\tau} = \frac{\omega_n^2}{s^2 + 2\zeta\omega_n s + \omega_n^2} \tag{11.63}$$

The closed-loop response is described by a second-order differential equation in which $\omega_n^2 = K_1/\tau$ and $2\zeta\omega_n = 1/\tau$ or $\zeta = 1/(2\sqrt{K_1\tau})$. Thus ζ and ω_n completely describe the transient behavior. To correlate the transient behavior with the frequency response, note that

$$M = \left|\frac{C(j\omega)}{R(j\omega)}\right| = \frac{\omega_n^2}{|(\omega_n^2 - \omega^2) + j(2\zeta\omega\omega_n)|} = \frac{1}{\sqrt{[1 - (\omega/\omega_n)^2]^2 + (2\zeta\omega/\omega_n)^2}} \tag{11.64}$$

The value of ω at which M is a maximum is obtained by differentiating Eq. (11.64) with respect to ω and then setting the resulting expression equal to zero. Thus,

$$\frac{\omega_p}{\omega_n} = \sqrt{1 - 2\zeta^2} \qquad 0 \le \zeta \le 0.707 \tag{11.65}$$

where ω_p is the value of ω at which M attains its peak or maximum value. Substituting ω_p/ω_n for ω/ω_n in Eq. (11.64) gives the peak or maximum value of M,

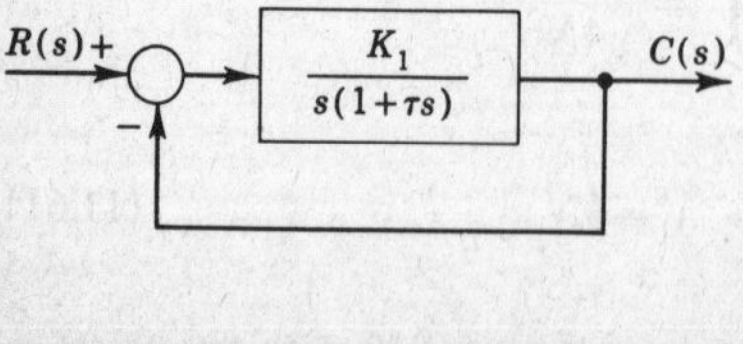

Figure 11.20 Second-order type 1 system.

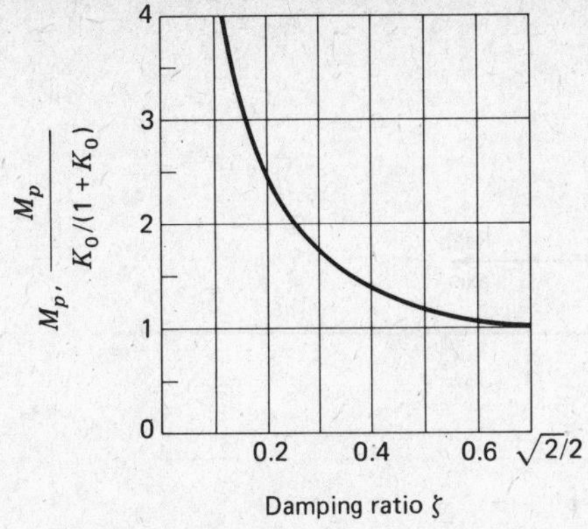

Figure 11.21 M_p versus ζ for a second-order system.

which is designated M_p. That is,

$$M_p = \frac{1}{2\zeta\sqrt{1-\zeta^2}} \qquad \begin{cases} 0 \le \zeta \le 0.707 \\ M_p \ge 1 \end{cases} \tag{11.66}$$

The preceding result has significance only for $0 \le \zeta \le 0.707$, in which case $M_p \ge 1$. In Fig. 11.21 is shown a plot of M_p versus ζ.

As previously discussed, the zeros of the characteristic function which are located nearest the imaginary axis have a predominant effect upon the transient behavior of higher-order systems. Thus, the transient behavior of a higher-order type 1 system for which $M_p \ge 1$ (the value of M_p may be obtained from a polar plot for the system) may be *approximated* by a second-order system whose damping ratio ζ as obtained from Fig. 11.21 corresponds to the value of M_p for the system.

Illustrative example 1 In Fig. 11.22 is shown the polar plot for a type 1 system for which $M_p = 1.6$ and $\omega_p = 3$. Determine the value of ζ and ω_n to be used for approximating the transient behavior.

SOLUTION From Fig. 11.21, it follows that for $M_p = 1.6$, the corresponding value of ζ is 0.33. The value of ω_n may now be ascertained from Eq. (11.65). That is,

$$\omega_n = \frac{\omega_p}{\sqrt{1-2\zeta^2}} = \frac{3}{\sqrt{1-2(0.33)^2}} = 3.4$$

It is to be noticed from Fig. 6.7 that for $\zeta > 0.707$ ($M_p < 1$) there is no overshoot of the response to a step change in the input. This is similar to the type of response that is obtained from a first-order system. Thus when M_p is less than 1, the transient response is approximated by an equivalent first-order system.

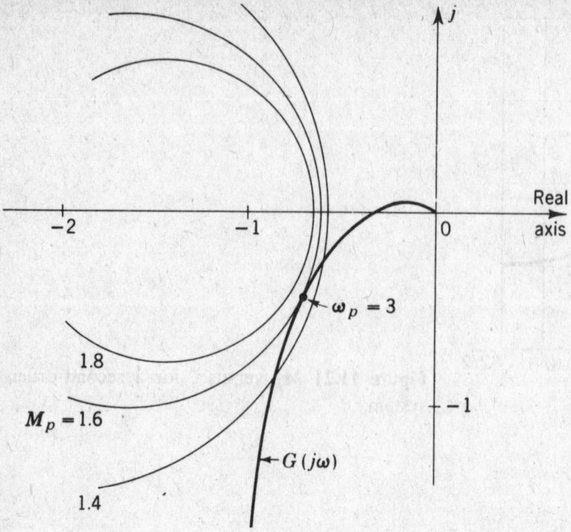

Figure 11.22 Polar plot for a type 1 system.

In Fig. 11.23 is shown a first-order type 1 system. The correlation between the frequency and the transient response for this system is obtained by first writing the equation for the closed-loop response.

$$\frac{C(s)}{R(s)} = \frac{K_1}{K_1 + s} = \frac{1}{1 + (1/K_1)s} = \frac{1}{1 + \tau_c s}$$

where $\tau_c = 1/K_1$ is the closed-loop time constant.

In Fig. 11.24 is shown a plot of the open-loop frequency response

$$G(j\omega) = \frac{K_1}{j\omega}$$

When the magnitude of $G(j\omega)$ is 1, then

$$|G(j\omega)| = \frac{K_1}{|j\omega_c|} = \frac{K_1}{\omega_c} = 1$$

where ω_c designates the value of ω at which $|G(j\omega)| = 1$. That is, ω_c is the value of ω at which the $G(j\omega)$ plot crosses the unit circle, as is illustrated in Fig. 11.24. Because $K_1 = \omega_c$ and $\tau_c = 1/K_1$, then

$$\tau_c = \frac{1}{K_1} = \frac{1}{\omega_c}$$

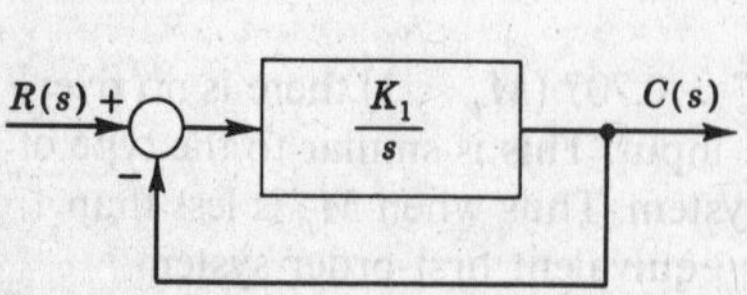

Figure 11.23 First-order type 1 system.

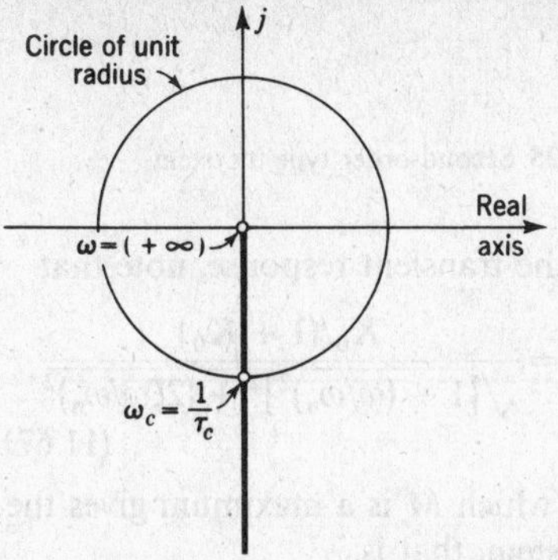

Figure 11.24 Polar plot for $G(j\omega) = K_1/j\omega$.

Thus, for type 1 systems in which $M_p < 1$, an indication of the equivalent time constant τ_c is obtained by taking the reciprocal of the angular frequency ω_c at which the $G(j\omega)$ plot crosses the unit circle.

The preceding results correlating transient and frequency response for type 1 systems are summarized in Table 11.2.

For $M_p < 1$, the response is approximated by a first-order system in which τ_c describes the transient behavior. For $M_p \geq 1$, the response is approximated by a second-order system in which ζ and ω_n describe the transient behavior.

Although the preceding correlation criteria are developed for type 1 systems, these criteria yield good approximations for type 2 systems, type 3 systems, etc. In the next section, it is shown that the preceding correlation criteria should be modified somewhat for the case of type 0 systems.

Type 0 Systems

In Fig. 11.25 is shown the block-diagram representation for a second-order type 0 system. The closed-loop transfer function $C(s)/R(s)$ is

$$\frac{C(s)}{R(s)} = \frac{K_0/b}{s^2 + (a/b)s + (1 + K_0)/b} = \frac{[K_0/(1 + K_0)]\omega_n^2}{s^2 + 2\zeta\omega_n s + \omega_n^2}$$

where $\omega_n^2 = (1 + K_0)/b$ and $2\zeta\omega_n = a/b$.

Table 11.2 Correlation Criteria for Type 1 Systems

$M_p < 1$	$M_p \geq 1$
$\tau_c = \dfrac{1}{\omega_c}$	$M_p = \dfrac{1}{2\zeta\sqrt{1-\zeta^2}}$ $\dfrac{\omega_p}{\omega_n} = \sqrt{1 - 2\zeta^2}$

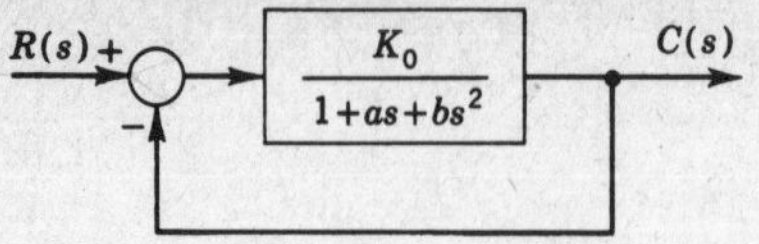

Figure 11.25 Second-order type 0 system.

To correlate the frequency response with the transient response, note that

$$M = \left|\frac{C(j\omega)}{R(j\omega)}\right| = \frac{K_0/(1+K_0)}{|1-(\omega/\omega_n)^2 + 2j\zeta(\omega/\omega_n)|} = \frac{K_0/(1+K_0)}{\sqrt{[1-(\omega/\omega_n)^2]^2 + (2\zeta\omega/\omega_n)^2}} \tag{11.67}$$

Differentiating to determine the value of ω at which M is a maximum gives the same result as for the corresponding type 1 system, that is,

$$\omega_p = \omega_n\sqrt{1-2\zeta^2} \qquad 0 \le \zeta \le 0.707$$

Substituting ω_p for ω in Eq. (11.67) gives

$$M_p = \frac{K_0/(1+K_0)}{2\zeta\sqrt{1-\zeta^2}}$$

or

$$\frac{M_p}{K_0/(1+K_0)} = \frac{1}{2\zeta\sqrt{1-\zeta^2}} \qquad \begin{cases} 0 \le \zeta \le 0.707 \\ \dfrac{M_p}{K_0/(1+K_0)} \ge 1 \end{cases} \tag{11.68}$$

Thus, for type 0 systems, the ordinate $M_p/[K_0/(1+K_0)]$ of Fig. 11.21 is to be used. It is to be noted that for large values of K_0, the preceding criterion becomes the same as that for a type 1 system.

Illustrative example 2 In Fig. 11.26 is shown the polar plot for a type 0 system in which $M_p = 1.6$, $\omega_p = 3$, and $K_0 = 4$. Determine the value of ζ and ω_n to be used in approximating the transient behavior of this system.

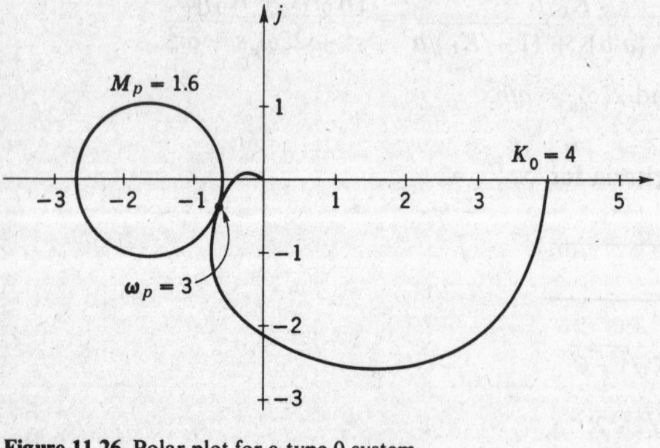

Figure 11.26 Polar plot for a type 0 system.

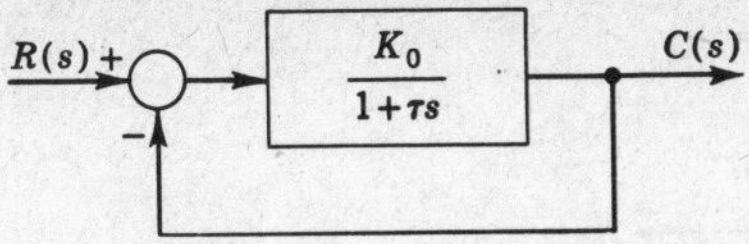

Figure 11.27 First-order type 0 system.

SOLUTION From Fig. 11.21, it follows that for $M_p/[K_0/(1+K_0)] = 1.6/0.8 = 2$, the corresponding value of ζ is 0.26. The value of ω_n is now ascertained from Eq. (11.65). Thus,

$$\omega_n = \frac{\omega_p}{\sqrt{1-2\zeta^2}} = \frac{3}{\sqrt{1-2(0.26)^2}} = 3.22$$

For a type 0 system in which $M_p/[K_0/(1+K_0)] < 1$, the transient behavior is best described by a first-order system. In Fig. 11.27 is shown a first-order type 0 system. The closed-loop transfer function is

$$\frac{C(s)}{R(s)} = \frac{K_0}{1+K_0+\tau s} = \frac{K_0/(1+K_0)}{1+\tau_c s}$$

where $\tau_c = \tau/(1+K_0)$ is the time constant for the closed-loop response. In Fig. 11.28 is shown a plot of the open-loop frequency response $G(j\omega)$. That is,

$$G(j\omega) = \frac{K_0}{1+j\tau\omega}$$

This plot crosses a circle of radius r at $\omega = \omega_c$. That is,

$$|G(j\omega)| = \frac{K_0}{\sqrt{1+(\tau\omega_c)^2}} = r \qquad (11.69)$$

The value of r such that ω_c is the reciprocal of the closed-loop time constant is obtained by substituting $\omega_c = 1/\tau_c = (1+K_0)/\tau$ into Eq. (11.69). This gives

$$K_0^2 = r^2[1+(1+K_0)^2]$$

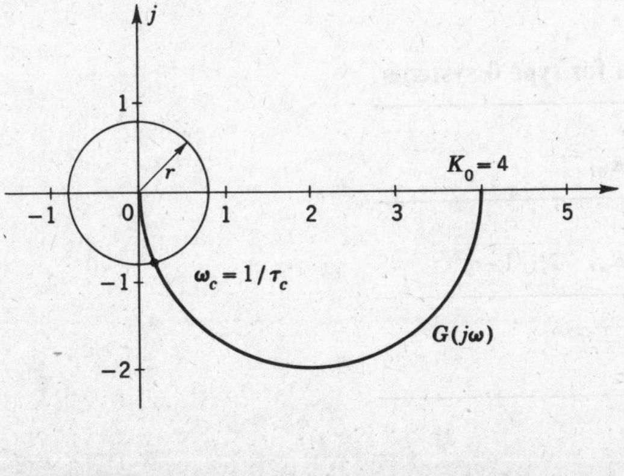

Figure 11.28 Polar plot for $G(j\omega) = K_0/(1+j\tau\omega)$.

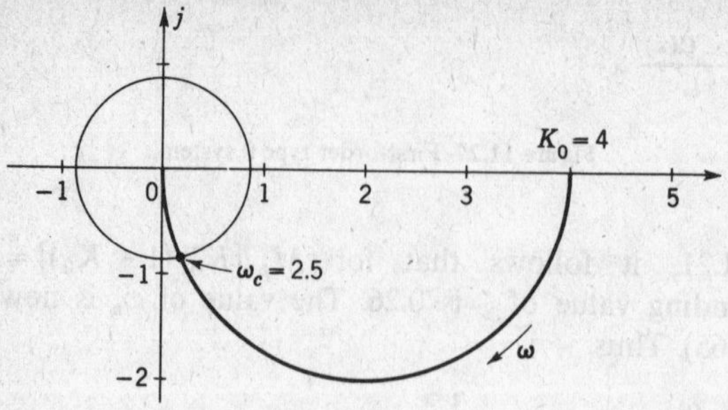

Figure 11.29 Polar plot for a type 0 system.

or

$$r = \frac{K_0}{\sqrt{1 + (1 + K_0)^2}}$$

For large values of K_0, the radius r approaches the unit circle and the preceding criterion becomes the same as that for a type 1 system.

Illustrative example 3 In Fig. 11.29 is shown the polar plot of a type 0 system. Determine the value of τ_c to be used in approximating the transient behavior of this system.

SOLUTION From the polar plot, it is seen that $K_0 = 4$. The value of r is

$$r = \frac{4}{\sqrt{1 + (5)^2}} = \frac{4}{\sqrt{26}} = 0.785$$

The polar plot shows that $\omega_c = 2.5$. Thus

$$\tau_c = \frac{1}{\omega_c} = 0.4$$

The preceding correlation criteria for type 0 systems are summarized in Table 11.3.

Table 11.3 Correlation criteria for type 0 systems

$\dfrac{M_p}{K_0/(1 + K_0)} < 1$	$\dfrac{M_p}{K_0/(1 + K_0)} \geq 1$
$\tau_c = \dfrac{1}{\omega_c}$	$\dfrac{M_p}{K_0/(1 + K_0)} = \dfrac{1}{2\zeta\sqrt{1 - \zeta^2}}$
$r = \dfrac{K_0}{\sqrt{1 + (1 + K_0)^2}}$	$\dfrac{\omega_p}{\omega_n} = \sqrt{1 - 2\zeta^2}$

Bandwidth

The closed-loop transfer function for the system of Fig. 11.27 is

$$\frac{C(s)}{R(s)} = \frac{K_0}{(1 + K_0) + \tau s} = \frac{K_0/(1 + K_0)}{1 + [\tau/(1 + K_0)]s} = \frac{K}{1 + \tau_c s}$$

where $K = K_0/(1 + K_0)$ is the steady-state gain and $\tau_c = \tau/(1 + K_0)$ is the closed-loop time constant. Replacing s by $j\omega$ yields for the closed-loop frequency response

$$\frac{C(j\omega)}{R(j\omega)} = \frac{K}{1 + j\tau_c\omega}$$

The amplitude ratio M of the closed-loop frequency response is

$$M(j\omega) = \left|\frac{C(j\omega)}{R(j\omega)}\right| = \frac{K}{\sqrt{1 + (\tau_c\omega)^2}}$$

A plot of the amplitude ratio is shown in Fig. 11.30*a*. For small values of ω, the

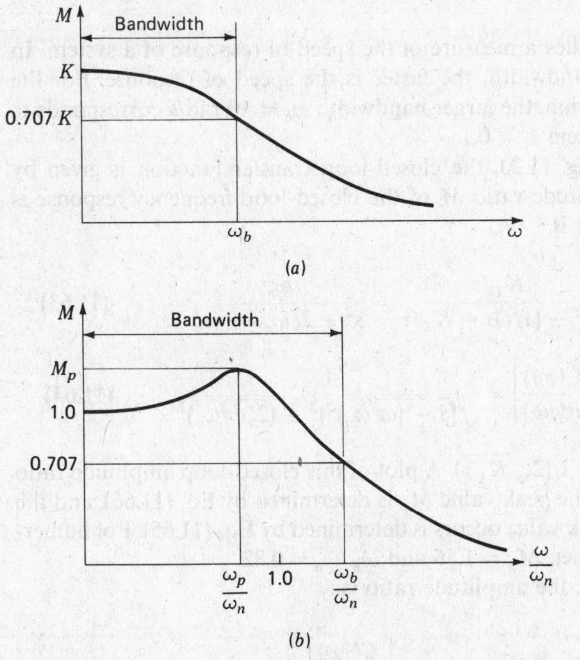

Figure 11.30 Closed-loop frequency response for (*a*) a type 0 system and (*b*) a type 1 system.

amplitude ratio is

$$M(j0) = \left|\frac{C(j\omega)}{R(j\omega)}\right|_{\omega=0} = K$$

The frequency $\omega = \omega_b$ at which the amplitude ratio decreases to $\sqrt{2}/2 = 0.707$ times its value for low frequencies $[M(j\omega) = 0.707M(j0)]$ is

$$M(j\omega) = \frac{K}{\sqrt{1 + (\tau_c \omega_b)^2}} = 0.707K$$

Squaring both sides and solving for ω_b gives

$$\omega_b = \frac{1}{\tau_c}$$

The frequency ω_b is called the bandwidth. For $\tau_c = 1$, the bandwidth is $\omega_b = 1$ rad/s. For $\tau_c = 0.1$, the bandwidth is $\omega_b = 1/0.1 = 10$ rad/s. The bandwidth is a measure of the frequency range $(0 < \omega < \omega_b)$ over which the closed-loop amplitude ratio is greater than $\sqrt{2}/2$ times its value for low frequencies. The response follows the input reasonably well for frequencies within the bandwidth. Note from Fig. 11.30*a* that the amplitude ratio decreases rapidly for frequencies greater than ω_b.

The bandwidth provides a measure of the speed of response of a system. In general, the larger the bandwidth, the faster is the speed of response. For the example under consideration, the larger bandwidth $\omega_b = 10$ rad/s corresponds to the faster-responding system $\tau_c = 0.1$.

For the system of Fig. 11.20, the closed-loop transfer function is given by Eq. (11.63) and the amplitude ratio M of the closed-loop frequency response is given by Eq. (11.64). That is,

$$\frac{C(s)}{R(s)} = \frac{K_1/\tau}{s^2 + (1/\tau)s + K_1/\tau} = \frac{\omega_n^2}{s^2 + 2\zeta\omega_n s + \omega_n^2} \tag{11.63}$$

$$M(j\omega) = \left|\frac{C(j\omega)}{R(j\omega)}\right| = \frac{1}{\sqrt{[1 - (\omega/\omega_n)^2]^2 + (2\zeta\omega/\omega_n)^2}} \tag{11.64}$$

where $\omega_n^2 = K_1/\tau$ and $\zeta = 1/(2\sqrt{K_1\tau})$. A plot of this closed-loop amplitude ratio is shown in Fig. 11.30*b*. The peak value M_p is determined by Eq. (11.66), and the frequency at which the peak value occurs is determined by Eq. (11.65). For numerical purposes, if $\zeta = 0.4$, then $M_p = 1.36$ and $\omega_p/\omega_n = 0.82$.

For small values of ω, the amplitude ratio is

$$M(j0) = M(j\omega)\Big|_{\omega=0} = \left|\frac{C(j\omega)}{R(j\omega)}\right|_{\omega=0} = 1$$

The frequency $\omega = \omega_b$ at which the amplitude ratio decreases to 0.707 times its value for low frequencies is

$$M(j\omega) = \frac{1}{\sqrt{[1-(\omega_b/\omega_n)^2]^2 + (2\zeta\omega_b/\omega_n)^2}} = 0.707M(j0) = 0.707$$

Squaring and solving for $(\omega_b/\omega_n)^2$ gives

$$\left(\frac{\omega_b}{\omega_n}\right)^2 = (1-2\zeta^2) + \sqrt{2-4\zeta^2(1-\zeta^2)}$$

For $\zeta = 0, 0.4$, and 0.707, the corresponding values of ω_b/ω_n are 1.55, 1.36, and 1.0.

11.8 DETERMINING THE GAIN K TO YIELD A DESIRED M_p

In Fig. 11.31 is shown a typical polar plot of $G(j\omega)$. If the gain K of the original function is doubled, the value of $G(j\omega)$ is doubled at every point. As shown in Fig. 11.31, it is not necessary to change the shape of the polar plot, but merely to change the scale by multiplying the old scale by the factor 2. Values of this new scale are shown in parentheses. It is now shown how the gain K can be adjusted so that the polar plot $G(j\omega)$ will be tangent to any desired $M_p > 1$ circle. This, in effect, is determining the gain K so that the system will have a desired M_p.

An M circle is shown in Fig. 11.32. From Eqs. (11.58) and (11.59), it follows that the center is located on the real axis at $-M^2/(M^2-1)$ and the radius is $M/(M^2-1)$. The line drawn from the origin, tangent to the M circle at the point P, has an included angle of ψ. The value of $\sin\psi$ is

$$\sin\psi = \frac{1}{M} \tag{11.70}$$

A characteristic feature of the point of tangency P is that a line drawn from the point P perpendicular to the negative real axis intersects this axis at the -1 point. This characteristic may be proved from the geometry of Fig. 11.32.

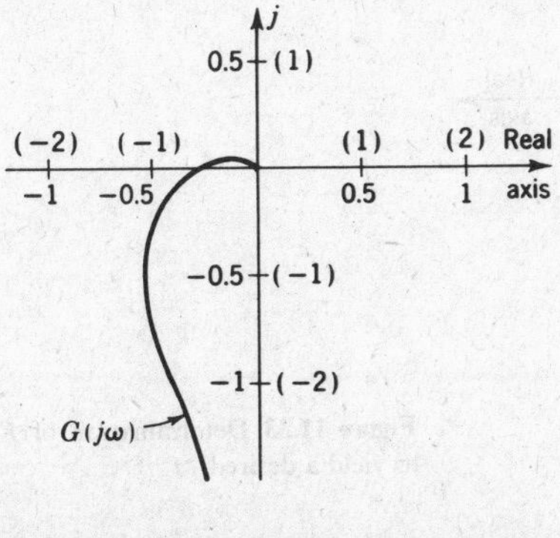

Figure 11.31 Typical polar plot.

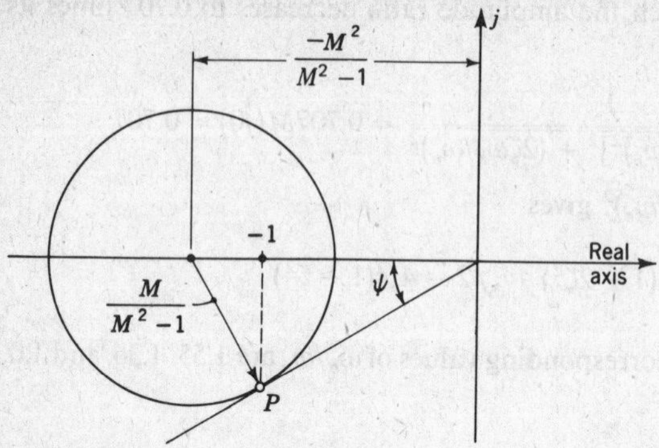

Figure 11.32 Tangent to an M circle.

The procedure for determining the gain K so that $G(j\omega)$ will have a desired value of M_p is as follows:

1. Draw the polar plot for $G(j\omega)/K$.
2. Draw the tangent line to the desired M_p circle [Eq. (11.70)].
3. Draw the circle with center on the negative real axis that is tangent to both the $G(j\omega)/K$ plot and the tangent line, as is shown in Fig. 11.33.
4. Erect the perpendicular to the negative real axis from point P, the point of tangency of this circle and the tangent line. This perpendicular intersects the negative real axis at a value $-A + j0 = -A$.
5. In order that the circle drawn in step 3 correspond to the desired M_p circle, this point should be $-1 + j0 = -1$ rather than $-A$. The desired gain is that value of K which changes the scale so that this does become the -1 point; thus $K(-A) = -1$ or $K = 1/A$.

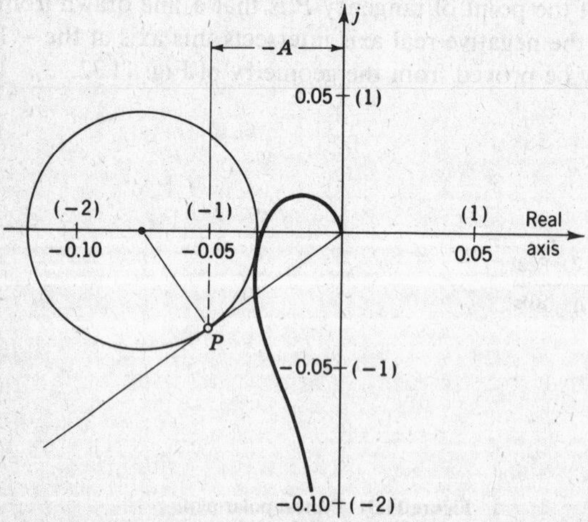

Figure 11.33 Determination of K to yield a desired M_p.

As is illustrated in Fig. 11.33, the perpendicular drawn from point P to the negative real axis intersects the negative real axis at a value of -0.05. However, this value should be -1. Multiplication of the scale by a factor of 20 (that is, $-0.05 \times 20 = -1$), as is shown in Fig. 11.33 by the numbers in parentheses, converts this point to the -1 point. Thus, the original function should have a gain of 20 in order that the circle drawn will be the desired M_p circle.

Illustrative example 1 Let it be desired to determine the gain K such that the unity-feedback system for which $G(s) = K/[s(1 + 0.1s)]$ will have a peak value $M_p = 1.4$. What values of ζ and ω_n should be used in approximating the transient behavior of this system?

SOLUTION First construct the polar plot for

$$\frac{G(j\omega)}{K} = \frac{1}{j\omega(1 + 0.1j\omega)}$$

as is shown in Fig. 11.34. The value of ψ is obtained from Eq. (11.70).

$$\psi = \sin^{-1}\frac{1}{M_p} = \sin^{-1}\frac{1}{1.4} = 45.6° \tag{11.71}$$

By trial and error, the circle which is tangent to both the $G(j\omega)/K$ plot and also to the line drawn at the angle $\psi = 45.6°$ is determined. The perpendicular drawn from point P intersects the negative real axis at the point $-A = -0.06$, or $A = 0.06$. Thus, the gain is $K = 1/0.06 = 16.7$.

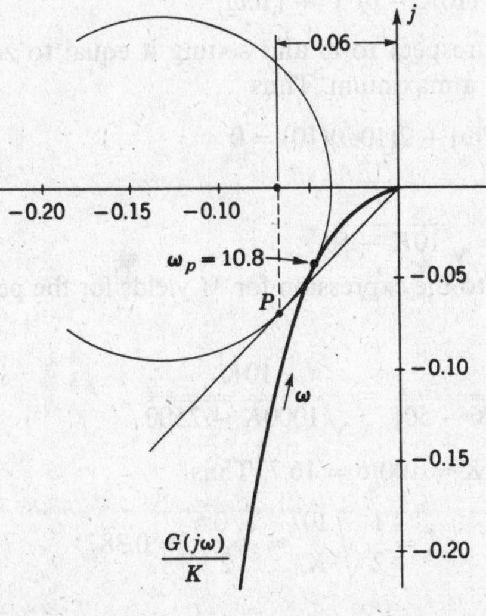

Figure 11.34 Polar plot for $G(j\omega)/K = 1/[j\omega(1 + j0.1\omega)]$.

From Fig. 11.21, for $M_p = 1.4$ the corresponding value of ζ is 0.387. From Fig. 11.34, $\omega_p = 10.8$; hence from Eq. (11.65) the value of ω_n is found to be

$$\omega_n = \frac{10.8}{\sqrt{1 - 2(0.387)^2}} = 12.9$$

Because the transfer function for this second-order system is known, the results of the preceding correlation between the frequency response and the transient response may be checked analytically. The open-loop transfer function is

$$G(s) = \frac{K}{s(1 + 0.1s)} = \frac{10K}{s(s + 10)}$$

The corresponding closed-loop transfer function for this unity-feedback system is

$$\frac{C(s)}{R(s)} = \frac{G(s)}{1 + G(s)} = \frac{10K}{s^2 + 10s + 10K}$$

From the characteristic function $(s^2 + 10s + 10K)$, it follows that $\omega_n^2 = 10K$ and $2\zeta\omega_n = 10$. Thus

$$\omega_n = \sqrt{10K} \quad \text{and} \quad \zeta = \frac{10}{2\omega_n} = \frac{1}{2}\sqrt{\frac{10}{K}}$$

Replacing s by $j\omega$ in the expression for the closed-loop transfer function gives

$$\frac{C(j\omega)}{R(j\omega)} = \frac{10K}{10K - \omega^2 + j10\omega}$$

The amplitude ratio M is

$$M = \left|\frac{C(j\omega)}{R(j\omega)}\right| = \frac{10K}{\sqrt{(10K - \omega^2)^2 + (10\omega)^2}}$$

Differentiating the denominator with respect to ω and setting it equal to zero yields the frequency ω_p at which M is a maximum. Thus

$$2(10K - \omega^2)(-2\omega) + 2(10\omega)(10) = 0$$

or

$$\omega = \omega_p = \sqrt{10K - 50}$$

Substitution of this value of $\omega = \omega_p$ into the expression for M yields for the peak value of the amplitude ratio M

$$M_p = \frac{10K}{\sqrt{(50)^2 + 100(10K - 50)}} = \frac{10K}{\sqrt{1000K - 2500}}$$

The value of K such that $M_p = 1.4$ is $K = 100/6 = 16.7$. Thus

$$\omega_n = \sqrt{10K} = \sqrt{167} = 12.9 \qquad \zeta = \frac{1}{2}\sqrt{\frac{10}{K}} = \frac{\sqrt{0.6}}{2} = 0.387$$

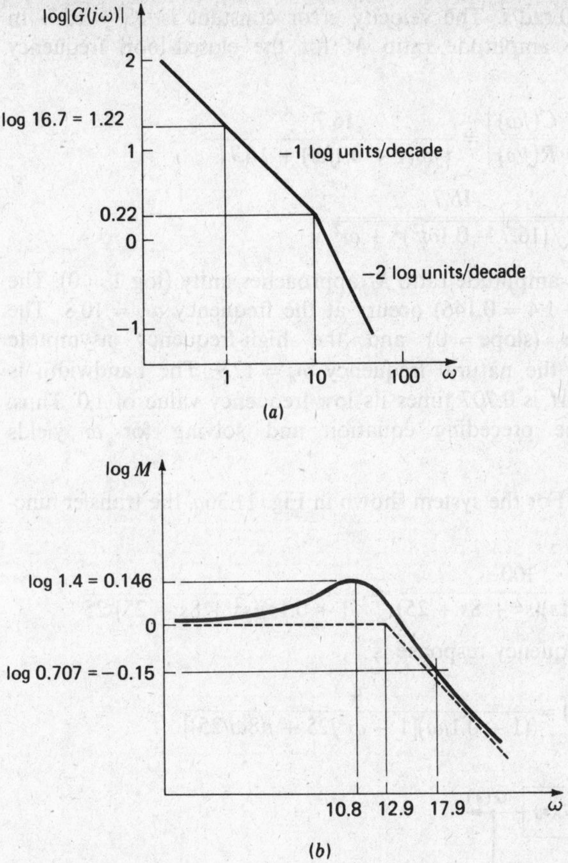

Figure 11.35 Log-magnitude plot of (*a*) open-loop frequency response and (*b*) closed-loop frequency response.

In Fig. 11.35*a* is shown the log-magnitude plot of the open-loop frequency response

$$G(j\omega) = \frac{16.7}{j\omega(1 + 0.1j\omega)}$$

The low-frequency asymptote is

$$|G(j\omega)| \approx \frac{16.7}{\omega} \qquad \omega \approx 0$$

The point on this asymptote at $\omega = 1$ is located by the coordinate, $\log|G(j\omega)| = \log 16.7 = 1.22$. The slope changes from -1 to -2 at the break frequency $1/\tau = 1/0.1 = 10$ rad/s. The velocity error constant is $K_v = 16.7$. In Fig. 11.35*b* is shown the amplitude ratio M for the closed-loop frequency response

$$M = \left|\frac{C(j\omega)}{R(j\omega)}\right| = \frac{16.7}{|j\omega(1 + 0.1j\omega) + 16.7|}$$

$$= \frac{16.7}{\sqrt{(16.7 - 0.1\omega^2)^2 + \omega^2}}$$

For small values of ω, the amplitude ratio M approaches unity ($\log 1 = 0$). The peak value $M_p = 1.4$ ($\log 1.4 = 0.146$) occurs at the frequency $\omega_p = 10.8$. The low-frequency asymptote (slope $= 0$) and the high-frequency asymptote (slope $= -2$) intersect at the natural frequency $\omega_n = 12.9$. The bandwidth is the value of ω such that M is 0.707 times its low-frequency value of 1.0. Thus, letting $M = 0.707$ in the preceding equation and solving for ω yields $\omega = \omega_b = 17.9$ rad/s.

Illustrative example 2 For the system shown in Fig. 11.36*a*, the transfer function $G(s)$ is

$$G(s) = \frac{100}{(1 + 0.1s)(s^2 + 8s + 25)} = \frac{4}{(1 + 0.1s)(s^2 + 8s + 25)/25}$$

The corresponding frequency response is

$$G(j\omega) = \frac{4}{(1 + 0.1j\omega)[1 - \omega^2/25 + j(8\omega/25)]}$$

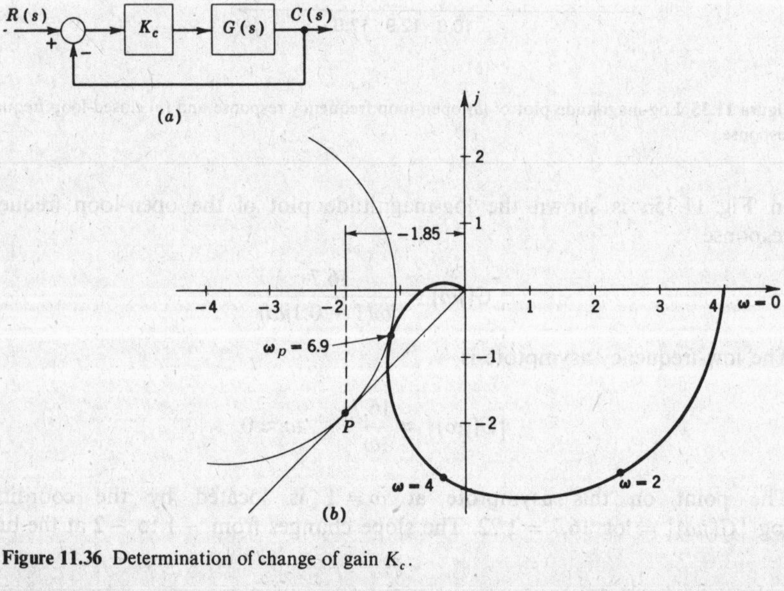

Figure 11.36 Determination of change of gain K_c.

1. Determine the factor K_c by which the gain of the system should be changed so that the resulting system will have an M_p of 1.4.
2. What values of ζ and ω_n should be used to approximate the transient behavior of this resulting system?

SOLUTION

1. For an M_p of 1.4, the tangent line is constructed at an angle of $\psi = 45.6°$. As shown in Fig. 11.36*b*, the perpendicular from the point *P* to the real axis intersects the real axis at the point -1.85. In order that this be the -1 point, the original scale must be changed by a factor of $1/1.85 = 0.54$. This is the factor K_c by which the gain of the system should be changed. Thus,

$$\text{New gain} = (K_c)(\text{original gain}) = (0.54)(4) = 2.16$$

2. For this type 0 system,

$$\frac{M_p}{K_0/(1+K_0)} = \frac{1.4}{2.16/3.16} = 2.05$$

From Fig. 11.21, the corresponding value of ζ is 0.25. The polar plot shows that $\omega_p = 6.9$. Hence from Eq. (11.65),

$$\omega_n = \frac{6.9}{\sqrt{1-2(0.25)^2}} = 7.37$$

This last example shows that if the $G(j\omega)$ plot is employed rather than the $G(j\omega)/K$ plot, then $-1/A$ is equal to the factor K_c by which the gain should be changed in order to obtain a desired M_p.

Log-Modulus Plots

In addition to log-magnitude and polar plots, another method of representing frequency-response information is log-modulus, or Nichols, plots.[1] The log-modulus curve is a plot of $\log|G(j\omega)|$ versus $\angle G(j\omega)$ for various values of angular velocity ω. The log-modulus curve for $G(j\omega)/K = 1/[j\omega(1+0.1j\omega)]$ is constructed in Fig. 11.37. From the equation for $G(j\omega)/K$ it is seen that, for a given angular velocity ω, the corresponding phase angle and amplitude ratio can be obtained. These values determine one point on the log-modulus plot. By repeating this process for other values of ω, the log-modulus plot of $G(j\omega)/K$ shown in Fig. 11.37 is obtained. Every point on the log-modulus plot corresponds to a certain value of $G(j\omega)$. Lines of constant M and constant α which are circles on the polar plot (Figs. 11.17 and 11.19) become contours when drawn on the log-modulus plot. These M and α contours are shown in Fig. 11.38. It is now shown how the log-modulus techniques may be used to determine the gain K so that a system will have a desired value of M_p.

[1] H. M. James, N. B. Nichols, and R. S. Phillips, "Theory of Servomechanisms," McGraw-Hill Book Company, New York, 1947.

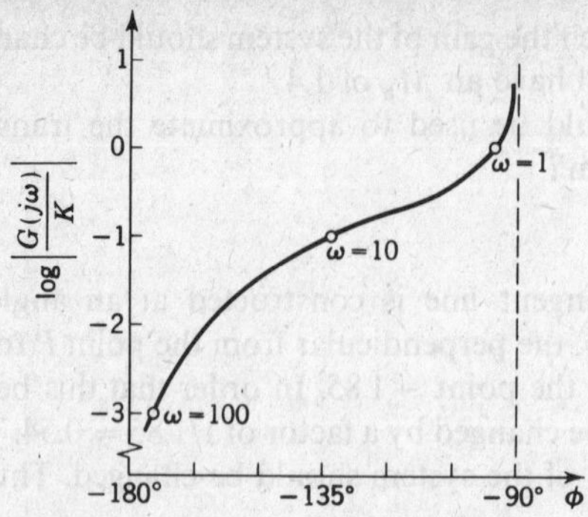

Figure 11.37 Log-modulus plot for $1/[j\omega(1 + j0.1\omega)]$.

Illustrative example 3 Same as Illustrative Example 1, except use log-modulus techniques.

SOLUTION In Fig. 11.39 is shown the log-modulus plot of $G(j\omega)/K$ corresponding to the polar plot of Fig. 11.34. Changing the gain K does not affect the phase angle, but merely moves the log-modulus curve vertically up for $K > 1$ and down for $K < 1$. In Fig. 11.39 it is to be noticed that the original function represented by the solid line must be moved up 1.22 log units so that it will be tangent to the desired M_p contour. Because $\log K = 1.22$, it follows that the required gain is $K = 16.7$. The values of ζ and ω_n are found as before.

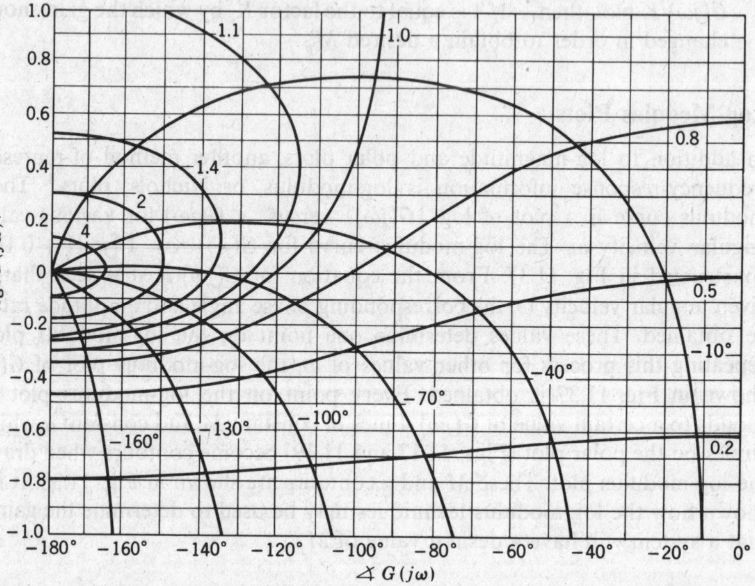

Figure 11.38 Log-modulus representation for lines of constant M and lines of constant α.

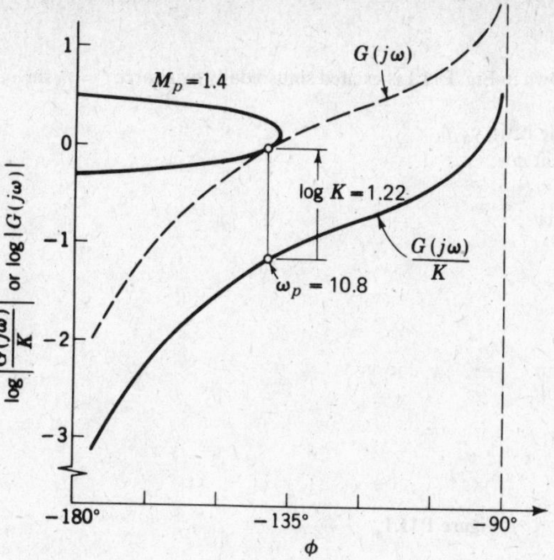

Figure 11.39 Determination of K for a desired M_p on the log-modulus plot.

Illustrative example 4 Same as Illustrative Example 2, except use log-modulus techniques.

SOLUTION In Fig. 11.40 is shown the log-modulus plot of $G(j\omega)$ corresponding to the polar plot of Fig. 11.36*b*. Because $\log K_c = -0.27$, then $K_c = 0.54$.

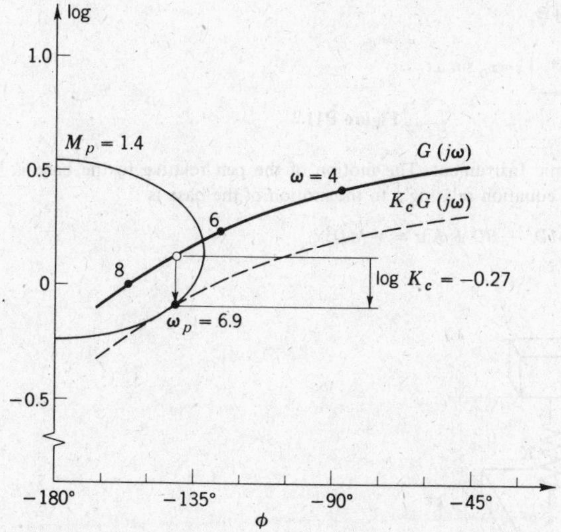

Figure 11.40 Determination of K_c for a desired M_p on the log-modulus plot.

PROBLEMS

11.1 Each of the mechanical systems shown in Fig. P11.1 is excited sinusoidally by a force $f = f_0 \sin \omega t$. For each system, determine

(*a*) The equation for the amplitude ratio y_0/f_0

(*b*) The equation for the phase shift ϕ

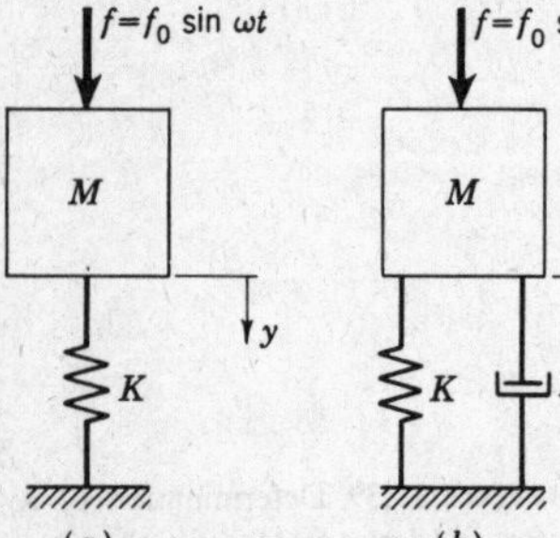

Figure P11.1

11.2 Each of the mechanical systems shown in Fig. P11.2 is excited sinusoidally by a motion of the support $x = x_0 \sin \omega t$. For each system, determine

(*a*) The equation for the amplitude ratio y_0/x_0

(*b*) The equation for the phase shift ϕ

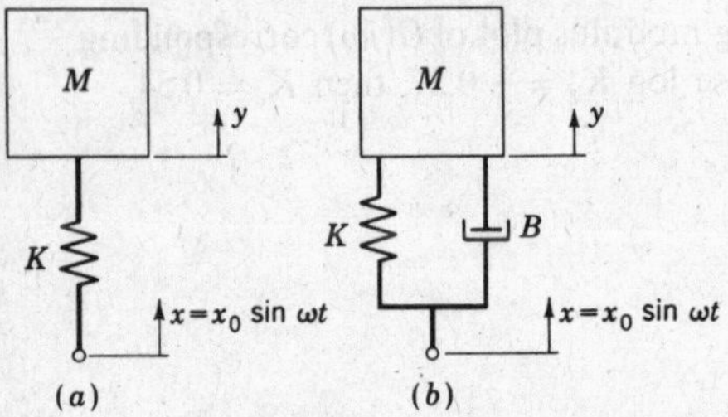

Figure P11.2

11.3 In Fig. P11.3 is shown a Seismic Instrument. The motion of the pen relative to the base is $z = y - x$. Show that the differential equation relating z to the motion of the base is

$$(MD^2 + BD + K)z = -MD^2x$$

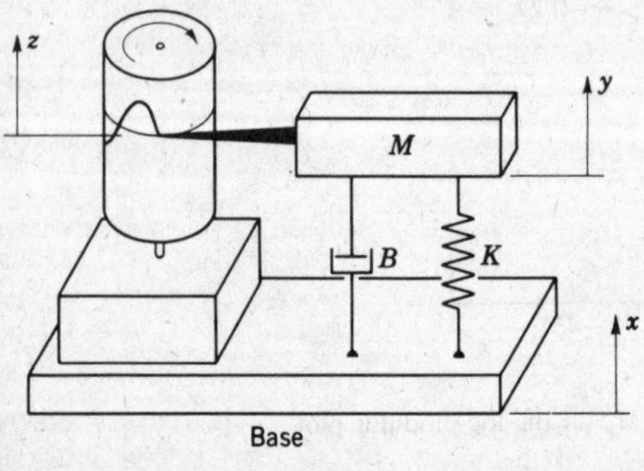

Figure P11.3

(*a*) Determine the equation for the amplitude ratio z_0/x_0 for the case in which the motion of the base is $x = x_0 \sin \omega t$.

(*b*) Show that for very large values of ω/ω_n, $z_0/x_0 = -1$. Such an instrument which may be used to measure displacements is called a vibrometer.

(*c*) Show that for small values of ω/ω_n,

$$\frac{z_0}{a_0} = \frac{1}{\omega_n^2}$$

where $$\ddot{x} = -x_0\omega^2 \sin \omega t = a_0 \sin \omega t$$

Such an instrument which measures acceleration is called an accelerometer.

11.4 For each of the following functions,

$$G(s) = \frac{10}{(1+s)(1+0.1s)}$$

$$G(s) = \frac{10(1+s)}{s(s^2+8s+100)/100}$$

(*a*) Draw the asymptotes for the log-magnitude diagram.

(*b*) Sketch the polar plot.

11.5 For each of the functions given below, evaluate $|G(j\omega)|$ and $\phi = \measuredangle G(j\omega)$ for $\omega = 4(1/0.25) = 16$, $\omega = 2(1/0.25) = 8$, $\omega = 1/0.25 = 4$, $\omega = \frac{1}{2}(1/0.25) = 2$, and $\omega = (\frac{1}{4})(1/0.25) = 1$. [Note that values of ω in the vicinity of the break frequency (1/0.25) yield the most significant information.] Construct the exact log-magnitude diagrams for each function, and sketch in the asymptotes.

(*a*) $G(j\omega) = \dfrac{10}{1+0.25j\omega}$ (*b*) $G(j\omega) = \dfrac{10}{j\omega(1+0.25j\omega)}$

(*c*) $G(j\omega) = \dfrac{10}{(1+0.25j\omega)^2}$

11.6 For the quadratic given below, evaluate $|G(j\omega)|$ and $\phi = \measuredangle G(j\omega)$ for values of $\omega/\omega_n = 4$, $\omega/\omega_n = 2$, $\omega/\omega_n = 1$, $\omega/\omega_n = \frac{1}{2}$, and $\omega/\omega_n = \frac{1}{4}$ and for $\zeta = 0.4$. Repeat for the case in which $\zeta = 0.1$. Construct the exact log-magnitude diagram, and sketch in the asymptotes.

$$G(j\omega) = \frac{10}{1-(\omega/\omega_n)^2 + j2\zeta(\omega/\omega_n)}$$

11.7 Construct the polar plot for each of the $G(j\omega)$ functions given in Probs. 11.5 and 11.6.

11.8 The asymptotes of the log-magnitude diagram for two $G(j\omega)$ functions are shown in Fig. P11.8. For each case, the value of ϕ is $-270°$ at very high frequencies. Determine the equation for $G(j\omega)$, and evaluate the gain K for each case.

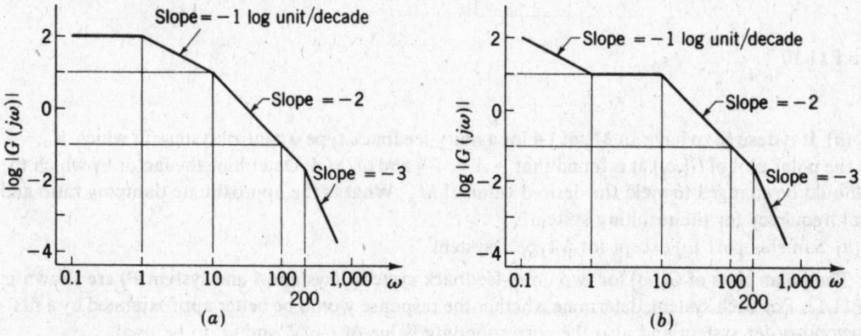

Figure P11.8

11.9 For the system shown in Fig. P11.9, the frequency-response curves for $G_1(j\omega)$ and $G_2(j\omega)$ were determined experimentally. For both $G_1(j\omega)$ and $G_2(j\omega)$ the phase angle at very high frequencies is $\phi_1 = \phi_2 = -90°$. Construct the log-magnitude plot for $G(j\omega) = G_1(j\omega)G_2(j\omega)$. Determine the equation for $G(j\omega)$, and evaluate the gain K.

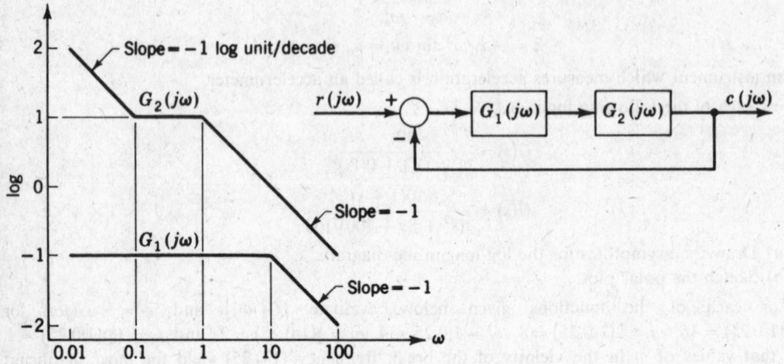

Figure P11.9

11.10 Convert each of the systems shown in Fig. P11.10 to an equivalent unity-feedback system.

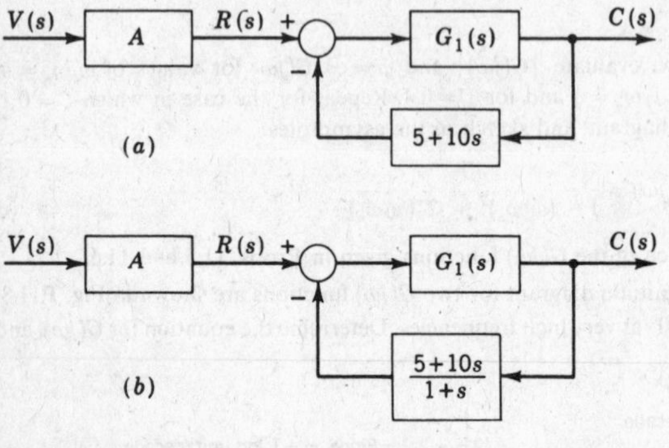

Figure P11.10

11.11 (*a*) It is desired to have an M_p of 1.4 for a unity-feedback type 0 control system in which $K_0 = 5$. From the polar plot of $G(j\omega)$, it is found that $-A = -\frac{1}{3}$ and $\omega_p = 4$. Determine the factor by which the gain should be changed to yield the desired value of M_p. What is the approximate damping ratio and natural frequency for the resulting system?

(*b*) Same as part (*a*) except for a type 1 system.

11.12 The polar plots of $G(j\omega)$ for two unity-feedback systems (system A and system B) are shown in Fig. P11.12. For each system, determine whether the response would be better approximated by a first- or a second-order system and also the corresponding value of τ or ζ and ω_n to be used.

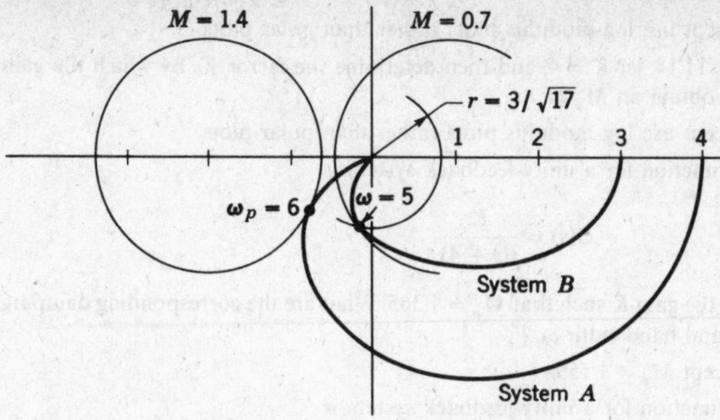

Figure P11.12

11.13 The open-loop transfer function for the system shown in Fig. P11.13 is

$$G(s) = \frac{3}{(s^2 + 2\zeta\omega_n s + \omega_n^2)/\omega_n^2} = \frac{3}{(s^2 + 8s + 4)/4}$$

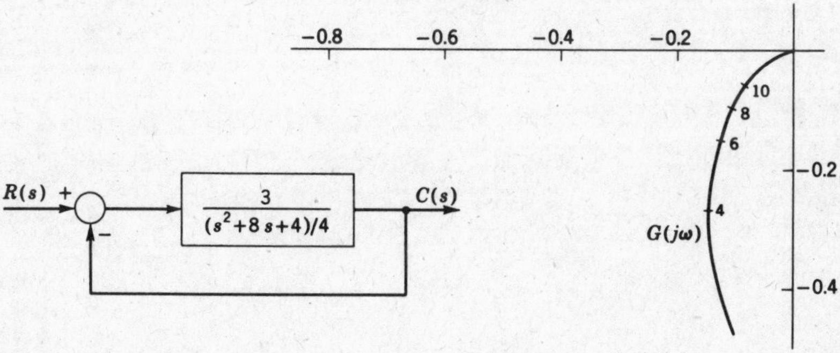

Figure P11.13

The polar plot is also shown.

(*a*) Determine the closed-loop transfer function $C(s)/R(s)$. What is the corresponding value of ζ and ω_n for this closed-loop transfer function?

(*b*) From the polar plot for $G(j\omega)$, determine the factor K_c by which the gain should be changed in order to yield an M_p of $2/\sqrt{3}$, ($\psi = \sin^{-1}\sqrt{3}/2 = 60°$). By using the correlation criterion between frequency response and transient response, determine the approximate value of ζ and ω_n for the resulting closed-loop system.

11.14 By use of polar plots, determine the value of K to yield an M_p of 1.4 for each of the following unity-feedback systems:

(*a*) $G(s) = \dfrac{K}{s(1 + 0.25s)}$ (*b*) $G(s) = \dfrac{K}{s(0.25s^2 + 0.40s + 1)}$

(*c*) $G(s) = \dfrac{K}{(1 + 0.25s)(0.25s^2 + 0.40s + 1)}$

11.15 Same as Prob. 11.14, except use log-modulus plots rather than polar plots.

11.16 For each system of Prob. 11.14, let $K = 4$, and then determine the factor K_c by which the gain should be changed in order to obtain an M_p of 1.4.

11.17 Same as Prob. 11.16, except use log-modulus plots rather than polar plots.

11.18 The open-loop transfer function for a unity-feedback system is

$$G(s) = \frac{K}{s(s+4)}$$

From the polar plot determine the gain K such that $M_p = 1.365$. What are the corresponding damping ratio ζ, natural frequency ω_n, and bandwidth ω_b?

11.19 Same as Prob. 11.18, except $M_p = 1.155$.

11.20 The open-loop transfer function for a unity-feedback system is

$$G(s) = \frac{K}{(s+4)^2}$$

From the polar plot determine the gain K such that $M_p = 1.365$. What are the corresponding values of the damping ratio ζ, natural frequency ω_n, and bandwidth ω_b?

11.21 Same as Prob. 11.20, except $M_p = 1.155$.

CHAPTER

TWELVE

SYSTEM COMPENSATION

Additional insight into the correlation between the shape of a polar plot and the dynamic behavior of a system is obtained by the Nyquist stability criterion.[1] For many design problems, it is not only necessary to change the gain K as discussed in the preceding chapter, but it is also necessary to reshape the polar plot. In this chapter, the significance of the Nyquist stability criterion is first presented, and then it is shown how system performance may be improved by reshaping the polar plot.

12.1 NYQUIST STABILITY CRITERION

Consider the function

$$F(s) = s - r$$

The vector from the origin to the point r and the vector from the origin to the point s are indicated in Fig. 12.1a. The term $s - r$ is represented by the vector from r to s. The point s travels around the closed path indicated as the path of values of s. That is, s goes along the path to point s_1, then to s_2, and then back to its original position. The point r is a fixed point located inside the path of values of s. The dotted vector from r to s_1 indicates the location of the $s - r$ vector when s is located at the point s_1. Similarly, the dotted vector from r to s_2 represents $s - r$ when s is at the point s_2. Figure 12.1a shows that when r is located inside the path of values of s, the vector $s - r$ rotates through one complete revolution as s

[1] H. Nyquist, Regeneration Theory, *Bell System Tech. J.*, **11**:126–147 (1932).

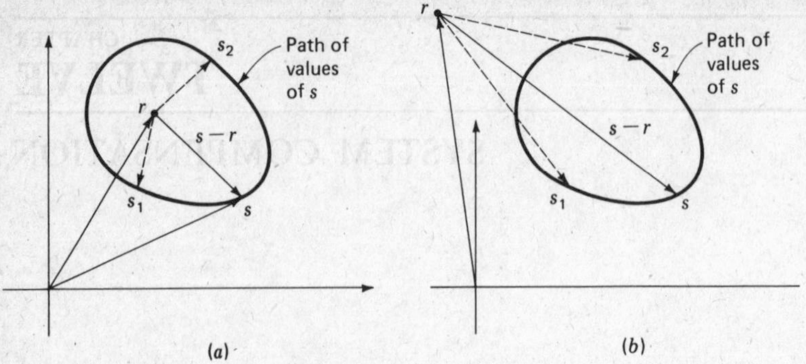

Figure 12.1 Rotation of $(s - r)$ vector when point r is (*a*) inside path of values of s; (*b*) outside path of values of s.

traverses the path from s to s_1 to s_2 and then back to s. Thus, the angle of the function $F(s) = s - r$ increases by 2π rad (one revolution) as s traverses the path of values of s.

For the reciprocal, $1/(s - r)$, the angle is the negative of the angle for the term $s - r$. Thus, the angle of the reciprocal decreases by 2π rad (one revolution) as s traverses the path.

The case in which r is located outside the path is shown in Fig. 12.1*b*. The vector $s - r$ goes from the point r to s. The angle of $(s - r)$ changes slightly as s travels from its initial position to the point s_1. In traveling from s_1 to the point s_2, the angle of the function returns to its initial value and then changes slightly in the opposite direction. In returning to its starting position the angle of the vector $s - r$ returns to its initial value. Thus, as s traverses the path of values, the vector $s - r$ eventually returns to its initial position, so that there is no net rotation of the vector.

Consider the function

$$F(s) = \frac{(s - z_1)(s - z_2) \cdots (s - z_m)}{(s - p_1)(s - p_2) \cdots (s - p_n)}$$

where $z_1, z_2, \ldots, z_m$ are the zeros of the function and $p_1, p_2, \ldots, p_n$ are the poles of the function. For each zero of $F(s)$ located within the path of values of s, the angle of the function $F(s)$ increases by 2π rad (one revolution) as s traverses the path. For each pole of $F(s)$ located within the path of values, the angle decreases by 2π rad as s traverses the path. Poles and zeros outside the path do not affect the angle.

The following general equation may be formulated:

$$N = Z - P \tag{12.1}$$

where P = number of poles of $F(s)$ located inside path of values for s
Z = number of zeros of $F(s)$ located inside path of values for s
N = net number of encirclements of origin of $F(s)$ plane

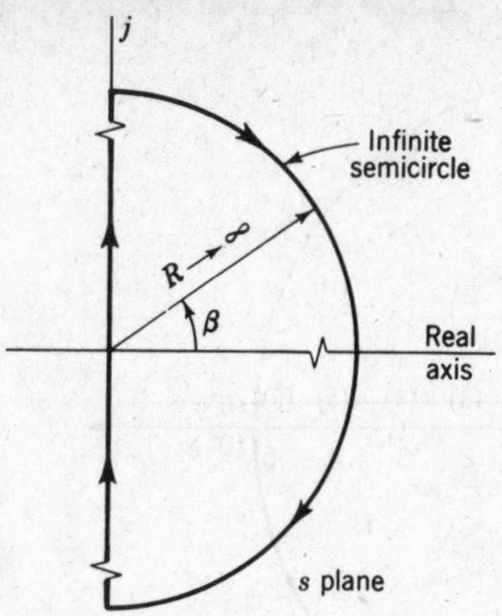

Figure 12.2 Path of values of s that encloses the entire right half plane.

When the net number of encirclements N is in the same sense as motion around the path of the s contour, an excess of zeros Z is indicated. The opposite sense signifies an excess of poles P. From Eq. (12.1), it follows that when N is in the same sense, N is a positive number. Similarly, when N is in the opposite sense, N is a negative number.[1] Generally, the path of values for s is traversed in a clockwise direction. Thus, for a net number of clockwise encirclements N is positive, and there is an excess of zeros. For a net number of counterclockwise encirclements N is negative, and there is an excess of poles.

For control work, the path of values for s is usually taken as shown in Fig. 12.2. This contour is seen to proceed from the origin up the imaginary axis to infinity; then an infinite semicircle ($R \to \infty$) sweeps around to the bottom of the imaginary axis; whence it returns to the origin. This contour, in effect, encloses the entire right half plane.

As is discussed in Chap. 6, a system is basically unstable if any zeros of the characteristic function are located in the right half plane. Note that

$$1 + G(s)H(s) = 1 + \frac{N_{G(s)} N_{H(s)}}{D_{G(s)} D_{H(s)}} = \frac{D_{G(s)} D_{H(s)} + N_{G(s)} N_{H(s)}}{D_{G(s)} D_{H(s)}} \tag{12.2}$$

It is apparent that the zeros of $1 + G(s)H(s)$ are the zeros of the characteristic function $(D_{G(s)} D_{H(s)} + N_{G(s)} N_{H(s)})$. Similarly, the poles of $1 + G(s)H(s)$ are the zeros of $D_{G(s)} D_{H(s)}$. By letting s assume the values indicated along the contour of Fig. 12.2, and by letting $F(s) = 1 + G(s)H(s)$, Eq. (12.1) becomes

$$Z = N + P \tag{12.3}$$

[1] Often Eq. (12.1) is written in the form $N = P - Z$. When this form is used, N is negative for a net number of encirclements in the same sense and is positive for the opposite sense.

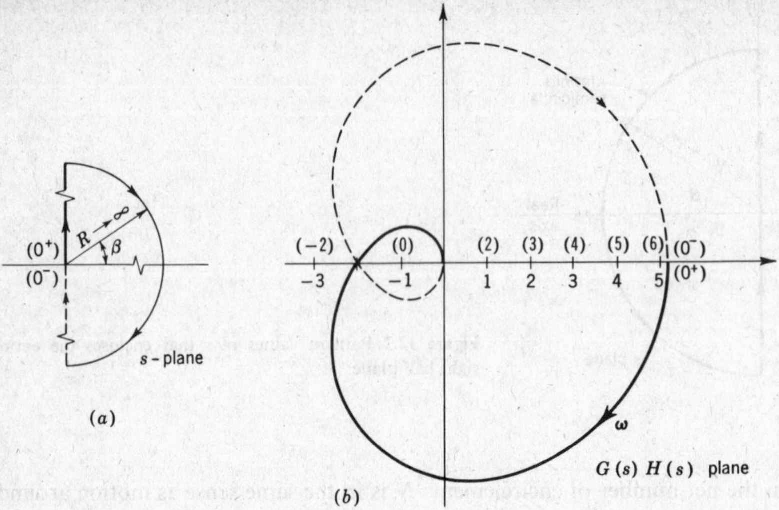

Figure 12.3 (*a*) Path of values of *s*; (*b*) map of $G(s)H(s)$ for a type 0 system.

where Z = number of zeros of characteristic function [i.e., zeros of $1 + G(s)H(s)$] in right half plane

P = number of zeros of $D_{G(s)}\, D_{H(s)}$ [that is, poles of $1 + G(s)H(s)$] in right half plane

N = net number of encirclements of origin of $1 + G(s)H(s)$ map

Because $G(s)H(s)$ is usually obtained in factored form, it is more convenient to construct the map for $G(s)H(s)$ rather than $1 + G(s)H(s)$. The effect of adding $+1$ to each point of the $G(s)H(s)$ map to obtain the $1 + G(s)H(s)$ map is accomplished simply by adding $+1$ to the scale of the real axis, as shown by the numbers in parentheses in Fig. 12.3*b*. It is seen that the -1 point of the $G(s)H(s)$ map corresponds to the origin of the $1 + G(s)H(s)$ map. Thus, N is equal to the net number of encirclements of the -1 point of the $G(s)H(s)$ plot. The application of the Nyquist stability criterion to type 0, type 1, and type 2 systems is now illustrated.

Type 0 System

Consider the following type 0 system:

$$G(s)H(s) = \frac{52}{(s+2)(s^2+2s+5)} = \frac{52/10}{(0.5s+1)(0.2s^2+0.4s+1)} \tag{12.4}$$

In Fig. 12.3*a* is shown the path of values of s that encloses the entire right half plane. Along the positive imaginary axis (indicated by the heavy line), s equals $j\omega$.

Thus, for this region Eq. (12.4) becomes

$$G(j\omega)H(j\omega) = \frac{5.2}{(1 + 0.5j\omega)(1 - 0.2\omega^2 + 0.4j\omega)}$$

This is the frequency response for the system. It is indicated by the heavy line in Fig. 12.3*b*. For values of s along the infinite semicircle of Fig. 12.3*a*, Eq. (12.4) becomes

$$G(s)H(s) = \lim_{R\to\infty} \frac{52}{(Re^{j\beta} + 2)(R^2e^{2j\beta} + 2Re^{j\beta} + 5)} = \lim_{R\to\infty} \frac{52}{R^3e^{3j\beta}} = 0$$

Thus, the $G(s)H(s)$ plot runs into the origin for values of s on the infinite semicircle.

For values of s on the negative imaginary axis (indicated by the dotted line), $s = -j\omega$. Because $G(-j\omega)H(-j\omega)$ is the complex conjugate of $G(j\omega)H(j\omega)$, the plot for $G(-j\omega)H(-j\omega)$ is obtained by reflecting the frequency response $G(j\omega)H(j\omega)$ about the real (horizontal) axis. The resulting $G(-j\omega)H(-j\omega)$ plot is shown dotted in Fig. 12.3*b*.

The poles of $1 + G(s)H(s)$ are the poles of $G(s)H(s)$. Because there are no poles of Eq. (12.4) in the right half plane (i.e., within the path of values of s), then $P = 0$. There are two clockwise encirclements of the -1 point of Fig. 12.3*b*; hence $N = 2$. Note that the -1 point of the $G(s)H(s)$ plot is the origin of the $1 + G(s)H(s)$ plot. Application of the Nyquist stability criterion to determine Z gives

$$Z = N + P = 2$$

Because there are two zeros of the characteristic function located in the right half plane, this system is basically unstable.

In general, for any type 0 system the frequency response $G(j\omega)H(j\omega)$ begins on the real axis for $\omega = 0$ and terminates at the origin for $\omega = \infty$. The $G(s)H(s)$ plot remains at the origin as the path of values of s traverses the infinite semicircle. For values of s along the negative imaginary axis (that is, $s = -j\omega$), then $G(-j\omega)H(-j\omega)$ is the complex conjugate of the frequency response $G(j\omega)H(j\omega)$.

At the intersection of a polar plot and the real axis the imaginary part of $G(j\omega)H(j\omega)$ is zero. The frequency at which a polar plot crosses the real axis is obtained by setting the imaginary part of $G(j\omega)H(j\omega)$ equal to zero. Substitution of this value of ω into the expression for $G(j\omega)H(j\omega)$ yields the location at which the polar plot crosses the real axis. Similarly, the location and frequency at which a polar plot crosses the imaginary axis are obtained by setting the real part of $G(j\omega)H(j\omega)$ equal to zero.

To illustrate this procedure, consider the system whose polar plot is shown in Fig. 12.3. The frequency response $G(j\omega)H(j\omega)$ may be written in the form

$$G(j\omega)H(j\omega) = \frac{5.2}{(1 + 0.5j\omega)(1 - 0.2\omega^2 + 0.4j\omega)} = \frac{5.2}{(1 - 0.4\omega^2) + j\omega(0.9 - 0.1\omega^2)}$$

Multiplying numerator and denominator by the complex conjugate of the denominator gives

$$G(j\omega)H(j\omega) = 5.2\frac{(1-0.4\omega^2) - j\omega(0.9-0.1\omega^2)}{(1-0.4\omega^2)^2 + \omega^2(0.9-0.1\omega^2)^2}$$

The imaginary part is zero when $0.9 - 0.1\omega^2 = 0$ or $\omega = 3$. Substitution of this value of ω into the expression for $G(j\omega)H(j\omega)$ yields the value at which $G(j\omega)H(j\omega)$ crosses the real axis. That is,

$$G(j3)H(j3) = \frac{5.2}{[1-0.4(3)^2] + j(0)} = \frac{5.2}{1-3.6} = -2.0$$

The real part is zero when $1 - 0.4\omega^2 = 0$ or $\omega = \sqrt{2.5} = 1.58$. This is the value of ω at which the polar plot crosses the imaginary axis. That is,

$$G(j2.5)H(j2.5) = \frac{5.2}{0 + j(1.58)(0.9-0.25)} = -\frac{j5.2}{1.027} = -j5.06$$

Type 1 System

For a type 1 system, there is an s term in the denominator of $G(s)H(s)$. For example, consider the system

$$G(s)H(s) = \frac{40}{s(s+1)(s+4)} = \frac{10}{s(1+s)(1+0.25s)} \tag{12.5}$$

In Fig. 12.4*a* it is to be noted that the assumed path of values of s excludes the origin. The reason for this will be made apparent in the following development.

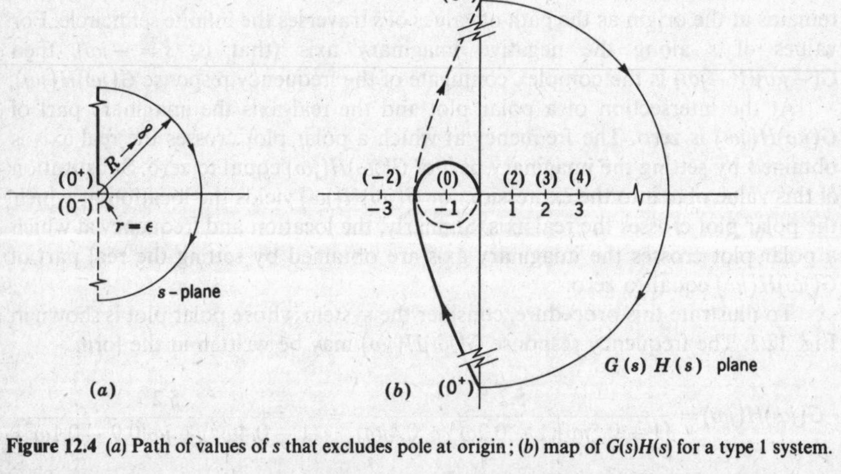

Figure 12.4 (*a*) Path of values of s that excludes pole at origin; (*b*) map of $G(s)H(s)$ for a type 1 system.

The portion of the plot for $s = j\omega$ as ω takes on values from $(0+)$ to $(+\infty)$ is indicated by the heavy line. This is the frequency response for the system

$$G(j\omega)H(j\omega) = \frac{10}{j\omega(1 + j\omega)(1 + 0.25j\omega)}$$

For values of s on the infinite semicircle, the $G(s)H(s)$ plot runs into the origin, that is,

$$G(s)H(s) = \lim_{R\to\infty} \frac{40}{Re^{j\beta}(Re^{j\beta} + 1)(Re^{j\beta} + 4)} \approx \lim_{R\to\infty} \frac{40}{R^3 e^{3j\beta}} = 0$$

The dotted portion of the $G(s)H(s)$ plot corresponds to $s = -j\omega$, where $G(-j\omega)H(-j\omega)$ is the complex conjugate of $G(j\omega)H(j\omega)$. To complete the Nyquist plot it is necessary to connect the ends corresponding to $\omega = (0-)$ and $\omega = (0+)$. If the path of values of s were to run through the origin, then for $s = 0$, the function $G(s)H(s)$ in Eq. (12.5) would be infinite and there would be no indication of how to join the $\omega = (0-)$ and $\omega = (0+)$ ends of the $G(s)H(s)$ plot in Fig. 12.4*b*. Hence a small semicircle of radius ε is constructed about the origin as illustrated in Fig. 12.4*a*. The equation for $G(s)H(s)$ is obtained by the substitution of $s = \varepsilon e^{j\beta}$, where β varies from $-90°$ to $0°$ to $+90°$ as s traverses the small semicircle. Hence

$$G(s)H(s) = \lim_{\varepsilon\to 0} \frac{40}{\varepsilon e^{j\beta}(\varepsilon e^{j\beta} + 1)(\varepsilon e^{j\beta} + 4)} \approx \frac{40}{\varepsilon e^{j\beta}(1)(4)} \approx \frac{10}{\varepsilon} e^{-j\beta} \approx \infty e^{-j\beta} \tag{12.6}$$

Thus $G(s)H(s)$ is an infinite semicircle. As β goes from $-90°$ to $0°$ to $+90°$, then $G(s)H(s)$ traverses an infinite semicircle from $+90°$ to $0°$ to $-90°$. The complete Nyquist plot is shown in Fig. 12.4*b*.

Because the origin has been excluded from the path of values of s, then from Eq. (12.5) it follows that there are no poles of $G(s)H(s)$ within the path of values of s, and thus $P = 0$. As indicated in Fig. 12.4*b*, there are two clockwise encirclements of the -1 point, so that $N = 2$. Application of the Nyquist stability criterion gives

$$Z = N + P = 2$$

Thus, there are two roots of the characteristic equation in the right half plane. Consequently the system is unstable.

The general procedure for constructing the complete Nyquist plot for a type 1 system is summarized as follows. A type 1 system always has a pole at the origin, so that it is necessary to exclude the origin from the path of values of s, as indicated in Fig. 12.4*a*. The frequency response $G(j\omega)H(j\omega)$ corresponds to values of $s = j\omega$ as the path of values of s traverses the positive imaginary axis from $0+$ to $+\infty$. For values of s on the infinite semicircle, the $G(s)H(s)$ plot runs into the origin. As s transverses the negative imaginary axis, then $G(s)H(s) = G(-j\omega)H(-j\omega)$ is the complex conjugate of the frequency response.

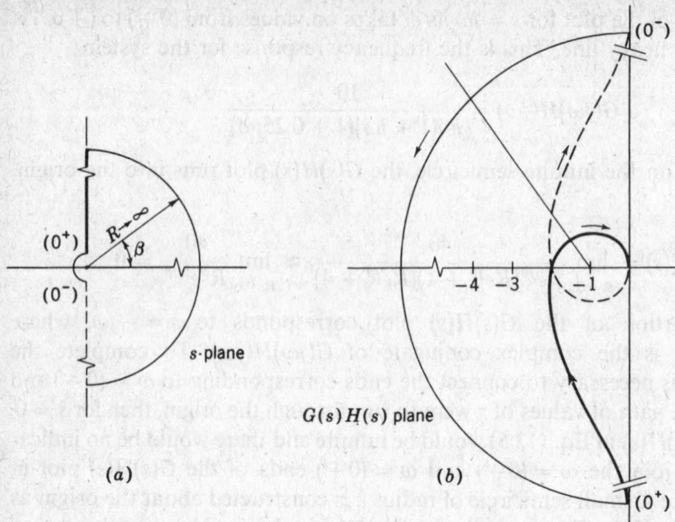

Figure 12.5 (*a*) Path of values of *s* that includes pole at origin; (*b*) map of $G(s)H(s)$ for a type 1 system.

This complex conjugate of the frequency response is obtained by "flipping" the frequency-response plot about the horizontal axis. To complete the Nyquist plot, the ends at $\omega = (0-)$ and $\omega = (0+)$ are joined by assuming values of *s* on the small semicircle of radius ε. Equation (12.6) holds for any type 1 system, that is,

$$G(s)H(s) = \infty e^{-j\beta}$$

This is an infinite semicircle.

In the application of the Nyquist stability criterion it would make no difference if the origin were included in the path of values of *s* as shown in Fig. 12.5*a* or if it were excluded as shown in Fig. 12.4*a*. For the case in which the origin is included, β varies from $-90°$ to $-180°$ to $-270°$ as *s* traverses the small semicircle. Thus from Eq. (12.6), the infinite semicircle goes from 90° to 180° to 270°. The resultant $G(s)H(s)$ plot is shown in Fig. 12.5*b*. For this case, $N = +1$. Because $s = 0$ is a pole of $G(s)H(s)$ which is now included in the path of values of *s*, $P = 1$. Hence

$$Z = N + P = 1 + 1 = 2$$

Thus, the same result ($Z = 2$) is obtained whether the pole at the origin is included in or excluded from the path of values of *s*. When a pole of $G(s)H(s)$ occurs at the origin ($s = 0$), it is customary to exclude the origin from the path of values of *s* as indicated in Fig. 12.4*a*.

A direct method for determining the net encirclements *N* of the -1 point is to draw a radial line from the -1 point out through the plot as illustrated in

Fig. 12.5*b*. Note the direction of the arrow on the loci at each point where the radial line crosses the loci. In Fig. 12.5*b*, the radial line crosses the loci three times. At two crossings the direction of the arrow is such as to rotate the radial line in a clockwise direction. At the third crossing the direction is such as to rotate the radial line in a counterclockwise direction. The value of N is the number of crossings at which the arrow on the loci tends to rotate the radial line clockwise minus the number of loci crossings at which the arrow tends to rotate the radial line counterclockwise. Thus, for this case $N = 2 - 1 = 1$. The radial line may be drawn at any angle from the -1 point.

Type 2 System

A type 2 system is characterized by the fact that there is a double pole at the origin. For example, consider the system

$$G(s)H(s) = \frac{4(1+s)}{s^2(1+0.1s)} \tag{12.7}$$

As for a type 1 system, the path of values of s is taken to exclude the origin, as shown in Fig. 12.6*a*. The frequency-response plot for this system is indicated by the heavy line in Fig. 12.6*b*. The $G(s)H(s)$ plot runs into the origin as s traverses the infinite semicircle. The $G(-j\omega)H(-j\omega)$ plot is merely the complex conjugate of the frequency response.

For values of s on the small semicircle which excludes the origin,

$$G(s)H(s) = \lim_{\varepsilon \to 0} \frac{4(1+\varepsilon e^{j\beta})}{\varepsilon^2 e^{2j\beta}(1+0.1\varepsilon e^{j\beta})} \approx \frac{4}{\varepsilon^2} e^{-j2\beta} \approx \infty e^{-j2\beta} \tag{12.8}$$

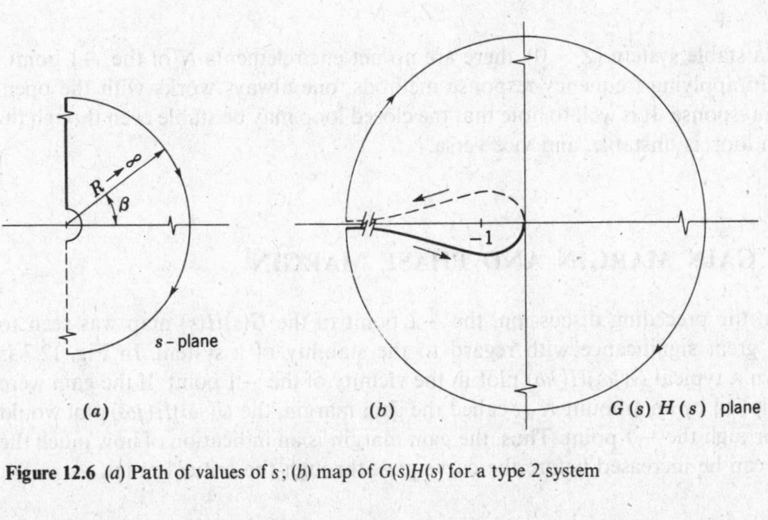

Figure 12.6 (*a*) Path of values of s; (*b*) map of $G(s)H(s)$ for a type 2 system

Equation (12.8) is valid for any type 2 system. As s traverses the small semicircle from $0-$ to $0+$, then β goes from $-90°$ to $0°$ to $+90°$. The corresponding infinite semicircle changes from $+180°$ to $0°$ to $-180°$ (i.e., the angle of the infinite semicircle is -2β).

For the $G(s)H(s)$ plot described by Eq. (12.7), there are no poles within the path of values of s, so that P is zero. Because there are no encirclements of the -1 point of Fig. 12.6*b*, N is also zero. Thus, $Z = N + P = 0$, so that the system is basically stable.

When the polar plot for $G(s)H(s)$ goes through the -1 point, the system is on the borderline between being stable and unstable. For this case the characteristic equation has roots on the imaginary axis. For example, from Fig. 12.3*b*, it is to be noticed that the polar plot crosses the negative real axis at a value of -2. If the gain were halved, the polar plot would go through the -1 point. For this case, the characteristic equation becomes

$$(s+2)(s^2+2s+5)+26 = s^3+4s^2+9s+36$$
$$= (s+4)(s^2+9) \tag{12.9}$$

Two roots, $s = \pm j3$, are seen to lie on the imaginary axis.

Similarly, from Fig. 12.4*b*, it is to be noticed that the polar plot crosses the negative real axis at -2, also. Halving the gain yields for the characteristic equation

$$s(s+1)(s+4)+20 = s^3+5s^2+4s+20$$
$$= (s+5)(s^2+4) \tag{12.10}$$

Two roots, $s = \pm j2$, are seen to lie on the imaginary axis.

For most systems, the open loop is stable. For this case, all the zeros of $D_G D_H$ lie in the left half plane ($P = 0$). Thus, the Nyquist stability criterion reduces to

$$Z = N$$

For a stable system ($Z = 0$), there are no net encirclements N of the -1 point.

In applying frequency-response methods, one always works with the open-loop response. It is well to note that the closed loop may be stable even though the open loop is unstable, and vice versa.

12.2 GAIN MARGIN AND PHASE MARGIN

From the preceding discussion, the -1 point of the $G(s)H(s)$ map was seen to have great significance with regard to the stability of a system. In Fig. 12.7 is shown a typical $G(j\omega)H(j\omega)$ plot in the vicinity of the -1 point. If the gain were multiplied by an amount K_M, called the gain margin, the $G(j\omega)H(j\omega)$ plot would go through the -1 point. Thus, the gain margin is an indication of how much the gain can be increased before the curve goes through the critical point.

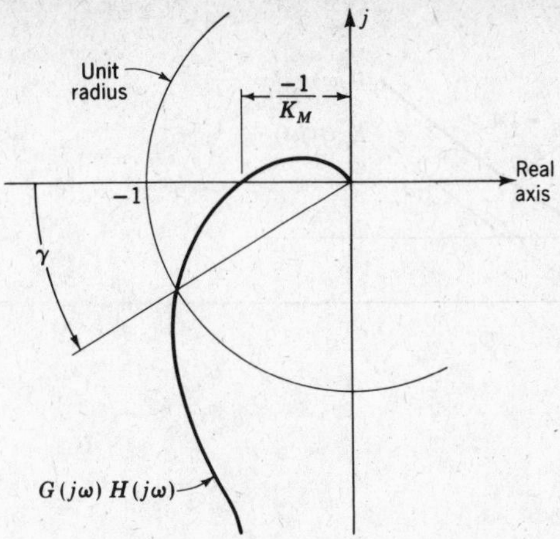

Figure 12.7 Gain margin and phase margin on the polar plot.

The angle γ in Fig. 12.7 is the angle measured from the negative real axis to where the polar plot crosses a circle of unit radius. If the angle γ is zero, the polar plot goes through the -1 point. The angle γ, called the phase margin, is thus seen to be another indication or measure of the closeness of the polar plot to the critical point.

Log-Modulus Plots

In Fig. 12.8 is shown the log-modulus plot corresponding to Fig. 12.7. Because log $1 = 0$, the $-1 + j0$ point on the log-modulus plot is defined by the ordinate $\log|G(j\omega)H(j\omega)| = 0$ and abscissa $\phi = -180°$. From Fig. 12.8, the vertical distance that the $G(j\omega)H(j\omega)$ plot may be raised before it goes through the -1 point is $\log K_M$.

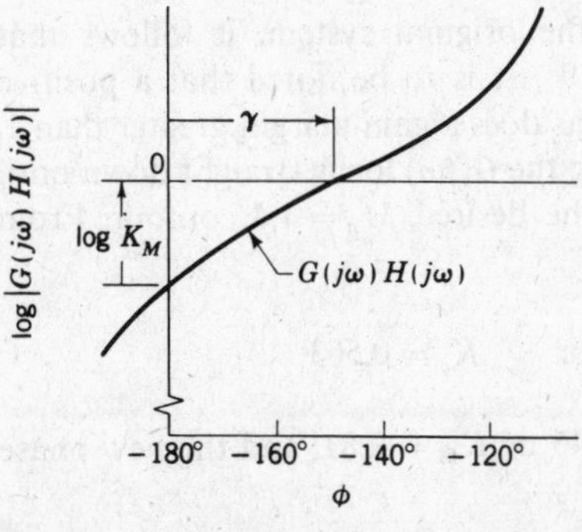

Figure 12.8 Gain margin and phase margin on the log-modulus plot.

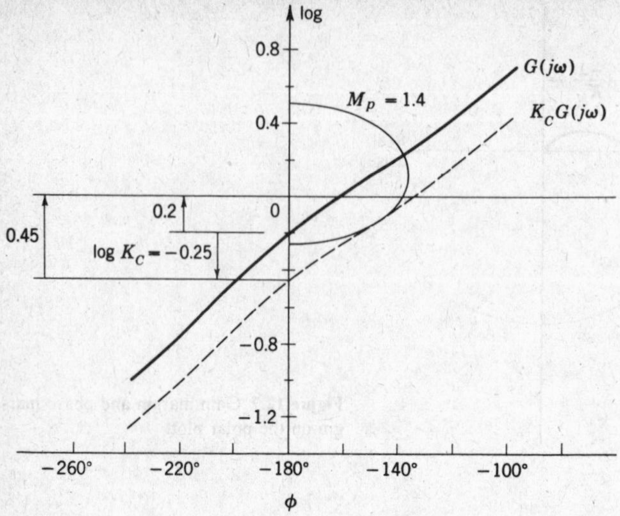

Figure 12.9 Log-modulus plot for a system.

The value of the phase margin may be obtained from a log-modulus plot as follows: The horizontal line in Fig. 12.8 of log $|G(j\omega)H(j\omega)| = \log 1 = 0$ corresponds to the unit circle of Fig. 12.7. The angle γ between the point where this horizontal line intersects the $G(j\omega)H(j\omega)$ plot and the value $\phi = -180°$ is the phase margin γ.

Illustrative example 1 The log-modulus plot of $G(j\omega)$ for a unity-feedback system is shown in Fig. 12.9. What is the value of the gain margin and the phase margin for this system? By what factor K_c should the gain of the system be changed so that M_p will be 1.4? What is the new value for the gain margin and the phase margin?

SOLUTION From the $G(j\omega)$ plot for the original system, it follows that $\log K_M = 0.2$, or $K_M = 1.59$, and $\gamma = 19°$. It is to be noted that a positive phase margin indicates a stable system, as does a gain margin greater than 1.

The factor K_c is obtained by moving the $G(j\omega)$ locus straight down until the new locus $K_c G(j\omega)$ is tangent to the desired $M_p = 1.4$ contour. From Fig. 12.9, it follows that

$$\log K_c = -0.25 \qquad \text{or} \qquad K_c = 0.563$$

The new gain margin is $\log K_M = +0.45$ or $K_M = 2.81$, and the new phase margin is $\gamma = 45°$.

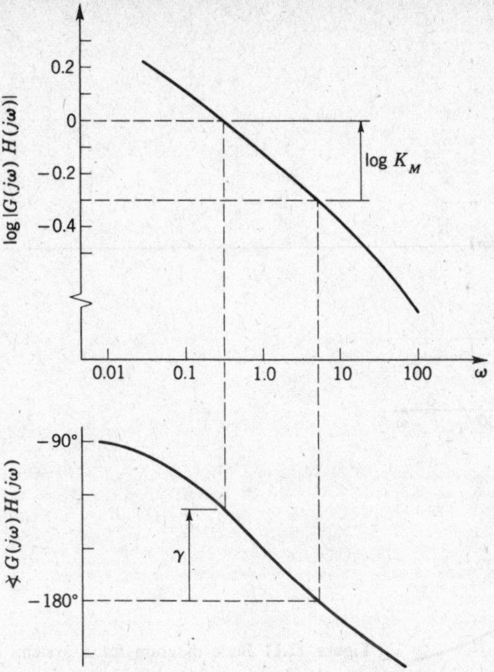

Figure 12.10 Gain margin and phase margin on the Bode diagram.

Bode Diagrams

In Fig. 12.10 is shown a Bode diagram. By entering the phase angle plot at $\phi = -180°$, it is noted that the corresponding value of log $|G(j\omega)H(j\omega)| = -0.3$. Hence, the gain of the system may be increased by $+0.3$ log unit before the $G(j\omega)H(j\omega)$ curve goes through the -1 point. Thus, the value of log K_M may be represented graphically as illustrated in Fig. 12.10.

The unit circle of the polar plot corresponds to the horizontal line through the log-magnitude plot at log $|G(j\omega)H(j\omega)| = 0$, in which case $|G(j\omega)H(j\omega)| = 1$. The phase margin γ is the difference between the corresponding angle and the angle $\phi = -180°$, as is illustrated in the angle diagram of Fig. 12.10.

Illustrative example 2 In Fig. 12.11 is shown the Bode diagram for a control system. By what factor K_c should the gain of the system be changed so that the resulting phase margin is 45°?

SOLUTION Entering the angle plot at $\phi = -180° + \gamma = -135°$, the corresponding value of log $|G(j\omega)H(j\omega)|$ is 0.3. To have a phase margin of 45°, the magnitude diagram must be lowered by 0.3 log unit. Thus,

$$\log K_c = -0.3 = 9.7 - 10.0$$

or $$K_c = 0.5$$

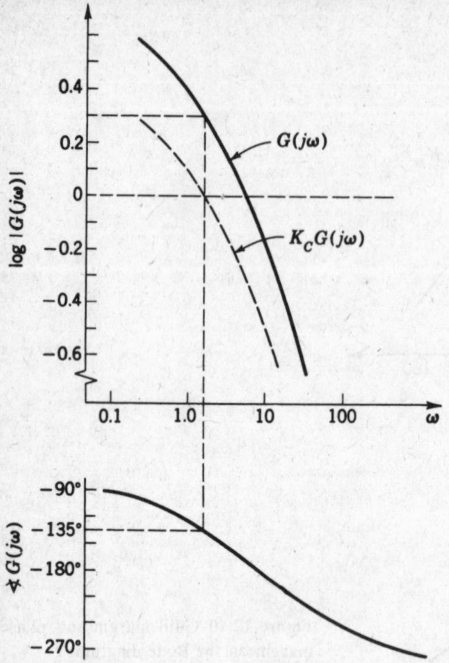

Figure 12.11 Bode diagram for a system.

In Sec. 11.7 the transient-response parameters ζ and ω_n were related to the frequency-response parameter M_p. This correlation is limited to use with polar or log-modulus plots. That is, M circles may be drawn on polar plots and M contours on log-modulus plots, but it is impossible to construct M lines on Bode diagrams because the magnitudes and phase are on separate plots. When designing with Bode diagrams, the transient and frequency responses are correlated by relating ζ and ω_n to the phase margin.

Correlation between ζ, ω_n, and Phase Margin

It is now shown that the transient-response parameters ζ and ω_n may also be related to the phase margin γ. Although the following analysis is for a second-order type 1 system, the results yield good approximations for higher-order systems and for systems of other type numbers, such as a type 0 or a type 2 system.

The closed-loop transfer function for the system of Fig. 11.20 is

$$\frac{C(s)}{R(s)} = \frac{K/\tau}{s^2 + (1/\tau)s + K/\tau} = \frac{\omega_n^2}{s^2 + 2\zeta\omega_n s + \omega_n^2} \tag{12.11}$$

where $\omega_n^2 = K/\tau$

$2\zeta\omega_n = 1/\tau$

The open-loop frequency response is

$$G(j\omega) = \frac{K}{j\omega(1 + j\tau\omega)} \tag{12.12}$$

By letting ω_c be the value of ω when $|G(j\omega)| = 1$, then

$$|G(j\omega)| = \frac{K}{\omega_c\sqrt{1 + \tau^2\omega_c^2}} = 1$$

Squaring gives

$$\tau^2\omega_c^4 + \omega_c^2 - K^2 = 0$$

or

$$\left(\frac{\tau}{K}\right)^2 \omega_c^4 + \frac{1}{K^2}\omega_c^2 - 1 = 0$$

Because $\tau/K = 1/\omega_n^2$ and $K = \omega_n^2\tau = \omega_n^2/2\zeta\omega_n = \omega_n/2\zeta$, then

$$\left(\frac{\omega_c}{\omega_n}\right)^4 + 4\zeta^2\left(\frac{\omega_c}{\omega_n}\right)^2 - 1 = 0$$

Application of the quadratic equation yields

$$\left(\frac{\omega_c}{\omega_n}\right)^2 = \sqrt{4\zeta^4 + 1} - 2\zeta^2 \tag{12.13}$$

The preceding expression relates ζ and the ratio ω_c/ω_n. A plot of this relationship is shown in Fig. 12.12*a*.

The phase angle γ is

$$\gamma = 180° + \measuredangle G(j\omega_c)$$

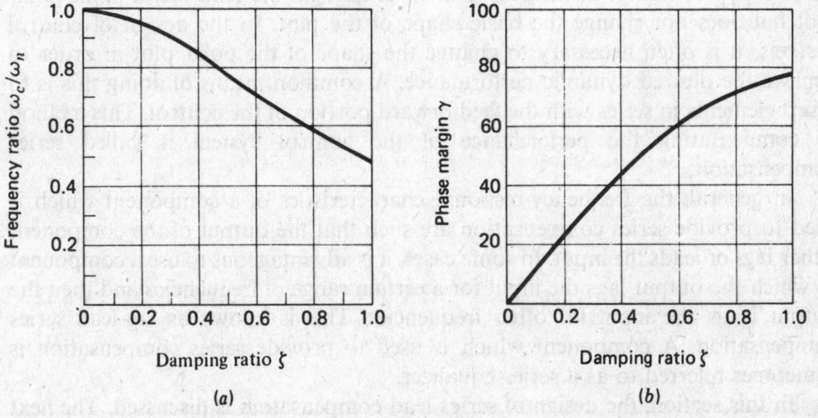

Figure 12.12 Correlation between ζ, ω_n, and phase margin γ. (*a*) Plot of (ω_c/ω_n) versus ζ; (*b*) plot of γ versus ζ.

where $\measuredangle G(j\omega_c)$ is the angle of $G(j\omega)$ at which the polar plot crosses the unit circle. From Eq. (12.12), it follows that

$$\measuredangle G(j\omega_c) = 0° - 90° - \tan^{-1} \tau\omega_c$$

Hence

$$\gamma = 90° - \tan^{-1} \tau\omega_c = \tan^{-1} \frac{1}{\tau\omega_c} = \tan^{-1} \frac{2\zeta}{\omega_c/\omega_n}$$

$$\gamma = \tan^{-1} \frac{2\zeta}{\sqrt{-2\zeta^2 + \sqrt{4\zeta^4 + 1}}} \tag{12.14}$$

In Fig. 12.12*b* is shown a plot of γ versus ζ. If γ is known, then the value of ζ may be determined from this plot. The corresponding value of ω_c/ω_n may then be ascertained from Fig. 12.12*a*.

Illustrative example 3 Determine the value of ζ and ω_n for the system shown by the dotted line in Fig. 12.11.

SOLUTION For this system, the phase margin γ is 45°. From Fig. 12.12*b*, the corresponding value of ζ is 0.425. Next, from Fig. 12.12*a*, the ratio ω_c/ω_n is found to be 0.84. The frequency ω_c is the value of ω at which $\log |G(j\omega)H(j\omega)| = 0$. From Fig. 12.11, it is found that $\omega_c = 1.7$, and thus $\omega_n = 2.03$.

12.3 LEAD COMPENSATION

In Sec. 11.8, it is shown how the gain K is selected in order to obtain a desired value of M_p. A change in the gain K in effect changes the scale factor of the polar plot but does not change the basic shape of the plot. In the design of control systems, it is often necessary to change the shape of the polar plot in order to achieve the desired dynamic performance. A common means of doing this is to insert elements in series with the feedforward portion of the control. This method of compensating the performance of the control system is called series compensation.

In general, the frequency-response characteristics of a component which is used to provide series compensation are such that the output of the component either lags or leads the input. In some cases, it is advantageous to use a component in which the output lags the input for a certain range of frequencies and then the output leads the input for other frequencies. This is known as lag-lead series compensation. A component which is used to provide series compensation is sometimes referred to as a series equalizer.

In this section, the design of series lead compensators is discussed. The next two sections consider series lag compensators and series lag-lead compensators, respectively.

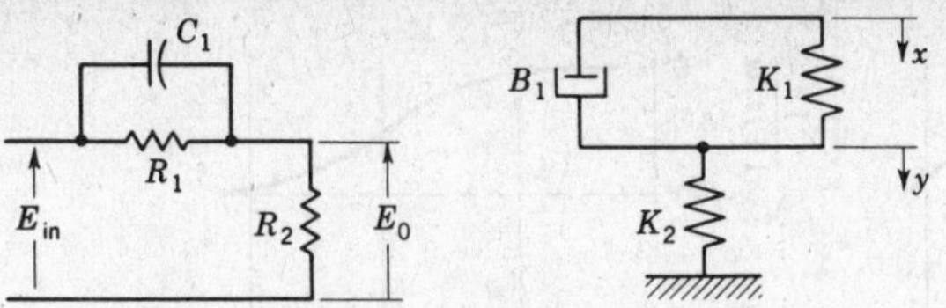

$$\frac{E_o(s)}{E_{in}(s)} = \frac{\tau_2}{\tau_1}\frac{1+\tau_1 s}{1+\tau_2 s} \qquad \frac{Y(s)}{X(s)} = \frac{\tau_2}{\tau_1}\frac{1+\tau_1 s}{1+\tau_2 s}$$

$$\tau_1 = R_1C_1 \qquad \tau_1 = \frac{B_1}{K_1}$$

$$\tau_2 = \frac{R_2}{R_1+R_2}R_1C_1 \qquad \tau_2 = \frac{B_1}{K_1+K_2}$$

$$= \frac{R_2}{R_1+R_2}\tau_1 \qquad = \frac{K_1}{K_1+K_2}\tau_1$$

Figure 12.13 An electrical and a mechanical component used to obtain phase lead.

In Fig. 12.13 is shown both an electrical and a mechanical component which have the general phase-lead characteristic given by

$$\frac{E_o(s)}{E_{in}(s)} = \frac{Y(s)}{X(s)} = \frac{\tau_2}{\tau_1}\frac{1+\tau_1 s}{1+\tau_2 s} \qquad \tau_1 > \tau_2$$

The frequency response for the preceding transfer function is

$$\frac{E_o(j\omega)}{E_{in}(j\omega)} = \frac{Y(j\omega)}{X(j\omega)} = \frac{\tau_2}{\tau_1}\frac{1+j\tau_1\omega}{1+j\tau_2\omega} \qquad \tau_1 > \tau_2 \tag{12.15}$$

Because the steady-state gain ($\omega \approx 0$) is τ_2/τ_1, additional amplification equal to τ_1/τ_2 must be provided to maintain the original system gain.

The construction of the log-magnitude diagram for Eq. (12.15) in which $\tau_2 = \tau_1/10$ is illustrated in Fig. 12.14. For the numerator, the break frequency occurs at $\omega = 1/\tau_1$, and for the denominator the break frequency occurs at $\omega = 1/\tau_2 = 10/\tau_1$. Adding the diagram for the numerator to that for the denominator yields the resultant diagram for phase lead.

The use of a phase-lead component placed in series with the feedforward portion of a control system to improve stability is now illustrated. In Fig. 12.15 the dashed curve is the frequency response $G(j\omega)H(j\omega)$ of the uncompensated control system. This control is one that would inherently be unstable. The addition of the lead compensator $G_c(j\omega)$ to reshape the high-frequency portion of the polar plot is shown by the solid-line curves of Fig. 12.15. It is to be noted that lead compensation rotates a typical vector such as that for $\omega = 2$ in a counterclockwise direction away from the -1 point. It is also to be noted that the length of this vector is increased. Because of the counterclockwise rotation of a typical vector, the effect of lead compensation is to increase ω_p. This tends to increase the speed of response of the system.

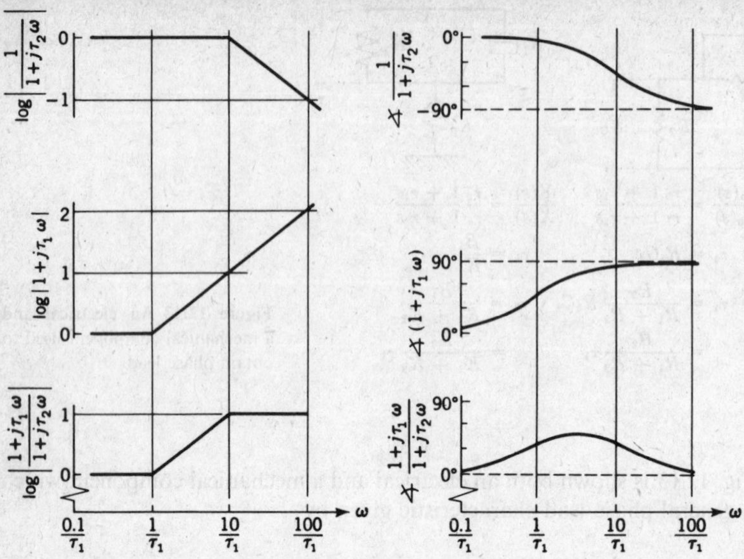

Figure 12.14 Construction of log-magnitude diagram for $(1 + j\tau_1\omega)/(1 + j\tau_2\omega)$ when $\tau_2 = \tau_1/10$.

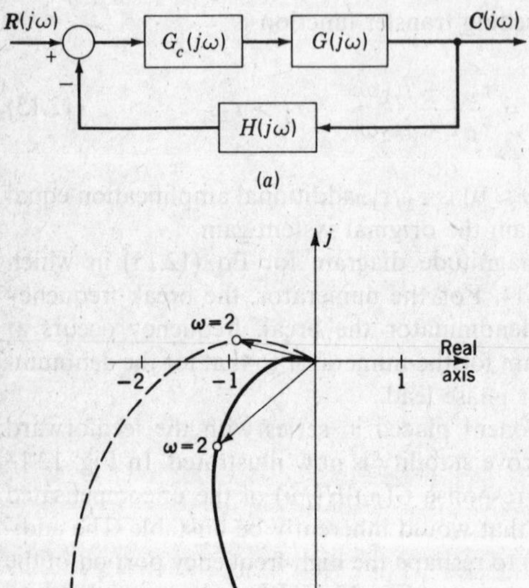

Figure 12.15 Use of phase lead to reshape a polar plot.

To select a lead compensator, it is necessary to be familiar with some of the general properties which are now derived. The phase shift ϕ due to a lead compensator is

$$\phi = \measuredangle \frac{1 + j\tau_1 \omega}{1 + j\tau_2 \omega} = \tan^{-1} \tau_1 \omega - \tan^{-1} \tau_2 \omega \tag{12.16}$$

Differentiating with respect to ω gives

$$\frac{d\phi}{d\omega} = \frac{\tau_1}{1 + (\tau_1 \omega)^2} - \frac{\tau_2}{1 + (\tau_2 \omega)^2}$$

Setting this derivative equal to zero and solving for ω yields the frequency $\omega = \omega_m$ at which the phase shift is a maximum. That is,

$$\tau_1[1 + (\tau_2 \omega_m)^2] - \tau_2[1 + (\tau_1 \omega_m)^2] = 0$$

$$(\tau_1 - \tau_2)(1 - \tau_1 \tau_2 \omega_m^2) = 0$$

$$\omega_m^2 = \frac{1}{\tau_1 \tau_2}$$

In Fig. 12.16*a* is shown the log-magnitude diagram for a lead compensator. It is to be noted that the maximum phase shift ϕ_m occurs at the frequency $\omega_m = 1/\sqrt{\tau_1 \tau_2}$. This frequency at which the maximum phase shift occurs is located at the midpoint between the break frequencies $\omega_1 = 1/\tau_1$ and $\omega_2 = 1/\tau_2$. Because frequency is plotted to a logarithmic scale, the midpoint is

$$\log \omega_m = \frac{1}{2}(\log \omega_1 + \log \omega_2) = \frac{1}{2} \log \omega_1 \omega_2 = \log \frac{1}{\sqrt{\tau_1 \tau_2}}$$

Hence,

$$\omega_m = 1/\sqrt{\tau_1 \tau_2} \tag{12.17}$$

The value of the maximum phase shift ϕ_m is obtained by substituting $\omega = \omega_m = 1/\sqrt{\tau_1 \tau_2}$ into Eq. (12.16). That is,

$$\phi_m = \measuredangle \frac{1 + j\sqrt{\tau_1/\tau_2}}{1 + j\sqrt{\tau_2/\tau_1}} \frac{1 - j\sqrt{\tau_2/\tau_1}}{1 - j\sqrt{\tau_2/\tau_1}} = \measuredangle \frac{1 + 1 + j(\sqrt{\tau_1/\tau_2} - \sqrt{\tau_2/\tau_1})}{1 + \tau_2/\tau_1}$$

$$= \tan^{-1} \frac{\sqrt{\tau_1/\tau_2} - \sqrt{\tau_2/\tau_1}}{2} = \tan^{-1} \frac{\tau_1/\tau_2 - 1}{2\sqrt{\tau_1/\tau_2}} \tag{12.18}$$

This result shows that ϕ_m is a function of the ratio τ_1/τ_2. In Fig. 12.16*b* is shown a plot of ϕ_m versus $\log \tau_1/\tau_2$. The double scale for the horizontal axis displays both $\log \tau_1/\tau_2$ and τ_1/τ_2.

In accordance with Eq. (12.18), ϕ_m may be regarded as the angle of a right triangle whose opposite side is $\tau_1/\tau_2 - 1$ and whose adjacent side is $2\sqrt{\tau_1/\tau_2}$. From this triangle, it follows that

$$\sin \phi_m = \frac{\tau_1/\tau_2 - 1}{\tau_1/\tau_2 + 1}$$

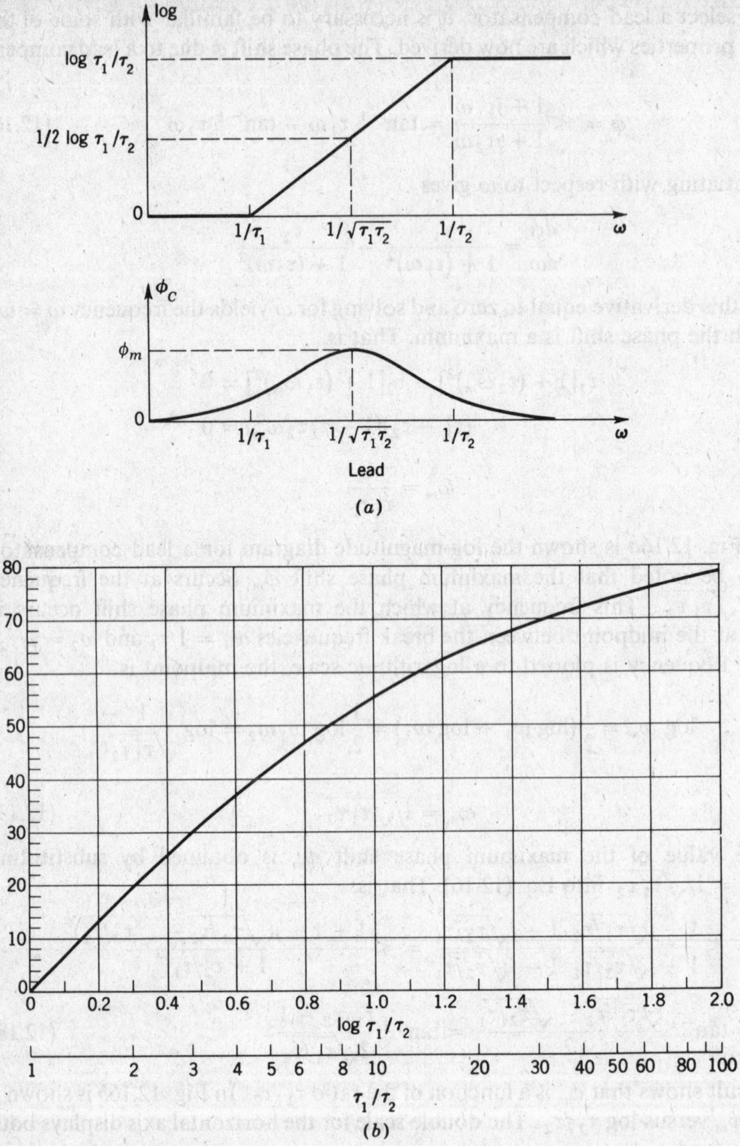

Figure 12.16 Lead compensator characteristics: (*a*) log-magnitude diagram; (*b*) maximum phase shift ϕ_m versus $\log \tau_1/\tau_2$.

Solving for the ratio τ_1/τ_2 shows that

$$\frac{\tau_1}{\tau_2} = \frac{1 + \sin \phi_m}{1 - \sin \phi_m} \tag{12.19}$$

To select a lead compensator, it is necessary to specify the values of both τ_1 and τ_2. Because of the two unknowns τ_1 and τ_2, the selection of a lead compensator to achieve a desired design specification is basically a trial-and-error process. However, a systematic procedure which rapidly converges the trial-and-error process is described in the following example, in which the procedure for obtaining a desired phase margin is described.

Illustrative example The log-modulus plot of $G(j\omega)$ for a unity-feedback system is shown in Fig. 12.17*a*. Determine the values of τ_1 and τ_2 for a series lead compensator such that the compensated system will have a phase margin of 45° ± 3°. What are the approximate values of ζ and ω_n for the resulting compensated system?

SOLUTION From Fig. 12.16*a*, it is to be noted that when the phase shift is a maximum, the lead compensator increases the gain by a factor of $\frac{1}{2} \log \tau_1/\tau_2$. The first step is to assume a value of τ_1/τ_2. For example, for $\tau_1/\tau_2 = 4$, Fig. 12.16*b* shows that $\log \tau_1/\tau_2 = 0.6$ and $\phi_m = 36°$. At the frequency $\omega_m = 1/\sqrt{\tau_1 \tau_2}$, the lead compensator increases the gain by a factor $\frac{1}{2} \log \tau_1/\tau_2 = 0.3$, and the phase angle is increased by $\phi_m = 36°$. Thus, by measuring down -0.3 log unit as shown in Fig. 12.17*a*, when the lead compensator is added, the point indicated by the circle which corresponds to ω_m will be raised vertically 0.3 log unit to the zero horizontal axis and shifted to the right 36°. The new location is indicated by the solid dot. To have a phase margin of 45°, the solid dot should be located at the ×. Thus, it is necessary to assume a larger value of τ_1/τ_2. The result for $\tau_1/\tau_2 = 10$ is illustrated in Fig. 12.17*b*. It is to be noted that this yields a phase margin of 43°, which is satisfactory. Because of the rapid convergence of this process, usually two or three trials suffice for obtaining the desired ratio τ_1/τ_2. The desired values of τ_1 and τ_2 are now computed from the relationships $\tau_1/\tau_2 = 10$ and $\omega_c = \omega_m = 1/\sqrt{\tau_1 \tau_2} = 2.6$. Hence,

$$\tau_1 = 1.2 \qquad \text{and} \qquad \tau_2 = 0.12$$

The complete log-modulus plot for the resulting $G_c(j\omega)G(j\omega)$ system may now be constructed as illustrated in Fig. 12.17*c*.

For a phase margin of 43°, Fig. 12.12*b* shows that the approximate value of ζ is 0.425. From Fig. 12.12*a*, it is found that $\omega_c/\omega_n = 0.84$. Thus, the approximate value of the natural frequency ω_n is found to be 3.1.

By putting an × at the point through which the resulting polar plot should pass, this procedure may be used to obtain a desired gain margin or a desired value of M_p.

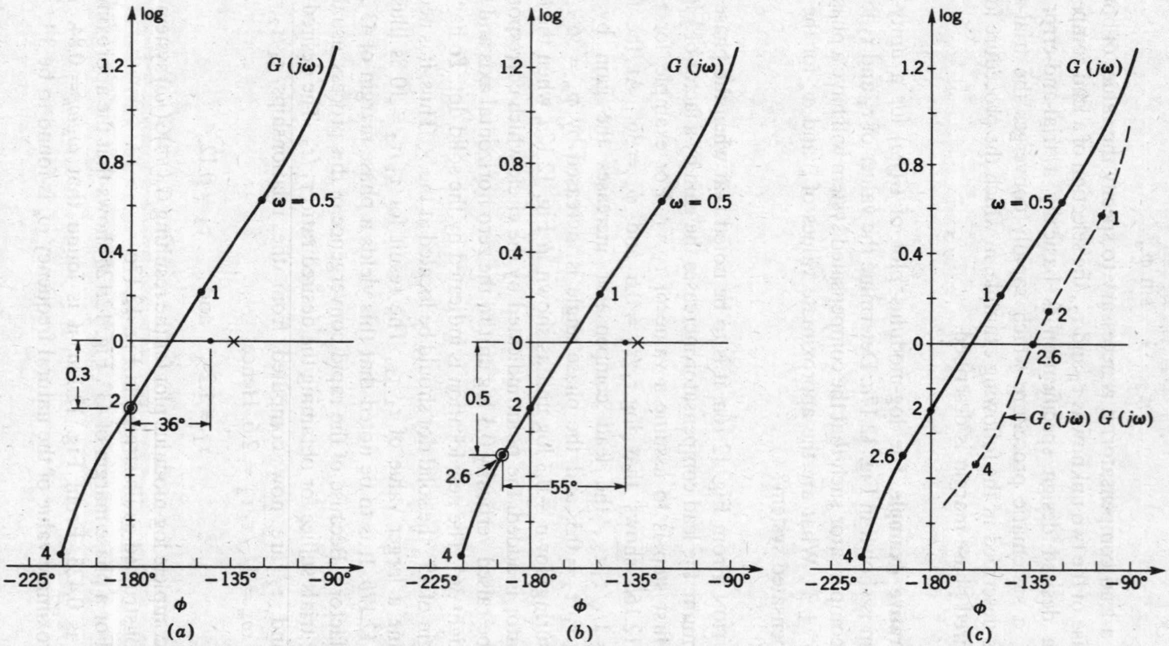

Figure 12.17 Use of series-lead compensation to obtain a desired phase margin.

12.4 LAG COMPENSATION

The output lags the input for any component which has a transfer function of the form

$$\frac{E_o(s)}{E_{in}(s)} = \frac{Y(s)}{X(s)} = \frac{1 + \tau_2 s}{1 + \tau_1 s} \qquad \tau_1 > \tau_2 \tag{12.20}$$

The frequency response for the preceding transfer function is

$$\frac{E_o(j\omega)}{E_{in}(j\omega)} = \frac{Y(j\omega)}{X(j\omega)} = \frac{1 + j\tau_2 \omega}{1 + j\tau_1 \omega} \qquad \tau_1 > \tau_2 \tag{12.21}$$

In Fig. 12.18 are shown both an electrical and a mechanical component in which the output lags the input, as is described by Eq. (12.21). The construction of the log-magnitude plot for Eq. (12.21) for the case in which $\tau_2 = \tau_1/10$ is illustrated in Fig. 12.19. For the term $1/(1 + j\tau_1 \omega)$, the break frequency occurs at $\omega = 1/\tau_1$, and for the numerator $1 + j\tau_2 \omega$ the break frequency occurs at $\omega = 1/\tau_2 = 10/\tau_1$. The addition of the log-magnitude diagram for the numerator to that for the denominator yields the resulting diagram for $(1 + j\tau_2 \omega)/(1 + j\tau_1 \omega)$.

The use of a phase-lag component placed in series with the feedforward portion of a control system to improve stability is now illustrated. In Fig. 12.20 the dashed curve is the frequency response $G(j\omega)H(j\omega)$ of the uncompensated control system. This control is one which would inherently be unstable. The addition of series compensation $G_c(j\omega)$ reshapes the polar plot, as shown by the solid-line curve of Fig. 12.20. The resultant system has good dynamic response. It is to be noted that the effect of lag compensation is to shorten a typical vector such as that for $\omega = 0.5$ and also to rotate it in a clockwise direction. The shortening is due to the attenuation. By attenuation is meant multiplication by a factor less than 1. The attenuation caused by use of lag compensation can be seen from Fig. 12.21*a*. The greater the spread in time constants τ_1 and τ_2, the more pronounced is the attenuation which occurs at higher frequencies. Series lag compensation has little effect on the low-frequency portion of the curve. By reshaping the polar plot, it has been possible to achieve good dynamic performance without changing the value of the gain K. Although it would have been possible to make

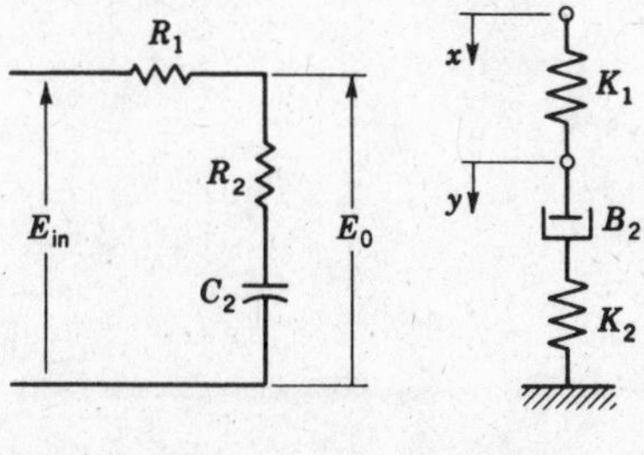

$$\frac{E_o(s)}{E_{in}(s)} = \frac{1 + \tau_2 s}{1 + \tau_1 s} \qquad \frac{Y(s)}{X(s)} = \frac{1 + \tau_2 s}{1 + \tau_1 s}$$

$$\tau_2 = R_2 C_2 \qquad \tau_2 = \frac{B_2}{K_2}$$

$$\tau_1 = (R_1 + R_2)C_2 = R_1 C_2 + \tau_2 \qquad \tau_1 = \frac{K_1 + K_2}{K_1}\tau_2$$

Figure 12.18 An electrical and a mechanical component used to provide lag compensation.

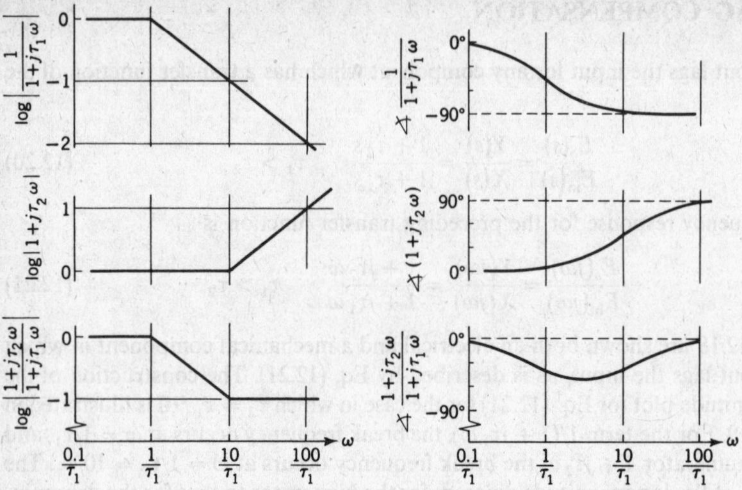

Figure 12.19 Construction of the log-magnitude diagram for $(1 + j\tau_2 \omega)/(1 + j\tau_1 \omega)$ when $\tau_2 = \tau_1/10$.

this system stable by decreasing the gain K only, errors caused by friction, hysteresis, backlash, etc., tend to predominate as the gain is decreased; thus, in general, the higher the value of K, the more accurate will be the control system.

In Fig. 12.21*a* is shown the log-magnitude diagram for a lag compensator. Comparison of Figs. 12.16*a* and 12.21*a* shows that the phase-shift characteristics

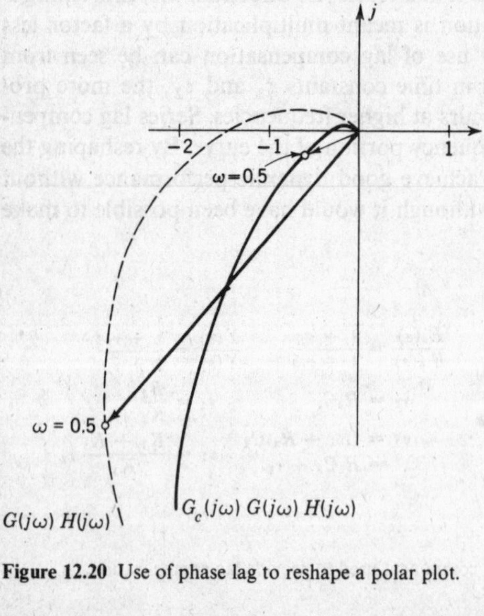

Figure 12.20 Use of phase lag to reshape a polar plot.

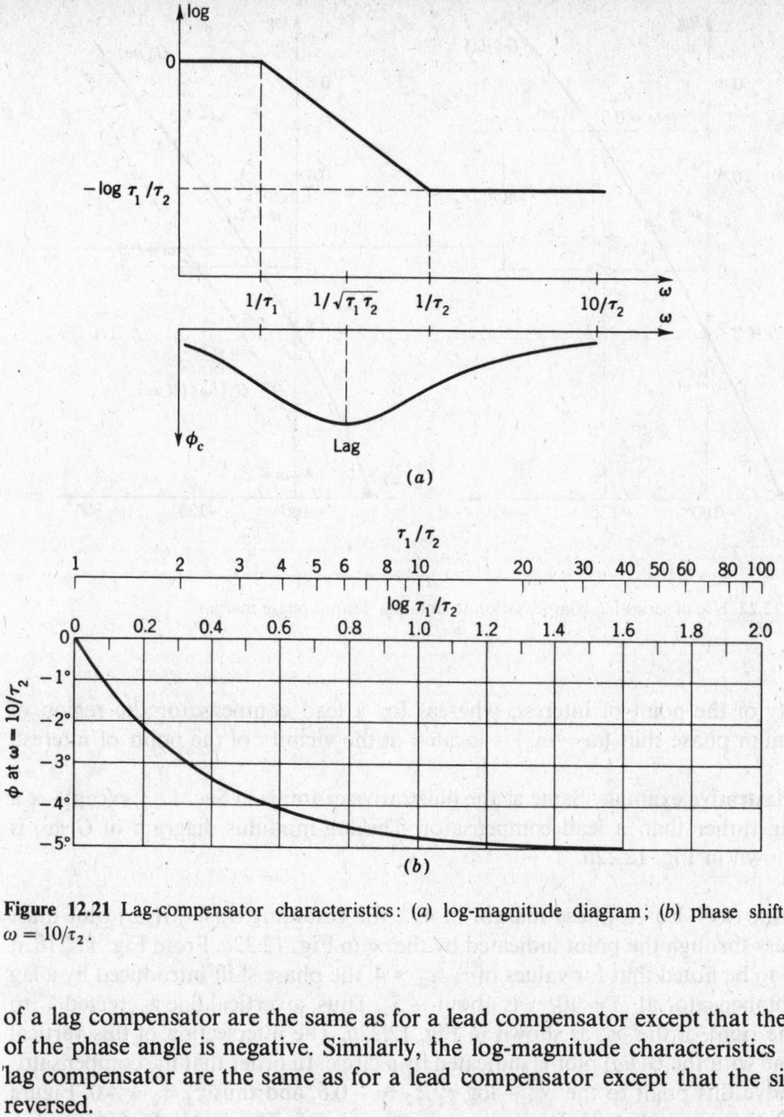

Figure 12.21 Lag-compensator characteristics: (*a*) log-magnitude diagram; (*b*) phase shift ϕ at $\omega = 10/\tau_2$.

of a lag compensator are the same as for a lead compensator except that the sign of the phase angle is negative. Similarly, the log-magnitude characteristics for a lag compensator are the same as for a lead compensator except that the sign is reversed.

The negative phase shift associated with lag compensation is usually undesirable. The effectiveness of lag compensation is attributed to the attenuation which occurs at higher frequencies. In Fig. 12.21*a*, it is to be noted that when $\omega = 10/\tau_2$, then the negative phase shift is very small. The solid-line curve in Fig. 12.21*b* is a plot of the value of the negative phase shift at $\omega = 10/\tau_2$. A significant difference between selecting a lag compensator and selecting a lead compensator is that for the lag compensator the region of small phase shift ($\omega = 10/\tau_2$) is located in the

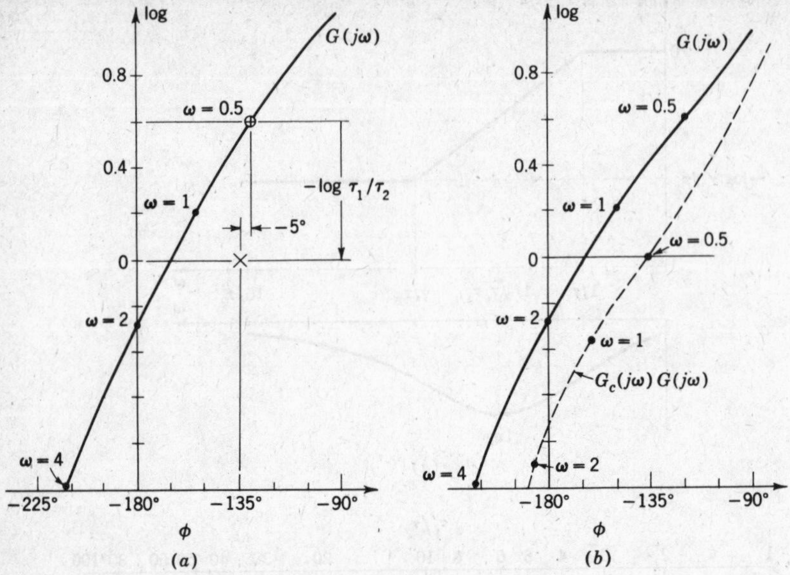

Figure 12.22 Use of series-lag compensation to obtain a desired phase margin.

vicinity of the point of interest, whereas for a lead compensator the region of maximum phase shift ($\omega = \omega_m$) is located in the vicinity of the point of interest.

Illustrative example Same as the illustrative example in Sec. 12.3, except use a lag rather than a lead compensator. The log-modulus diagram of $G(j\omega)$ is shown in Fig. 12.22*a*.

SOLUTION For a phase margin of 45°, the resultant $G_c(j\omega)G(j\omega)$ plot must pass through the point indicated by the × in Fig. 12.22*a*. From Fig. 12.21*b*, it is to be noted that for values of $\tau_1/\tau_2 > 4$, the phase shift introduced by a lag compensator at $\omega = 10/\tau_2$ is about $-5°$. Thus, a vertical line is erected 5° to the right of the ×, as shown in Fig. 12.22*a*. The intersection of this vertical line with the $G(j\omega)$ plot is indicated by a circle. In order that the compensator move this point to the ×, $-\log \tau_1/\tau_2 = -0.6$, and thus $\tau_1/\tau_2 = 4.0$. Figure 12.22*a* shows that the frequency $\omega = 10/\tau_2$ is 0.5. The particular values of τ_1 and τ_2 are now computed from the relationships $\tau_1/\tau_2 = 4$ and $10/\tau_2 = 0.5$. Thus,

$$\tau_1 = 80 \qquad \text{and} \qquad \tau_2 = 20$$

With these values of τ_1 and τ_2, the log-modulus diagram for the resultant compensated system $G_c(j\omega)G(j\omega)$ may now be constructed as shown in Fig. 12.22*b*.

For a phase margin of 45°, it follows from Fig. 12.12*b* that the approximate value of ζ is 0.425. Similarly, from Fig. 12.12*a* the ratio ω_c/ω_n is found to be 0.84. Because the cross-over frequency ω_c is 0.5, then the approximate natural frequency ω_n is found to be 0.6.

It is to be noted that the values of τ_1 and τ_2 for this lag compensator are larger than the values of τ_1 and τ_2 for the corresponding lead compensator. Thus, the system with lag compensation is slower than the corresponding system with lead compensation. This fact is also substantiated by noting that the approximate natural frequency for the system with lag compensation is considerably smaller ($\omega_n = 0.6$) than the approximate natural frequency for the system with lead compensation ($\omega_n = 3.1$).

By proceeding in a similar manner, it is possible to select lag compensators to yield a desired M_p or a desired gain margin. When selecting a compensator to yield a desired phase margin or a desired gain margin, one may use either Bode diagrams or log-modulus diagrams. Because it is not possible to construct M contours on Bode diagrams, it is necessary to use log-modulus diagrams for obtaining a compensator to yield a desired value of M_p.

12.5 LAG-LEAD COMPENSATION

A lag-lead compensator is a series combination of a lag and a lead network. The general transfer function for a lag-lead compensator is

$$\frac{E_o(s)}{E_{in}(s)} = \frac{Y(s)}{X(s)} = \frac{1 + c\tau_2 s}{1 + c\tau_1 s} \frac{1 + \tau_1 s}{1 + \tau_2 s} \qquad \tau_1 > \tau_2 \tag{12.22}$$

where $c > 1$ is a constant. The substitution of $j\omega$ for s gives

$$\frac{E_o(j\omega)}{E_{in}(j\omega)} = \frac{Y(j\omega)}{X(j\omega)} = \frac{1 + jc\tau_2\omega}{1 + jc\tau_1\omega} \frac{1 + j\tau_1\omega}{1 + j\tau_2\omega} \tag{12.23}$$

Rather than using a lag and a lead compensator in series, it is possible to use a single compensator, as is shown in Fig. 12.23.

The log-magnitude diagram for a typical lag-lead compensator is shown in Fig. 12.24. Because $c\tau_1 > c\tau_2 > \tau_1 > \tau_2$, the first break frequency occurs at $1/c\tau_1$. This break frequency belongs to a denominator term, so that the magnitude plot has a slope of -1 log unit/decade between $1/c\tau_1$ and $1/c\tau_2$. The second break frequency, $1/c\tau_2$, is associated with a numerator term, and thus the magnitude plot again becomes horizontal. The third break frequency, $1/\tau_1$, also occurs in the numerator. This results in a slope of $+1$ log unit/decade in the region from $1/\tau_1$ to $1/\tau_2$. Finally the break frequency $1/\tau_2$, which occurs in the denominator, causes the magnitude curve to become horizontal again. It is to be noted that the maximum phase shift ϕ_m occurs at $\omega = 1/\sqrt{\tau_1 \tau_2}$, and the corresponding attenuation is $-\frac{1}{2} \log \tau_1/\tau_2$. This is the same as for a lead compensator only (see Fig. 12.16*a*) except that the sign of the log of the magnitude is negative. This feature makes the lag-lead compensator considerably more effective than the lead compensator only.

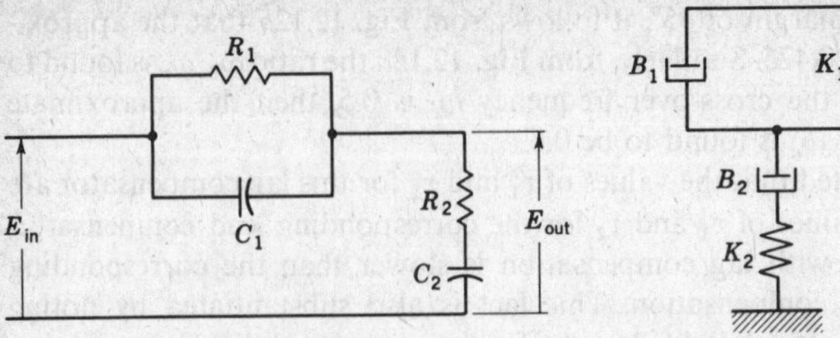

$$\frac{E_0(s)}{E_{in}(s)} = \left(\frac{1+c\tau_2 s}{1+c\tau_1 s}\right)\left(\frac{1+\tau_1 s}{1+\tau_2 s}\right) \qquad \frac{Y(s)}{X(s)} = \left(\frac{1+c\tau_2 s}{1+c\tau_1 s}\right)\left(\frac{1+\tau_1 s}{1+\tau_2 s}\right)$$

$$\tau_1 = R_1 C_1 \qquad \tau_2 = \frac{R_2 C_2}{c} \qquad \tau_1 = \frac{B_1}{K_1} \qquad \tau_2 = \frac{B_2}{cK_2}$$

$$c = 1 + \frac{R_1 C_2}{\tau_1 - \tau_2} \qquad c = 1 + \frac{B_2/K_1}{\tau_1 - \tau_2}$$

Figure 12.23 An electrical and a mechanical component used to provide lag-lead compensation.

Illustrative example Same as the illustrative example of Sec. 12.3, except use a lag-lead compensator rather than a lead compensator.

SOLUTION In Fig. 12.25*a* is shown the log-modulus plot for the uncompensated system $G(j\omega)$. As a first trial, it is assumed that $\tau_1/\tau_2 = 2$; thus $\phi_m = 20°$ and $-\frac{1}{2}\log \tau_1/\tau_2 = -0.15$ log unit. The circle in Fig. 12.25*a* will be shifted downward -0.15 log unit and it will be moved to the right 20°. The resulting location is indicated by the ×. The corresponding phase margin is $\gamma = 45°$.

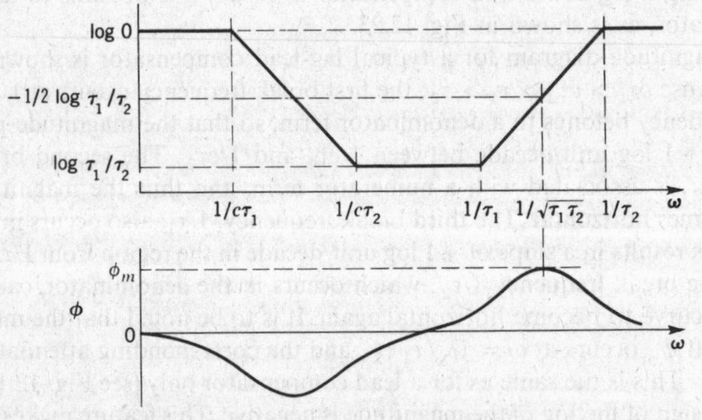

Figure 12.24 Log-magnitude diagram for a lag-lead compensator.

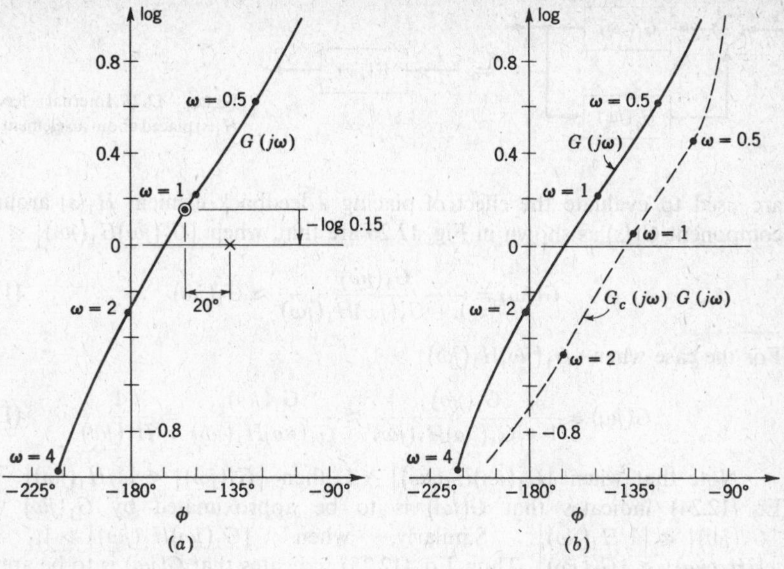

Figure 12.25 Use of series lag-lead compensation to obtain a desired phase margin.

The particular values of τ_1 and τ_2 for this lag-lead compensator are determined from the relationships $\tau_1/\tau_2 = 2$ and $\omega_m = 1/\sqrt{\tau_1 \tau_2} = 1.1$. Thus, it is found that $\tau_1 = 1.30$ and $\tau_2 = 0.65$.

A factor of 5 provides a reasonable separation between the second and third break frequencies (see Fig. 12.24), that is, $1/\tau_1 = 5(1/c\tau_2)$. Solving this relationship for c gives

$$c = 5\frac{\tau_1}{\tau_2} = 10$$

With the compensator specified, the log-modulus diagram for the resulting compensated system may now be constructed as shown in Fig. 12.25*b*. As is indicated by Fig. 12.24, lag-lead compensation does not affect the low- or high-frequency regions but rather the mid-frequency region.

12.6 INTERNAL FEEDBACK

Another method commonly used to alter frequency-response characteristics is that of providing a separate internal-feedback path about certain components. In employing log-magnitude diagrams to investigate the effect of internal feedback, the use of a few approximations affords much simplification. This approximate analysis in effects puts the designer in the right " ball park." In the latter design stages, it may be desirable to make an exact analysis. The approximations which

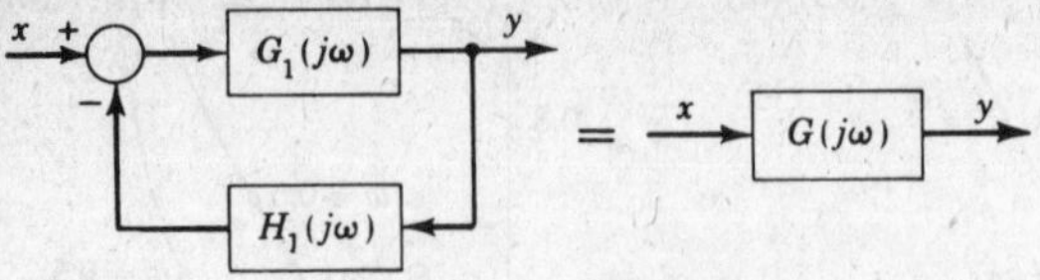

Figure 12.26 Internal feedback $H_1(s)$ placed about an element $G_1(s)$.

are used to evaluate the effect of placing a feedback element $H_1(s)$ around a component $G_1(s)$ as shown in Fig. 12.26 are that, when $|G_1(j\omega)H_1(j\omega)| \ll 1$,

$$G(j\omega) = \frac{G_1(j\omega)}{1 + G_1(j\omega)H_1(j\omega)} \approx G_1(j\omega) \tag{12.24}$$

For the case when $|G_1(j\omega)H_1(j\omega)| \gg 1$,

$$G(j\omega) = \frac{G_1(j\omega)}{1 + G_1(j\omega)H_1(j\omega)} \approx \frac{G_1(j\omega)}{G_1(j\omega)H_1(j\omega)} = \frac{1}{H_1(j\omega)} \tag{12.25}$$

Note that when $|G_1(j\omega)H_1(j\omega)| \ll 1$, then $|G_1(j\omega)| \ll |1/H_1(j\omega)|$. Thus Eq. (12.24) indicates that $G(j\omega)$ is to be approximated by $G_1(j\omega)$ when $|G_1(j\omega)| \ll |1/H_1(j\omega)|$. Similarly, when $|G_1(j\omega)H_1(j\omega)| \gg 1$, then $|1/H_1(j\omega)| \ll |G_1(j\omega)|$. Thus, Eq. (12.25) indicates that $G(j\omega)$ is to be approximated by $1/H_1(j\omega)$ when $|1/H_1(j\omega)| \ll |G_1(j\omega)|$. In summary, $G(j\omega)$ is always approximated by the smaller of $G_1(j\omega)$ or $1/H_1(j\omega)$.

When $|G_1(j\omega)H_1(j\omega)| = 1$, then $|G_1(j\omega)| = |1/H_1(j\omega)|$. Thus, the intersection of the log-magnitude diagram for $|G_1(j\omega)|$ and that for $|1/H_1(j\omega)|$ determines the point at which $|G_1(j\omega)H_1(j\omega)| = 1$. Usually at high frequencies $|G_1(j\omega)H_1(j\omega)| \ll 1$, in which case $|G_1(j\omega)| \ll |1/H_1(j\omega)|$. Thus, the high-frequency response is approximated by $G_1(j\omega)$, and the low-frequency response is approximated by $1/H_1(j\omega)$.

In summary, this approximation converts an internal-feedback path to an approximate open-loop element for which a standard analysis can be made. With the use of inverse polar plots, as is next described, no approximations are employed.

12.7 INVERSE POLAR PLOTS

A plot of the function $G^{-1}(j\omega) = 1/G(j\omega)$ is called an inverse polar plot. In Fig. 12.27 is shown a typical inverse polar plot of the function $G^{-1}(j\omega)$. At any frequency ω, the vector from the origin to the graph defines the vector $G^{-1}(j\omega)$ for that frequency. The length of the vector is $|G^{-1}(j\omega)| = |1/G(j\omega)|$, and the angle is

$$\measuredangle G^{-1}(j\omega) = \measuredangle \frac{1}{G(j\omega)} = -\measuredangle G(j\omega)$$

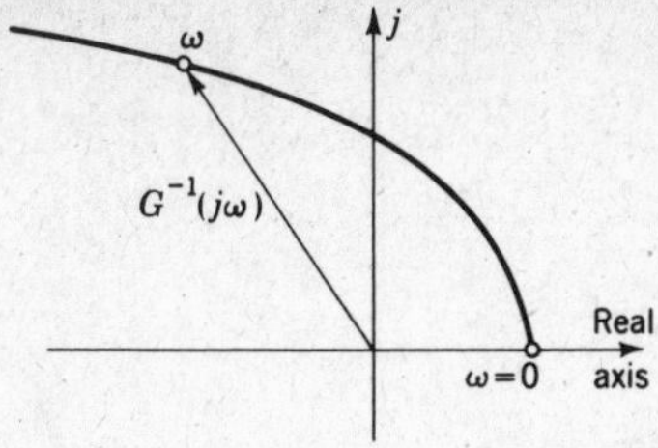

Figure 12.27 Typical inverse polar plot $G^{-1}(j\omega)$.

A plot of M circles and α lines for inverse polar plots is accomplished by first taking the reciprocal of Eq. (11.52), i.e.,

$$\frac{R(j\omega)}{C(j\omega)} = \frac{1 + G(j\omega)}{G(j\omega)} = G^{-1}(j\omega) + 1 \tag{12.26}$$

A typical vector $G^{-1}(j\omega)$ as shown in Fig. 12.27 may be written in the general form $G^{-1}(j\omega) = x + jy$. Substitution of this general representation for $G^{-1}(j\omega)$ into Eq. (12.26) gives

$$\frac{R(j\omega)}{C(j\omega)} = x + 1 + jy \tag{12.27}$$

Because $M = |C(j\omega)/R(j\omega)|$, from the magnitude of Eq. (12.27) it follows that

$$\left|\frac{R(j\omega)}{C(j\omega)}\right| = \frac{1}{M} = \sqrt{(x+1)^2 + y^2}$$

Squaring this result gives

$$(x+1)^2 + y^2 = \frac{1}{M^2} \tag{12.28}$$

Thus, on the inverse plane, lines of constant M are circles of radius $1/M$. The center of these concentric M circles is at the point $x = -1$ and $y = 0$, that is, the -1 point. A plot of these M circles on the inverse plane is shown in Fig. 12.28. Because the reciprocal of -1 is still -1, this point has the same significance for an inverse polar plot as for a direct polar plot. Polar plots are referred to as direct polar plots when it is necessary to distinguish them from inverse polar plots.

The lines of constant $\alpha = \sphericalangle[C(j\omega)/R(j\omega)] = -\sphericalangle[R(j\omega)/C(j\omega)]$ are determined from Eq. (12.27) as follows:

$$\alpha = -\sphericalangle\frac{R(j\omega)}{C(j\omega)} = -\tan^{-1}\frac{y}{x+1} \tag{12.29}$$

When plotted on the inverse plane, as is shown in Fig. 12.28, constant α contours are radial straight lines which pass through the $-1 + j0$ point.

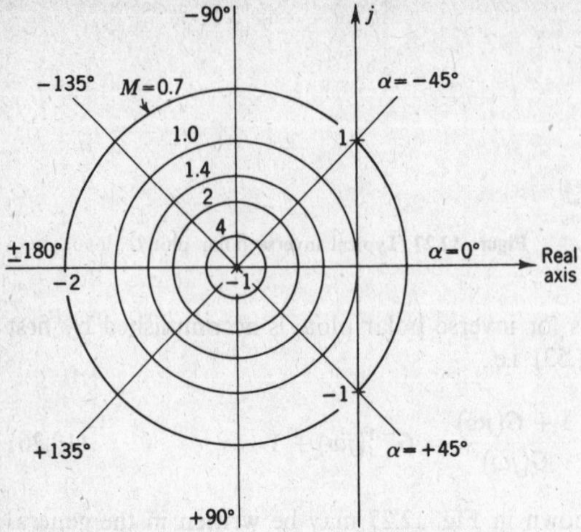

Figure 12.28 M circles and α lines on the inverse plane.

As is illustrated in Fig. 12.29, the angle ψ of a radial line drawn from the origin tangent to any M circle is

$$\sin \psi = \frac{1}{M} \tag{12.30}$$

The use of the inverse polar plot for determining the gain K to yield a desired value of M_p is similar to that for the direct polar plot. Consider the same function $G(j\omega) = K/[j\omega(1 + 0.1j\omega)]$ discussed in Sec. 11.8. The plot of the inverse function

$$\frac{K}{G(j\omega)} = KG^{-1}(j\omega) = j\omega(1 + 0.1j\omega) \tag{12.31}$$

is shown in Fig. 12.30. For a desired $M_p = 1.4$, the angle ψ of the tangent line is

$$\psi = \sin^{-1}\frac{1}{M_p} = \sin^{-1}\frac{1}{1.4} = 45.6° \tag{12.32}$$

Next construct by trial and error the circle which is tangent to both the $KG^{-1}(j\omega)$ plot and the tangent line. In order for this circle to be the desired M_p circle, its

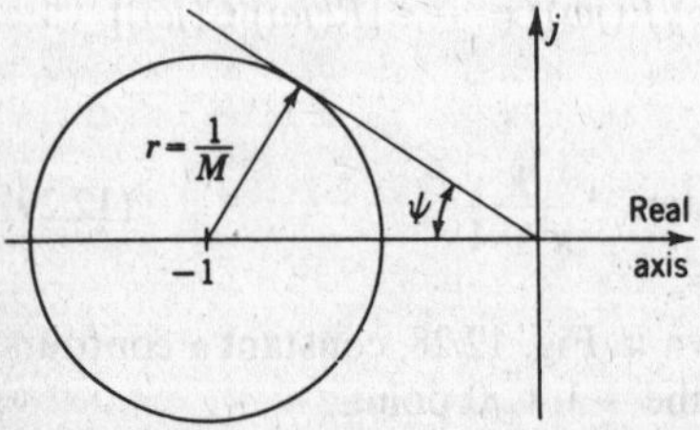

Figure 12.29 Tangent line to an M circle.

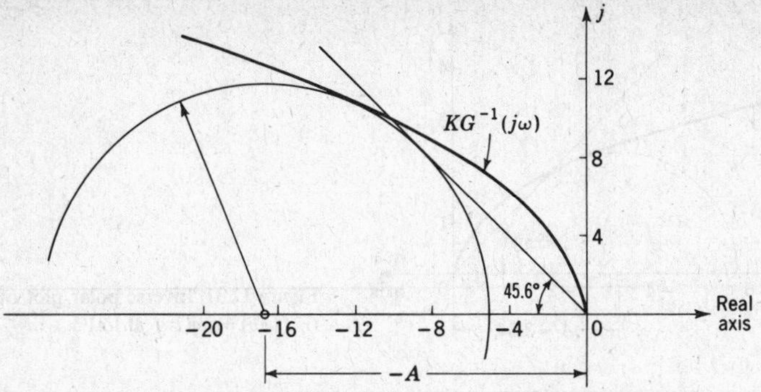

Figure 12.30 Inverse polar plot of $KG^{-1}(j\omega) = j\omega(1 + 0.1j\omega)$.

center must be at the -1 point. From Fig. 12.30, it is to be seen that the center is at $-A = -16.7$. To convert this to the -1 point, the scale factor must be multiplied by $1/A = 1/16.7 = 0.06$. The resulting function $G^{-1}(j\omega)$, which is tangent to the desired M circle, is

$$G^{-1}(j\omega) = \frac{1}{A}[KG^{-1}(j\omega)] = 0.06j\omega(1 + 0.1j\omega)$$

or

$$G(j\omega) = \frac{16.7}{j\omega(1 + 0.1j\omega)}$$

Thus, the value of A yields directly the required gain K.

The general procedure for obtaining K by use of the inverse polar plot is:

1. Plot the inverse function $KG^{-1}(j\omega)$.
2. Construct the tangent line in accordance with Eq. (12.30).
3. By trial and error, determine the circle which is tangent to both the $KG^{-1}(j\omega)$ plot and the tangent line.
4. The desired gain is $K = A$.

When the function $G^{-1}(j\omega)$ is plotted rather than $KG^{-1}(j\omega)$, then A is equal to the factor K_c by which the gain should be changed to yield the desired M_p.

Illustrative example 1 Consider the function

$$G(j\omega) = \frac{5}{j\omega(1 + 0.1j\omega)}$$

The inverse polar plot $G^{-1}(j\omega)$ is shown in Fig. 12.31. Determine the factor K_c by which the gain should be changed so that the resulting plot is tangent to the $M_p = 1.4$ circle.

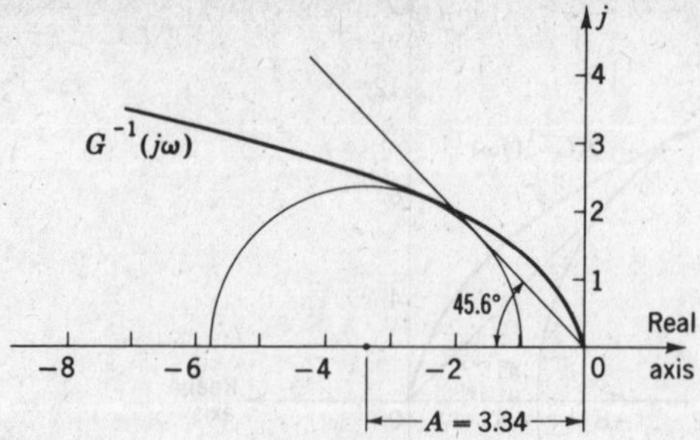

Figure 12.31 Inverse polar plot of $G^{-1}(j\omega) = j\omega(1 + j0.1\omega)/5$.

SOLUTION In order that the point $-A$ in Fig. 12.31 be the -1 point, the scale factor must be multiplied by $1/A$. The resulting function is

$$\frac{1}{A}G^{-1}(j\omega) = \frac{1}{AG(j\omega)} = \frac{1}{K_c G(j\omega)}$$

or
$$K_c G(j\omega) = \frac{(3.34)(5)}{j\omega(1 + 0.1j\omega)} = \frac{16.7}{j\omega(1 + 0.1j\omega)}$$

The preceding analysis shows that $K_c = A$.

The major advantage of using the inverse plane is realized for systems with internal feedback. The reciprocal of Eq. (12.24) is

$$G^{-1}(j\omega) = \frac{1 + G_1(j\omega)H_1(j\omega)}{G_1(j\omega)} = G_1^{-1}(j\omega) + H_1(j\omega) \tag{12.33}$$

The vectors $G_1^{-1}(j\omega)$ and $H_1(j\omega)$ may be added as vector quantities to yield $G^{-1}(j\omega)$, as is illustrated in Fig. 12.32.

Illustrative example 2 For the system shown in Fig. 12.33*a*, the value of K_1 is 10 and K_2 is 2.5. From the inverse polar plot $1/K_2 G_1(j\omega)$ of Fig. 12.33*b*, the value of M_p is found to be 5. It is desired to obtain an M_p of 1.4 by the use of

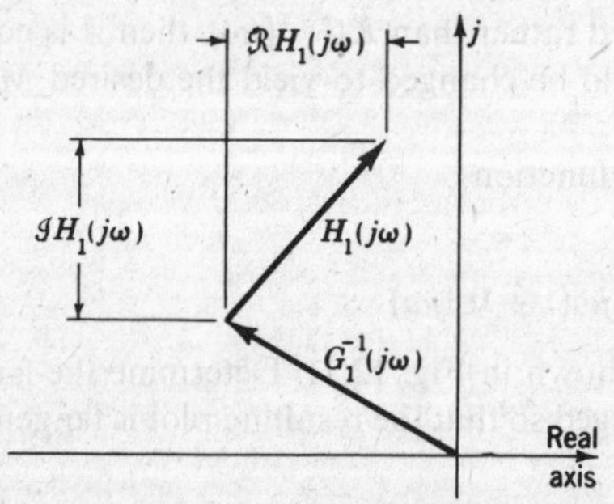

Figure 12.32 Vector addition of $G_1^{-1}(j\omega)$ and $H_1(j\omega)$ to yield $G^{-1}(j\omega)$.

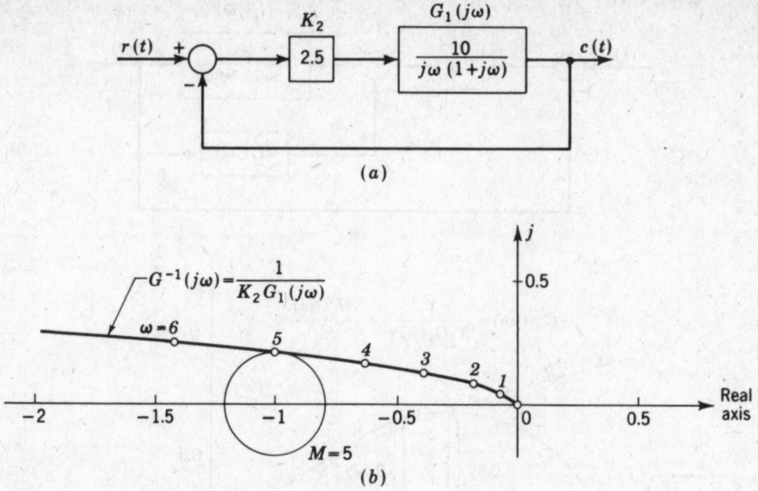

Figure 12.33 System without internal feedback.

an internal-feedback loop as shown in Fig. 12.34*a*. What feedback element $H_1(j\omega)$ should be used?

SOLUTION The equation for the inverse polar plot with internal feedback is

$$\frac{1}{G(j\omega)} = \frac{1}{K_2}\frac{1 + G_1(j\omega)H_1(j\omega)}{G_1(j\omega)} = \frac{1}{K_2G_1(j\omega)} + \frac{H_1(j\omega)}{K_2} \tag{12.34}$$

The quantity $H_1(j\omega)/K_2$ must be such that when it is added to $1/[K_2 G_1(j\omega)]$, the resulting plot will be tangent to the $M = 1.4$ circle. To obtain this, it is necessary only to raise the original plot vertically. It is to be seen from Fig. 12.32 that the horizontal component of $H_1(j\omega)$ is its real part $\mathscr{R}H_1(j\omega)$ and the vertical component is its imaginary part $\mathscr{I}H_1(j\omega)$. It is thus necessary only that $H_1(j\omega)$ be purely imaginary, i.e., of the form $H_1(s) = \beta s$ or $H_1(j\omega) = j\beta\omega$. In Fig. 12.34*b*, it is to be noted that, at $\omega = 5$, the addition of $H_1(j5)/K_2 = 0.5j$ to the $1/[K_2 G_1(j5)]$ vector causes the resulting curve to pass through the top of the $M = 1.4$ circle. For this case, the value of β is $j\beta 5/2.5 = 0.5j$, or $\beta = 0.25$. The resulting curve may now be constructed as indicated by the dashed line in Fig. 12.34*b*. Because this curve is not tangent to the $M = 1.4$ circle, another trial value must be taken. From the dashed loci of Fig. 12.34*b*, it now appears that the point of tangency is more likely to occur in the neighborhood of $\omega = 4.5$. The addition of $H_1(j4.5)/K_2 = 0.47j$ to $1/[K_2 G_1(j4.5)]$ causes the new resulting curve to be tangent to the desired M circle. In this case $j\beta 4.5/2.5 = 0.47j$, or $\beta = 0.26$. Thus, the desired result is $H_1(j\omega) = 0.26j\omega$.

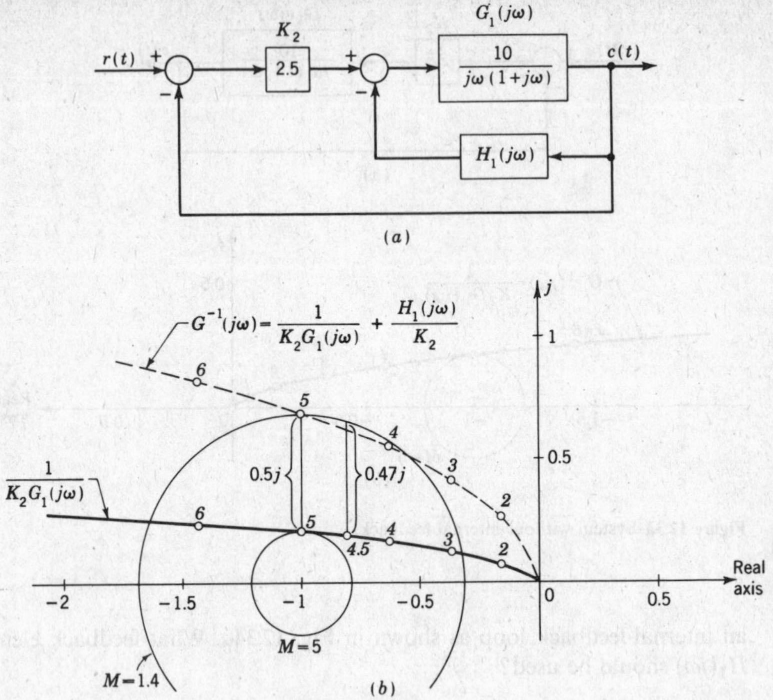

Figure 12.34 System of Fig. 12.33 with internal feedback.

When $H_1(j\omega)$ is a constant, $H_1(j\omega)$ is entirely real. As may be seen from Fig. 12.34*b*, the effect of a constant $H_1(j\omega)$ is to shift the inverse plot horizontally to the right. Suppose in the preceding problem that it is desired to increase the speed of response by having ω_p equal to 6 rather than 4.5. After assuming a few trial values for $H_1(j6)/K_2$, it is found that $H_1(j6)/K_2 = 0.6 + 0.4j$ makes the resultant plot tangent to the $M = 1.4$ circle at $\omega = 6$, as is illustrated in Fig. 12.35. Because $H_1(j6)/K_2 = 0.6 + 0.4j = 0.6 + j\beta 6$, then $\beta = 0.4/6 = 0.067$, whence the required $H_1(j\omega)$ is

$$H_1(j\omega) = K_2(0.6 + j\beta\omega) = 1.5 + j0.167\omega \tag{12.35}$$

The general procedure followed in this illustrative example was to assume a value of $H_1(j\omega)$ which makes a point lie on the desired M circle. From this assumed value, the general equation for the resulting plot was obtained. When the assumed point is not the point of tangency, then another trial point must be selected.

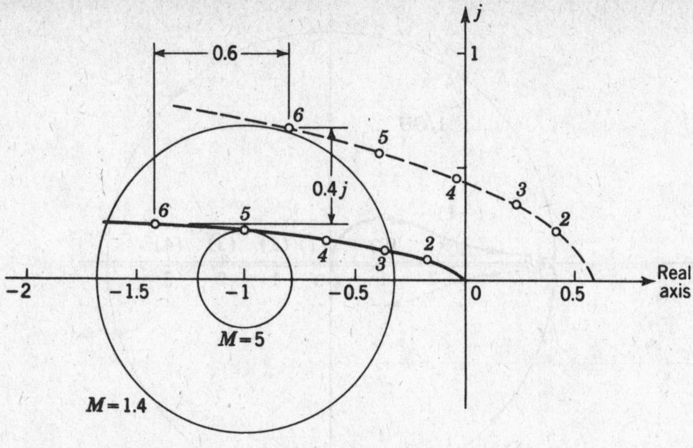

Figure 12.35 Use of inverse polar plots to increase speed of response.

12.8 STABILITY CRITERIA IN THE INVERSE PLANE

The inverse function $1/[G(s)H(s)]$ may be expressed in terms of numerator and denominator terms as follows:

$$\frac{1}{G(s)H(s)} = \frac{D_G D_H}{N_G N_H}$$

In Fig. 12.36 is shown the complete inverse polar plot for the function

$$G(s)H(s) = \frac{10(s+2)}{s(s+1)(s+4)}$$

or

$$\frac{1}{G(s)H(s)} = \frac{s(s+1)(s+4)}{10(s+2)}$$

As s proceeds up the vertical (imaginary) axis of Fig. 12.36*a*, then the corresponding inverse plot in Fig. 12.36*b* is indicated by the heavy line.

For values of s on the infinite semicircle $s = Re^{j\beta}$, then

$$\frac{1}{G(s)H(s)} \approx \frac{R^3 e^{3j\beta}}{Re^{j\beta}} = R^2 e^{2j\beta}$$

In general, if n is the highest order of s in the denominator of $G(s)H(s)$ and m is the highest order of s in the numerator of $G(s)H(s)$, then for values of s on the infinite semicircle,

$$\frac{1}{G(s)H(s)} = R^{n-m} e^{j(n-m)\beta}$$

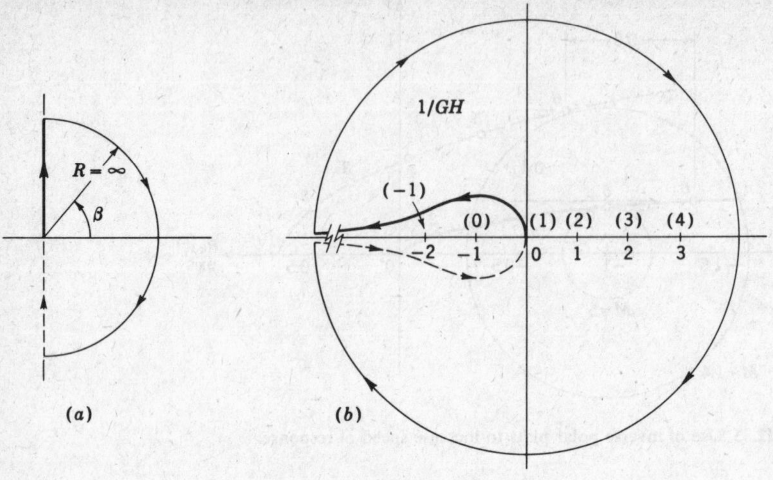

Figure 12.36 Complete inverse polar plot for $\dfrac{1}{G(s)H(s)} = \dfrac{s(s+1)(s+4)}{10(s+2)}$.

Because β changes by an angle of $-\pi$, the corresponding inverse plot transcribes an infinite semicircle which goes through the angle $-(n-m)\pi$. The negative imaginary axis $s = -j\omega$ is the complex conjugate of the positive imaginary axis $s = j\omega$; thus the portion shown dotted is the mirror image of the heavy-line portion.

The effect of adding $(+1)$ to the $1/GH$ plot is obtained by the new scale shown in parentheses above the real axis of Fig. 12.36*b*. Thus, the -1 point of the $1/GH$ plot is seen to be the origin of the $(1/GH) + 1$ plot. With respect to the numerator and denominator terms, this new plot is

$$\frac{1}{GH} + 1 = \frac{D_G D_H}{N_G N_H} + 1 = \frac{N_G N_H + D_G D_H}{N_G N_H}$$

Application of the Nyquist stability criterion to the inverse plot shows that

$$Z = N + P$$

where Z = number of zeros of the characteristic function $(N_G N_H + D_G D_H)$ in the right half plane
P = number of zeros of $N_G N_H$ in the right half plane
N = net number of encirclements of the origin of the $1 + 1/GH$ plot (that is, -1 point of the $1/GH$ plot)

It is to be noted that N and Z have the same meaning for inverse plots as for direct plots. However, P is the number of zeros of $N_G N_H$ when using inverse polar plots, whereas P is the number of zeros of $D_G D_H$ when using direct polar plots.

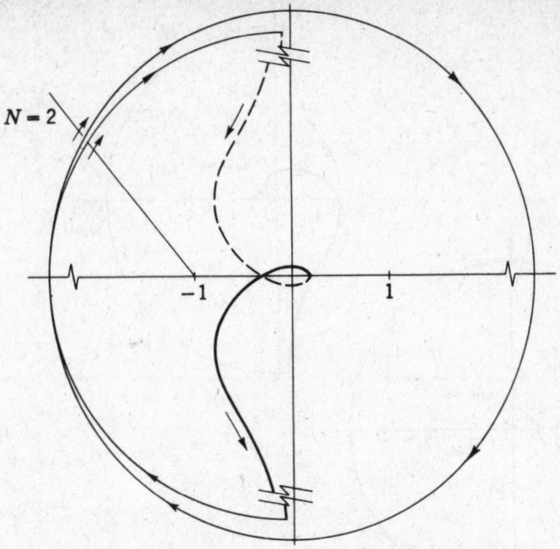

Figure 12.37 Complete inverse polar plot for

$$\frac{1}{G(s)H(s)} = \frac{(s+2)(s^2+2s+5)}{52}.$$

For the system of Fig. 12.36, $N = 0$ and $P = 0$. Application of the Nyquist stability criterion shows that $Z = N + P = 0$. Hence, the system is stable.

Illustrative example Determine the inverse polar plot and the value of Z for the type 0 system whose direct polar plot is shown in Fig. 12.3.

SOLUTION For a type 0 system the inverse polar plot begins on the positive real axis at the value $1/K$. The heavy-line portion of Fig. 12.37 is the portion of the inverse plot for $s = j\omega$. The dotted line is the portion for $s = -j\omega$. From Eq. 12.4, it is to be noted that $n - m = 3$. Thus, the inverse plot transcribes an infinite semicircle which goes through the angle $-(n - m)\pi = -3\pi$. For the system of Fig. 12.37, $N = 2$ and $P = 0$. Application of the Nyquist stability criterion gives $Z = N + P = 2$. Thus, the system is basically unstable, as was previously determined using the direct polar plot.

On direct polar plots instability is indicated when the frequency response crosses the negative real axis outside the -1 point (e.g., see Fig. 12.3). On inverse polar plots instability is indicated when the frequency response crosses the negative real axis inside the -1 point (e.g., see Fig. 12.37).

PROBLEMS

12.1 For each of the $G(s)H(s)$ plots shown in Fig. P12.1, the path of values for s is the same as that shown in Fig. 12.2. For each plot, determine the number of roots of the characteristic equation which are located in the right half plane ($P = 0$ in all cases).

For each stable system, determine the factor by which the gain should be changed so that the system will just become unstable.

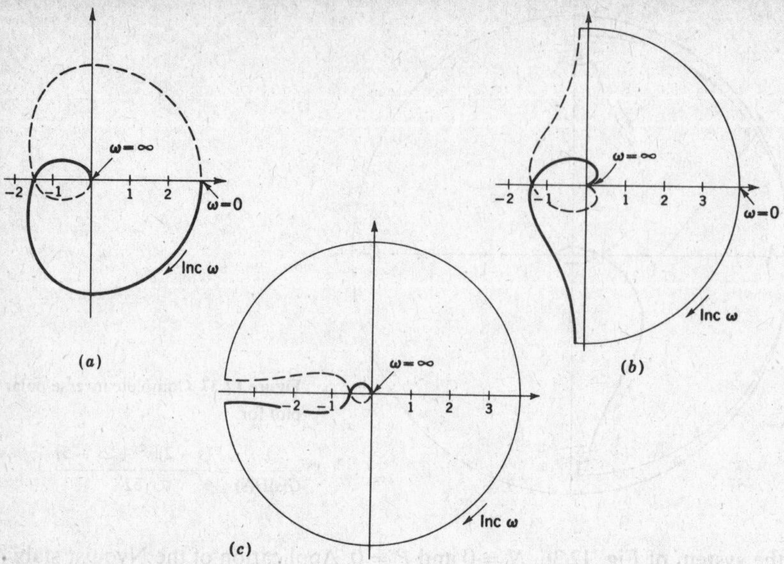

Figure P12.1

For each unstable system, determine the factor by which the gain should be changed so that the system will just become stable.

12.2 For each of the following unity-feedback systems, sketch the complete $G(s)$ plot, and determine the number of roots of the characteristic equation that lie in the right half plane:

(a) $G(s) = \dfrac{10}{(1 + 0.25s)(0.25s^2 + 0.40s + 1)}$

(b) $G(s) = \dfrac{10}{s(1 + 0.25s)}$

(c) $G(s) = \dfrac{10}{s^2(1 + 0.25s)}$ (d) $G(s) = \dfrac{10(1 + s)}{s^2(1 + 0.25s)}$

12.3 Plot the log-magnitude diagram for the system given in Prob. 12.2(a). For this system, determine

(a) The gain margin and the phase margin

(b) The factor by which the gain should be changed to yield a gain margin of 5

(c) The factor by which the gain should be changed to yield a phase margin of 40°

12.4 The open-loop transfer function for a unity-feedback system is

$$G(s) = \frac{2}{s(1 + s)(1 + 2s)}$$

The Bode diagram for this system is shown in Fig. P12.4.

(a) Determine the factor K_c by which the gain should be changed so that the resulting system will have a phase margin of 45°.

(b) Determine the factor K_c by which the gain should be changed so that the resulting system will have a gain margin of 5.

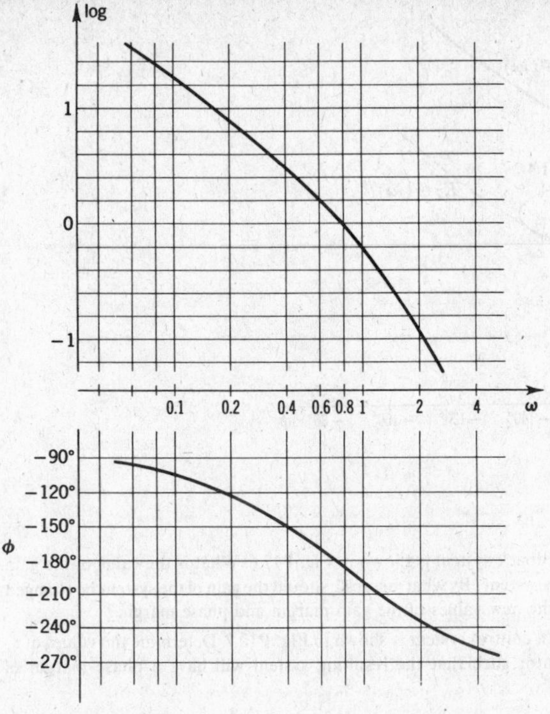

Figure P12.4

12.5 The Nichols plot of $G(j\omega)$ for a unity-feedback system is shown in Fig. P12.5.

(*a*) Determine the gain margin and the phase margin for this system.

(*b*) By what factor K_c should the gain K of the system be changed so that the system will have a phase margin of 45°?

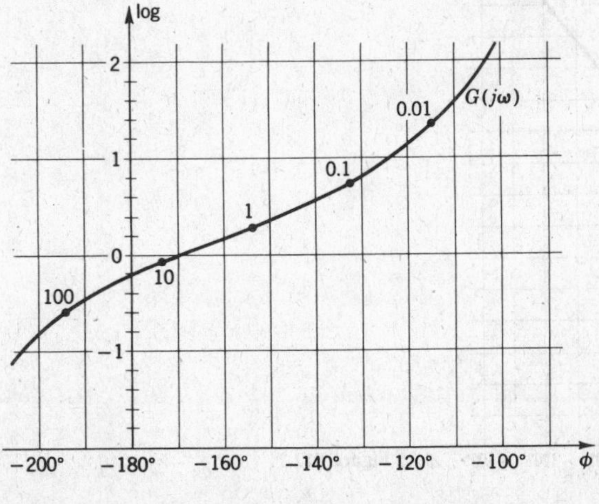

Figure P12.5

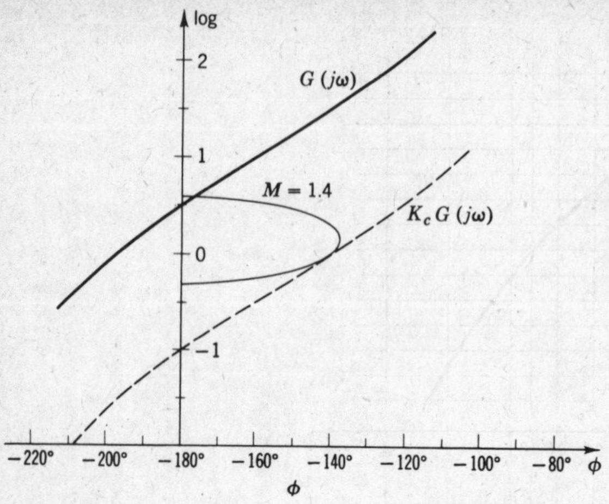

Figure P12.6

12.6 A plot of $G(j\omega)$ for a unity-feedback system is shown in Fig. P12.6. What is the value of the gain margin and the phase margin for this system? By what factor K_c should the gain of the system be changed so that M_p will be 1.4? What are the new values of the gain margin and phase margin?

12.7 The log-modulus diagram for a control system is shown in Fig. P12.7. Determine the values of τ_1 and τ_2 for a series lead compensator such that the resulting system will have a phase margin of $35° \pm 3°$.

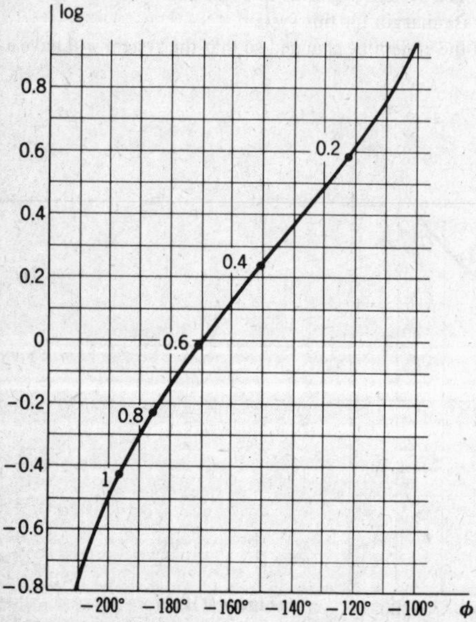

Figure P12.7

12.8 Same as Prob. 12.7 except use a lag compensator.

12.9 Same as Prob. 12.7 except use a lag-lead compensator.

12.10 The log-magnitude diagram shown in Fig. P12.10 is for the unity-feedback system

$$G(s) = \frac{4}{(s + 1)[(s^2 + 8s + 25)/25]}$$

(*a*) Find the values of τ_1 and τ_2 for a series lag-lead compensator such that the resulting system will have a phase margin of 45° ± 3°.

(*b*) Use Fig. P12.10 to construct the log-modulus plot for this system. Using this plot, verify the results of part (*a*).

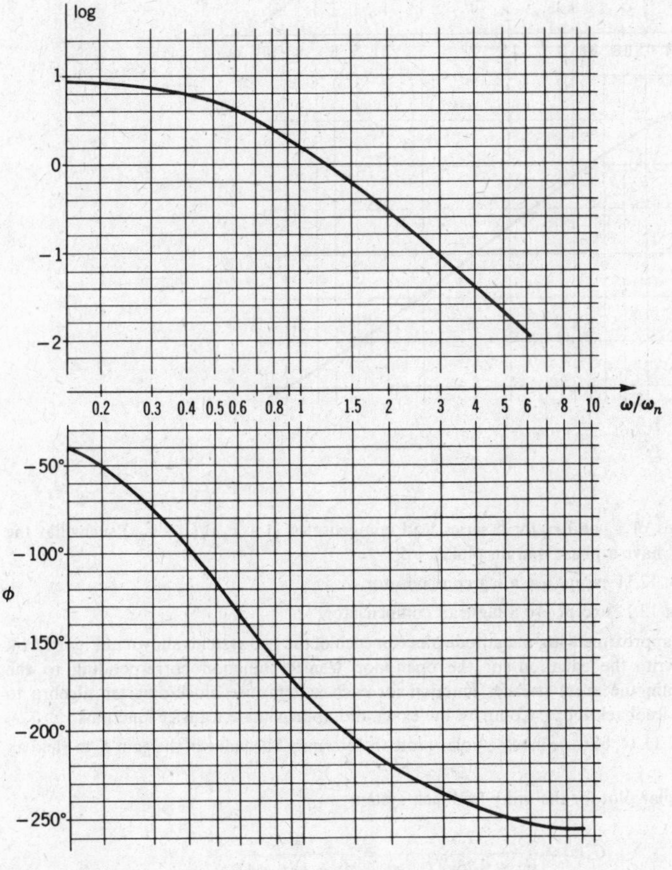

Figure P12.10

12.11 In Fig. P12.11 is shown the log-magnitude diagram for the unity-feedback system

$$G(s) = \frac{2.5}{s(1 + 0.25s)(1 + s)}$$

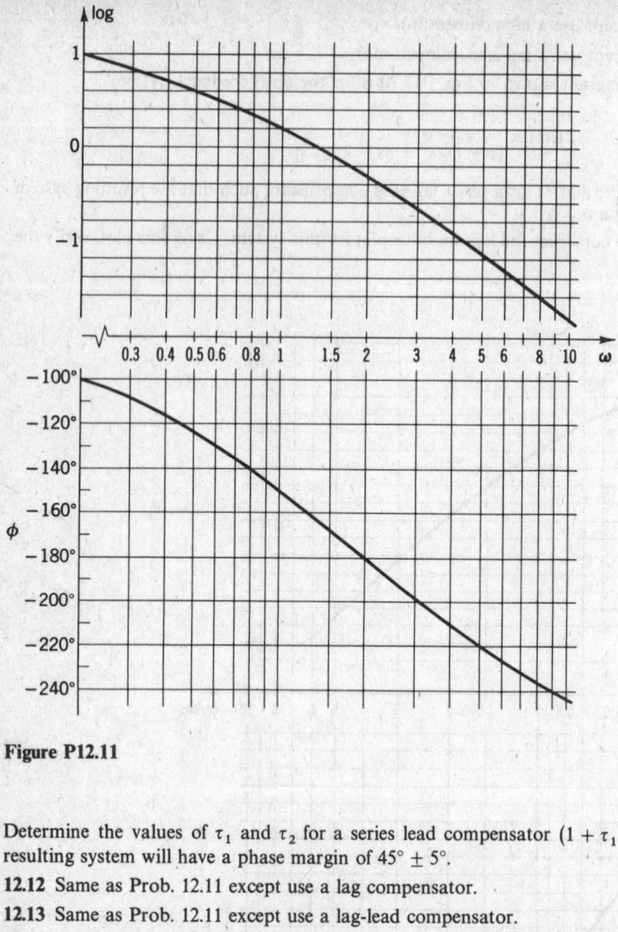

Figure P12.11

Determine the values of τ_1 and τ_2 for a series lead compensator $(1 + \tau_1 s)/(1 + \tau_2 s)$ such that the resulting system will have a phase margin of $45° \pm 5°$.

12.12 Same as Prob. 12.11 except use a lag compensator.

12.13 Same as Prob. 12.11 except use a lag-lead compensator.

12.14 Construct the approximate log-magnitude plots for each of the two systems shown in Fig. P12.14. For each system, write the equation for the open-loop transfer function corresponding to the asymptotes. To obtain the exact transfer function for each system, use block-diagram algebra to eliminate the minor feedback loops. Compare the exact and approximate transfer functions.

12.15 Same as Prob. 11.14, but use inverse polar plots to determine the value of the gain K to yield an M_p of 1.4.

12.16 The inverse polar plot for the unity-feedback system

$$G_1(s) = \frac{2.5}{s(1 + 0.25s)(1 + s)} = \frac{10}{s(s + 1)(s + 4)}$$

is shown in Fig. P12.16. For internal feedback compensation of the form $H_1(s) = \alpha + \beta s$, determine the values of α and β such that the resulting system will have an M_p of 1.4 and ω_p occurs at $\omega = 2$.

12.17 Use inverse polar plots to determine the value of β such that the system of Fig. P12.17 will have an M_p of 1.4.

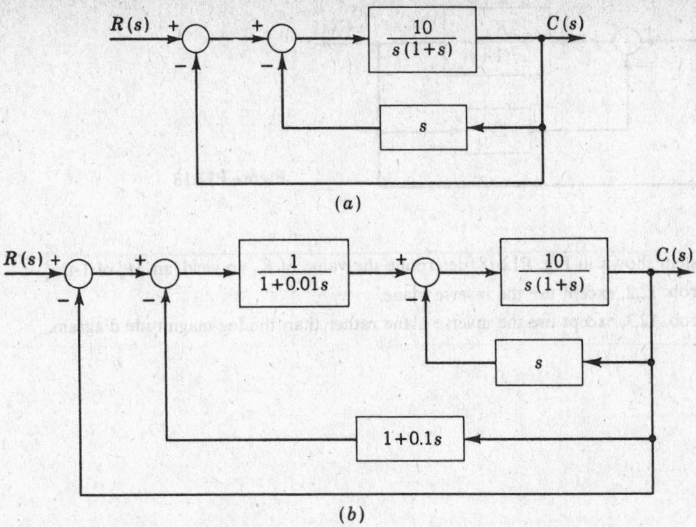

Figure P12.14

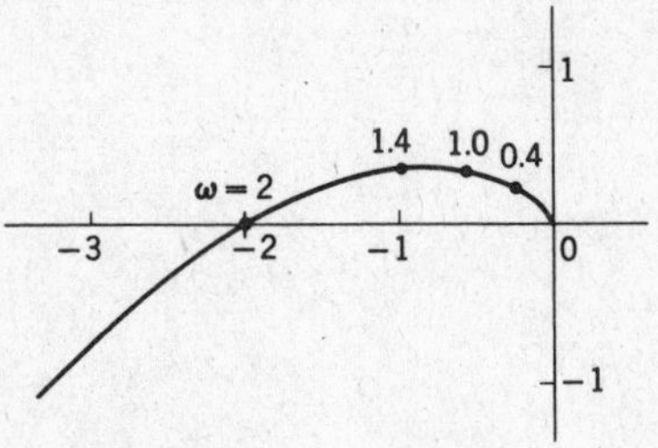

Figure P12.16

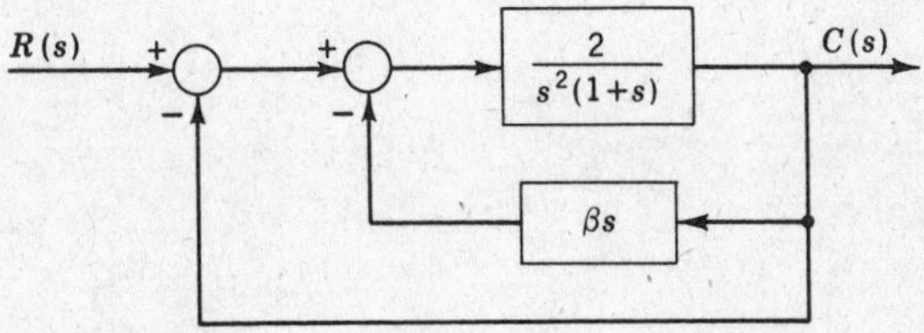

Figure P12.17

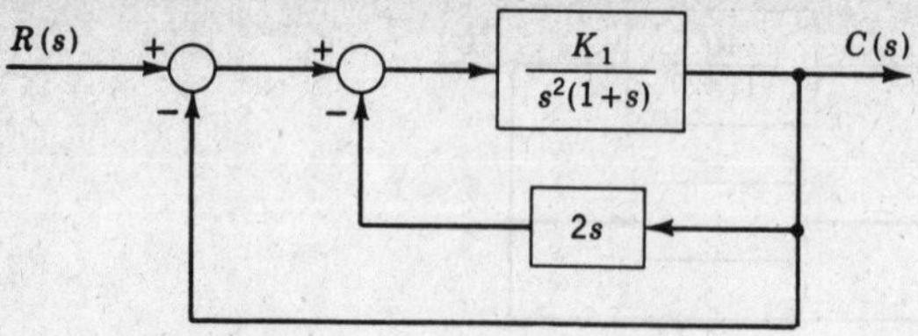

Figure P12.18

12.18 For the system shown in Fig. P12.18, determine the value of K_1 to yield an M_p of 1.4.

12.19 Same as Prob. 12.2, except use the inverse plane.

12.20 Same as Prob. 12.3, except use the inverse plane rather than the log-magnitude diagram.

CHAPTER

THIRTEEN

DESCRIBING FUNCTIONS

In Fig. 13.1 is shown a nonlinear element N in which x is the input and y is the output. The describing function method is applicable for any nonlinearity N which has the characteristic that if the input is a sinusoid ($x = x_0 \sin \omega t$), the output y is a periodic function.[1] Because of its simplicity and wide range of applicability, the describing function method is probably the most versatile technique for investigating nonlinear effects.

13.1 THE DESCRIBING FUNCTION

The operating characteristics of an on-off control element are shown in Fig. 13.2. When the input x is greater than zero, the value of the output is Y_0. When x is less than zero, the output is $-Y_0$. The equation for this element is

$$y = \begin{cases} Y_0 & x > 0 \\ -Y_0 & x < 0 \end{cases} \tag{13.1}$$

A plot of the sinusoidal input $x = x_0 \sin \omega t$ is drawn vertically down from the on-off contactor characteristic of Fig. 13.2. The corresponding output is shown horizontally to the right.

[1] R. J. Kochenburger, A Frequency Response Method for Analyzing and Synthesizing Contactor Servomechanisms, *Trans. AIEE*, **69**: 270–284 (1950).

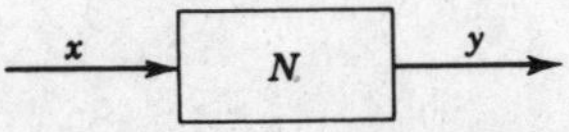

Figure 13.1 Nonlinear element N.

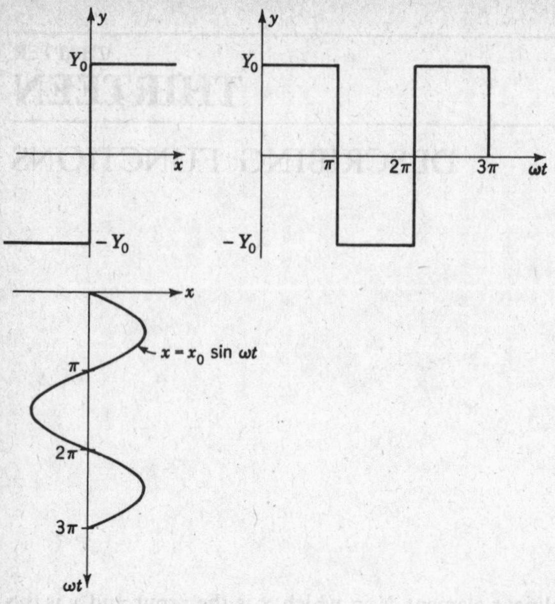

Figure 13.2 Characteristics of an on-off element.

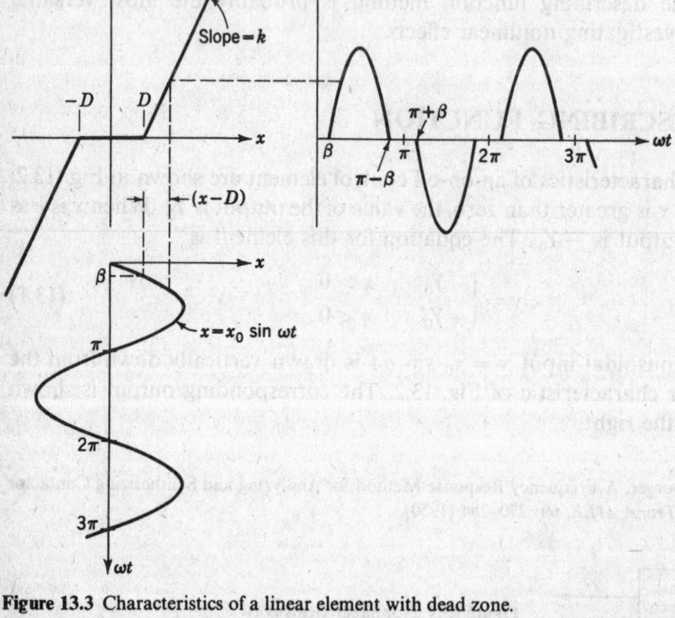

Figure 13.3 Characteristics of a linear element with dead zone.

Another nonlinearity which is frequently encountered is that of dead zone, or dead band, which is illustrated in Fig. 13.3. For $x > D$, the output is $k(x - D) = k(x_0 \sin \omega t - D)$. The overall equation of operation is

$$y = \begin{cases} k(x_0 \sin \omega t - D) & x > D \\ 0 & 0 \le x \le D \end{cases} \tag{13.2}$$

From the $x = x_0 \sin \omega t$ curve of Fig. 13.3, note that when $x = D$, then $\omega t = \beta$. Thus,

$$D = x_0 \sin \beta$$

or

$$\beta = \sin^{-1} \frac{D}{x_0} \tag{13.3}$$

Nonlinearities are usually such that for a sinusoidal input ($x = x_0 \sin \omega t$), the output y is an odd function of period 2π. As is illustrated in Fig. 13.4, an odd function has symmetry such that if the portion for the first half of the period (0 to π) is reflected about a vertical axis through π, and then reflected about the horizontal axis, it falls upon (coincides with) the function for the second half of the period (π to 2π). The Fourier series representation for an odd function of period 2π is

$$f(\theta) = B_1 \sin \theta + B_2 \sin 2\theta + B_3 \sin 3\theta + \cdots \tag{13.4}$$

where

$$B_n = \frac{1}{\pi} \int_0^{2\pi} f(\theta) \sin n\theta \, d\theta$$

$$= \frac{2}{\pi} \int_0^{\pi} f(\theta) \sin n\theta \, d\theta \qquad n = 1, 2, 3, \ldots \tag{13.5}$$

The value of B_n for the on-off element of Fig. 13.2 is

$$B_n = \frac{2}{\pi} \int_0^{\pi} Y_0 \sin n\theta \, d\theta = -\frac{2Y_0}{n\pi} [\cos n\theta]_0^{\pi}$$

$$= \begin{cases} \dfrac{4Y_0}{n\pi} & n = 1, 3, 5, \ldots \\ 0 & n = 2, 4, 6, \ldots \end{cases}$$

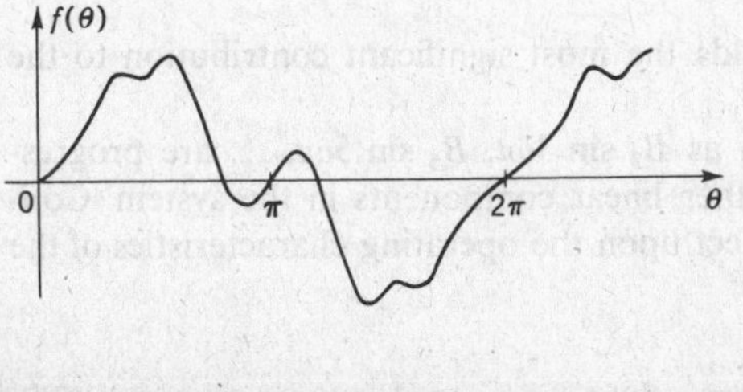

Figure 13.4 Odd function.

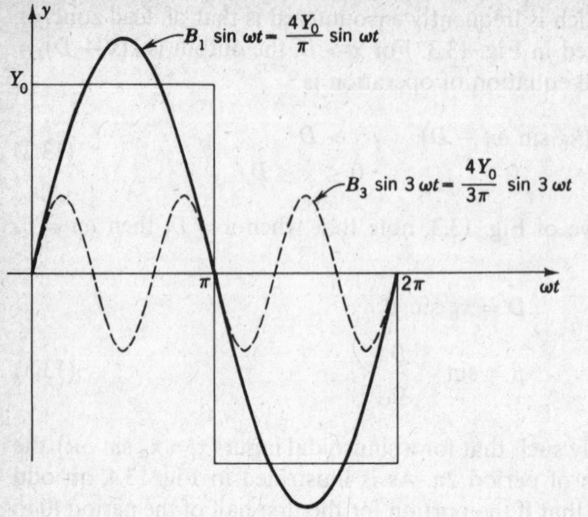

Figure 13.5 Graphical interpretation of series expansion for a square wave.

The resulting Fourier series representation for y is

$$y = \frac{4Y_0}{\pi}\left(\sin \omega t + \frac{1}{3}\sin 3\omega t + \frac{1}{5}\sin 5\omega t + \cdots\right) \tag{13.6}$$

where $\theta = \omega t$. The coefficients $B_2, B_4, B_6, \ldots$ are zero whenever the function has the additional symmetry such that if the portion from 0 to $\pi/2$ is reflected about a vertical axis through $\pi/2$, it falls upon (coincides with) the portion for the interval from $\pi/2$ to π. Thus, in the interval 0 to π the function is an even function with respect to the vertical axis through $\pi/2$. This is the case for the functions shown in Figs. 13.2 and 13.3.

In Fig. 13.5 is shown the original output y of Fig. 13.2, and also the first two terms of the series expansion for this function. The sum of all the terms would yield the original function which is a square wave. However, the fundamental component $B_1 \sin \omega t$ is seen to yield the most significant contribution. Good results are obtained in the analysis of such nonlinear control elements by approximating the output by its fundamental component.

$$y \approx B_1 \sin \omega t \tag{13.7}$$

The two major reasons why the fundamental component yields good results in approximating the characteristics of a nonlinear element are:

1. The fundamental component yields the most significant contribution to the output.
2. The higher-frequency terms such as $B_3 \sin 3\omega t$, $B_5 \sin 5\omega t$, ... are progressively attenuated more by the other linear components in the system. Consequently, they have less of an effect upon the operating characteristics of the system.

The operation of the on-off element of Fig. 13.2 is thus approximated by the ratio

$$N = \frac{y}{x} \approx \frac{B_1 \sin \omega t}{x_0 \sin \omega t} = \frac{B_1}{x_0} = \frac{4Y_0}{\pi x_0} \tag{13.8}$$

where $N = y/x$ is called the describing function because it describes the relationship between the output and input.

For tne element with dead zone shown in Fig. 13.3, it follows that when $x_0 > D$,

$$B_1 = \frac{2}{\pi}\int_0^{\pi} f(\theta)\sin\theta\, d\theta = \frac{2}{\pi}\int_{\beta}^{\pi-\beta} k(x_0 \sin\theta - x_0 \sin\beta)\sin\theta\, d\theta$$

$$= \frac{2kx_0}{\pi}\left[\left(\frac{\theta}{2} - \frac{\sin 2\theta}{4}\right) + \cos\theta\sin\beta\right]_{\beta}^{\pi-\beta}$$

$$= \frac{2kx_0}{\pi}\left(\frac{\pi - 2\beta}{2} - \frac{\sin 2\beta}{2}\right)$$

Thus, the describing function N is

$$N = \frac{y}{x} \approx \frac{B_1}{x_0} = \begin{cases} \dfrac{k}{\pi}(\pi - 2\beta - \sin 2\beta) & x_0 > D \\ 0 & 0 \le x_0 \le D \end{cases} \tag{13.9}$$

When $0 \le x_0 \le D$, the output is zero.

Because $\beta = \sin^{-1}(D/x_0)$, a plot of N/k versus x_0/D may be constructed as shown in Fig. 13.6.

Adding (or subtracting) the describing function for known nonlinearities yields the describing function for the sum (or difference) of the nonlinearities. As is illustrated in Fig. 13.7, the input $x = x_0 \sin \omega t$ enters both the nonlinear element N_a and the nonlinear element N_b. The fundamental component of the output from

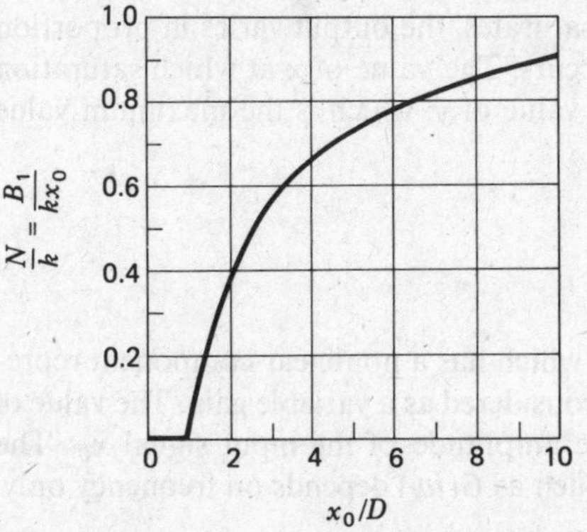

Figure 13.6 Describing function for linear element with dead zone.

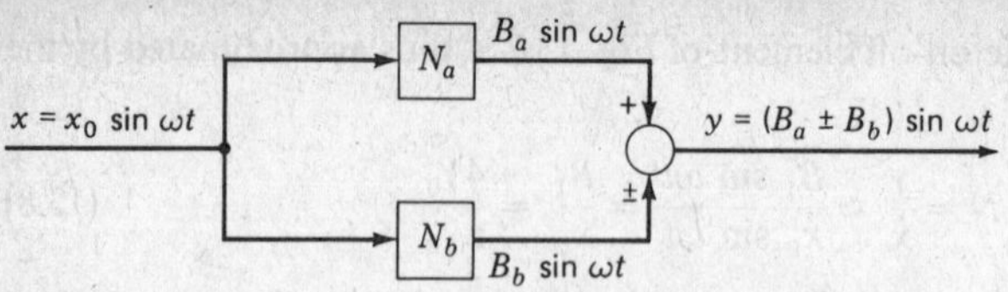

Figure 13.7 Adding or subtracting describing functions.

N_a is $B_a \sin \omega t$, and the fundamental component of the output from N_b is $B_b \sin \omega t$. The resultant fundamental component of the output y is $B_a \sin \omega t \pm B_b \sin \omega t$. Thus, the overall describing function is

$$N = \frac{y}{x} \approx \frac{(B_a \pm B_b) \sin \omega t}{x_0 \sin \omega t} = \frac{B_a}{x_0} \pm \frac{B_b}{x_0} = N_a \pm N_b$$

As is illustrated in Fig. 13.8, subtracting N_2 from N_1 yields the nonlinearity N whose characteristic is

$$N = N_1 - N_2 \tag{13.10}$$

The equation for N_1 is

$$N_1 = \frac{y}{x} = k \qquad \text{or} \qquad \frac{N_1}{k} = 1 \tag{13.11}$$

For convenience in graphically subtracting the describing function for N_2 from N_1, the horizontal scale is made the same for both describing functions (that is, x_0/D). The function $N_1/k = 1$ is independent of x_0 and thus is also independent of x_0/D.

The equation for N is obtained by subtracting Eq. (13.9) from (13.11). Thus,

$$N = \begin{cases} \dfrac{k}{\pi}(2\beta + \sin 2\beta) & x_0 > D \quad \text{or} \quad \dfrac{x_0}{D} > 1 \\ k & 0 \le x_0 \le D \quad \text{or} \quad 0 \le \dfrac{x_0}{D} \le 1 \end{cases} \tag{13.12}$$

The resultant nonlinearity $N = N_1 - N_2$ is the characteristic of an element which saturates. For an element which saturates, the output varies in proportion to the input ($y = kx$) until saturation occurs. The value of x at which saturation occurs is $D = S$, and the corresponding value of y, which is the maximum value that y attains, is $kD = kS$.

13.2 STABILITY ANALYSIS

In Fig. 13.9a is shown a control system which has a nonlinear component represented by N. The component N may be considered as a variable gain. The value of N, the variable gain, depends upon the amplitude of the input signal x_0. The frequency response for linear elements such as $G(j\omega)$ depends on frequency only.

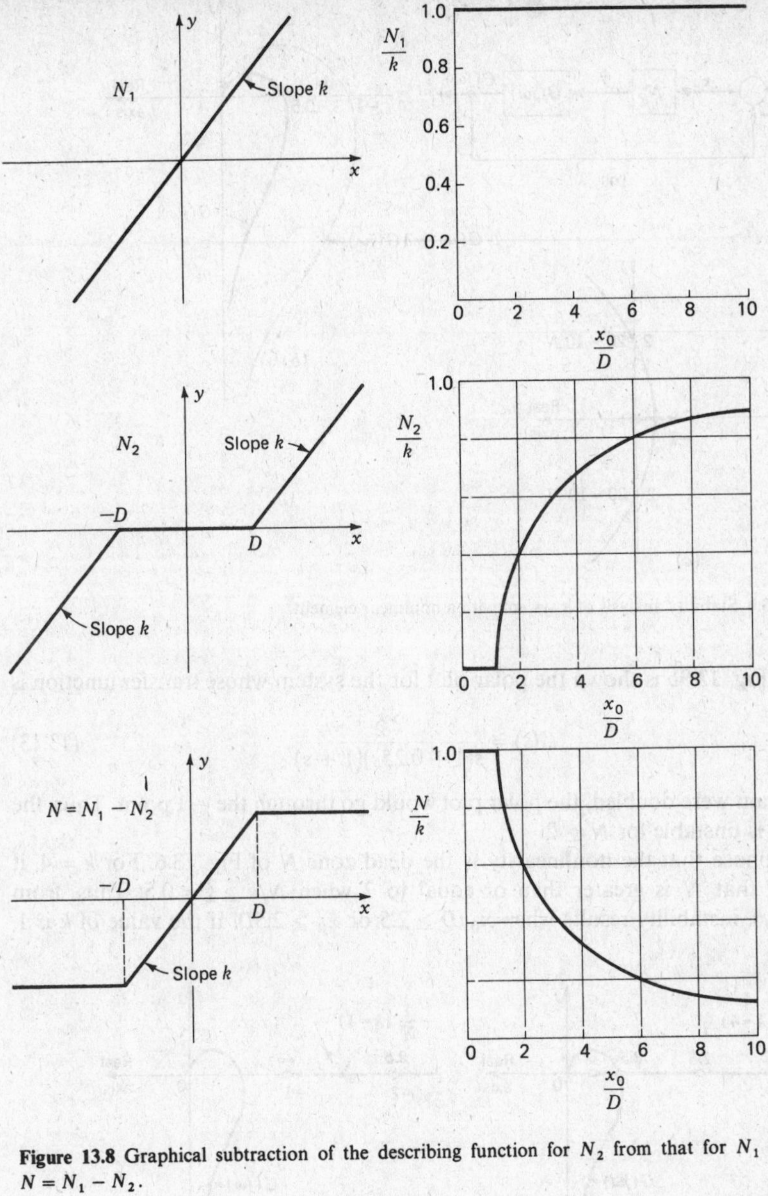

Figure 13.8 Graphical subtraction of the describing function for N_2 from that for N_1 to obtain $N = N_1 - N_2$.

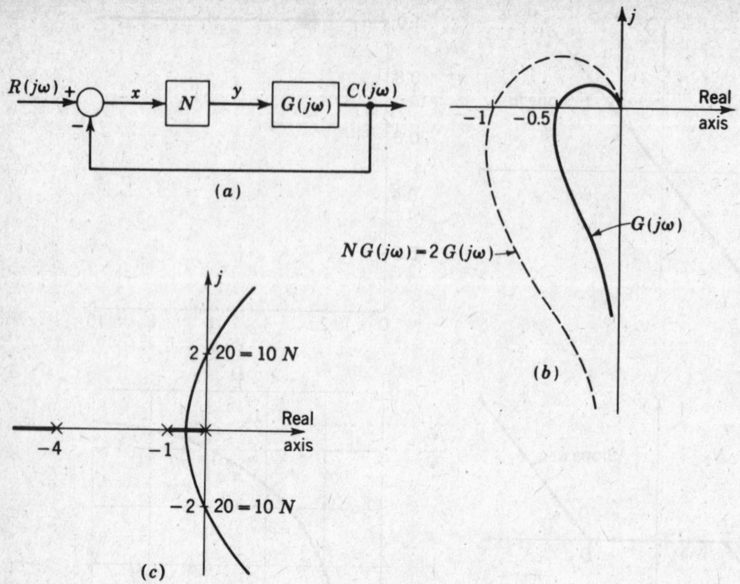

Figure 13.9 Stability analysis of a system with a nonlinear element.

In Fig. 13.9*b* is shown the polar plot for the system whose transfer function is

$$G(s) = \frac{2.5}{s(1 + 0.25s)(1 + s)} \tag{13.13}$$

If the gain were doubled, the polar plot would go through the −1 point. Thus, the system is unstable for $N \geq 2$.

Suppose that the nonlinearity is the dead zone N of Fig. 13.6. For $k = 4$, it follows that N is greater than or equal to 2 when $N/k \geq \frac{2}{4} = 0.5$. Thus, from Fig. 13.6, instability results when $x_0/D \geq 2.5$ or $x_0 \geq 2.5D$. If the value of k is 1,

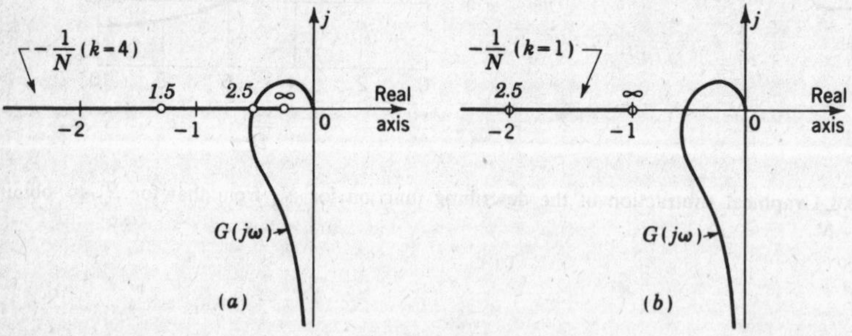

Figure 13.10 Plot of $-1/N$ for dead zone for (*a*) $k = 4$ and (*b*) $k = 1$.

instability results when $N/k \geq 2$. Instability cannot occur for this case because the maximum attainable value of N/k is 1.

Instead of the polar plot of Fig. 13.9*b*, the same information could also have been obtained by use of the log-magnitude diagram, the log-modulus plot, or the inverse polar plot. The root-locus method is also well suited to this type of problem. The characteristic equation for this system is

$$s(s+1)(s+4) + 10N = 0 \tag{13.14}$$

The corresponding root-locus plot is shown in Fig. 13.9*c*. Application of Routh's criterion shows that

$$s^3 + 5s^2 + 4s + 10N = 0$$

$$\begin{array}{ccc} 1 & 4 & 0 \\ 5 & 10N & 0 \\ \dfrac{(20-10N)}{5} & & \\ 10N & & \end{array}$$

The system becomes unstable when the gain $10N$ is 20. Thus instability results for $N \geq 2$.

Another method for investigating stability is to note that the overall system response is

$$\frac{C(j\omega)}{R(j\omega)} = \frac{NG(j\omega)}{1 + NG(j\omega)} \tag{13.15}$$

Instability results if

$$NG(j\omega) = -1$$

or

$$G(j\omega) = -\frac{1}{N} \tag{13.16}$$

When $G(j\omega)$ and $-1/N$ are plotted as shown in Fig. 13.10, an unstable system is indicated if the two curves intersect. The function $-1/N$ is plotted by obtaining N/k for various values of x_0/D from Fig. 13.6, and then computing $-1/N$ from the equation

$$-\frac{1}{N} = -\frac{1}{k(N/k)} \tag{13.17}$$

For example, when $x_0/D = \infty$, then $N/k = 1$. Thus, $-1/N = -1/k$. For $k = 4$, then $-1/N = -\frac{1}{4}$. Similarly, for $x_0/D = 2.5$, then $-1/N = 0.5$; and for $x_0/D = 1.5$, then $-1/N = -1.2$. In Fig. 13.10*a* values of x_0/D of 1.5, 2.5, and ∞ are italicized along the $-1/N$ curve. The location of the $-1/N$ point plays the same role with regard to stability as does the -1 point for a linear system. For $0 < x_0/D < 2.5$, the $-1/N$ point lies outside the $G(j\omega)$ curve, and the resulting

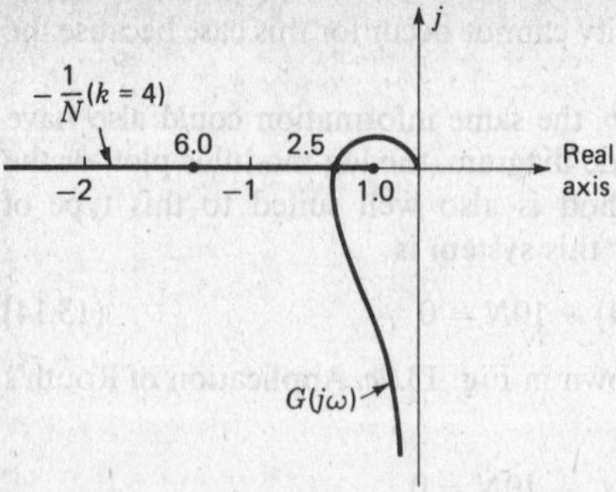

Figure 13.11 Plot of $-1/N$ for saturation ($k = 4$).

system is stable. In this region, the amplitude x_0 decreases in such a way that the $-1/N$ point moves toward the value $x_0/D = 0$. For $2.5 < x_0/D < \infty$, the $-1/N$ point lies inside the $G(j\omega)$ curve and the resulting system is unstable. In this region, the amplitude x_0 increases in such a way that the $-1/N$ point moves toward the value $x_0/D = \infty$. Thus, if the amplitude x_0 ever exceeds the value $x_0/D = 2.5$, the system becomes unstable.

The case in which $k = 1$ rather than 4 is shown in Fig. 13.10*b*. Because the $-1/N$ and $G(j\omega)$ curves do not intersect, the system is always stable.

A substantially different $-1/N$ curve results when the nonlinear element is saturation rather than dead zone. In Fig. 13.11 is shown the $-1/N$ plot for $k = 4$. From Fig. 13.8, it follows that for $x_0/D = 1$, then $N/k = 1$. Thus $-1/N = -1/[k(N/k)] = -\frac{1}{4}$. For $x_0/D = 2.5$, then $N/k = 0.5$. Thus $-1/N = -\frac{1}{2}$. For $1.0 < x_0/D < 2.5$, the $-1/N$ point lies inside the $G(j\omega)$ plot. Because the system is unstable, the amplitude x_0 increases in such a way that the $-1/N$ point moves toward the point of intersection, where $x_0/D = 2.5$. For $x_0/D > 2.5$, the $-1/N$ point lies outside the $G(j\omega)$ plot. Because the resulting system is stable, the amplitude x_0 decreases, so that the $-1/N$ point moves toward the point of intersection, where $x_0/D = 2.5$. Thus, this system always tends to operate at the point of intersection of the $-1/N$ plot and the $G(j\omega)$ plot. The amplitude and frequency of the signal at the point of intersection are obtained by noting that at the intersection

$$G(j\omega) = -\frac{1}{N} \qquad \text{or} \qquad N = -\frac{1}{G(j\omega)}$$

Substitution of numerical values gives

$$N = \frac{-j\omega(1 + 0.25j\omega)(1 + j\omega)}{2.5} = \frac{\frac{5}{4}\omega^2 - j\omega(1 - \omega^2/4)}{5/2}$$

For the equality to hold, the real parts must be equal and the imaginary parts must be equal. Because N is real, it follows from the imaginary parts that

$$1 - \frac{\omega^2}{4} = 0 \qquad \text{or} \qquad \omega = 2$$

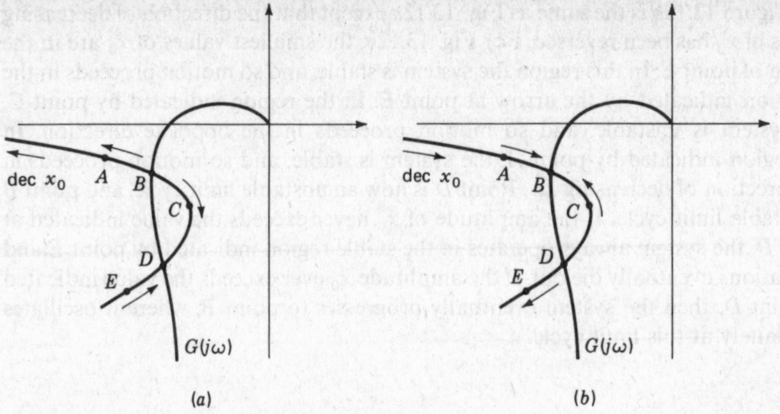

Figure 13.12 Stability analysis indentifying limit cycles.

At the point of intersection, the value of ω is 2. From the real parts, the value of N at the point of intersection is found to be

$$N = \frac{5\omega^2/4}{5/2} = \frac{\omega^2}{2} = \frac{(2)^2}{2} = 2$$

This verifies that the critical value of N is 2, and so $N/k = \frac{2}{4} = \frac{1}{2}$ and the corresponding value of x_0/D is 2.5. This system tends to want to oscillate at the frequency $\omega = 2$ and at the amplitude $x_0/D = 2.5$. Such an oscillatory type of motion is called a limit cycle.

In Fig. 13.12*a* is shown a general $-1/N$ curve and a typical $G(j\omega)$ plot. The direction of decreasing amplitude x_0 along the $-1/N$ curve is indicated. The point A lies outside the $G(j\omega)$ plot. This indicates a stable system, and so the amplitude of motion x_0 tends to decrease. As indicated by the arrow at point A, the amplitude moves in the direction of decreasing x_0. When the amplitude x_0 is such that operation is at point C, the system is unstable and the amplitude x_0 increases. As indicated by the arrow at point C, motion proceeds in the direction of increasing x_0. Point E is located in a region of stable operation. The arrow at point E indicates that the amplitude x_0 decreases in this region. It should be noted that in the vicinity of the intersection indicated by point B, the motion always proceeds away from point B. In the vicinity of the intersection indicated by point D, the motion always proceeds toward point D. If the amplitude x_0 never exceeds the value indicated at point B, the system always operates in the stable range and oscillations eventually die out. If the amplitude is ever such that x_0 is in the region indicated by points C or E, then operation will eventually progress to point D. The system then oscillates indefinitely at this limit cycle. The frequency ω of the oscillation is the value of ω at point D on the $G(j\omega)$ plot, and the value of N is obtained from the $-1/N$ plot at point D. Point B is an unstable limit cycle, and point D is a stable limit cycle.

Figure 13.12*b* is the same as Fig. 13.12*a* except that the direction of decreasing values of x_0 has been reversed. For Fig. 13.12*b*, the smallest values of x_0 are in the region of point *E*. In this region the system is stable, and so motion proceeds in the direction indicated by the arrow at point *E*. In the region indicated by point *C*, the system is unstable, and so motion proceeds in the opposite direction. In the region indicated by point *A*, the system is stable, and so motion proceeds in the direction of decreasing x_0. Point *D* is now an unstable limit cycle, and point *B* is a stable limit cycle. If the amplitude of x_0 never exceeds the value indicated at point *D*, the system always operates in the stable region indicated by point *E* and oscillations eventually die out. If the amplitude x_0 ever exceeds the value indicated at point *D*, then the system eventually progresses to point *B*, where it oscillates indefinitely at this limit cycle.

13.3 DESCRIBING FUNCTIONS WITH A PHASE SHIFT

The preceding discussion was limited to describing functions in which there was no phase shift between the input $x = x_0 \sin \omega t$ and the fundamental component $y \approx B_1 \sin \omega t$. In Fig. 13.13 is shown the input-output relationship for an on-off (contactor) element which has a hysteresis loop of width 2Δ. Starting from $x = 0$, as the amplitude of the input x is increased, the contactor does not close until x exceeds the value $x = \Delta$. The angle β at which the contactor closes is obtained from Fig. 13.13 as follows:

$$\Delta = x_0 \sin \beta$$

or

$$\beta = \sin^{-1} \frac{\Delta}{x_0} \tag{13.18}$$

The contactor now remains closed until the value of x is less than $-\Delta$. As indicated by the arrows in Fig. 13.13, in the region $-\Delta < x < \Delta$ the value of the output y depends on the past history (i.e., whether x is increasing or decreasing). There is a phase shift ϕ associated with the describing function for such nonlinearities in which for any one value of the input x there may be more than one value of the output y. In Fig. 13.14 is shown an enlarged view of the contactor output and the first harmonic component. The square-wave output begins at the angle β and terminates at $\pi + \beta$. Thus it is symmetrical about the angle $[\beta + (\pi + \beta)]/2 = \beta + \pi/2$. The equation for the fundamental harmonic is $B_1 \sin(\omega t + \phi)$. When $\omega t = \beta + \pi/2$, the fundamental is a maximum, $\sin(\omega t + \phi) = 1$ or $\omega t + \phi = \pi/2$. Thus, the phase shift ϕ is

$$\phi = \frac{\pi}{2} - \left(\beta + \frac{\pi}{2}\right) = -\beta = -\sin^{-1} \frac{\Delta}{x_0} \tag{13.19}$$

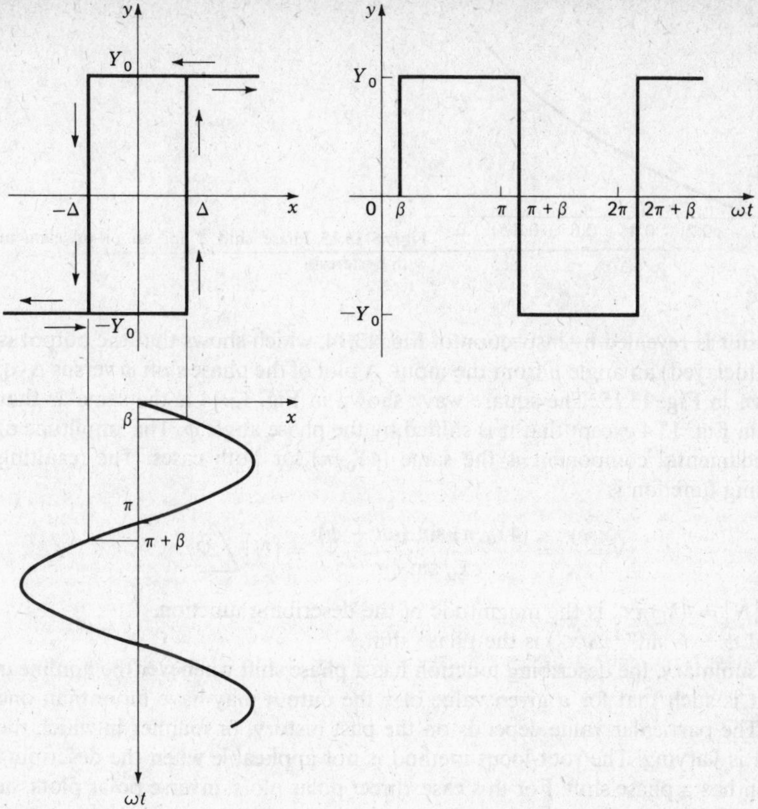

Figure 13.13 Characteristics of an on-off element with hysteresis.

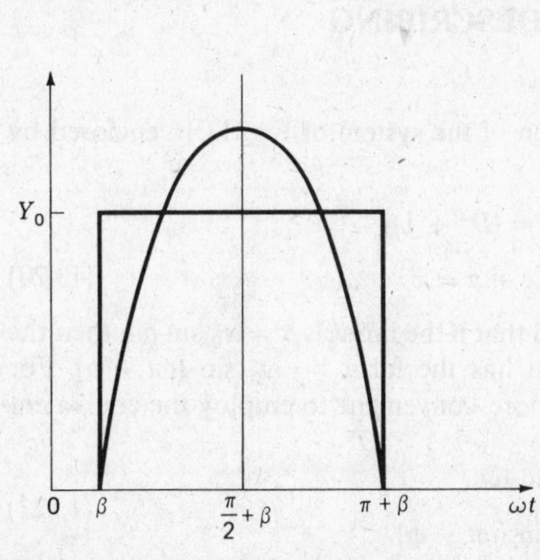

Figure 13.14 Fundamental component of on-off element with hysteresis.

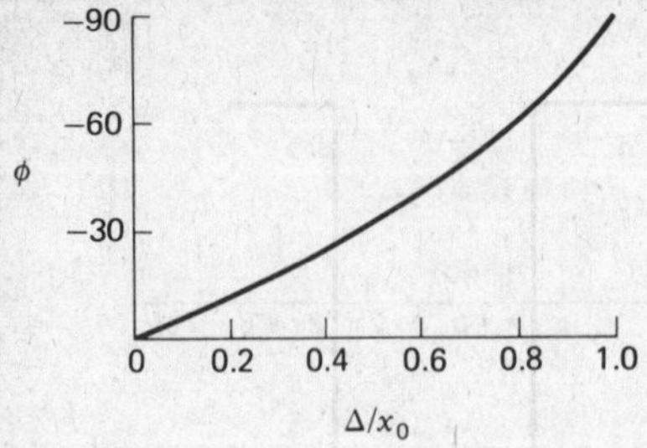

Figure 13.15 Phase shift ϕ for an on-off element with hysteresis.

This result is revealed by inspection of Fig. 13.14, which shows that the output is shifted (delayed) an angle β from the input. A plot of the phase shift ϕ versus Δ/x_0 is shown in Fig. 13.15. The square wave shown in Fig. 13.14 is the same as that shown in Fig. 13.4 except that it is shifted by the phase angle ϕ. The amplitude of the fundamental component is the same $(4Y_0/\pi)$ for both cases. The resulting describing function is

$$N = \frac{y}{x} = \frac{(4Y_0/\pi)\sin(\omega t + \phi)}{x_0 \sin \omega t} = |N|\angle\phi$$

where $|N| = 4Y_0/\pi x_0$ is the magnitude of the describing function and $\phi = -\sin^{-1}(\Delta/x_0)$ is the phase shift.

In summary, the describing function has a phase shift whenever the nonlinear element is such that for a given value of x the output may have more than one value. The particular value depends on the past history, or manner in which the input x is varying. The root-locus method is not applicable when the describing function has a phase shift. For this case, direct polar plots, inverse polar plots, or log-modulus diagrams must be used.

13.4 FREQUENCY-SENSITIVE DESCRIBING FUNCTIONS

The differential equation for the portion of the system of Fig. 13.16 enclosed by the dotted box is

$$(x - Dy^3) = (D^2 + 1)y$$

or

$$\ddot{y} + 3y^2\dot{y} + y = x \tag{13.20}$$

In the preceding sections it was assumed that if the input is $x = x_0 \sin \omega t$, then the fundamental component of the output has the form $y = y_0 \sin(\omega t + \phi)$. For nonlinear differential equations, it is more convenient to employ the equivalent form

$$\begin{aligned} y &= y_0 \sin \omega t \\ x &= x_0 \sin(\omega t - \phi) \end{aligned} \tag{13.21}$$

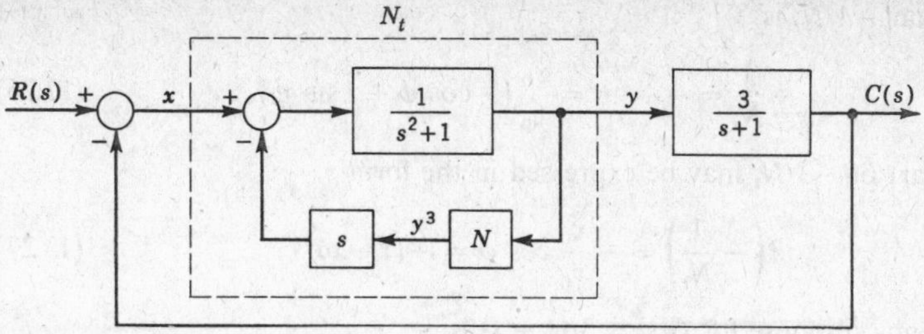

Figure 13.16 System with a frequency-sensitive describing function.

Substitution of these forms for x and y into Eq. (13.20) gives

$$-y_0\omega^2 \sin \omega t + 3y_0^3\omega \sin^2 \omega t \cos \omega t + y_0 \sin \omega t = x_0 \sin(\omega t - \phi)$$

or

$$y_0(1-\omega^2) \sin \omega t + 3y_0^3\omega(\cos \omega t - \cos^3 \omega t) = x_0 \sin(\omega t - \phi)$$

Replacing $\cos^3 \omega t$ by $(3 \cos \omega t + \cos 3\omega t)/4$ and neglecting higher-order harmonics (that is, $\cos 3\omega t$) gives

$$y_0(1-\omega^2) \sin \omega t + \tfrac{3}{4}y_0^3\omega \cos \omega t = x_0(\cos \phi \sin \omega t - \sin \phi \cos \omega t)$$

Equating $\sin \omega t$ terms and $\cos \omega t$ terms shows that

$$y_0(1-\omega^2) = x_0 \cos \phi \tag{13.22}$$

$$\tfrac{3}{4}y_0^3\omega = -x_0 \sin \phi \tag{13.23}$$

The total describing function N_t for the portion of the system of Fig. 13.16 enclosed by the dotted box is

$$N_t = \frac{y_0}{x_0} e^{j\phi} = \rho(\cos \phi + j \sin \phi)$$

where $\rho = y_0/x_0$.

Dividing Eq. (13.23) by (13.22) gives

$$\phi = \tan^{-1} \frac{3\omega(\rho x_0/2)^2}{1-\omega^2} \tag{13.24}$$

Similarly, squaring Eqs. (13.22) and (13.23) and adding gives

$$x_0^2 = \frac{4}{3\omega\rho^3}[1 - \rho^2(1-\omega^2)^2]^{1/2} \tag{13.25}$$

From Eq. (13.25), a family of curves of ρ versus x_0 for constant values of ω can be constructed. Similarly, from Eq. (13.24), a family of curves of ρ versus ϕ for constant values of ω may be constructed.

The function $-1/N_t$ is

$$-\frac{1}{N_t} = -\frac{e^{-j\phi}}{\rho} = \frac{x_0}{y_0}(-\cos\phi + j\sin\phi) \tag{13.26}$$

The real part of $-1/N_t$ may be expressed in the form

$$\mathscr{R}\left(-\frac{1}{N_t}\right) = -\frac{x_0}{y_0}\cos\phi = -(1-\omega^2) \tag{13.27}$$

The frequency response for $G(s) = 3/(1+s)$ is

$$G(j\omega) = \frac{3}{1+j\omega}\,\frac{1-j\omega}{1-j\omega} = \frac{3}{1+\omega^2} - j\frac{3\omega}{1+\omega^2} \tag{13.28}$$

Equating the real part of $G(j\omega)$ and the real part of $(-1/N_t)$ shows that these are equal when $\omega = \sqrt{2}$. In Fig. 13.17*a* is shown the polar plot $G(j\omega)$ and the $-1/N_t$ plot for $\omega = \sqrt{2}$. The real part of $-1/N_t$, given by Eq. (13.27), is $-(1-2) = 1.0$. The imaginary part of $-1/N_t$ is

$$\mathscr{I}\left(-\frac{1}{N_t}\right) = \frac{x_0}{y_0}\sin\phi = -\frac{3}{4}y_0^2\omega = \frac{-3\sqrt{2}}{4}\,y_0^2$$

Equating the imaginary parts of $-1/N_t$ and $G(j\omega)$ shows that at the intersection $\omega = \sqrt{2}$, the value of y_0 is $2/\sqrt{3}$. At this intersection, $|G(j\omega)| = \sqrt{3}$ and $|1/N_t| = \sqrt{3}$; hence sustained oscillations result, since the loop gain $|N_t|\,|G(j\omega)| = 1$. For $y_0 < 2/\sqrt{3}$, then $|N_t| > 1/\sqrt{3}$. The amplitude of y_0 increases because the loop gain

$$|N_t|\,|G(j\omega)| > 1$$

For $y_0 > 2/\sqrt{3}$, then $|N_t| < 1/\sqrt{3}$. The amplitude of y_0 now decreases because the loop gain is less than 1. Thus, the intersection $\omega = \sqrt{2}$ and $y_0 = 2/\sqrt{3}$ represents a point of sustained oscillation.

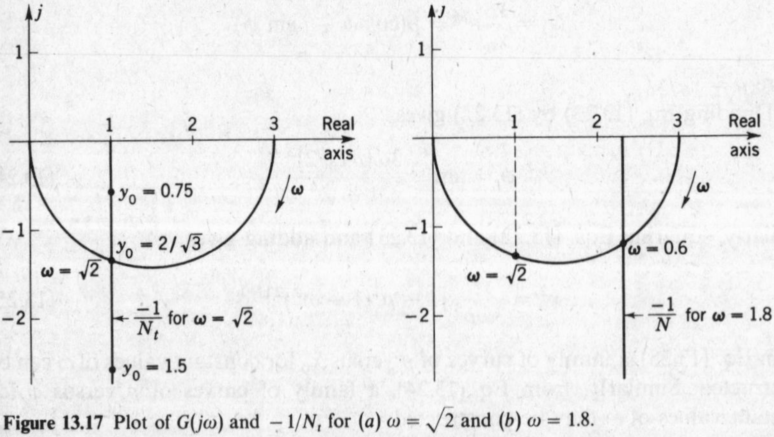

Figure 13.17 Plot of $G(j\omega)$ and $-1/N_t$ for (*a*) $\omega = \sqrt{2}$ and (*b*) $\omega = 1.8$.

In Fig. 13.17*b* is shown the $-1/N_t$ plot for $\omega = 1.8$. The real part of $-1/N_t$ is $-(1 - 3.24) = 2.24$. The value of ω on the $G(j\omega)$ plot at which the real part of $G(j\omega)$ is 2.24 is $\mathscr{R}\ G(j\omega) = 3/(1 + \omega^2)$. Solving for ω gives $\omega = 0.6$. Such a mismatch does not represent a sustained oscillation. In summary, although many $-1/N_t$ plots for various constant values of ω may intersect the $G(j\omega)$ plot, instability results only when the $-1/N_t$ curve drawn for a certain value of ω intersects the $G(j\omega)$ plot at the same frequency.

An alternative method of solving this problem is to obtain the describing function for the nonlinearity only, and then to proceed to construct the root-locus plot for the system. The output from the nonlinear element is

$$y_0^3 \sin^3 \omega t = y_0^3 \frac{3 \sin \omega t - \sin 3\omega t}{4}$$

Neglecting the higher-order harmonic yields for the describing function

$$N = \frac{3y_0^3 \sin \omega t}{4y_0 \sin \omega t} = \frac{3}{4} y_0^2 \tag{13.29}$$

The transfer function for the portion of the system enclosed by the dotted box of Fig. 13.16 is

$$\frac{G}{1 + GH} = \frac{1/(s^2 + 1)}{1 + Ns/(s^2 + 1)} = \frac{1}{s^2 + Ns + 1}$$

Thus, the characteristic equation for the entire system is

$$s^3 + (N + 1)s^2 + (N + 1)s + 4 = 0 \tag{13.30}$$

Application of Routh's criterion to determine the value of N at which the system becomes unstable gives

$$\begin{array}{ccc} 1 & N+1 & 0 \\ N+1 & 4 & 0 \\ \dfrac{[(N+1)^2 - 4]}{N+1} & 0 & 0 \\ 4 & 0 & 0 \end{array}$$

Thus, instability results when $(N + 1) \le 2$ or $N \le 1.0$. From Eq. (13.29), it follows that $y_0 \le 2/\sqrt{3}$.

To construct the root-locus plot, the characteristic equation is written in the form

$$(s^3 + 4) + Ks(s + 1) = 0$$

where $K = N + 1$. The three cube roots of (-4) are $1.59\underline{/60°}$, $1.59\underline{/180°}$, and $1.59\underline{/-60°}$. The root-locus plot is shown in Fig. 13.18. When the locus crosses the imaginary axis, the value of $K = N + 1$ is 2. Thus, the characteristic equation is

$$s^3 + 2s^2 + 2s + 4 = (s^2 + 2)(s + 2)$$

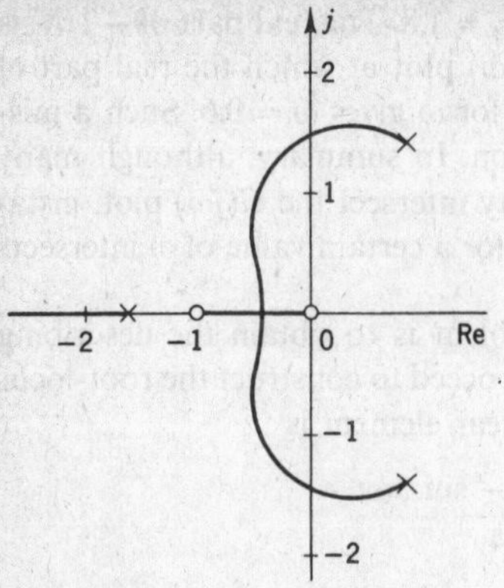

Figure 13.18 Root-locus plot for $(s^3 + 4) + Ks(s + 1)$ where $K = N + 1$.

The corresponding three roots are $s = \pm j\omega = \pm j\sqrt{2}$ and $s = -2$. Thus, $\omega = \sqrt{2}$ is the frequency of oscillation.

For the case in which $y_0 < 2/\sqrt{3}$, and thus $K = (N + 1) < 2$, the system has a pair of roots in the right half plane. The oscillation grows until $y_0 = 2/\sqrt{3}$. If the oscillations are such that $y_0 > 2/\sqrt{3}$, and thus $K = (N + 1) > 2$, all the roots of the characteristic equation are in the left half plane. The oscillations now decrease until $y_0 = 2/\sqrt{3}$. In summary, $y_0 = 2/\sqrt{3}$ and $\omega = \sqrt{2}$ represents an oscillatory state toward which the system tends. Such a state is referred to as a stable limit cycle.

PROBLEMS

13.1 Determine the describing function N for each of the nonlinear elements shown in Fig. P13.1.

13.2 The equation for B_n for a function of period 2π may be written in the form

$$B_n = \frac{1}{\pi}\int_0^{\pi} f(\theta)\sin n\theta\, d\theta + \frac{1}{\pi}\int_{\pi}^{2\pi} f(\theta)\sin n\theta\, d\theta$$

For an odd function, $f(\theta) = -f(2\pi - \theta)$ in the interval π to 2π. By making the change of variable from θ to $(2\pi - \theta)$ in the second integral for B_n, show that

$$B_n = \frac{2}{\pi}\int_0^{\pi} f(\theta)\sin n\theta\, d\theta$$

13.3 When the function $f(\theta)$ of Prob. 13.2 has the additional symmetry such that in the interval 0 to π it is an even function about the vertical $\theta = \pi/2$ axis, then $f(\theta) = f(\pi - \theta)$. The result of Prob. 13.2 may be written in the form

$$B_n = \frac{2}{\pi}\int_0^{\pi/2} f(\theta)\sin n\theta\, d\theta + \frac{2}{\pi}\int_{\pi/2}^{\pi} f(\theta)\sin n\theta\, d\theta$$

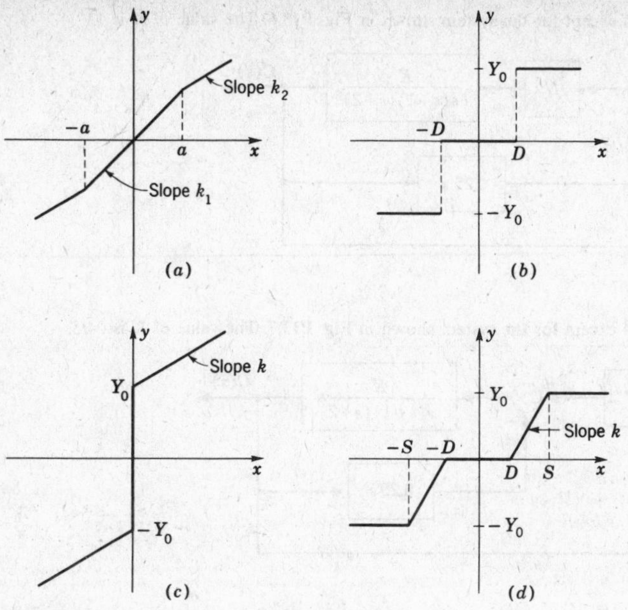

Figure P13.1

By making the change of variable from θ to $(\pi - \theta)$ in the last integral, show that

$$B_n = \begin{cases} \dfrac{4}{\pi}\displaystyle\int_0^{\pi/2} f(\theta) \sin n\theta \, d\theta & n = 1, 3, 5, \dots \\ 0 & n = 2, 4, 6, \dots \end{cases}$$

13.4 For the system shown in Fig. P13.4, the gain is $K = 3$. Determine the range of values of x_0 for which the system is stable if

(a) The nonlinear element is dead zone for which $k = 4$.
(b) The nonlinear element is saturation for which $k = 5$.
(c) The nonlinear element is an on-off device for which $Y_0 = 10$.

Determine the amplitude and frequency of the stable limit cycles.

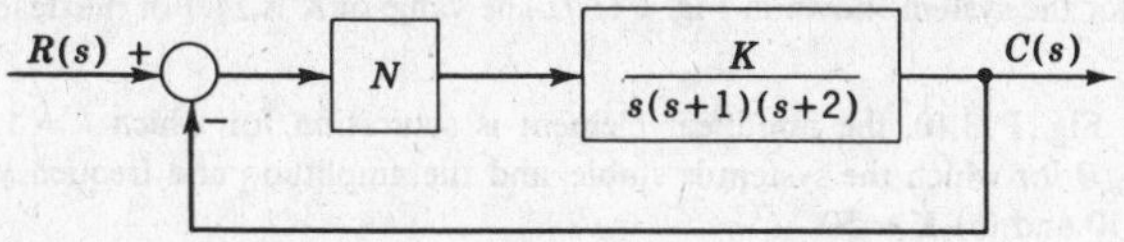

Figure P13.4

13.5 Same as Prob. 13.4 except for the system shown in Fig. P13.5. The value of K is 3.

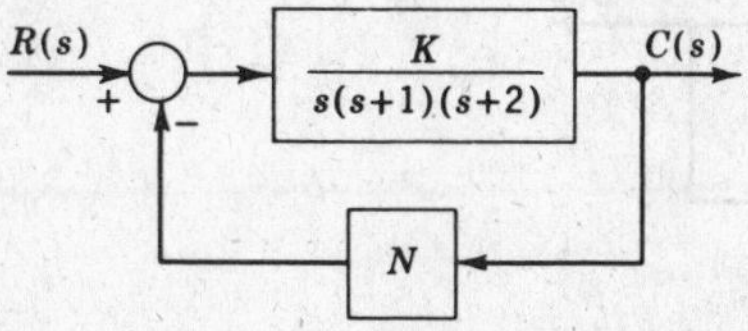

Figure P13.5

13.6 Same as Prob. 13.4 except for the system shown in Fig. P13.6. The value of K is 12.

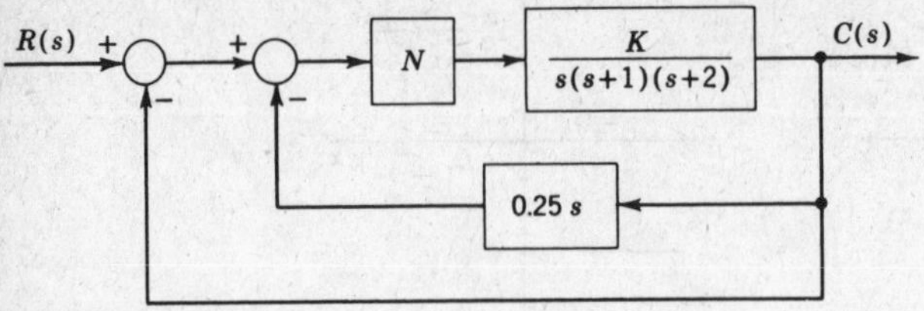

Figure P13.6

13.7 Same as Prob. 13.4 except for the system shown in Fig. P13.7. The value of K is 24/5.

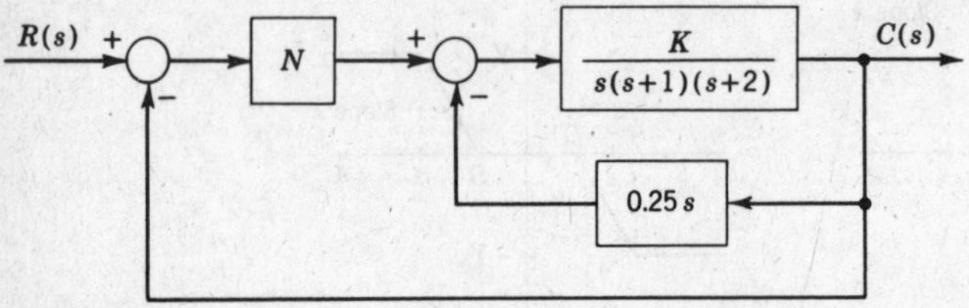

Figure P13.7

13.8 Same as Prob. 13.4 except for the system shown in Fig. P13.8. The value of K is 24. For the dead zone and saturation use $k = 2$.

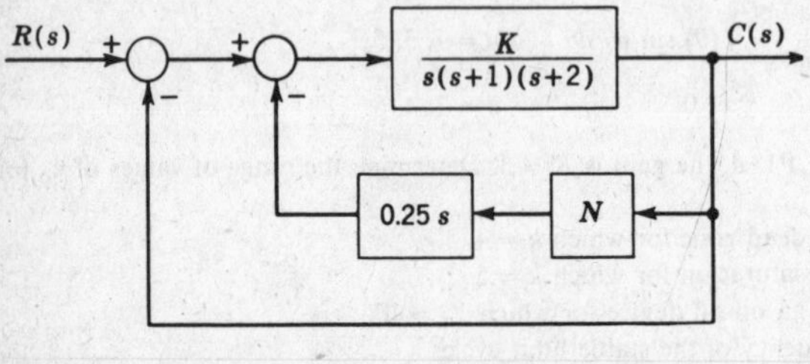

Figure P13.8

13.9 Same as Prob. 13.4 except for the system shown in Fig. P13.7. The value of K is 24. For the dead zone and saturation use $k = 2$.

13.10 For the system shown in Fig. P13.10, the nonlinear element is saturation for which $k = 1$. Specify the range of values of x_0/D for which the system is stable, and the amplitude and frequency of the limit cycle when (*a*) $K = 10$ and (*b*) $K = 50$.

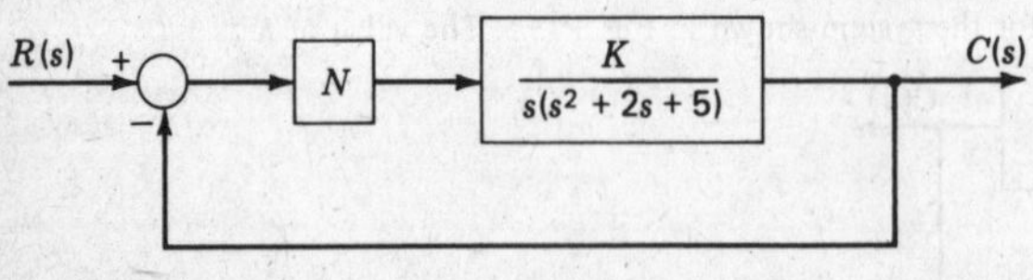

Figure P13.10

13.11 Same as Prob. 13.10 except that the nonlinear element is the on-off contactor with hysteresis shown in Fig. 13.13, for which $Y_0 = 2\pi$ and $\Delta = 1$.

13.12 Determine the describing function N for the nonlinear element shown in Fig. P13.12.

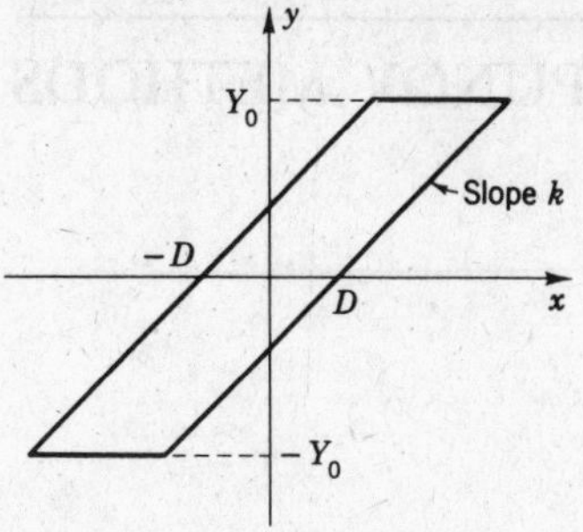

Figure P13.12

13.13 Determine the equation for the magnitude and the equation for the phase of the describing function N for the following nonlinear equation:

$$\ddot{y} + y^3 = x$$

13.14 The dotted box of Fig. 13.16 is replaced by the nonlinearity

$$y^2\dot{y} - y = x$$

Determine the frequency and amplitude of oscillation of the resulting system.

CHAPTER

FOURTEEN

THE PHASE-PLANE AND LIAPUNOV METHODS

The phase-plane method is basically a graphical procedure for determining the transient response of first- or second-order nonlinear systems. The Liapunov method is an extension of these stability concepts to higher-order nonlinear systems.

14.1 THE PHASE-PLANE METHOD

Consider the second-order nonlinear differential equation

$$\ddot{y} + f_1(y, \dot{y})\dot{y} + f_2(y, \dot{y})y = f(y, \dot{y}) \tag{14.1}$$

where $f_1(y, \dot{y})$, $f_2(y, \dot{y})$, and $f(y, \dot{y})$ are various functions of y and $\dot{y}$.

For the case in which $f_1(y, \dot{y})$ and $f_2(y, \dot{y})$ are both constant, Eq. (14.1) reduces to a linear differential equation with constant coefficients.

By letting

$$\dot{y} = v \tag{14.2}$$

then

$$\ddot{y} = \frac{dv}{dt} = \frac{dy}{dt}\frac{dv}{dy} = v\frac{dv}{dy} \tag{14.3}$$

The substitution of these values of $\dot{y}$ and $\ddot{y}$ into Eq. (14.1) gives

$$v\frac{dv}{dy} + f_1(y, v)v + f_2(y, v)y = f(y, v)$$

or

$$\frac{dv}{dy} = -f_1(y, v) - \frac{f_2(y, v)}{v}y + \frac{f(y, v)}{v} \tag{14.4}$$

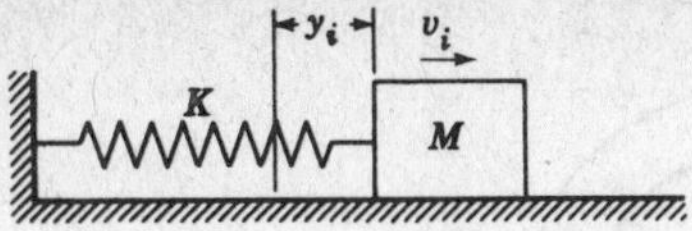

Figure 14.1 Mass-spring system.

The second-order differential equation, Eq. (14.1), may thus be represented by the two first-order equations, Eqs. (14.2) and (14.4).

To illustrate the basic principles involved in the phase-plane method, consider the mass-spring system shown in Fig. 14.1. The equation of motion is

$$M\ddot{y} + Ky = 0 \tag{14.5}$$

For $\dot{y} = v$, then $\ddot{y} = v(dv/dy)$. Thus,

$$Mv\frac{dv}{dy} = -Ky$$

The solution of this first-order differential equation is obtained directly by integration.

$$\int v\,dv = -\frac{K}{M}\int y\,dy$$

Thus

$$v^2 + \frac{K}{M}y^2 = C \tag{14.6}$$

The constant of integration is obtained by evaluating this result at $t = 0$.

$$C = v_i^2 + \frac{K}{M}y_i^2$$

where y_i = initial displacement
v_i = initial velocity

Equation (14.6) is the equation for an ellipse in the (y, v) coordinate system. Any ellipse may be plotted as a circle by changing the scale factor. Thus, with v as the vertical axis and $\sqrt{K/M}\,y$ as the horizontal axis, Eq. (14.6) is the equation of a circle with center at the origin and radius $R = \sqrt{C}$.

A phase-plane trajectory is a plot of all corresponding values of y and v that satisfy the system equation for a given set of initial conditions. A particular phase-plane trajectory for Eq. (14.6) is shown in Fig. 14.2*a*. The starting point has the coordinates $(\sqrt{K/M}\,y_i, v_i)$. Different trajectories corresponding to different values of the constant, $v_i^2 + (K/M)y_i^2$, are shown in Fig. 14.2*b*. The initial conditions determine the value of the constant, which in turn, determines the particular trajectory. The family of trajectories for a given system is called a phase portrait.

The trajectory for any conservative system in which there is no damping to dissipate energy must be a closed path. If there were damping in the system, the

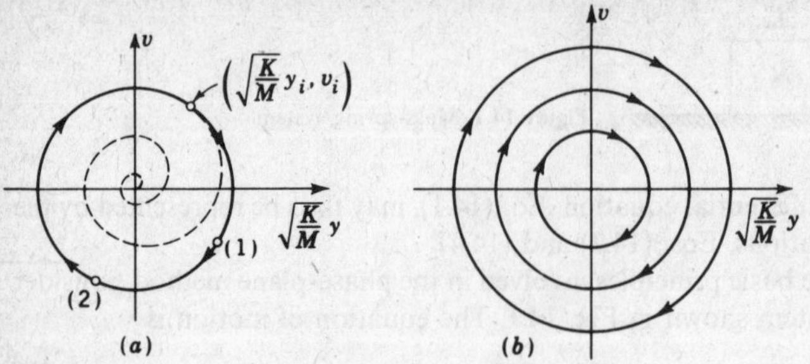

Figure 14.2 Phase-plane trajectories for mass-spring system.

path of operation would be a spiral in toward the origin, as is indicated by the dashed line in Fig. 14.2*a*.

From Eq. (14.3), the slope of the phase trajectory dv/dy is

$$\frac{dv}{dy} = \frac{1}{v}\ddot{y}$$

On the y axis the value of v is zero. Thus, each trajectory crosses the y axis at right angles ($dv/dy = \infty$).

Because $y = \int v\,dt$, for positive values of v the position y increases. That is, for values of v above the horizontal axis $v > 0$, the arrows on the trajectories indicate y moving to the right. For negative values of v (i.e., below the horizontal axis), the arrows on the trajectories show y decreasing by going to the left. Thus, as time increases, corresponding values of y and v proceed in a clockwise direction along the phase trajectory.

The time required for the operating point to move from any point (1) on a trajectory to a second point (2), as indicated in Fig. 14.2*a*, may be computed by integrating the equation

$$dt = \frac{dy}{v}$$

Thus,

$$t_2 - t_1 = \int_{y_1}^{y_2} \frac{dy}{v} = \int_{y_1}^{y_2} \frac{dy}{\sqrt{C - (K/M)y^2}}$$

When v is a more complicated function, this integration can become very difficult to evaluate. A graphical technique for approximating $\Delta t = t_2 - t_1$ is illustrated in Fig. 14.3. If the change is sufficiently small so that v does not vary much from its average value, then

$$\Delta t \approx \frac{\Delta y}{v_{av}}$$

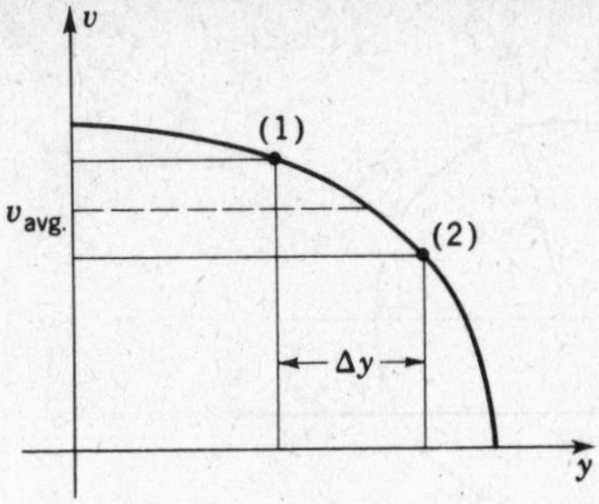

Figure 14.3 Graphical interpretation of $t_2 - t_1 = \Delta y / v_{av}$.

A more accurate procedure for approximating Δt is obtained by considering the system described by the differential equation

$$\ddot{y} + \omega_n^2 (y - y_c) = 0$$

Letting $\dot{y} = v$ and $\ddot{y} = v\, dv/dy$, then

$$v\, dv + \omega_n^2 (y - y_c)\, dy = 0$$

Integration yields

$$v^2 + \omega_n^2 (y^2 - 2y_c) = C$$

Adding $\omega_n^2 y_c^2$ to both sides yields the desired form

$$v^2 + \omega_n^2 (y - y_c)^2 = R^2 \tag{14.7}$$

where $R^2 = C + \omega_n^2 y_c^2$. When the horizontal axis is $\omega_n y$ and the vertical axis is v, this is the equation for a circle with center at $(\omega_n y_c, 0)$ and radius R. The radius is obtained by evaluating Eq. (14.7) at time $t = 0$. A typical trajectory is shown in Fig. 14.4*a*. As a point P travels along this trajectory, the horizontal component of the velocity of point P is $d(\omega_n y)/dt = \omega_n dy/dt = \omega_n \dot{y} = \omega_n v$, and the vertical component of velocity is $dv/dt = \ddot{y} = -\omega_n^2 (y - y_c)$. The magnitude of the velocity, which is the speed of point P along the path, is

$$\sqrt{(\omega_n v)^2 + (\ddot{y})^2} = \sqrt{\omega_n^2 [v^2 + \omega_n^2 (y - y_c)^2]} = \omega_n R$$

The distance along the circular path from point (1) to point (2) is the product of the speed $\omega_n R$ and the corresponding time Δt. The length of this circular arc is the product of the radius R and the included angle $\Delta\theta$. Because $\omega_n R\, \Delta t = R\, \Delta\theta$, then

$$\Delta t = \frac{\Delta\theta}{\omega_n}$$

When ω_n is unity, the plot of Fig. 14.4*a* becomes the phase-plane plot shown in Fig. 14.4*b*. The speed of point P in Fig. 14.4*b* is R, and

$$\Delta t = \Delta\theta$$

Thus, the time Δt is equal to the included angle $\Delta\theta$ measured in radians. A general path which is not circular is shown in Fig. 14.4*c*. Segments of such paths may be approximated by circular arcs. This is accomplished by first connecting points (1)

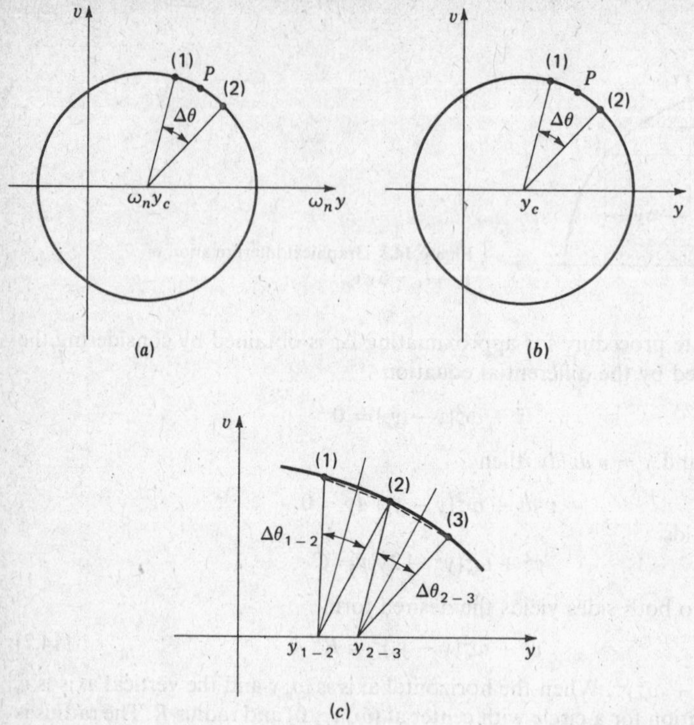

Figure 14.4 Determination of time to go from point (1) to point (2) on a phase trajectory.

and (2) by a straight line. The perpendicular bisector of this line intersects the horizontal axis at y_{1-2}, which is the center of the circular arc that passes from point (1) to point (2). The time required to go from point (1) to point (2) is equal to the subtended angle $\Delta\theta_{1-2}$. Similarly, points (2) and (3) are connected by a straight line. The perpendicular bisector of this line intersects the horizontal axis at y_{2-3}, which is the center of the circular arc that passes through points (2) and (3). The time required to go from point (2) to point (3) is equal to the subtended angle $\Delta\theta_{2-3}$. The total time required to go from point (1) to point (3) is

$$\Delta t_{1-3} = \Delta t_{1-2} + \Delta t_{2-3} = \Delta\theta_{1-2} + \Delta\theta_{2-3}$$

Coulomb Friction

When there is coulomb friction existing between the mass M of Fig. 14.1 and the surface over which it is sliding, the equation of motion is

$$M\ddot{y} + Ky = -\mu Mg \qquad v > 0 \tag{14.8}$$

$$M\ddot{y} + Ky = \mu Mg \qquad v < 0 \tag{14.9}$$

where μ is the coefficient of friction.

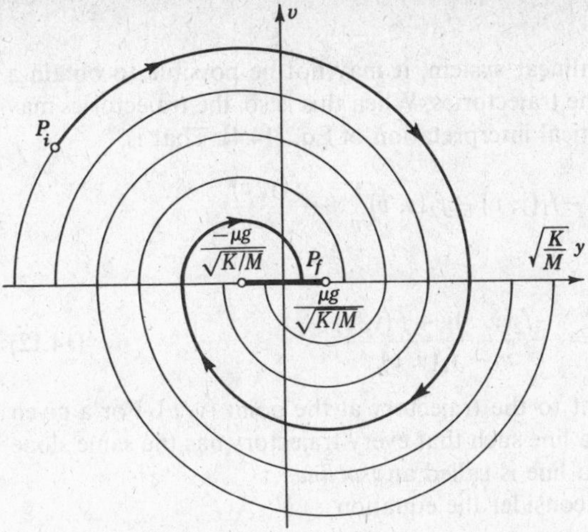

Figure 14.5 Phase-plane portrait for mass-spring system with friction.

By making the substitution $y_r = y + \mu Mg/K$ where y_r indicates motion to the right ($v > 0$), Eq. (14.8) becomes

$$M\ddot{y}_r + Ky_r = 0$$

It is seen that $\dot{y}_r = \dot{y} = v$ and $\ddot{y}_r = \ddot{y}$. The preceding equation is similar to Eq. (14.5), and thus its solution is

$$v^2 + \frac{K}{M}y_r^2 = v^2 + \frac{K}{M}\left(y + \frac{\mu Mg}{K}\right)^2 = C_r \tag{14.10}$$

This is the equation for a family of ellipses in the (y, v) coordinate system. On $(\sqrt{K/M}\,y, v)$ coordinates the phase portrait for Eq. (14.10) is a family of circles of radius $\sqrt{C_r}$. The center $(y = -\mu Mg/K)$ is located at $\sqrt{K/M}\,y = \sqrt{K/M}(-\mu Mg/K) = -\mu g/\sqrt{K/M}$. Because Eq. (14.10) is valid for $v > 0$, only semicircles above the y axis may be obtained from this expression, as shown in Fig. 14.5. For the case in which $v < 0$, the substitution $y_L = y - \mu Mg/K$ is made in Eq. (14.9). This yields

$$M\ddot{y}_L + Ky_L = 0$$

The solution of the preceding expression is

$$v^2 + \frac{K}{M}y_L^2 = v^2 + \frac{K}{M}\left(y - \frac{\mu Mg}{K}\right)^2 = C_L \tag{14.11}$$

Equation (14.11) yields the family of semicircles drawn below the y axis of Fig. 14.5.

If P_i is the starting point, as indicated in Fig. 14.5, the path of motion is that of the heavy line. The final position at which the mass comes to rest is indicated by P_f. Because of coulomb friction, the at-rest position is not at the origin of the phase portrait. Note at point P_f that $\sqrt{K/M}\,y < \mu g/\sqrt{K/M}$ or $Ky < \mu Mg$. Thus, the spring force Ky is less than the frictional force μMg.

Isoclines

For the general case of a nonlinear system, it may not be possible to obtain a mathematical expression for the trajectories. When this is so, the trajectories may be constructed by a mathematical interpretation of Eq. (14.4). That is,

$$m = \frac{dv}{dy} = -f_1(y, v) - f_2(y, v)\frac{y}{v} + \frac{f(y, v)}{v}$$

Solving for v gives

$$v = \frac{-f_2(y, v)y + f(y, v)}{m + f_1(y, v)} \tag{14.12}$$

where $m = dv/dy$ is the tangent to the trajectory at the point (y, v). For a given slope m, Eq. (14.12) describes a line such that every trajectory has the same slope m as it crosses this line. Such a line is called an *isocline*.

To illustrate this method, consider the equation

$$\ddot{y} + 2\dot{y} + 5y = 3 \tag{14.13}$$

where $f_1(y, v) = 2$, $f_2(y, v) = 5$, and $f(y, v) = 3$. The equation for the isoclines is

$$v = \frac{-5y + 3}{m + 2} \tag{14.14}$$

The isoclines for $m = -8, -4, -2, 0, 4$, and ∞ are shown in Fig. 14.6. The short crosslines on the isoclines are drawn at the slope indicated by the value of m for the isocline. These crosslines are horizontal on the $m = 0$ isocline and vertical

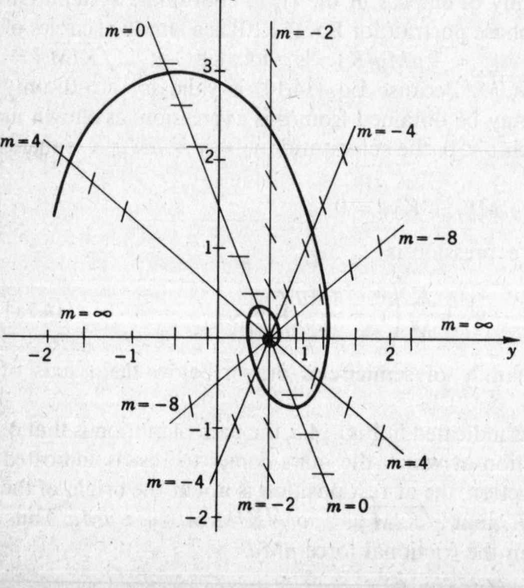

Figure 14.6 Construction of phase portrait from isoclines.

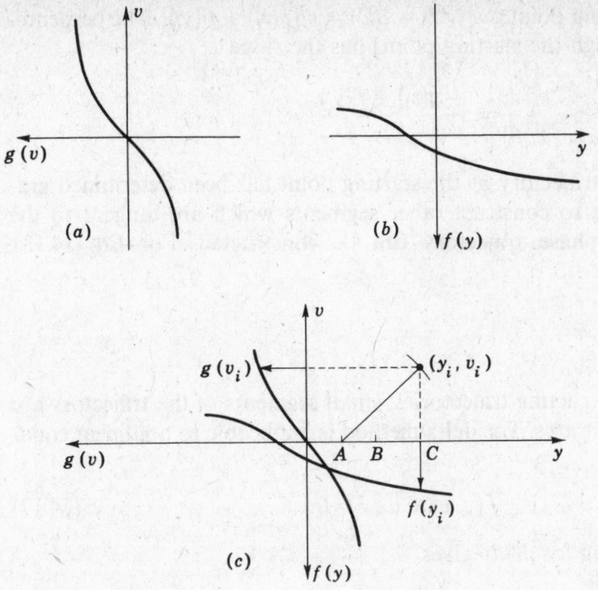

Figure 14.7 Construction of phase portrait by Pell's method.

on the $m = \infty$ isocline. As indicated in Fig. 14.6, the phase trajectory is drawn so that it is always tangent to these crosslines. From Eq. (14.12) it follows that the isoclines are straight lines when $f_1(y, v)$, $f_2(y, v)$, and $f(y, v)$ are constant.

Pell's Method

This method for constructing phase trajectories is applicable for equations of the form

$$\ddot{y} + g(\dot{y}) + f(y) = 0 \tag{14.15}$$

or

$$v\frac{dv}{dy} + g(v) + f(y) = 0$$

The slope dv/dy is

$$\frac{dv}{dy} = \frac{-g(v) - f(y)}{v} \tag{14.16}$$

To apply Pell's method, first construct the $g(v)$ versus v plot and the $f(y)$ versus y plot as per the coordinate directions shown in Fig. 14.7*a* and 14.7*b*. The two plots are then superimposed upon each other as shown in Fig. 14.7*c*. To obtain the tangent to the trajectory at the point (y_i, v_i), transfer with a divider the value $f(y_i)$ to BC on the y axis, and then transfer $g(v_i)$ to AB on the y axis. The slope of the line from A to the starting point is $v/(AB + BC) = v/[g(v_i) + f(y_i)]$. The perpendicular to this line (through the starting point) has the slope

$$\frac{dv}{dy} = \frac{-g(v_i) - f(y_i)}{v_i}$$

Thus, the slope to the trajectory at the starting point has been determined graphically. By proceeding to construct other segments which are tangent to the trajectory, the entire phase trajectory can be constructed. For Eq. (14.13), $g(v) = 2v$ and $f(y) = 5y - 3$.

The Delta Method

In this method for constructing trajectories, small segments of the trajectory are approximated by circular arcs. The delta method is applicable to nonlinear equations of the form

$$\ddot{y} + f(y, v) + \omega_n^2 y = 0 \tag{14.17}$$

Letting $v = \dot{y}$ and solving for dv/dy gives

$$\frac{dv}{dy} = -\frac{[\omega_n^2 y + f(y, v)]}{v}$$

In the vicinity of a point in the (y, v) plane, the function $f(y, v)$ may be regarded as remaining constant. By letting $f(y, v) = \omega_n^2 \delta$, then the preceding equation becomes

$$\frac{v\,dv}{\omega_n^2} + (y + \delta)\,dy = 0$$

Integration gives

$$\frac{v^2}{\omega_n^2} + (y^2 + 2\delta y) = C$$

or

$$\left(\frac{v}{\omega_n}\right)^2 + (y + \delta)^2 = C + \delta^2 = R^2 \tag{14.18}$$

With v/ω_n as the vertical axis and y as the horizontal axis, this is recognized as the equation for a circle with center at $y = -\delta$, $(v/\omega_n) = 0$, and radius R.

In Fig. 14.8 is shown the application of the delta method to the nonlinear differential equation

$$\ddot{y} + \frac{y\dot{y}}{2} + y = 0$$

This equation has the form of Eq. (14.17) in which $f(y, v) = yv/2$ and $\omega_n^2 = 1$. Because $f(y, v) = \omega_n^2 \delta$, it follows that $\delta = f(y, v)/\omega_n^2 = yv/2$.

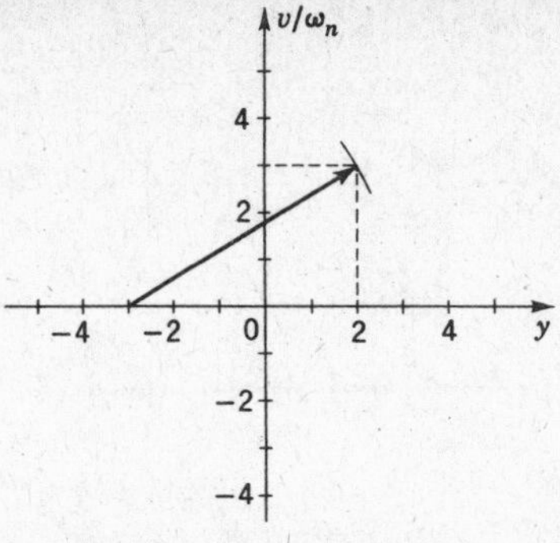

Figure 14.8 Construction of phase portrait by the delta method.

For $y = 2$ and $v/\omega_n = v = 3$, the center of the circle is $y = -\delta = -yv/2 = -3$, and the radius is $R = \sqrt{3^2 + (2+3)^2} = \sqrt{34}$. To put a nonlinear equation in the proper form for the application of the delta method, it is sometimes necessary to add and subtract a term proportional to y.

14.2 FEEDBACK SYSTEMS

The same phase-plane plot may be used to determine the response of a feedback system for various input excitations such as an impulse, step, or ramp function. The differential equation for the feedback system shown in Fig. 14.9*a* is

$$\ddot{c} + \dot{c} + c = r(t) \tag{14.19}$$

Impulse Response

When $r(t)$ is an impulse of area k, the differential equation for $t > 0$ is

$$\ddot{c} + \dot{c} + c = 0 \tag{14.20}$$

The phase plane which describes the response for $t > 0$ is obtained by writing the preceding expression in the form

$$\dot{c}\frac{d\dot{c}}{dc} + \dot{c} + c = 0$$

Replacing $d\dot{c}/dc$ by m yields the following equation for the isoclines:

$$\dot{c} = \frac{-1}{m+1}c \tag{14.21}$$

The resulting isoclines are shown in Fig. 14.9*b*. To construct the trajectory it is necessary to know $c(0+)$ and $\dot{c}(0+)$. When all initial conditions are zero and $r(t)$ is an impulse of area k, the Laplace transform of Eq. (14.19) is

$$C(s) = \frac{R(s)}{s^2+s+1} = \frac{k}{s^2+s+1}$$

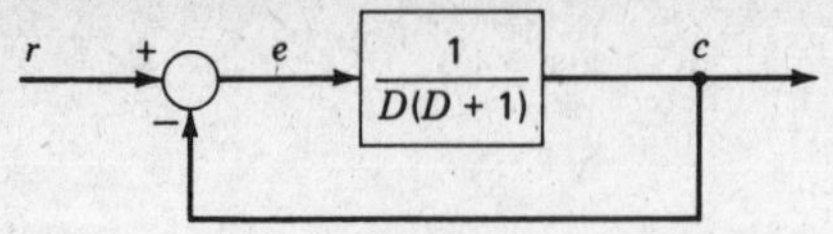

(a)

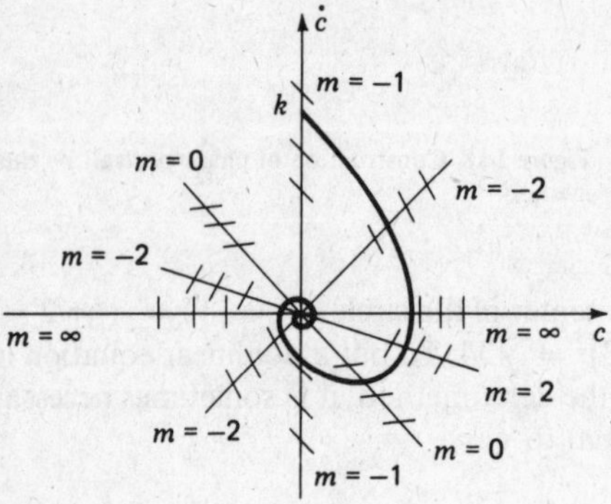

(b)

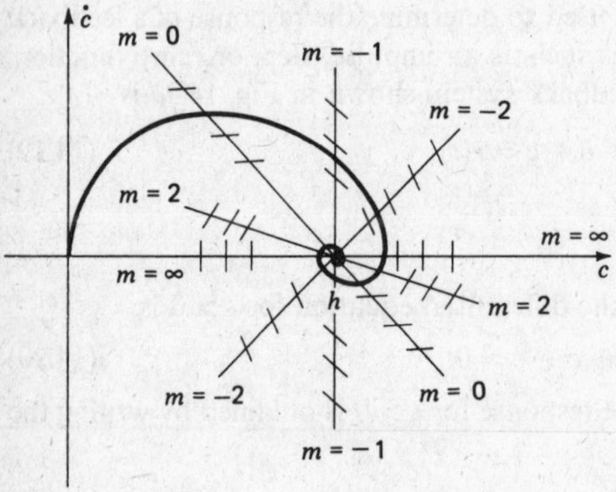

(c)

Figure 14.9 Impulse response and step-function response on the phase plane.

Application of the initial-value theorem to determine $c(0+)$ and $\dot{c}(0+)$ shows that

$$c(0+) = \lim_{s\to\infty} s\mathscr{L}[c(t)] = [sC(s)]_{s=\infty} = 0$$

$$\dot{c}(0+) = \lim_{s\to\infty} s\mathscr{L}[\dot{c}(t)] = \{s[sC(s) - c(0)]\}_{s=\infty} = [s^2C(s)]_{s=\infty} = k$$

Thus, the starting point for the impulse response is $c(0+) = 0$ and $\dot{c}(0+) = k$, where k is the area of the impulse. The corresponding phase plane is shown in Fig. 14.9b.

Step-Function Response

When the input $r(t)$ is a step function of height h, the differential equation for $t > 0$ is

$$\ddot{c} + \dot{c} + c = h \tag{14.22}$$

Application of the initial-value theorem shows that $c(0+) = \dot{c}(0+) = 0$. The equation for the isoclines is obtained by expressing the differential equation in the form

$$\dot{c}\frac{d\dot{c}}{dc} + \dot{c} + c = h$$

$$(m + 1)\dot{c} = -(c - h)$$

Thus,

$$\dot{c} = \frac{-1}{m+1}(c - h) \tag{14.23}$$

These isoclines are the same as those given by Eq. (14.21) except that they are shifted a distance h to the right. The isoclines and resulting trajectory are shown in Fig. 14.9c. The trajectory originates at $c(0+) = \dot{c}(0+) = 0$ and terminates at $c(\infty) = h$.

Ramp-Function Response

A ramp-function excitation is characterized by the input $r(t) = at$. Successive differentiation shows that $\dot{r} = a$ and $\ddot{r} = 0$. For a ramp-function input, it is more convenienent to make a phase-plane plot of $\dot{e}$ or e, where e is the error signal. The substitution of $c = r - e$ in the differential equation of operation, Eq. (14.19), gives

$$\ddot{e} + \dot{e} + e = \ddot{r} + \dot{r} = a$$

Application of the initial-value theorem shows that $e(0+) = 0$ and $\dot{e}(0+) = 0$. The equation for the isoclines is obtained by writing the preceding equation in the form

$$\dot{e}\frac{d\dot{e}}{de} + \dot{e} + e = a$$

Thus

$$\dot{e} = \frac{-1}{m+1}(e - a)$$

These isoclines are the same as those for the step-function response except that c is replaced by e and h is replaced by a.

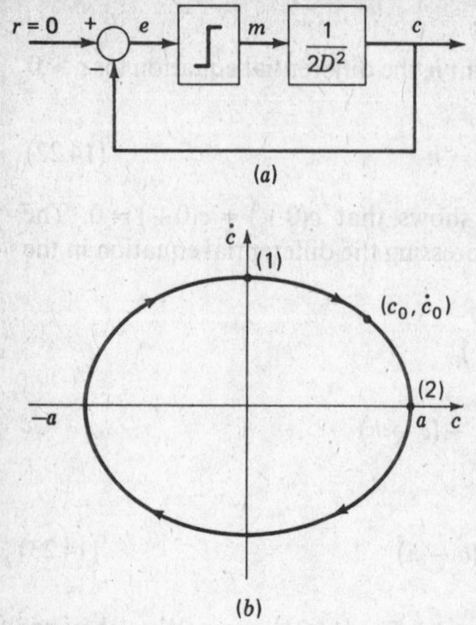

Figure 14.10 On-off system and phase-plane trajectory.

Nonlinear Feedback System

For the system shown in Fig. 14.10*a*, the nonlinear element is an on-off contactor. For negative values of e, the output is -1. For positive values of e, the output is $+1$. Because $e = -c$, then $e < 0$ corresponds to $c > 0$. Similarly, $e > 0$ corresponds to $c < 0$. Thus

$$m = -1 \qquad (e < 0 \text{ or } c > 0)$$

$$m = 1 \qquad (e > 0 \text{ or } c < 0)$$

The relationship between m and the output c is

$$m\left(\frac{1}{2D^2}\right) = c$$

or

$$2\ddot{c} = m$$

Replacing $\ddot{c}$ by $\dot{c}\, d\dot{c}/dc$ and integrating shows that

$$2\int \dot{c}\, d\dot{c} = m\int dc$$

or
$$\dot{c}^2 = mc + a$$

Evaluation at time $t = 0$ shows that the constant of integration is $a = \dot{c}_0^2 - mc_0$.

Because $m = -1$ for $c > 0$ and $m = 1$ for $c < 1$, the preceding becomes

$$\begin{aligned} \dot{c}^2 &= -(c - a) \qquad c > 0 \\ \dot{c}^2 &= c + a \qquad c < 0 \end{aligned} \tag{14.24}$$

These are equations for parabolas. The parabolas $y^2 = -x$ and $y^2 = -(x - a)$ both face to the left. The parabola $y^2 = -x$ passes through the origin ($x = 0$, $y = 0$). The parabola $y^2 = -(x - a)$ is shifted a distance a to the right of the parabola $y^2 = -x$. As shown in Fig. 14.10*b*, the parabola for $c > 0$ faces to the left and intersects the horizontal axis at the value $a = \dot{c}_0^2 + c_0$. The starting point $(c_0, \dot{c}_0)$ is indicated on the trajectory. For $c < 0$, the parabola faces to the right and intersects the horizontal axis at the value $-a$. Because this trajectory forms a closed path, the motion is periodic. The time required to travel along the trajectory from point (1) to point (2) is determined by noting that $\dot{c} = dc/dt$ or $dt = \dot{c}/c$. Thus, integration gives

$$t = \int_0^a \frac{dc}{\sqrt{a - c}} = -2\sqrt{a - c}\,\Big|_0^a = 2\sqrt{a} = 2\sqrt{\dot{c}_0^2 + c_0} \tag{14.25}$$

By symmetry of the trajectory, this is one-fourth of the total period. The system shown in Fig. 14.11*a* is the same as that shown in Fig. 14.10*a* except that the feedback element is $D + 1$ rather than unity. The new relationship between e and c is

$$e = -(D + 1)c = -c - \dot{c}$$

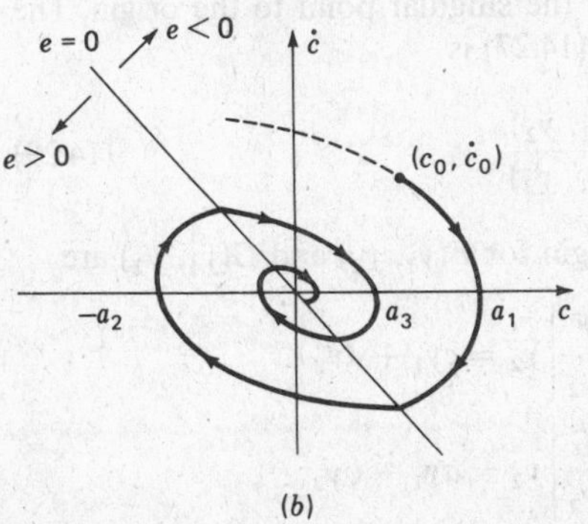

Figure 14.11 On-off system and phase-plane trajectory.

Hence

$$\dot{c} = -c - e \tag{14.26}$$

The line $\dot{c} = -c$ corresponding to $e = 0$ is shown in Fig. 14.11*b*. For $e < 0$, corresponding values of c and $\dot{c}$ are above this line. For $e > 0$, corresponding values of c and $\dot{c}$ are below this line. Because $m = -1$ for $e < 0$ and $m = 1$ for $e > 0$, the equations for the trajectories are

$$\dot{c}^2 = -(c - a) \qquad e < 0$$

$$\dot{c}^2 = \quad c + a \qquad e > 0$$

As shown in Fig. 14.11*b*, for $e < 0$ the parabolas face to the left and for $e > 0$ the parabolas face to the right. Because the transition is not symmetric about the vertical $c = 0$ axis, the parabolas progressively get smaller and the trajectory proceeds toward the origin.

14.3 SINGULAR POINTS

In general, the differential equation for a nonlinear second-order system may be written in the form

$$\begin{aligned} \dot{y} &= Q(y, v) \\ \dot{v} &= P(y, v) \end{aligned} \tag{14.27}$$

Dividing $\dot{v}$ by $\dot{y}$ yields the form

$$\frac{dv}{dy} = \frac{P(y, v)}{Q(y, v)} \tag{14.28}$$

A singular point is a point at which $P(y, v) = Q(y, v) = 0$. Thus, $dv/dy = 0/0$ is indeterminate at a singular point. A singular point is transferred to the origin by making the change of variable $y_1 = y - y_s$ and $y_2 = v - v_s$. The following analysis loses none of its generality by transferring the singular point to the origin. The transferred equation corresponding to Eq. (14.27) is

$$\frac{dy_2}{dy_1} = \frac{F(y_1, y_2)}{G(y_1, y_2)} \tag{14.29}$$

The Taylor series expansions about the origin for $F(y_1, y_2)$ and $G(y_1, y_2)$ are

$$F(y_1, y_2) = \left.\frac{\partial F}{\partial y_1}\right| y_1 + \left.\frac{\partial F}{\partial y_2}\right| y_2 = cy_1 + dy_2$$

$$G(y_1, y_2) = \left.\frac{\partial G}{\partial y_1}\right| y_1 + \left.\frac{\partial G}{\partial y_2}\right| y_2 = ay_1 + by_2$$

Evaluation of each of the preceding partial derivatives at the origin ($y_1 = 0$, $y_2 = 0$) yields the constants a, b, c, and d. The resulting linearized form for Eq. (14.29) is

$$\frac{dy_2}{dy_1} = \frac{cy_1 + dy_2}{ay_1 + by_2} \tag{14.30}$$

The solution of this differential equation is simplified by further transforming it to the canonical form

$$\frac{dx_2}{dx_1} = \frac{K_2}{K_1}\frac{x_2}{x_1} \tag{14.31}$$

To determine the equations for K_1 and K_2 in terms of the known constants (a, b, c, d), write the denominator and numerator of Eqs. (14.30) and (14.31) in the form

$$\begin{aligned} \dot{y}_1 &= ay_1 + by_2 \\ \dot{y}_2 &= cy_1 + dy_2 \end{aligned} \tag{14.32}$$

and

$$\begin{aligned} \dot{x}_1 &= K_1 x_1 + 0 \\ \dot{x}_2 &= 0 + K_2 x_2 \end{aligned} \tag{14.33}$$

The corresponding matrix representations are

$$\begin{bmatrix} \dot{y}_1 \\ \dot{y}_2 \end{bmatrix} = \begin{bmatrix} a & b \\ c & d \end{bmatrix} \begin{bmatrix} y_1 \\ y_2 \end{bmatrix} \quad \text{or} \quad \dot{\mathbf{y}} = A\mathbf{y} \tag{14.34}$$

and

$$\begin{bmatrix} \dot{x}_1 \\ \dot{x}_2 \end{bmatrix} = \begin{bmatrix} K_1 & 0 \\ 0 & K_2 \end{bmatrix} \begin{bmatrix} x_1 \\ x_2 \end{bmatrix} \quad \text{or} \quad \dot{\mathbf{x}} = K\mathbf{x} \tag{14.35}$$

Boldface notation is used to designate a column matrix, and capital letters designate coefficient matrices. The matrix B which transforms the y_1, y_2 coordinate system to the (x_1, x_2) system is

$$\begin{bmatrix} x_1 \\ x_2 \end{bmatrix} = \begin{bmatrix} \alpha & \beta \\ \gamma & \delta \end{bmatrix} \begin{bmatrix} y_1 \\ y_2 \end{bmatrix} \quad \text{or} \quad \mathbf{x} = B\mathbf{y}$$

Differentiation shows that

$$\dot{\mathbf{x}} = B\dot{\mathbf{y}} = BA\mathbf{y}$$

Another representation for $\dot{\mathbf{x}}$ is

$$\dot{\mathbf{x}} = K\mathbf{x} = KB\mathbf{y}$$

Subtracting the second representation for $\dot{\mathbf{x}}$ from the first gives

$$[BA - KB]\mathbf{y} = 0$$

Multiplying out this matrix shows that

$$\begin{aligned} [(a - K_1)\alpha + c\beta]y_1 + [b\alpha + (d - K_1)\beta]y_2 &= 0 \\ [(a - K_2)\gamma + c\delta]y_1 + [b\gamma + (d - K_2)\delta]y_2 &= 0 \end{aligned}$$

Because y_1 and y_2 cannot be zero, all the coefficients must be zero.

$$(a - K_1)\alpha + c\beta = 0 \qquad (a - K_2)\gamma + c\delta = 0$$

$$b\alpha + (d - K_1)\beta = 0 \qquad b\gamma + (d - K_2)\delta = 0$$

In order that the solution of each of these sets of equations not be trivial (that is, $\alpha = \beta = \gamma = \delta = 0$), each determinant must vanish.

$$\begin{vmatrix} a - K_1 & c \\ b & d - K_1 \end{vmatrix} = 0 \qquad \begin{vmatrix} a - K_2 & c \\ b & d - K_2 \end{vmatrix} = 0$$

Solving for K_1 and K_2 gives

$$K_{1,2} = \frac{(a + d) \pm \sqrt{(a - d)^2 + 4bc}}{2} \tag{14.36}$$

The behavior of the phase-plane trajectories in the vicinity of the singular point is now analyzed for various combinations of K_1 and K_2.

Case I K_1 and K_2 are real and $K_2/K_1 > 0$. From Eq. (14.36), it follows that K_1 and K_2 are real if

$$(a - d)^2 + 4bc > 0 \tag{14.37}$$

In order that K_1 and K_2 have the same sign ($K_2/K_1 > 0$), it is necessary that $[(a - d)^2 + 4bc] < (a + d)^2$, or

$$bc - ad < 0 \tag{14.38}$$

For Case I, Eq. (14.31) becomes

$$\frac{dx_2}{x_2} = \frac{K_2}{K_1}\frac{dx_1}{x_1}$$

The solution is

$$x_2 = Cx_1^{K_2/K_1} \tag{14.39}$$

If the root having the larger magnitude is designated as K_2, then $K_2/K_1 > 1$. A plot of the corresponding trajectories is shown in Fig. 14.12. Such singular points are called *nodes*. To determine the direction of the arrows on these

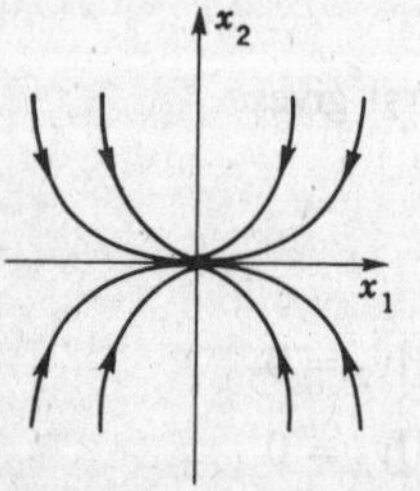

Figure 14.12 Stable node.

trajectories, replace $\dot{y}_1$ by Dy_1 and $\dot{y}_2$ by Dy_2 in Eqs. (14.32). Eliminating y_2 from the resulting expressions gives

$$[D^2 - (a + d)D + (ad - bc)]y_1 = (D - K_1)(D - K_2)y_1 = 0 \quad (14.40)$$

Similarly, eliminating y_1 gives

$$[D^2 - (a + d)D + (ad - bc)]y_2 = (D - K_1)(D - K_2)y_2 = 0$$

The nature of the response y_1 or y_2 is governed by the same differential equation. The solution of each differential equation is

$$y_1 = C_1 e^{K_1 t} + C_2 e^{K_2 t}$$

$$y_2 = C_3 e^{K_1 t} + C_4 e^{K_2 t}$$

In general, the initial conditions for y_1 are different from those for y_2, so that C_1 is not equal to C_3 and C_2 is not equal to C_4. Note that the roots K_1 and K_2 determine not only the shape of the trajectories but also the transient response. The system has a stable response when the roots K_1 and K_2 are both negative. This is so when

$$a + d < 0 \quad (14.41)$$

If the trajectory is stable in the (y_1, y_2) plane, it will also be stable in the (x_1, x_2) plane. Thus, the arrows in Fig. 14.12 are for a stable system in that the trajectories go into the origin, and thus come to rest.

When K_1 and K_2 are positive, the response is unstable. This is so when

$$a + d > 0 \quad (14.42)$$

The arrows in Fig. 14.12 should be reversed to indicate unstable nodes when $a + d > 0$.

The phase-plane plot for a typical node is drawn in the (y_1, y_2) coordinate system shown in Fig. 14.13. It is to be noted that all the trajectories cross the y_1 axis at right angles. Also, all the trajectories approach the origin tangent to the x_1 axis except for the trajectories that originate on the x_2 axis and follow it directly into the origin. The x_1 axis is called the slow eigenvector, and the x_2 axis is called the fast eigenvector. A trajectory that originates on the x_2 axis proceeds into the origin at a faster rate than one that originates on the x_1 axis. The location of the x_1 axis in the (y_1, y_2) plane is obtained by letting $x_2 = 0$, then expressing x_1 in terms of y_1 and y_2. Similarly, the location of the x_2 axis in the (y_1, y_2) plane is obtained by letting $x_1 = 0$, then expressing y_1 and y_2 in terms of x_2. The relationship between $\mathbf{x}$ and $\mathbf{y}$ is

$$\begin{bmatrix} y_1 \\ y_2 \end{bmatrix} = \begin{bmatrix} p_{11} & p_{12} \\ p_{21} & p_{22} \end{bmatrix} \begin{bmatrix} x_1 \\ x_2 \end{bmatrix} \qquad \text{or} \qquad \mathbf{y} = P\mathbf{x}$$

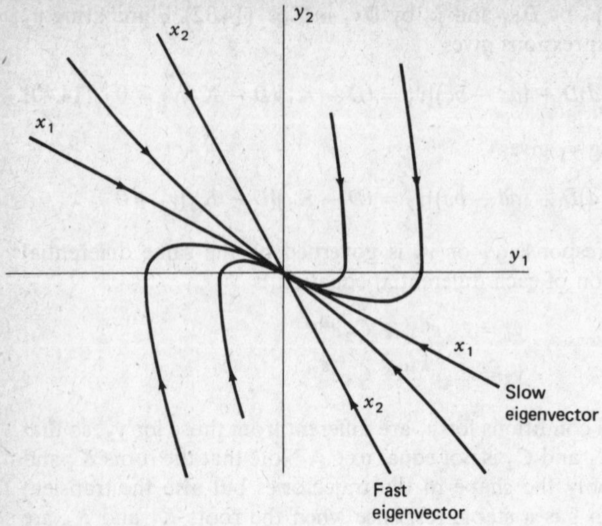

Figure 14.13 (x_1, x_2) axes on the phase-plane plot.

For $x_2 = 0$, it follows that the x_1 axis is such that $y_1 = p_{11}x_1$ and $y_2 = p_{21}x_1$. The slope m_1 of the x_1 axis in the (y_1, y_2) plane is

$$m_1 = \frac{y_2}{y_1} = \frac{p_{21}}{p_{11}}$$

Similarly, the slope m_2 of the x_2 axis is found to be

$$m_2 = \frac{y_2}{y_1} = \frac{p_{22}}{p_{12}}$$

Differentiation of $\mathbf{x} = P^{-1}\mathbf{y}$ gives

$$\dot{\mathbf{x}} = P^{-1}\dot{\mathbf{y}} = P^{-1}A\mathbf{y} = P^{-1}AP\mathbf{x}$$

This has the same form as Eq. (14.35); hence

$$K = P^{-1}AP$$

Multiplying through by P gives

$$PK = AP$$

Substitution of the appropriate matrices for P, K, and A into the preceding relationship yields the equations

$$p_{11}K_1 = ap_{11} + bp_{21}$$

$$p_{21}K_1 = cp_{11} + dp_{21}$$

$$p_{12}K_2 = ap_{12} + bp_{22}$$

$$p_{22}K_2 = cp_{12} + dp_{22}$$

From the first two equations, it follows that

$$m_1 = \frac{p_{21}}{p_{11}} = \frac{K_1 - a}{b} = \frac{c}{K_1 - d}$$

Similarly, the last two equations show that

$$m_2 = \frac{p_{22}}{p_{12}} = \frac{K_2 - a}{b} = \frac{c}{K_2 - d}$$

Usually $\dot{y}_1 = ay_1 + by_2 = y_2$, in which case $a = 0$ and $b = 1$. Thus

$$m_1 = K_1 \qquad \text{and} \qquad m_2 = K_2$$

Illustrative example 1 Identify the singular point for the system

$$\ddot{y} + 2.5\dot{y} + y = (D + 0.5)(D + 2.0)y = 0$$

SOLUTION By letting $y = y_1$ and $\dot{y} = \dot{y}_1 = y_2$, this system may be expressed in the form

$$\dot{y}_1 = y_2$$
$$\dot{y}_2 = -y_1 - 2.5y_2$$

Comparison with Eq. (14.32) shows that $a = 0, b = 1, c = -1$, and $d = -2.5$. Because Eqs. (14.37) and (14.38) are satisfied, the singular point is a node. Because Eq. (14.41) is satisfied, the node is stable. The slope of the slow eigenvector is $K_1 = -0.5$, and the slope of the fast eigenvector is $K_2 = -2.0$. The phase plane for this system is that shown in Fig. 14.13. From the system equation, it follows that the equation for the isoclines is

$$y_2 \frac{dy_2}{dy_1} + 2.5y_2 = -y_1$$

or

$$y_2 = \frac{-y_1}{m + 2.5}$$

where $m = dy_2/dy_1$.

Note that when $m = -0.5$, then $y_2 = -y_1/2 = -0.5y_1$. Similarly, when $m = -2.0$, then $y_2 = -y_1/0.5 = -2y_1$. On an eigenvector, m is equal to the slope of the isocline. When a trajectory reaches an eigenvector, it follows it back to the origin. For equal roots ($K_1 = K_2$), the eigenvectors are identical.

Case II K_1 and K_2 are real, and $K_2/K_1 < 0$. As given by Eq. (14.37), the roots are real when

$$(a - d)^2 + 4bc > 0$$

In order that K_1 and K_2 have different signs ($K_2/K_1 < 0$), it is necessary that

$$bc - ad > 0 \tag{14.43}$$

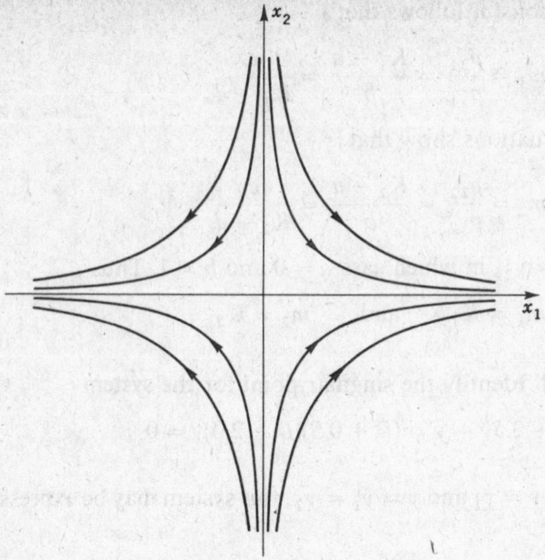

Figure 14.14 Saddle point.

The equation for the trajectories for Case II is the same as Eq. (14.39) except that K_2/K_1 is now negative. A plot of the corresponding trajectories is shown in Fig. 14.14. This type of singularity is called a *saddle point*. Because one root is negative and the other positive, Case II always represents an unstable response.

Illustrative example 2 Identify the singular point for the system

$$\ddot{y} + 3\dot{y} - 10y = 0$$

SOLUTION By letting $y = y_1$ and $\dot{y} = \dot{y}_1 = y_2$, this system may be expressed in the form

$$\dot{y}_1 = y_2$$
$$\dot{y}_2 = 10y_1 - 3y_2$$

For $a = 0$, $b = 1$, $c = 10$, and $d = -3$, the roots are

$$K_{1,2} = \frac{-3 \pm \sqrt{3^2 + 40}}{2} = \frac{-3 \pm 7}{2} = 2, -5$$

Both roots are real. Because one is negative and one is positive, the singular point is a saddle point.

The relationship $\dot{y}_1 = y_2$ is arbitrary. To illustrate that any linear relationship yields the same result, let $\dot{y}_1 = y_1 + y_2$. For $y = y_1$, then $\dot{y} = \dot{y}_1 = y_1 + y_2$. The system equation now becomes

$$(\dot{y}_1 + \dot{y}_2) + 3(y_1 + y_2) - 10y_1 = (y_1 + y_2) + \dot{y}_2 + 3(y_1 + y_2) - 10y_1$$
$$= \dot{y}_2 - 6y_1 + 4y_2 = 0$$

Thus

$$\dot{y}_1 = y_1 + y_2$$
$$\dot{y}_2 = 6y_1 - 4y_2$$

For $a = 1$, $b = 1$, $c = 6$, and $d = -4$, the roots are $K_{1,\,2} = 2, -5$.

Case III K_1 and K_2 are complex conjugates. From Eq. (14.36), K_1 and K_2 are complex conjugates when

$$(a - d)^2 + 4bc < 0 \tag{14.44}$$

When $d = a$ and $c = -b$, then from Eq. (14.36) the complex conjugate roots are $K_{1,\,2} = a \pm jb$. Thus, Eq. (14.30) becomes

$$\frac{dy_2}{dy_1} = \frac{-by_1 + ay_2}{ay_1 + by_2} \tag{14.45}$$

The polar representation for y_1 and y_2 is

$$y_1 = r \cos \phi$$
$$y_2 = r \sin \phi$$

Thus, Eq. (14.45) becomes

$$\frac{r \cos \phi \, d\phi + \sin \phi \, dr}{-r \sin \phi \, d\phi + \cos \phi \, dr} = \frac{-br \cos \phi + ar \sin \phi}{ar \cos \phi + br \sin \phi}$$

After cross-multiplying this reduces to

$$\frac{dr}{r} = -\frac{a}{b} \, d\phi$$

The solution is

$$r = Ce^{-a(\phi/b)} \tag{14.46}$$

For positive values of a, the singular point is an unstable focus, as shown in Fig. 14.15*a*. For negative values of a, the singular point is a stable focus, as shown in Fig. 14.15*b*. When a is zero, the singular point is a vortex, or center, as shown in Fig. 14.15*c*.

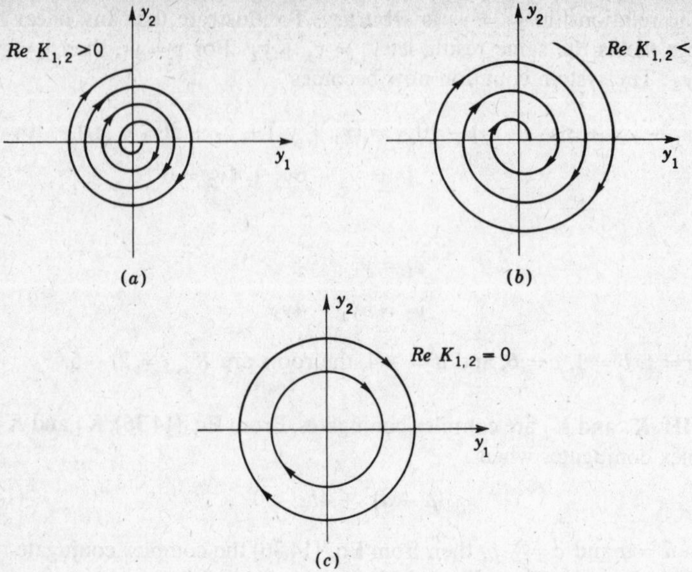

Figure 14.15 Focal point. (*a*) Unstable; (*b*) stable; (*c*) center.

For the more general case, the real part of $K_{1,2}$ is $(a + d)/2$. By designating $K_{1,2}$ as $A \pm jB$, then Eq. (14.31) becomes

$$\frac{\dot{x}_2}{\dot{x}_1} = \frac{Ax_2 + jBx_2}{Ax_1 - jBx_1}$$

Letting $x_1 = u_1 + ju_2$ and $x_2 = u_1 - ju_2$ shows that

$$\frac{\dot{u}_2}{\dot{u}_1} = \frac{-Bu_1 + Au_2}{Au_1 + Bu_2}$$

This has the same form as Eq. (14.45). Thus, when the real part $A = (a + d)/2$ is positive, the singular point is an *unstable focus*. When the real part is negative, the singular point is a *stable focus*. When the real part is zero, the singular point is a *vortex*, or *center*.

Illustrative example 3 In Fig. 14.6 is shown the phase-plane plot for Eq. (14.13). That is,

$$\ddot{y} + 2\dot{y} + 5y = 3 \tag{14.13}$$

Identify the singular point.

SOLUTION By letting $\dot{y} = v$, Eq. (14.13) may be represented in the form

$$\dot{y} = v$$
$$\dot{v} = -5y - 2v + 3$$

The singular point occurs at $\dot{y} = \dot{v} = 0$. In order that $\dot{y} = 0$, then $v = 0$. In order that $\dot{v} = 0$, then $(-5y + 3) = 0$ or $y = 0.6$. The singular point $(y = 0.6, v = 0)$ is transferred to the origin by letting $y_1 = y - 0.6$ and $y_2 = v$. Substitution of $y = y_1 + 0.6$, $\dot{y} = \dot{y}_1$, $v = y_2$, and $\dot{v} = \dot{y}_2$ into the preceding gives

$$\dot{y}_1 = y_2$$
$$\dot{y}_2 = -5y_1 - 2y_2$$

For $a = 0$, $b = 1$, $c = -5$, and $d = -2$, the roots are $K_{1,2} = -1 \pm j2$. Because the real part of these complex conjugate roots is negative, the singular point is a stable focus.

Illustrative example 4 The differential equation for a pendulum is

$$\ddot{\phi} + \frac{g}{L} \sin \phi = 0$$

Identify the singular points.

SOLUTION By letting $\phi = y$ and $\dot{\phi} = \dot{y} = v$, the equation of motion becomes

$$\dot{y} = v$$
$$\dot{v} = -\frac{g}{L} \sin y$$

In order that $\dot{y} = \dot{v} = 0$, then $v = 0$ and $\sin y = 0$. Thus singular points occur at $(y = n\pi, v = 0)$, where $n = 0, \pm 1, \pm 2, \ldots$. The singular point at $(y = n\pi, v = 0)$ is transferred to the origin by letting $y_1 = y - n\pi$ and $y_2 = v$. Thus the system equations are

$$\dot{y}_1 = y_2$$
$$\dot{y}_2 = -\frac{g}{L} \sin (y_1 + n\pi)$$

For $F(y_1, y_2) = y_2$ and $G(y_1, y_2) = -(g/L) \sin (y_1 + n\pi)$, $a = \partial F/\partial y_1 = 0$, $b = \partial F/\partial y_2 = 1$, $c = \partial G/\partial y_1 = [-(g/L) \cos (y_1 + n\pi)]_{y_1=0} = -(g/L) \cos n\pi$, and $d = \partial G/\partial y_2 = 0$. The resulting linearized form is

$$\dot{y}_1 = y_2$$
$$\dot{y}_2 = \left(-\frac{g}{L} \cos n\pi\right) y_1$$

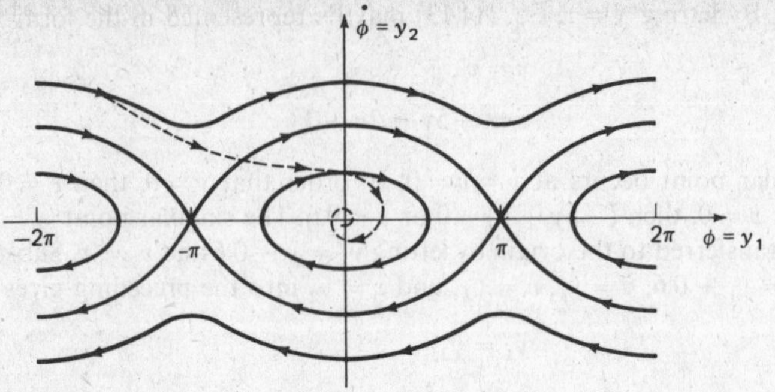

Figure 14.16 Phase portrait for motion of a pendulum.

The roots are

$$K_{1,2} = \pm\sqrt{-\frac{g}{L}\cos n\pi}$$

For $n = 0$ and for even values of $n(\cos n\pi = 1)$, the roots are imaginary and the singular points are centers. For odd values of n, the roots are real but have opposite signs, so that these singular points are saddle points.

The phase-plane plot is shown in Fig. 14.16. The singular point at the origin ($\phi = 0$, $\dot{\phi} = 0$) is a stable focus. The pendulum is in its lowest position. For the closed path about the origin, the amplitude ϕ is always less than π. Because the pendulum never reaches the top vertical position, it oscillates back and forth. Similar singular points occur at ($\phi = -2\pi$, $\dot{\phi} = 0$) and ($\phi = 2\pi$, $\dot{\phi} = 0$).

The singular point at ($\phi = \pi$, $\dot{\phi} = 0$) is a saddle point. The pendulum is at rest in the top vertical position. This is an unstable point of equilibrium. If the pendulum falls in one direction ($\dot{\phi} > 0$), then its trajectory will be the path connecting $\phi = \pi$ to $\phi = 3\pi$. If the pendulum falls in the opposite direction ($\dot{\phi} < 0$), then its trajectory will be the path connecting $\phi = \pi$ to $\phi = -\pi$, whence it again comes to rest at the top. For the top path of Fig. 14.16, the pendulum passes the vertical position $\phi = -\pi$ or π with a positive velocity $\dot{\phi}$. This pendulum keeps making full swings. The bottom path is the same motion in the opposite direction. The dotted path shows a typical trajectory in which there is damping to absorb energy, so that the pedulum eventually comes to rest.

14.4 LIAPUNOV'S DIRECT METHOD

For second-order systems, the coordinates for the phase plane are position and velocity. Third-order systems require a phase space with coordinates of position, velocity, and acceleration. Because of the difficulties of working graphically in

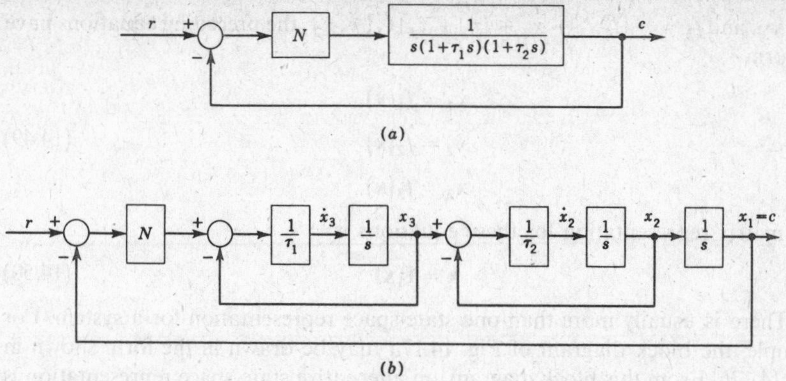

Figure 14.17 Nonlinear system.

three-dimensional space, the phase-plane method becomes exceedingly cumbersome. Thus, for third- and higher-order nonlinear systems, it has become necessary to develop other methods of analysis. One of the most promising methods for investigating the behavior of higher-order systems is the method known as Liapunov's second method or more simply Liapunov's direct method.[1,2]

The state-space notation is a convenient symbolism for representing higher-order systems. To illustrate this notation, consider the third-order feedback control system with the nonlinear element N shown in Fig. 14.17*a*. The differential equation relating the output c and input r is

$$\dddot{c} + \frac{\tau_1 + \tau_2}{\tau_1 \tau_2}\ddot{c} + \frac{1}{\tau_1 \tau_2}\dot{c} + \frac{N}{\tau_1 \tau_2}c = \frac{N}{\tau_1 \tau_2}r \tag{14.47}$$

By letting $x_1 = c$, $x_2 = \dot{c}$, and $x_3 = \ddot{c}$, the preceding third-order equation is converted to the following three first-order equations:

$$\begin{aligned} \dot{x}_1 &= x_2 \\ \dot{x}_2 &= x_3 \\ \dot{x}_3 &= -\frac{\tau_1 + \tau_2}{\tau_1 \tau_2}x_3 - \frac{1}{\tau_1 \tau_2}x_2 - \frac{N}{\tau_1 \tau_2}x_1 + \frac{N}{\tau_1 \tau_2}r \end{aligned} \tag{14.48}$$

The terms x_1, x_2, and x_3 are called the state variables. For investigating stability, one is not interested in the particular excitation r. Thus, by letting $f_1 = x_2$,

[1] A. M. Liapunov, "On the General Problem of Stability of Motion," Ph.D. Thesis, Kharkov, 1892. Princeton University Press, Princeton, N.J., 1949.

[2] J. LaSalle and S. Lefschetz, "Stability by Liapunov's Direct Method," Academic Press Inc., New York, 1961.

$f_2 = x_3$, and $f_3 = -[Nx_1 + x_2 + (\tau_1 + \tau_2)x_3]/\tau_1\tau_2$, the preceding equations have the form

$$\begin{aligned} \dot{x}_1 &= f_1(\mathbf{x}) \\ \dot{x}_2 &= f_2(\mathbf{x}) \\ \dot{x}_3 &= f_3(\mathbf{x}) \end{aligned} \tag{14.49}$$

The matrix representation for these equations is

$$\dot{\mathbf{x}} = \mathbf{f}(\mathbf{x}) \tag{14.50}$$

There is usually more than one state-space representation for a system. For example, the block diagram of Fig. 14.17*a* may be drawn in the form shown in Fig. 14.17*b*. From this block diagram, an alternative state-space representation is

$$\begin{aligned} \dot{x}_1 &= x_2 \\ \dot{x}_2 &= \frac{1}{\tau_2}x_3 - \frac{1}{\tau_2}x_2 \\ \dot{x}_3 &= -\frac{N}{\tau_1}x_1 - \frac{1}{\tau_1}x_3 + \frac{N}{\tau_1}r \end{aligned} \tag{14.51}$$

By letting $f_1 = x_2$, $f_2 = (x_3 - x_2)/\tau_2$, and $f_3 = -(Nx_1 + x_3)/\tau_1$, then for $r = 0$ the preceding set of equations has the same form as Eq. (14.50). Regardless of the particular state-space representation, Eq. (14.50) is a general representation for an nth-order nonlinear system.

Illustrative example Consider the mass-spring-damper system shown in Fig. 14.18*a*. The equation of motion for this system is

$$M\ddot{y} + B\dot{y} + Ky = 0$$

Letting $x_1 = y$ and $x_2 = \dot{x}_1 = \dot{y}$, the state-space representation is

$$\begin{aligned} \dot{x}_1 &= x_2 = f_1 \\ \dot{x}_2 &= -\frac{Kx_1 + Bx_2}{M} = f_2 \end{aligned} \tag{14.52}$$

The potential energy stored in the spring is the area under the force-deflection curve shown in Fig. 14.18*b*. The static deflection δ_{st} is due to the load W. The potential energy stored in the spring at this reference position is

$$(PE)_i = \tfrac{1}{2}W\delta_{st}$$

The additional potential energy in the spring due to a deflection y from the reference position is

$$PE = \int_0^y (W + Ky)\,dy = Wy + \int_0^y Ky\,dy = Wy + \frac{Ky^2}{2}$$

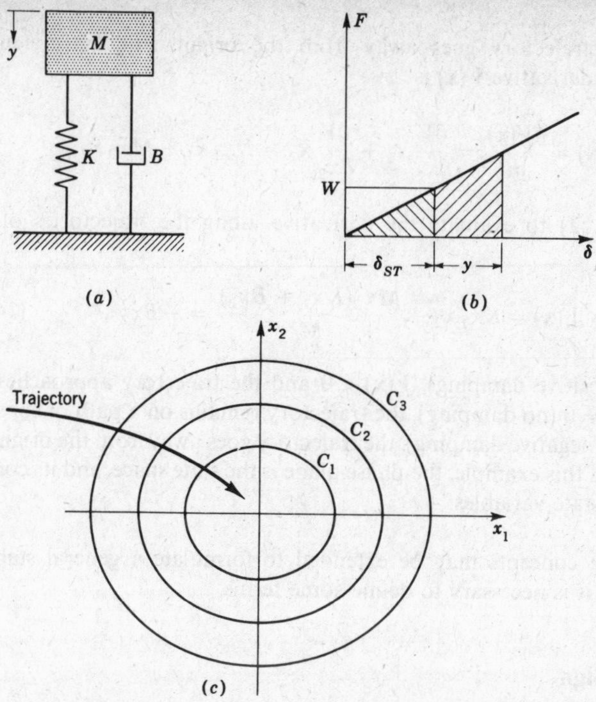

Figure 14.18 (*a*) Mass-spring-damper system; (*b*) potential energy stored in spring; (*c*) plot of energy function for the system.

The potential energy of the mass is

$$PE = -W(\delta_{st} + y)$$

The kinetic energy of the mass is

$$KE = \tfrac{1}{2}M\dot{y}^2$$

After replacing y by x_1 and $\dot{y}$ by x_2, the sum of the potential and kinetic energy for the system is $Kx_1^2/2 + Mx_2^2 - (PE)_i$. Consider now the function

$$V(\mathbf{x}) = \frac{Kx_1^2}{2} + \frac{Mx_2^2}{2} = C \qquad (14.53)$$

A plot of this scalar function for constant values $C_3 > C_2 > C_1$ is shown in Fig. 14.18*c*. As a point $\mathbf{x}$ in the phase plane proceeds across C_3 to C_2 to C_1 toward the origin, the value of $V(\mathbf{x})$ is decreasing. Thus, if $\dot{V}(\mathbf{x}) < 0$, then $V(\mathbf{x})$ decreases with time, and the trajectory approaches the origin, as shown in Fig. 14.18*c*. For $\dot{V}(\mathbf{x}) = 0$, the trajectory remains on a path of constant C. For

$\dot{V}(\mathbf{x}) > 0$, the trajectory goes away from the origin. For the system of Fig. 14.18, the derivative $\dot{V}(\mathbf{x})$ is

$$\dot{V}(\mathbf{x}) = \frac{dV(\mathbf{x})}{dt} = \frac{\partial V}{\partial x_1}\dot{x}_1 + \frac{\partial V}{\partial x_2}\dot{x}_2 = Kx_1\dot{x}_1 + Mx_2\dot{x}_2$$

Using Eq. (14.52) to evaluate the derivative along the trajectories of the system gives

$$\dot{V}(\mathbf{x}) = Kx_1x_2 - \frac{Mx_2(Kx_1 + Bx_2)}{M} = -Bx_2^2 \tag{14.54}$$

For $B > 0$ (positive damping), $\dot{V}(\mathbf{x}) < 0$ and the trajectory approaches the origin. For $B = 0$ (no damping), the trajectory remains on a path of constant C. For $B < 0$ (negative damping), the trajectory goes away from the origin. As is illustrated in this example, the phase plane is the state space, and its coordinates are the state variables.

The preceding concepts may be extended to formulate a general stability criterion, but first it is necessary to define some terms.

Definiteness of Sign

A scalar function $V(\mathbf{x}) = V(x_1, x_2, \ldots, x_n)$ is positive definite in some neighborhood of the origin if in this neighborhood

1. $V(\mathbf{x})$ is continuous
2. $V(\mathbf{x}) > 0 \quad (\mathbf{x} \neq 0)$
3. $V(\mathbf{0}) = 0$

When the neighborhood includes all values of $x_1, x_2, \ldots, x_n$, the function is said to be globally positive definite. Equation (14.53) is globally positive definite. Unless otherwise stated, it is assumed that the function is global.

A scalar function is positive semidefinite in some neighborhood of the origin if

1. $V(\mathbf{x})$ is continuous
2. $V(\mathbf{x}) \geq 0 \quad (\mathbf{x} \neq 0)$
3. $V(\mathbf{0}) = 0$

Positive semidefinite and positive definite functions are distinguished by condition (2). For a positive semidefinite function, $V(\mathbf{x})$ goes to zero even though all the x's are not zero. An example of a positive semidefinite function for the two-dimensional case (x_1, x_2) is

$$V(\mathbf{x}) = x_1^2$$

For $x_2 \neq 0$, this function is zero along the entire $x_1 = 0$ axis.

Changing the sign of a positive definite function yields a negative definite function. Likewise, changing the sign of a positive semidefinite function yields a negative semidefinite function.

A scalar function $V(\mathbf{x})$ is indefinite if it takes on both positive and negative values in some neighborhood of the origin. An example of an indefinite function is

$$V(\mathbf{x}) = x_1 x_2$$

A Liapunov function $V(\mathbf{x})$ is a scalar function which is positive definite, such that $V(\mathbf{x}) = C$ represents a family of closed surfaces in n-dimensional space. The linearly independent variables $x_1, x_2, \ldots, x_n$ are the coordinates of the n-dimensional state space. As shown in Fig. 14.18c, these closed surfaces should be such that the closed surface formed for $V(\mathbf{x}) = C$ contains within itself all the surfaces for smaller values of C. Thus, the surfaces progressively become larger as C increases and do not intersect. This requires that $V(\mathbf{x})$ increase as any one of the state variables increases. In order for a Liapunov function to be global, it must have the additional requirement that $V(\mathbf{x})$ becomes infinite if any one of the state variables becomes infinite.

Stability Criteria

If a system possesses a Liapunov function such that $\dot{V}(\mathbf{x})$ is negative definite or negative semidefinite along the trajectories of the system (trajectory approaches origin when $\dot{V}(\mathbf{x}) < 0$), then the origin is said to be asymptotically stable. For this case, equilibrium is obtained at the origin.

If a system possesses a Liapunov function such that $\dot{V}(\mathbf{x}) > 0$ is positive definite or positive semidefinite along the trajectories of the system, then the origin is said to be unstable. For this case, the trajectories move away from the origin.

If a system possesses a Liapunov function such that $\dot{V}(\mathbf{x})$ remains zero, the trajectory remains on a path of constant $V(\mathbf{x})$. Such a trajectory is called a limit cycle.

If $\dot{V}(\mathbf{x})$ is indefinite, the test fails, as neither stability nor instability has been proved. Thus, one must try a different $V(\mathbf{x})$ function. A system may have many Liapunov functions. However, if one has been found to prove that the origin is stable, then it is stable. Similarly, if a function is found which shows that the origin is unstable, then it is unstable. The major obstacle in applying Liapunov's method is that of obtaining a satisfactory Liapunov function to prove stability or instability, as the case may be.

14.5 GENERATING LIAPUNOV FUNCTIONS

Because a Liapunov function must be positive definite, one is initially tempted to assume that $V(\mathbf{x})$ has a general form, such as the square of the Euclidean norm. That is,

$$V(\mathbf{x}) = \|\mathbf{x}\|^2 = x_1^2 + x_2^2 + \cdots + x_n^2 \tag{14.55}$$

It is immediately apparent that the quadratic form is even more general. That is,

$$V(\mathbf{x}) = \sum_{i=1}^{n} \sum_{j=1}^{n} a_{ij} x_i x_j \tag{14.56}$$

where $a_{ij} = a_{ji}$. Malkin[1] has shown that such a Liapunov function will prove stability or instability for linear systems. Unfortunately, for nonlinear systems such functions usually fail to prove stability or instability.

Illustrative example The mass-spring-damper system shown in Fig. 14.19 has a nonlinear spring $K = g(y)$ and a nonlinear damper $B = f(\dot{y})$. The equation of motion is

$$M\ddot{y} + f(\dot{y})\dot{y} + g(y)y = 0$$

By letting $x_1 = y$ and $x_2 = \dot{x}_1 = \dot{y}$, the state-space representation is

$$\dot{x}_1 = x_2 = f_1$$

$$\dot{x}_2 = -\frac{g(x_1)}{M} x_1 - \frac{f(x_2)}{M} x_2 = f_2 \tag{14.57}$$

Consider the function

$$V(\mathbf{x}) = \tfrac{1}{2} M x_2^2 + \int_0^{x_1} g(x_1) x_1 \, dx_1 \tag{14.58}$$

If $g(x_1)x_1 > 0$ for $x_1 > 0$ and $g(x_1)x_1 < 0$ for $x_1 < 0$ [that is, $g(x_1) > 0$ for $x_1 \neq 0$], then $V(\mathbf{x})$ satisfies the requirements for a Liapunov function.

The value of $\dot{V}(\mathbf{x})$ for this system is

$$\dot{V}(\mathbf{x}) = \frac{\partial V}{\partial x_1} \dot{x}_1 + \frac{\partial V}{\partial x_2} \dot{x}_2 = g(x_1)x_1 \dot{x}_1 + M x_2 \dot{x}_2$$

Using Eq. (14.57) to evaluate the derivative along the trajectories of the system gives

$$\dot{V}(\mathbf{x}) = g(x_1)x_1 x_2 + x_2[-g(x_1)x_1 - f(x_2)x_2] = -f(x_2)x_2^2 \tag{14.59}$$

[1] I. G. Malkin, "Theory of Stability of Motion," Gostekhizdat, Moscow, 1952. English translation, Commerce Department, AEC translation 3352, Washington, D.C.

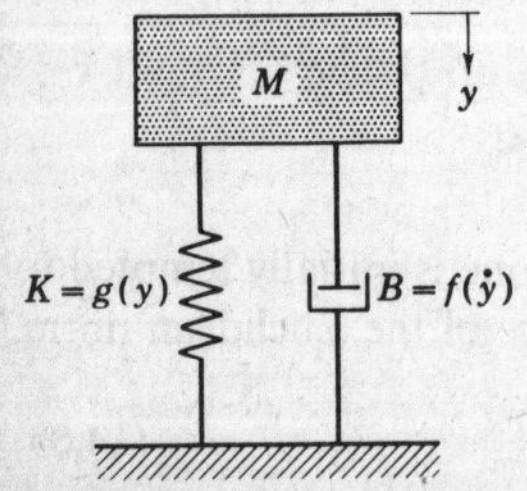

Figure 14.19 Nonlinear mass-spring-damper system.

The system thus approaches equilibrium at the origin $[\dot{V}(\mathbf{x}) < 0]$ for any damping function such that $f(x_2) > 0$.

General techniques for generating Liapunov functions for nonlinear systems are described in Secs. 14.6 and 14.7. The derivation of the Liapunov function for the preceding illustrative example, Eq. (14.58), is presented in Illustrative Example 2 of Sec. 14.7.

Some Mathematics

Before the discussion of various techniques for generating Liapunov functions for nonlinear systems, some basic mathematics will be reviewed.

The operator ∇ (said "del") is defined as follows:

$$\nabla = \frac{\partial}{\partial x}\mathbf{i} + \frac{\partial}{\partial y}\mathbf{j} + \frac{\partial}{\partial z}\mathbf{k}$$

The gradient of a scalar function $F(x, y, z)$ is

$$\text{Gradient of } F = \nabla F = \left(\frac{\partial}{\partial x}\mathbf{i} + \frac{\partial}{\partial y}\mathbf{j} + \frac{\partial}{\partial z}\mathbf{k}\right)F = \left(\frac{\partial F}{\partial x}\mathbf{i} + \frac{\partial F}{\partial y}\mathbf{j} + \frac{\partial F}{\partial z}\mathbf{k}\right)$$

Insight into the meaning of ∇F is obtained by considering the vector $\Delta\mathbf{r}$ in Fig. 14.20. The angle between the x axis and $\Delta\mathbf{r}$ is α, the angle between the y axis and $\Delta\mathbf{r}$ is β, and the angle between the z axis and $\Delta\mathbf{r}$ is γ. In terms of its components,

$$\Delta\mathbf{r} = \Delta r(\cos\alpha\mathbf{i} + \cos\beta\mathbf{j} + \cos\gamma\mathbf{k}) = \Delta r\mathbf{e}$$

where $\mathbf{e} = \cos\alpha\mathbf{i} + \cos\beta\mathbf{j} + \cos\gamma\mathbf{k}$ is a unit vector in the direction of $\Delta\mathbf{r}$. From calculus, it follows that the change in F is

$$\Delta F = \frac{\partial F}{\partial x}\Delta x + \frac{\partial F}{\partial y}\Delta y + \frac{\partial F}{\partial z}\Delta z$$

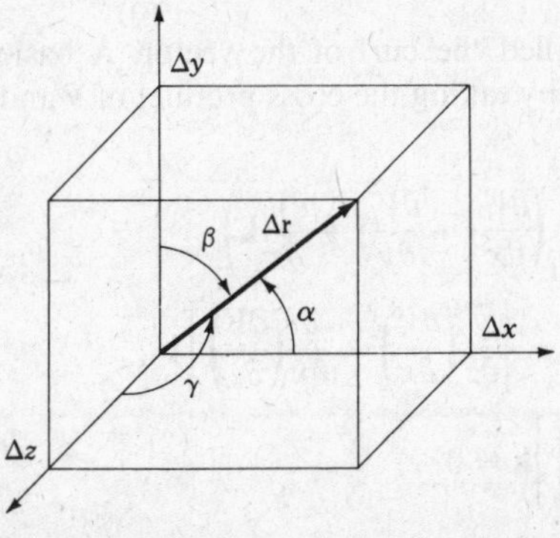

Figure 14.20 Vector $\Delta\mathbf{r} = \Delta x\mathbf{i} + \Delta y\mathbf{j} + \Delta z\mathbf{k}$.

When Δx, Δy, and Δz are the components of $\Delta\mathbf{r}$, then ΔF is the change of F in the direction of $\Delta\mathbf{r}$. The rate of change of F in the direction of $\Delta\mathbf{r}$ or $\mathbf{e}$ is

$$\frac{dF}{dr} = \lim_{\Delta r \to 0} \frac{\Delta F}{\Delta r} = \frac{\partial F}{\partial x}\frac{\Delta x}{\Delta r} + \frac{\partial F}{\partial y}\frac{\Delta y}{\Delta r} + \frac{\partial F}{\partial z}\frac{\Delta z}{\Delta r}$$

$$= \left(\frac{\partial F}{\partial x}\mathbf{i} + \frac{\partial F}{\partial y}\mathbf{j} + \frac{\partial F}{\partial z}\mathbf{k}\right) \cdot (\cos\alpha\mathbf{i} + \cos\beta\mathbf{j} + \cos\gamma\mathbf{k})$$

$$= \nabla F \cdot \mathbf{e}$$

Because $\nabla F \cdot \mathbf{e}$ is the component of ∇F in the direction of $\mathbf{e}$, the gradient ∇F must be the maximum rate of change of the function F.

Next consider the scalar function $V(x_1, x_2, x_3)$ of the three variables x_1, x_2, and x_3. The derivative with respect to time is

$$\frac{dV}{dt} = \frac{\partial V}{\partial x_1}\frac{dx_1}{dt} + \frac{\partial V}{\partial x_2}\frac{dx_2}{dt} + \frac{\partial V}{\partial x_3}\frac{dx_3}{dt} = \frac{\partial V}{\partial x_1}\dot{x}_1 + \frac{\partial V}{\partial x_2}\dot{x}_2 + \frac{\partial V}{\partial x_3}\dot{x}_3$$

By noting that

$$\nabla V = \frac{\partial V}{\partial x_1}\mathbf{i} + \frac{\partial V}{\partial x_2}\mathbf{j} + \frac{\partial V}{\partial x_3}\mathbf{k}$$

and

$$\dot{\mathbf{x}} = \dot{x}_1\mathbf{i} + \dot{x}_2\mathbf{j} + \dot{x}_3\mathbf{k}$$

then dV/dt may be written in the form

$$\frac{dV}{dt} = \nabla V \cdot \dot{\mathbf{x}}$$

The function V may be obtained by integrating $\dot{V} = \nabla V \cdot \dot{\mathbf{x}}$ as follows:

$$V = \int_0^t \dot{V}\,dt = \int_0^t \nabla V \cdot \dot{\mathbf{x}}\,dt = \int_0^{\mathbf{x}} \nabla V \cdot d\mathbf{x}$$

The cross product of ∇ and a vector is called the curl of the vector. A basic property of a gradient vector ∇V is revealed by taking the cross product of ∇ and ∇V. That is,

$$\nabla \times \nabla V = \left(\frac{\partial}{\partial x}\mathbf{i} + \frac{\partial}{\partial y}\mathbf{j} + \frac{\partial}{\partial z}\mathbf{k}\right) \times \left(\frac{\partial V}{\partial x}\mathbf{i} + \frac{\partial V}{\partial y}\mathbf{j} + \frac{\partial V}{\partial z}\mathbf{k}\right)$$

$$= \left[\frac{\partial}{\partial y}\left(\frac{\partial V}{\partial z}\right) - \frac{\partial}{\partial z}\left(\frac{\partial V}{\partial y}\right)\right]\mathbf{i} + \left[\frac{\partial}{\partial z}\left(\frac{\partial V}{\partial x}\right) - \frac{\partial}{\partial x}\left(\frac{\partial V}{\partial z}\right)\right]\mathbf{j}$$

$$+ \left[\frac{\partial}{\partial x}\left(\frac{\partial V}{\partial y}\right) - \frac{\partial}{\partial y}\left(\frac{\partial V}{\partial x}\right)\right]\mathbf{k} = 0$$

Letting $x_1 = x$, $x_2 = y$, $x_3 = z$, and $v_1 = \partial V/\partial x$, $v_2 = \partial V/\partial y$, and $v_3 = \partial V/\partial z$, the preceding **i**, **j**, and **k** components are

$$\frac{\partial}{\partial x_2} v_3 = \frac{\partial}{\partial x_3} v_2 \qquad \frac{\partial}{\partial x_3} v_1 = \frac{\partial}{\partial x_1} v_3 \qquad \frac{\partial}{\partial x_1} v_2 = \frac{\partial}{\partial x_2} v_1$$

These are referred to as the curl relationships. There are $n(n-1)/2$ curl equations. In order that ∇V be a gradient vector, it is necessary that the curl equations be satisfied. The matrix form for dV/dt is

$$\frac{dV}{dt} = \nabla V \cdot \dot{\mathbf{x}} = \begin{bmatrix} \dfrac{\partial V}{\partial x_1} & \dfrac{\partial V}{\partial x_2} & \dfrac{\partial V}{\partial x_3} \end{bmatrix} \begin{bmatrix} \dot{x}_1 \\ \dot{x}_2 \\ \dot{x}_3 \end{bmatrix} = \nabla V^T \dot{\mathbf{x}}$$

where $\nabla V = \begin{bmatrix} \partial V/\partial x_1 \\ \partial V/\partial x_2 \\ \partial V/\partial x_3 \end{bmatrix} = \begin{bmatrix} v_1 \\ v_2 \\ v_3 \end{bmatrix}$ and $\dot{\mathbf{x}} = \begin{bmatrix} \dot{x}_1 \\ \dot{x}_2 \\ \dot{x}_3 \end{bmatrix}$

The matrix representation has the obvious advantage that it is applicable for functions of n variables.

14.6 THE VARIABLE-GRADIENT METHOD[1,2]

To develop this method, first note that the derivative $\dot{V}(\mathbf{x})$ is

$$\begin{aligned} \dot{V}(\mathbf{x}) = \frac{dV}{dt} &= \frac{\partial V}{\partial x_1}\dot{x}_1 + \frac{\partial V}{\partial x_2}\dot{x}_2 + \cdots + \frac{\partial V}{\partial x_n}\dot{x}_n \\ &= \frac{\partial V}{\partial x_1} f_1 + \frac{\partial V}{\partial x_2} f_2 + \cdots + \frac{\partial V}{\partial x_n} f_n \\ &= \nabla V \cdot \mathbf{f} \end{aligned} \tag{14.60}$$

In the variable-gradient method, the gradient vector ∇V is assumed to have the general form

$$\nabla V = \begin{bmatrix} a_{11}x_1 + a_{12}x_2 + \cdots + a_{1n}x_n \\ a_{21}x_1 + a_{22}x_2 + \cdots + a_{2n}x_n \\ \cdots\cdots\cdots\cdots\cdots\cdots\cdots \\ a_{n1}x_1 + a_{n2}x_2 + \cdots + a_{nn}x_n \end{bmatrix} = \begin{bmatrix} v_1 \\ v_2 \\ \cdots \\ v_n \end{bmatrix} \tag{14.61}$$

[1] D. G. Schultz and J. E. Gibson, The Variable Gradient Method for Generating Liapunov Functions, *Trans. AIEE*, **81**: (2), 203–210 (1962).

[2] D. G. Schultz, "The Variable Gradient Method of Generating Liapunov Functions with Applications to Automatic Control Systems," Ph.D. Thesis, Purdue University, 1962.

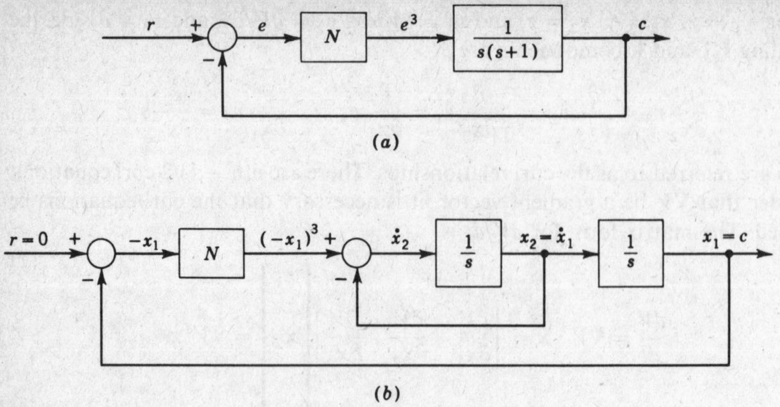

Figure 14.21 System with a nonlinear element.

where

1. $$a_{ij} = k_{ij} + f_{ij}(x_1, x_2, \ldots, x_{n-1})$$
2. $$a_{ii} = k_{ii} + f_{ii}(x_i) \tag{14.62}$$
3. $$a_{nn} = 2$$

Thus, each coefficient a_{ij} is assumed to be composed of a constant part k_{ij} and a variable part f_{ij}. For the diagonal coefficient a_{ii}, the variable part is a function of x_i only. In order that the curl equations be satisfied, it is necessary that $k_{ij} = k_{ji}$.

Illustrative example In Fig. 14.21*a* is shown a feedback control system in which the nonlinear element N cubes the actuating signal e. From the equivalent representation for this system, Fig. 14.21*b*, the state-space equations are found to be

$$\begin{aligned} \dot{x}_1 &= x_2 = f_1 \\ \dot{x}_2 &= -x_1^3 - x_2 = f_2 \end{aligned} \tag{14.63}$$

SOLUTION Assume ∇V is of the form

$$\nabla V = \begin{bmatrix} (a_{11}x_1 + a_{12}x_2) \\ (a_{12}x_1 + 2x_2) \end{bmatrix} \tag{14.64}$$

Thus,

$$\begin{aligned} \dot{V}(\mathbf{x}) = \nabla V^T \mathbf{f} &= [(a_{11}x_1 + a_{12}x_2)\ (a_{21}x_1 + 2x_2)] \begin{bmatrix} x_2 \\ -x_2 - x_1^3 \end{bmatrix} \\ &= (a_{11} - a_{21} - 2x_1^2)x_1x_2 - (2 - a_{12})x_2^2 - a_{21}x_1^4 \end{aligned} \tag{14.65}$$

By choosing $a_{11} = a_{21} + 2x_1^2$, the first term vanishes. Furthermore, if $0 < a_{12} < 2$, then each of the last two terms is negative. With these constraints it is seen that $\dot{V}(\mathbf{x})$ is negative definite. For a constant a_{21}, tnen $a_{12} = a_{21}$. The gradient ∇V that has been constructed is

$$\nabla V = \begin{bmatrix} (a_{21}x_1 + 2x_1^3 + a_{21}x_2) \\ (a_{21}x_1 + 2x_2) \end{bmatrix} \tag{14.66}$$

For a second-order system, there is but one curl equation. For this system, it is

$$\frac{\partial v_1}{\partial x_2} = a_{21} = \frac{\partial v_2}{\partial x_1}$$

With the curl equation satisfied, we now proceed to construct $V(\mathbf{x})$ from ∇V.

$$V(\mathbf{x}) = \int_0^{\mathbf{x}} \nabla V \cdot d\mathbf{x} = \int_0^{x_1} (a_{21}x_1 + 2x_1^3 + a_{21}x_2)\, dx_1 + \int_0^{x_2} (a_{21}x_1 + 2x_2)\, dx_2$$

$$= \left(\frac{a_{21}}{2} + \frac{x_1^2}{2}\right)x_1^2 + a_{21}x_1x_2 + x_2^2 \tag{14.67}$$

A line integral is independent of the path. For the path (0, 0) to $(x_1, 0)$ to (x_1, x_2), $x_2 = 0$ in the first integral. For the path (0, 0) to $(0, x_2)$ to (x_1, x_2), $x_1 = 0$ in the second integral. Because $V(\mathbf{x})$ has the quadratic form, it may be expressed as

$$V(\mathbf{x}) = \mathbf{x}^T A \mathbf{x}$$

where

$$A = \begin{bmatrix} \dfrac{a_{21} + x_1^2}{2} & \dfrac{a_{21}}{2} \\ \dfrac{a_{21}}{2} & 1 \end{bmatrix}$$

If the matrix A is positive definite, then $V(\mathbf{x})$ is positive definite. By Sylvester's theorem, a matrix A is positive definite if all its minors are positive definite. The minors of A are

$$\frac{a_{21} + x_1^2}{2} > 0$$

$$\frac{a_{21} + x_1^2}{2} - \frac{a_{21}^2}{4} = \frac{a_{21}(2 - a_{21})}{4} + \frac{x_1^2}{2} > 0$$

The first minor requires that $a_{21} > 0$ and the second requires that $(2 - a_{21}) > 0$. Thus, $V(\mathbf{x})$ is positive definite if

$$0 < a_{21} < 2 \tag{14.68}$$

This is the same constraint that was placed on a_{21} in the construction of ∇V.

In effect, Eq. (14.67) describes an infinite set of Liapunov functions for this system in that $0 < a_{12} < 2$. Because

$$\dot{V}(\mathbf{x}) = -(2 - a_{21})x_2^2 - a_{21}x_1^4$$

is globally negative definite, this system is globally asymptotically stable.

14.7 THE FORMAT METHOD

This method was developed by Dr. J. L. Peczkowski.[1,2] The following properties of vectors are needed to prove the theorem which is fundamental to the method.

Property I For any n vector $\mathbf{x}$ ($\mathbf{x} \neq 0$), the scalar product

$$P\mathbf{x} \cdot \mathbf{x} = \mathbf{x} \cdot P\mathbf{x} = \mathbf{x}^T P\mathbf{x} = 0 \tag{14.69}$$

if and only if P is any real $n \times n$ skew-symmetric matrix[3] (that is, $P = -P^T$). For $n = 2$, the preceding is

$$\mathbf{x}^T P\mathbf{x} = [x_1 \quad x_2]\begin{bmatrix} 0 & p \\ -p & 0 \end{bmatrix}\begin{bmatrix} x_1 \\ x_2 \end{bmatrix} = [x_1 \quad x_2]\begin{bmatrix} px_2 \\ -px_1 \end{bmatrix} = [px_1x_2 - px_1x_2] = 0$$

Property II Every n vector $\mathbf{y}$ which satisfies the scalar product

$$\mathbf{x} \cdot \mathbf{y} = F \tag{14.70}$$

where $\mathbf{x} \neq 0$ and F is any scalar, is represented by

$$\mathbf{x} = [D + P]\mathbf{y} \tag{14.71}$$

if and only if D is any $n \times n$ matrix satisfying $D\mathbf{y} \cdot \mathbf{y} = F$ and P is any real $n \times n$ skew-symmetric matrix. From the two preceding equations, it follows that

$$\mathbf{x} \cdot \mathbf{y} = [D + P]\mathbf{y} \cdot \mathbf{y} = D\mathbf{y} \cdot \mathbf{y} + P\mathbf{y} \cdot \mathbf{y} = D\mathbf{y} \cdot \mathbf{y} = F \tag{14.72}$$

By Property I, $P\mathbf{y} \cdot \mathbf{y} = 0$.

Because $\dot{V} = \nabla V \cdot \dot{\mathbf{x}}$, replacing $\mathbf{x}$ by ∇V and $\mathbf{y}$ by $\dot{\mathbf{x}}$ in Eq. (14.70) shows that the scalar F is $\dot{V}$. The basic theorem for the format method is obtained by making the change of variable $\mathbf{x} = \nabla V$, $\mathbf{y} = \dot{\mathbf{x}} = \mathbf{f}$, and $F = \dot{V}$ in Eqs. (14.70) to (14.72).

[1] J. L. Peczkowski, "A Format Method for Generating Liapunov Functions," Ph.D. Thesis, University of Notre Dame, 1966.

[2] J. L. Peczkowski and R. W. Liu, "A Format Method for Generating Liapunov Functions," *Trans. ASME*, **89:** (2) Series D (June 1967).

[3] R. W. Liu and R. J. Leake, "Exhaustive Equivalence Classes of Optimal Control Systems with Separable Controls," Technical Report EE-652, Department of Elec. Engineering, University of Notre Dame, March 1965.

The new relationships are

$$\dot{V} = \nabla V \cdot \dot{\mathbf{x}}$$
$$\nabla V = [D + P]\mathbf{f}$$
$$\nabla V \cdot \mathbf{x} = D\dot{\mathbf{x}} \cdot \dot{\mathbf{x}} = D\mathbf{f} \cdot \mathbf{f} = V$$

Theorem Every vector ∇V which satisfies $\dot{V} = \nabla V \cdot \dot{\mathbf{x}}$ may be written

$$\nabla V = [D + P]\mathbf{f} \tag{14.73}$$

where D is any $n \times n$ matrix satisfying $D\mathbf{f} \cdot \mathbf{f} = V$ and $P = -P^T$ is any real $n \times n$ skew-symmetric matrix satisfying $P\mathbf{f} \cdot \mathbf{f} = 0$. This theorem is a restatement of Property II.

To reduce computational effort, the matrix $D(\mathbf{x})$ is usually taken as a diagonal matrix. A diagonal matrix has elements on the principal diagonal only. For example,

$$D(\mathbf{x}) = \begin{bmatrix} d_{11}(\mathbf{x}) & 0 & 0 \\ 0 & d_{22}(\mathbf{x}) & 0 \\ 0 & 0 & d_{33}(\mathbf{x}) \end{bmatrix}$$

When $D(\mathbf{x})$ has but one element, $d_{ii} = L(\mathbf{x})$, then

$$\dot{V}(\mathbf{x}) = D\mathbf{f} \cdot \mathbf{f} = d_{ii} f_i^2 = L(\mathbf{x}) f_i^2$$

Because f_i^2 is positive, $\dot{V}(\mathbf{x})$ will be semidefinite or definite if $L(\mathbf{x})$ is sign definite. A skew-symmetric matrix has no elements on the diagonal, and in addition, $p_{ji} = -p_{ij}$. Thus,

$$P(\mathbf{x}) = \begin{bmatrix} 0 & -p_{12} & -p_{13} \\ p_{12} & 0 & -p_{23} \\ p_{13} & p_{23} & 0 \end{bmatrix}$$

To generate Liapunov functions by the format method,

1. Write the vector format
$$\nabla V = [D + P]\mathbf{f} \tag{14.73}$$
2. Choose the arbitrary functions p_{ij} and d_{ii}, to satisfy the curl equations, and thus obtain P and D.
3. The functions $V(\mathbf{x})$ and $\dot{V}(\mathbf{x}) = D\mathbf{f} \cdot \mathbf{f}$ may now be constructed.

Because $D(\mathbf{x})$ may have different forms, it is customary to assume first that $D(\mathbf{x})$ contains only the d_{11} element [that is, $\dot{V}(\mathbf{x}) = d_{11} f_1^2$]. If this does not yield a satisfactory Liapunov function, then assume that $D(\mathbf{x})$ contains only the d_{22} element. After all the single-element possibilities are exhausted, different forms are tried.

Illustrative example 1 Use the format method to generate a satisfactory Liapunov function for the system of Fig. 14.21.

SOLUTION Write the vector format

$$\nabla V = [D + P]\mathbf{f} = \begin{bmatrix} L(\mathbf{x}) & -p(\mathbf{x}) \\ p(\mathbf{x}) & 0 \end{bmatrix} \begin{bmatrix} x_2 \\ -x_2 - x_1^3 \end{bmatrix}$$

where $\mathbf{f}$ is obtained from Eq. (14.63).

Performing the preceding matrix multiplication gives

$$\nabla V = \begin{bmatrix} Lx_2 + px_2 + px_1^3 \\ px_2 \end{bmatrix}$$

The curl equation $\partial v_1/\partial x_2 = \partial v_2/\partial x_1$ shows that

$$\frac{\partial[(L+p)x_2]}{\partial x_2} + x_1^3 \frac{\partial p}{\partial x_2} = x_2 \frac{\partial p}{\partial x_1}$$

For the first trial, assume that p is constant. Thus,

$$\frac{\partial[(L+p)x_2]}{\partial x_2} = 0$$

The curl equation is satisfied if $L = -p$ is constant. Thus, ∇V becomes

$$\nabla V = \begin{bmatrix} px_1^3 \\ px_2 \end{bmatrix}$$

Integration to obtain the Liapunov function gives

$$V(\mathbf{x}) = \int_0^{\mathbf{x}} \nabla V \cdot d\mathbf{x} = \int_0^{x_1} px_1^3\, dx_1 + \int_0^{x_2} px_2\, dx_2 = \frac{px_1^4}{4} + \frac{px_2^2}{2} \qquad (14.74)$$

The derivative along the trajectories is

$$\dot{V}(\mathbf{x}) = \nabla V \cdot \mathbf{f} = -px_2^2 \qquad (14.75)$$

For $p > 0$, then $V(\mathbf{x})$ is positive definite and $\dot{V}(\mathbf{x})$ is negative semidefinite. For $p < 0$, then $V(\mathbf{x})$ is negative definite and $\dot{V}(\mathbf{x})$ is positive semidefinite. The stability theorems are unaffected if all the signs are reversed.

Thus, this system is globally asymptotically stable for all values of p. There is no need to assume other forms of D or other forms of the p functions to obtain other Liapunov functions. It is to be noted that although the Liapunov functions of Eqs. (14.67) and (14.74) are different, they both yield the same result.

Illustrative example 2 Use the format method to generate the Liapunov function for the illustrative example of Sec. 14.5. The differential equation is

$$M\ddot{y} + f(\dot{y})\dot{y} + g(y)y = 0 \qquad (14.56)$$

SOLUTION In phase coordinates this equation becomes

$$\dot{x}_1 = x_2$$
$$\dot{x}_2 = -[g(x_1)x_1 + f(x_2)x_2]/M \tag{14.76}$$

The vector format is

$$\nabla V = \begin{bmatrix} L & -p \\ p & 0 \end{bmatrix} \begin{bmatrix} f_1 \\ f_2 \end{bmatrix} = \begin{bmatrix} Lx_2 + p[g(x_1)x_1 + f(x_2)x_2]/M \\ px_2 \end{bmatrix}$$

For the first trial it is assumed that p is constant. Thus, the curl equation is

$$\frac{\partial}{\partial x_2}\left[\left(L + \frac{pf(x_2)}{M}\right)x_2\right] = 0$$

The curl equation is satisfied if $L = -pf(x_2)/M$. Thus, ∇V becomes

$$\nabla V = \begin{bmatrix} pg(x_1)x_1/M \\ px_2 \end{bmatrix}$$

Line integration gives

$$V(\mathbf{x}) = \frac{p}{M}\int_0^{x_1} g(x_1)\, x_1\, dx_1 + \frac{px_2^2}{2} \tag{14.77}$$

The derivative $\dot{V}(\mathbf{x})$ is

$$\dot{V}(\mathbf{x}) = \nabla V \cdot f = -(p/M)f(x_2)x_2^2 \tag{14.78}$$

For $p = M$, Eq. (14.77) reduces to Eq. (14.58), which is the Liapunov function for the illustrative example of Sec. 14.5. Similarly, Eq. (14.78) becomes the $\dot{V}(\mathbf{x})$ function given by Eq. (14.59).

The Inverse Liapunov Problem

Applications of Liapunov's direct method have been concerned primarily with the problem of finding a suitable Liapunov function to prove stability or instability for a given system. The inverse problem may be briefly stated as follows: Find a system or class of systems that satisfy a given Liapunov function. The inverse problem makes it possible to design systems which satisfy given performance specifications. Dr. J. L. Peczkowski has shown[1,2] that his format method is also applicable to the solution of the inverse problem. In addition, it is possible to determine relative stability.

[1] J. L. Peczkowski, "Synthesis by Liapunov's Direct Method," *Trans. ASME, Journal of Dynamics, Systems, Measurement, and Control*, (Sept. 1971), pp. 151–156.

[2] J. L. Peczkowski, "A Format Method for Generating Liapunov Functions," Ph.D. Thesis, University of Notre Dame, 1966.

By making the change of variable $\mathbf{x} = \dot{\mathbf{x}}$, $\mathbf{y} = \nabla V$, and $F = \dot{V}$, then Eqs. (14.70) to (14.72) become

$$\dot{\mathbf{x}} \cdot \nabla V = \nabla V \cdot \dot{\mathbf{x}} = \dot{V}$$
$$\dot{\mathbf{x}} = [D + P]\nabla V$$
$$D\nabla V \cdot \nabla V = \dot{V}$$

The following theorem is a restatement of Property II in which the preceding change of variable is made.

Theorem I All systems which satisfy the scalar equation $\dot{V} = \nabla V \cdot \dot{\mathbf{x}}$ are represented by the vectors

$$\dot{\mathbf{x}} = [D + P]\nabla V \tag{14.79}$$

if and only if D is any real $n \times n$ matrix such that $D\nabla V \cdot \nabla V = \dot{V}$ and $P = -P^T$ is any real $n \times n$ skew-symmetric matrix. Note that

$$\dot{V} = \nabla V \cdot \dot{\mathbf{x}} = \nabla V \cdot [D + P]\nabla V = \nabla V \cdot D\nabla V + \nabla V \cdot P\nabla V = D\nabla V \cdot \nabla V$$

where $\nabla V \cdot P\nabla V = P\nabla V \cdot \nabla V = 0$ as per Property I.

Theorem II All system vectors which satisfy $\dot{V} = \nabla V \cdot \dot{\mathbf{x}}$ are represented by

$$\dot{\mathbf{x}} = [(G^T)^{-1}K + PG]\mathbf{x} \tag{14.80}$$

if and only if

$G(\mathbf{x})$ is any $n \times n$ matrix which satisfies $\nabla V = G\mathbf{x}$ and G^{-1} exists

$K(\mathbf{x})$ is any $n \times n$ matrix which satisfies $\dot{V} = \mathbf{x}^T K \mathbf{x}$

$P(\mathbf{x})$ is any $n \times n$ skew-symmetric matrix

To prove Eq. (14.80), first write Theorem I in the form

$$\dot{\mathbf{x}} = [D + P]\nabla V = [D + P]G\mathbf{x} \tag{14.81}$$

Noting that $\nabla V = G\mathbf{x}$ and $\nabla V^T = \mathbf{x}^T G^T$, it follows that

$$\dot{V} = D\nabla V \cdot \nabla V = \nabla V \cdot D\nabla V = \nabla V^T D \nabla V = \mathbf{x}^T G^T D G \mathbf{x} = \mathbf{x}^T K \mathbf{x}$$

where

$$G^T D G = K$$

Premultiplying both sides by $(G^T)^{-1}$ shows that

$$DG = (G^T)^{-1}K$$

Substitution of DG into Eq. (14.81) verifies the result given by Eq. (14.80).

Illustrative example 3 Find all linear systems which satisfy $V = (x_1^4 + x_2^8)/4$ and $\dot{V} = -kx_1^4$, where k is a constant. The components of the gradient vector ∇V are $v_1 = \partial V/\partial x_1 = x_1^3$ and $v_2 = \partial V/\partial x_2 = 2x_2^7$. The $\nabla V = G\mathbf{x}$ form is

$$\nabla V = \begin{bmatrix} x_1^3 \\ 2x_2^7 \end{bmatrix} = \begin{bmatrix} x_1^2 & 0 \\ 0 & 2x_2^6 \end{bmatrix} \begin{bmatrix} x_1 \\ x_2 \end{bmatrix} = G\mathbf{x}$$

Similarly, the $\dot{V} = \mathbf{x}^T K \mathbf{x}$ form is

$$\dot{V} = [x_1 \quad x_2] \begin{bmatrix} -k_1 & 0 \\ 0 & -k_2 \end{bmatrix} \begin{bmatrix} x_1 \\ x_2 \end{bmatrix}$$

In order that $\dot{V} = -kx_1^4$, then $k_1 = kx_1^2$ and $k_2 = 0$. The resulting system equations are

$$\dot{\mathbf{x}} = [(G^T)^{-1}K + P]G\mathbf{x} = \begin{bmatrix} -k & 2px_2^6 \\ -px_1^2 & 0 \end{bmatrix} \mathbf{x} = \begin{bmatrix} -kx_1 + 2px_2^7 \\ -px_1^3 \end{bmatrix}$$

Because V is positive definite, $\dot{V}$ is negative semidefinite, and $\dot{\mathbf{x}}(0) = \mathbf{f}(0) = 0$, the system is asymptotically stable.

Quadratic Forms

For Liapunov functions expressed in quadratic form, a unique representation is obtained for the corresponding system equation. Thus, consider the pair of scalar functions given by

$$V = \tfrac{1}{2}\mathbf{x}^T A \mathbf{x} \qquad \text{and} \qquad \dot{V} = \mathbf{x}^T K \mathbf{x}$$

where A and K are any constant $n \times n$ matrices. The gradient vector ∇V is

$$\nabla V = \frac{\partial V}{\partial \mathbf{x}} = \frac{1}{2}\frac{\partial}{\partial \mathbf{x}}(\mathbf{x} \cdot A\mathbf{x})$$

$$= \frac{1}{2}(A + A^T)\mathbf{x} = G\mathbf{x}$$

Thus, it follows that

$$G^T = \tfrac{1}{2}(A^T + A) \qquad \text{and} \qquad (G^T)^{-1} = 2(A^T + A)^{-1}$$

The systems which satisfy the scalar equations are now obtained by application of the synthesis equation. That is,

$$\dot{\mathbf{x}} = [(G^T)^{-1}K + PG]\mathbf{x} = [2(A^T + A)^{-1}K + P(A + A^T)/2]\mathbf{x} \qquad (14.82)$$

If A is symmetric, $A + A^T = 2A$; thus

$$\dot{\mathbf{x}} = (A^{-1}K + PA)\mathbf{x} \qquad (14.83)$$

Equations (14.82) and (14.83) represent all linear and nonlinear systems whose stability in the state space is described by the scalar functions $V = \frac{1}{2}\mathbf{x}^T A \mathbf{x}$ and $\dot{V} = \mathbf{x}^T K \mathbf{x}$.

Illustrative example 4 Find all linear systems which satisfy

$$V = x_1^2 + 2x_2^2 + 4x_3^2 \qquad \text{and} \qquad \dot{V} = -k_1 x_1^2 - k_3 x_3^2$$

SOLUTION For $V = \frac{1}{2}\mathbf{x}^T A\mathbf{x}$ and $\dot{V} = \mathbf{x}^T K\mathbf{x}$, it follows that

$$A = \begin{bmatrix} 2 & 0 & 0 \\ 0 & 4 & 0 \\ 0 & 0 & 8 \end{bmatrix} \quad K = \begin{bmatrix} -k_1 & 0 & 0 \\ 0 & 0 & 0 \\ 0 & 0 & -k_3 \end{bmatrix} \quad A^{-1} = \begin{bmatrix} \frac{1}{2} & 0 & 0 \\ 0 & \frac{1}{4} & 0 \\ 0 & 0 & \frac{1}{8} \end{bmatrix}$$

Application of Eq. (14.83) yields for the system equations

$$\dot{\mathbf{x}} = [A^{-1}K + PA]\mathbf{x} = \begin{bmatrix} -k_1/2 & 4p_{12} & 8p_{13} \\ -2p_{12} & 0 & 8p_{23} \\ -2p_{13} & -4p_{23} & -k_3/8 \end{bmatrix} \mathbf{x}$$

To satisfy a stability theorem, the k's must be selected so that $\dot{V}$ is negative definite or negative semidefinite.

Asymptotic Response

In state space, $V(\mathbf{x}) = C$ may be regarded as a contour. If $T(t)$ is an increasing function of time such that $T(t)$ approaches infinity as t approaches infinity, then $V(\mathbf{x}) = C/T(t)$ approaches the origin as t approaches infinity. Thus, consider the function

$$Q(\mathbf{x}, t) = T(t)V(\mathbf{x}) = T_0 V_0 = C$$

Differentiation with respect to time shows that

$$\dot{T}V + T\dot{V} = 0$$

Hence

$$\frac{\dot{V}}{V} = -\frac{\dot{T}}{T}$$

For exponential asymptotic stability, choose $T(t) = e^{at}$. For this function, $\dot{T}/T = ae^{at}/e^{at} = a$. Thus

$$\dot{V} = -\frac{\dot{T}}{T}V = -aV$$

This relationship ($\dot{V} = -aV$) is a characteristic feature of systems which exhibit exponential response and stability. Integration of this relationship shows that

$$V = V_0 e^{-at} = Ce^{-at}$$

Because $T_0 = e^0 = 1$, then $V_0 = C/T_0 = C$. Note that $V(\mathbf{x}) = Ce^{-at}$ decreases exponentially with time.

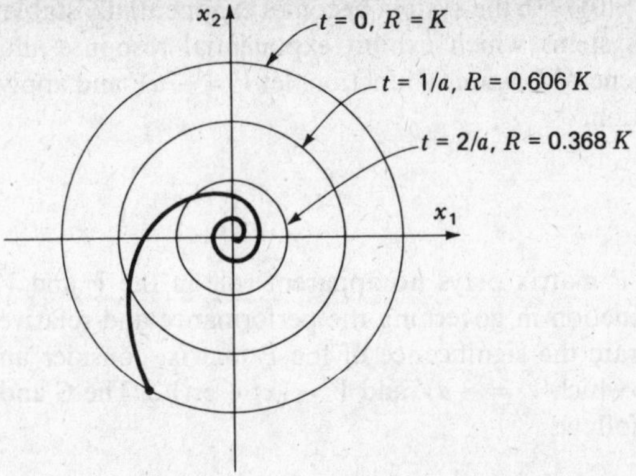

Figure 14.22 Asymptotic response.

For the two-dimensional case in which $V(\mathbf{x}) = x_1^2 + x_2^2$, then

$$Q = e^{at}V(\mathbf{x}) = e^{at}(x_1^2 + x_2^2) = C$$

For $t = 0$, $V(\mathbf{x}) = V_0 = x_1^2 + x_2^2 = C$. This is the equation for a circle of radius $R = \sqrt{C} = K$, where $C = K^2$. For $t = 1/a$, $V(\mathbf{x}) = x_1^2 + x_2^2 = K^2/e = 0.368K^2$. This is a circle of radius $R = 0.606K$. For $t = 2/a$, $V(\mathbf{x}) = x_1^2 + x_2^2 = K^2/e^2$. This is a circle of radius $R = e^{-1}K = 0.368K$. A typical phase-plane trajectory is shown in Fig. 14.22.

Illustrative example 5 Find systems which give exponential response and stability with respect to the Liapunov function

$$V(\mathbf{x}) = x_1^n + x_2^m$$

SOLUTION The gradient vector ∇V is

$$\nabla V = \begin{bmatrix} \dfrac{\partial V}{\partial x_1} \\ \dfrac{\partial V}{\partial x_2} \end{bmatrix} = \begin{bmatrix} nx_1^{n-1} \\ mx_2^{m-1} \end{bmatrix} = \begin{bmatrix} nx_1^{n-2} & 0 \\ 0 & mx_2^{m-2} \end{bmatrix} \begin{bmatrix} x_1 \\ x_2 \end{bmatrix} = G\mathbf{x}$$

For exponential asymptotic stability,

$$\dot{V} = -aV = -ax_1^n - ax_2^m$$

$$= \mathbf{x}^T \begin{bmatrix} -ax_1^{n-2} & 0 \\ 0 & -ax_2^{m-2} \end{bmatrix} \mathbf{x} = \mathbf{x}^T K \mathbf{x}$$

Application of the synthesis equation $\dot{\mathbf{x}} = [(G^T)^{-1}K + PG]\mathbf{x}$ yields for the desired result

$$\begin{bmatrix} \dot{x}_1 \\ \dot{x}_2 \end{bmatrix} = \begin{bmatrix} -\dfrac{a}{n} & pmx_2^{m-2} \\ -pnx_1^{n-2} & -\dfrac{a}{m} \end{bmatrix} \begin{bmatrix} x_1 \\ x_2 \end{bmatrix} = \begin{bmatrix} -\dfrac{a}{n}x_1 + pmx_2^{m-1} \\ -pnx_1^{n-1} - \dfrac{a}{m}x_2 \end{bmatrix}$$

By selecting $p(\mathbf{x})$ such that $\dot{\mathbf{x}}(0) = 0$, the system becomes exponentially stable. In general, to determine systems which exhibit exponential response and stability with respect to a general Liapunov function, let $\dot{V} = -aV$ and apply the general synthesis equation.

Relative Stability

Although the skew-symmetric P matrix plays no apparent role in the V and $\dot{V}$ relationships, it has a major function in governing the performance and relative stability of a system. To illustrate the significance of the P matrix, consider an exponentially stable system for which $\dot{V} = -aV$ and $V = (x_1^2 + x_2^2)/2$. The G and K matrices are determined as follows:

$$\nabla V = \begin{bmatrix} \dfrac{\partial V}{\partial x_1} \\ \dfrac{\partial V}{\partial x_2} \end{bmatrix} = \begin{bmatrix} x_1 \\ x_2 \end{bmatrix} = \begin{bmatrix} 1 & 0 \\ 0 & 1 \end{bmatrix} \mathbf{x} = G\mathbf{x}$$

$$\dot{V} = -a(x_1^2 + x_2^2)/2 = \mathbf{x}^T \begin{bmatrix} -a/2 & 0 \\ 0 & -a/2 \end{bmatrix} \mathbf{x} = \mathbf{x}^T K \mathbf{x}$$

Application of Eq. (14.82) yields for the system equations

$$\dot{\mathbf{x}} = [(G^T)^{-1}K + PG]\mathbf{x} = \begin{bmatrix} -a/2 & p \\ -p & -a/2 \end{bmatrix} \begin{bmatrix} x_1 \\ x_2 \end{bmatrix}$$

Hence

$$\dot{x}_1 = -\frac{a}{2}x_1 + px_2$$

$$\dot{x}_2 = -\frac{a}{2}x_2 - px_1$$

For $p = 0$, the solution of these equations is

$$x_1 = x_1(0)e^{-(a/2)t} \qquad \text{and} \qquad x_2 = x_2(0)e^{-(a/2)t}$$

To obtain the solution when $p \neq 0$, replace $\dot{x}_1$ by Dx_1 and $\dot{x}_2$ by Dx_2 and then eliminate x_2 to obtain the following differential equation for x_1:

$$\left[\left(D + \frac{a}{2}\right)^2 + p^2\right] x_1 = 0$$

Similarly, eliminating x_1 yields the following differential equation for x_2:

$$\left[\left(D + \frac{a}{2}\right)^2 + p^2\right] x_2 = 0$$

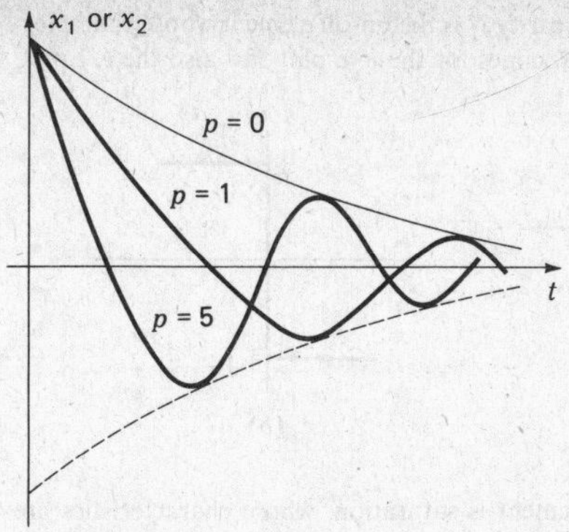

Figure 14.23 System response as a function of p.

The general solution of these equations is

$$x_1 = C_1 e^{-(a/2)t} \sin(pt + \phi_1)$$
$$x_2 = C_2 e^{-(a/2)t} \sin(pt + \phi_2)$$

The phase trajectories for $p = 0$, 1, and 5 are sketched in Fig. 14.23. All systems approach the origin at the identical rate $e^{-at/2}$. The Liapunov function has broadly specified the rate of decay or settling time, but not the relative stability. This situation is analogous to one in which the envelope of the response is specified but not the action within.

PROBLEMS

14.1 Determine the general equation for the phase trajectory for each of the following:

(*a*) $\dot{y} + y = 0$
(*b*) $\ddot{y} + \dot{y} = 0$
(*c*) $\ddot{y} + y^3 = 0$
(*d*) $\ddot{y} + \sin y = 0$

Sketch the trajectories for each of these cases.

14.2 Determine the equation for the isoclines for each of the following systems:

(*a*) $\ddot{y} + y = 0$
(*b*) $\ddot{y} + 2\dot{y} + 4y = 0$
(*c*) $\ddot{y} + |\dot{y}|\dot{y} + y = 0$

Sketch the trajectories for each of these systems.

14.3 Use Pell's method to sketch the trajectories in the vicinity of the point $y = 2$ and $\dot{y} = 3$ for each of the systems of Prob. 14.2.

14.4 Use the delta method to sketch the trajectories in the vicinity of the point $y = 2$ and $\dot{y} = 3$ for each of the systems of Prob. 14.2.

14.5 Determine the equation of the isoclines for each of the following:

(*a*) $\ddot{y} + B\dot{y} + Ky = 0$
(*b*) $\ddot{y} + B\dot{y} + Ky^3 = 0$

Sketch the trajectories for the case in which $B = K = 1$ and for the case in which $B = -1$ and $K = 1$.

14.6 For the nonlinear system of Fig. P14.6*a*, the nonlinearity N is the on-off element whose characteristics are shown in Fig. P14.6*b*. For $r = 0$, sketch the isoclines for the c, $\dot{c}$ plot and also the e, $\dot{e}$ plot.

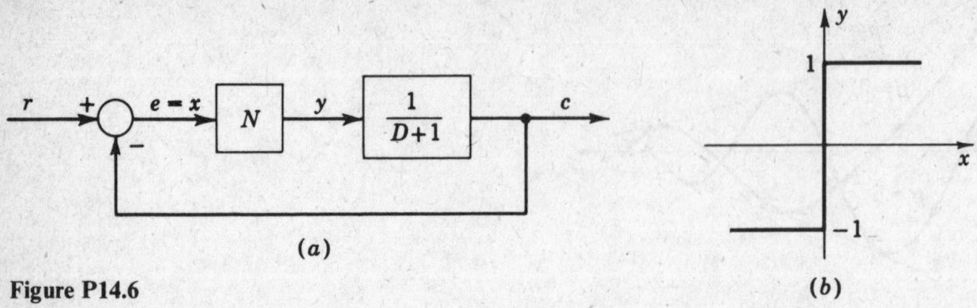

Figure P14.6

14.7 Same as Prob. 14.6 except that the nonlinear element is saturation, whose characteristics are shown in Fig. P14.7.

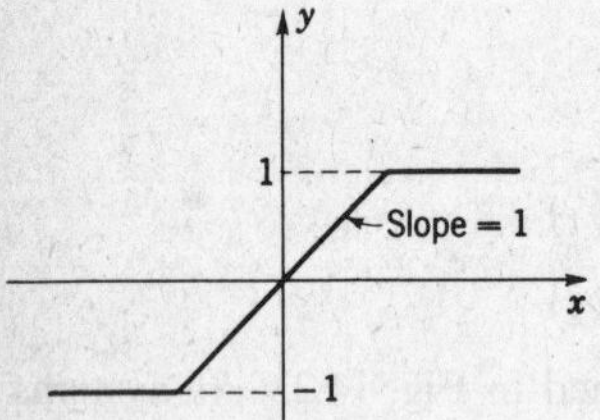

Figure P14.7

14.8 Same as Prob. 14.6 except that the nonlinear element is dead zone, whose characteristics are shown in Fig. P14.8.

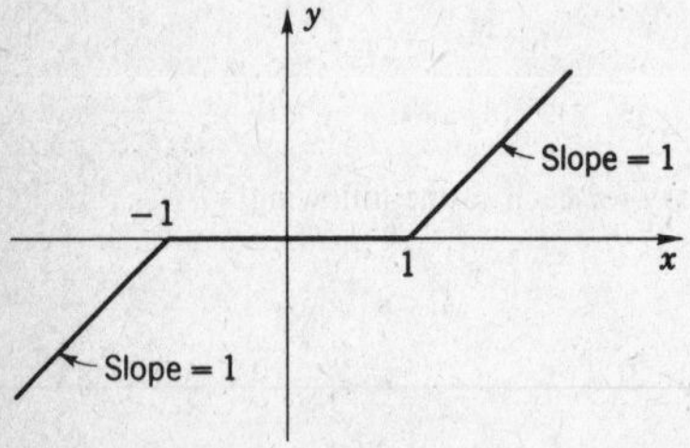

Figure P14.8

14.9 For the system shown in Fig. P14.9*a*, the nonlinear element N is saturation, whose characteristics are shown in Fig. P14.9*b*. For $r = 0$, sketch the c, $\dot{c}$ plot and also the e, $\dot{e}$ plot.

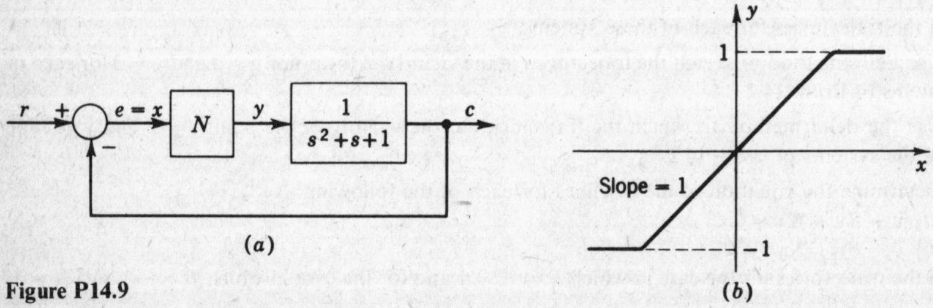

Figure P14.9

14.10 Same as Prob. 14.9 except that the nonlinear element N is dead zone, whose characteristics are shown in Fig. P14.8.

14.11 For the system shown in Fig. P14.11, the nonlinearity N is the on-off element whose characteristics are shown in Fig. P14.6*b*. For $r = 0$, sketch the isoclines for the c, $\dot{c}$ plot and also the e, $\dot{e}$ plot.

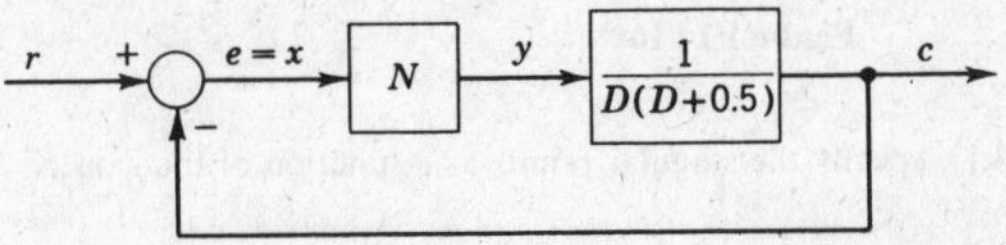

Figure P14.11

14.12 For the system shown in Fig. P14.12*a*, the nonlinearity N is the on-off element whose characteristics are shown in Fig. P14.12*b*. For $r = 0$, sketch the isoclines for the c, $\dot{c}$ plot and also the e, $\dot{e}$ plot.

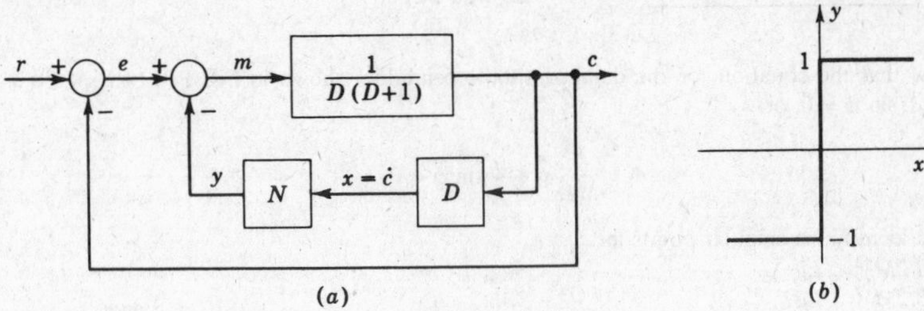

Figure P14.12

14.13 For the system shown in Fig. P14.6, sketch the phase plane of c versus $\dot{c}$ when the nonlinear element is:

(*a*) $m = e$
(*b*) $m = e^2$
(*c*) $m = e^3$

Comment on the stability of each case.

14.14 For the system shown in Fig. P14.14, use the phase-plane method to construct the response to a

(*a*) unit impulse
(*b*) unit step function

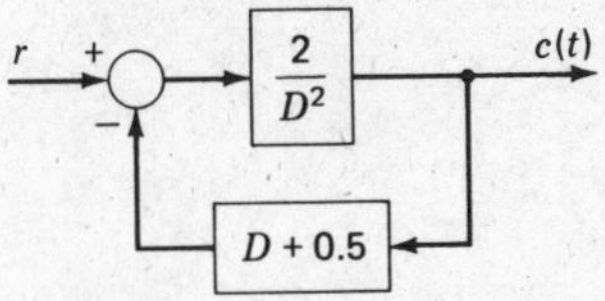

Figure P14.14

14.15 For the differential equation

$$\ddot{y} + 2\zeta\omega_n \dot{y} + \omega_n^2 y = 0$$

specify the type of singular point for

(*a*) $\zeta \geq 1$
(*b*) $0 < \zeta < 1$
(*c*) $\zeta = 0$
(*d*) $-1 < \zeta < 0$
(*e*) $-1 \leq \zeta$

14.16 For the system shown in Fig. P14.16, specify the singular points as a function of the gain K.

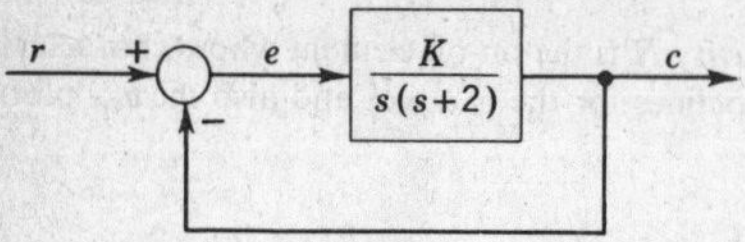

Figure P14.16

14.17 For the system shown in Fig. P14.17, specify the singular points as a function of the gain K.

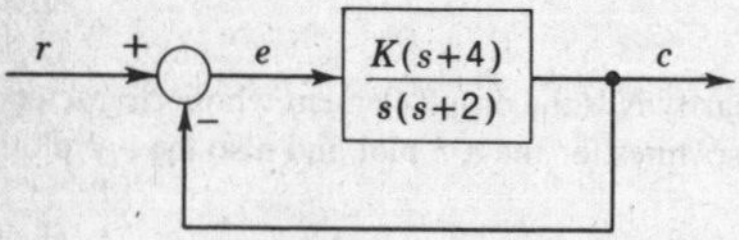

Figure P14.17

14.18 Show that the equation for the damped simple pendulum shown in Fig. P14.18 is $ML^2\ddot{\phi} + BL\dot{\phi} + MgL \sin \phi = 0$, or

$$\ddot{\phi} + \frac{B}{ML}\dot{\phi} + \frac{g}{L}\sin \phi = 0$$

Locate and identify the singular points for

(a) $(B/2M)^2 < Lg$
(b) $(B/2M)^2 > Lg$

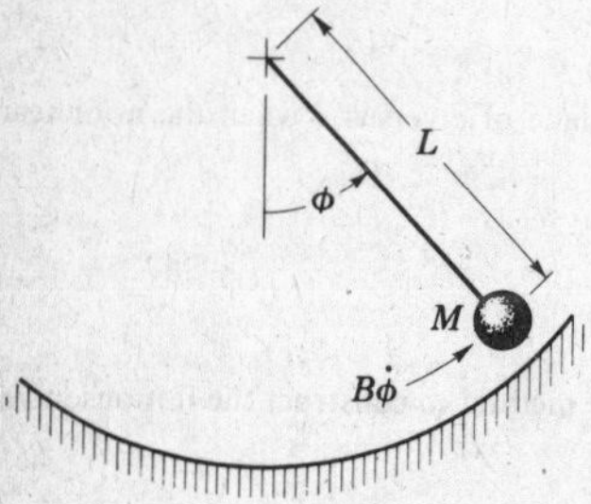

Figure P14.18

14.19 The Van der Pol equation is

$$\ddot{y} - \mu(1 - y^2)\dot{y} + y = 0$$

where μ is a constant. Locate and identify the singular points.

14.20 Consider the system

$$\ddot{x} - 2a\dot{x} + (a^2 + b^2)x = 0$$

Write the state-space representation in which $x = x_1$ and $\dot{x} = \dot{x}_1 = x_2$, and then apply the format method to determine the constraints on a and b such that the system is stable.

14.21 The differential equation for a pendulum with viscous damping is

$$\ddot{\phi} + \frac{B}{ML}\dot{\phi} + \frac{g}{L}\sin \phi = 0$$

Let $\phi = x_1$ and $\dot{\phi} = \dot{x}_1 = x_2$, and then apply the format method to determine the necessary conditions for stability.

14.22 Figure P14.22 shows a feedback control system with an unknown nonlinearity $g(x)$. Use the format method to show that a suitable $V(\mathbf{x})$ function is

$$V(\mathbf{x}) = p\left[B\int_0^{x_1} g(x_1)x_1\, dx_1 + \tfrac{1}{2}x_2^2\right]$$

where $x = x_1$ and $\dot{x} = \dot{x}_1 = x_2$. Show that the corresponding $\dot{V}(\mathbf{x})$ function is

$$\dot{V}(\mathbf{x}) = -p\left(1 + \frac{dy}{dx_1}\right)x_2^2$$

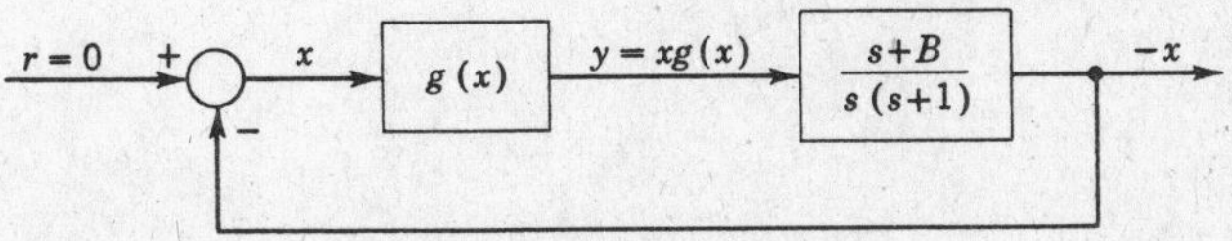

Figure P14.22

14.23 Same as Prob. 14.22 except use the variable-gradient method.

14.24 Use the format method to obtain a Liapunov function for Van der Pol's equation, which is given in Prob. 14.19.

14.25 The transfer function of the feedforward elements for a feedback control system is

$$G(s) = \frac{1}{s(s+1)}$$

The feedback path contains a nonlinear element $f(x_1)$. Use the format method to show that the system will be stable if the feedback element is such that $\int_0^{x_1} f(x_1)x_1\, dx_1 \geq 0$.

14.26 Determine the equation $\dot{\mathbf{x}} = \mathbf{f}(\mathbf{x})$ for all systems which satisfy $V = (a_2 x_1^2 + x_2^2)/2$ and $\dot{V} = -a_1 x_2^2$.

14.27 Determine the equation $\dot{\mathbf{x}} = \mathbf{f}(\mathbf{x})$ for all systems which satisfy $V = (x_1^4 + x_2^4)/4$ and $\dot{V} = -k_1 x_1^2 - k_2 x_2^2$.

14.22 Figure P14-22 shows [illegible] form [illegible] in the [illegible]

[illegible]

where [illegible] Show that the [illegible]

Figure P14-22

14.23 Using [illegible] 14.22 [illegible] the variable gradient method.

14.24 Can the [illegible] method [illegible]

14.25 The [illegible] of the feedforward elements for a feedback control system [illegible]

[illegible]

The feedback path contains a nonlinear element [illegible] show that [illegible] will [illegible] the feedback element [illegible] such that [illegible]

14.26 Determine the equation [illegible]

14.27 Determine [illegible]

APPENDIX

I

EQUILIBRIUM FLOW

Many pneumatic components use two orifices in series to obtain a controlled pressure in the chamber between the orifices. If the component is available, the chamber pressure may be experimentally determined for various operating conditions. However, in the initial design stages, before any parts have been manufactured, it is desirable to be able to predict the value of the chamber pressure. This may be accomplished by use of the nondimensional family of curves shown in Fig. I.1*a*. As is illustrated by the insert above Fig. I.1*a*, the pressures P_1, P_2, and P_3 represent the inlet pressure, chamber pressure, and discharge pressure, respectively. The symbol A_1 is the area of the first orifice times the coefficient of discharge, and A_2 is the area of the second orifice times the coefficient of discharge.

Usually, the overall pressure ratio P_1/P_3 is known, and also the ratio A_2/A_1 is known, so that the ratio P_2/P_1 can be found from Fig. I.1*a*. The value of the chamber pressure P_2 is then computed as the product of the ratio P_2/P_1 and the value of the inlet pressure P_1. In using Fig. I.1*a*, it is necessary to use absolute pressures. Because these are nondimensional curves, any consistent set of units may be used.

The derivation of this nondimensional family of curves is accomplished as follows: Assuming that the fluid is a perfect gas and that the kinetic energy at the inlet is negligible compared with other terms in the energy equation, the mass rate of flow through the first orifice is

$$M_1 = \frac{A_1 P_1}{\sqrt{T_1}} \left\{ 2g \frac{k}{k-1} \frac{1}{R} \left[\left(\frac{P_{1_t}}{P_1} \right)^{2/k} - \left(\frac{P_{1_t}}{P_1} \right)^{(k+1)/k} \right] \right\}^{1/2} \tag{I.1}$$

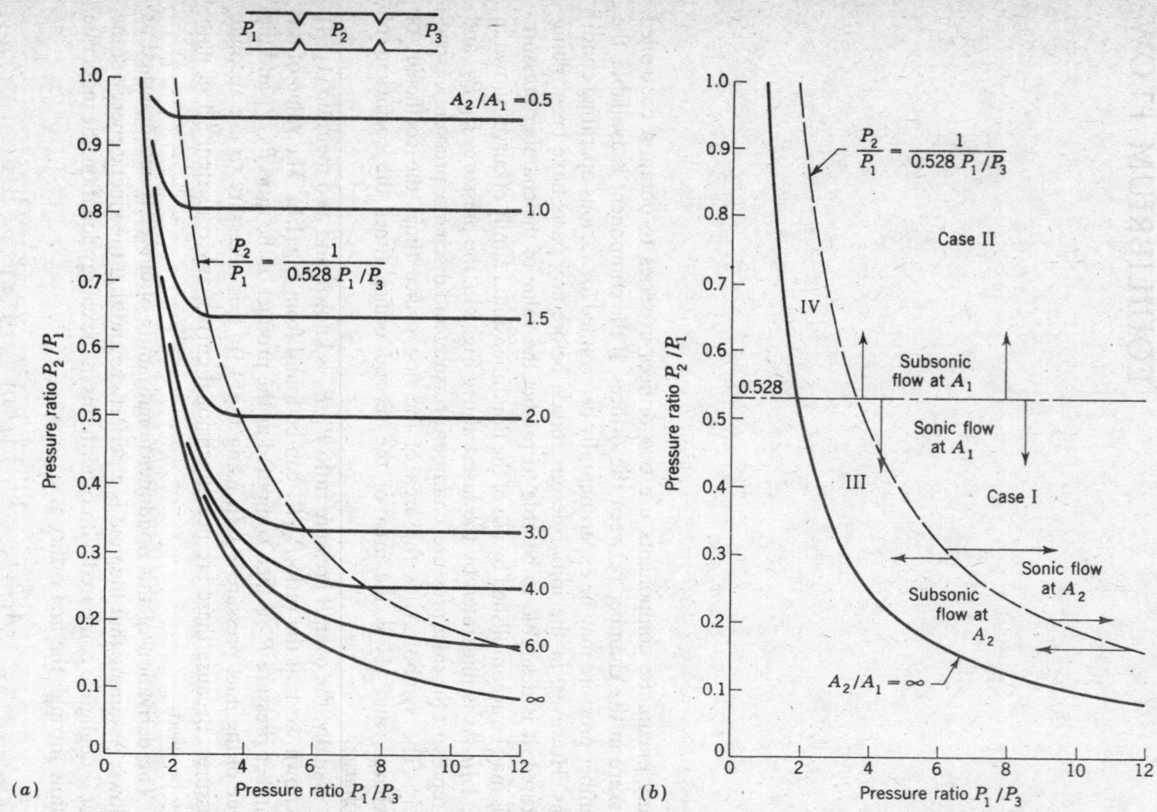

Figure I.1 Nondimensional curve for determining equilibrium conditions for flow through two orifices in series.

where T_1 = stagnation temperature at inlet
g = gravitational conversion factor
k = ratio of specific heat at constant pressure to that at constant volume
P_{1_t} = throat pressure at first orifice
R = gas constant

By replacing the subscript 1 in Eq. (I.1) by 2 and the subscript 1_t by 2_t, the equation for the mass rate of flow through the second orifice is obtained. For equilibrium to exist, the mass rate of flow in must equal that out, so that

$$\frac{A_1 P_1}{\sqrt{T_1}} B_1^{1/2} = \frac{A_2 P_2}{\sqrt{T_2}} B_2^{1/2} \tag{I.2}$$

where
$$B_1 = \left(\frac{P_{1_t}}{P_1}\right)^{2/k} - \left(\frac{P_{1_t}}{P_1}\right)^{(k+1)/k}$$

$$B_2 = \left(\frac{P_{2_t}}{P_2}\right)^{2/k} - \left(\frac{P_{2_t}}{P_2}\right)^{(k+1)/k}$$

Because there is little time for heat transfer to take place, the flow may be considered to be adiabatic, so that $T_1 = T_2$. Thus Eq. (I.2) becomes

$$A_1 P_1 B_1^{1/2} = A_2 P_2 B_2^{1/2} \tag{I.3}$$

In the following analysis, it is assumed that the fluid is air, for which $k = 1.4$, and the critical pressure ratio is $P_2/P_1 = P_3/P_2 = 0.528$. By using the appropriate value of k and the critical ratio, this analysis is applicable for any gas.

When sonic flow exists at the first orifice, $B_1^{1/2} = 0.259$, and similarly for sonic flow at the second orifice $B_2^{1/2} = 0.259$. Thus, for sonic flow at both orifices Eq. (I.3) reduces to

$$\frac{P_2}{P_1} = \frac{1}{A_2/A_1} \tag{I.4}$$

When sonic flow exists at the first orifice,

$$\frac{P_2}{P_1} \leq 0.528$$

Above the line $P_2/P_1 = 0.528$ shown in Fig. I.1*b*, subsonic flow exists at A_1, and below this line sonic flow exists at A_1.

The equation for the line of separation between subsonic and sonic flow at A_2 is obtained by noting that the critical ratio is $P_3/P_2 = 0.528$; thus

$$\frac{P_2}{P_1} = \frac{1}{(P_3/P_2)(P_1/P_3)} = \frac{1}{0.528(P_1/P_3)} \tag{I.5}$$

The curve defined by the preceding expression is shown in Fig. I.1*b*. To the right of this curve sonic flow exists at A_2, and to the left of this curve subsonic flow exists at A_2. The regions in which each of the four possible combinations of sonic or subsonic flow may exist at the first and second orifices are shown in Fig. I.1*b*, that is,

Case I sonic flow at both orifices
Case II subsonic flow at the first orifice and sonic at the second
Case III sonic flow at the first orifice and subsonic at the second
Case IV subsonic flow at both orifices

For case I, it follows from Eq. (I.4) that the lines of constant values of A_2/A_1 are horizontal straight lines as shown in Fig. I.1*a*.

For case II, $P_2 = P_{1_t}$, and $B_2^{1/2} = 0.259$, so that Eq. (I.3) reduces to

$$\frac{P_2}{P_1}\frac{1}{B_1^{1/2}} = \frac{1}{0.259(A_2/A_1)} \tag{I.6}$$

For a given area ratio A_2/A_1, there is but one value of P_2/P_1 which makes the left-hand side of Eq. (I.6) equal to the right-hand side. Thus, for case II, lines of constant A_2/A_1 are also horizontal.

By applying these techniques to case III and case IV, the complete family of curves shown in Fig. I.1*a* is obtained. This method of analysis may be extended to determine equilibrium flow conditions for three or more orifices in series.[1]

Equation (I.1) is in an awkward form for computing partial derivatives. However, for the case of sonic flow, this expression reduces to

$$M_1 = \frac{0.53}{\sqrt{T_1}} A_1 P_1 \tag{I.7}$$

where the preceding expression has units of pounds-mass (lb_m), pounds-force (lb_f), feet, degrees Rankine, and seconds. For the usual design case in which the stagnation temperature of the inlet air is 60°F or 520°R, then $M_1 = 0.0074 A_1 P_1$.

For the case of subsonic flow $P_{1_t} = P_2$, Eq. (I.1) may be approximated by noting that a plot of the function B_1 versus $(P_1 - P_2)P_2/P_1^2$ is very nearly a straight line. The slope of this line is such that

$$B_1 \approx \frac{0.261(P_1 - P_2)P_2}{P_1^2} \tag{I.8}$$

Substitution of the preceding approximation into Eq. (I.1) gives

$$M_1 \approx \frac{2.06}{\sqrt{T_1}} A_1 \sqrt{0.261(P_1 - P_2)P_2}$$

$$= \frac{1.05}{\sqrt{T_1}} A_1 \sqrt{(P_1 - P_2)P_2} \tag{I.9}$$

[1] The author wishes to express his appreciation to Mr. Stanley Best, Chief of Analysis, Hamilton Standard Division, United Aircraft Corporation, Windsor Locks, Conn., for his fine comments and suggestions concerning the development of the preceding method for determining equilibrium flow conditions.

where $\sqrt{(2g/R)[k/(k-1)]} = 2.06$. For a stagnation temperature of 520°R, Eq. (I.9) is

$$M_1 = 0.046A_1\sqrt{(P_1 - P_2)P_2} \tag{I.10}$$

The length units cancel in Eqs. (I.7) to (I.10), hence any unit of length may be used.

Because the curves shown in Fig. I.1 are nondimensional, they are valid for SI units as well as British gravitational units. When using SI units (kg, m, N, s, K), the g_c term does not appear in Eq. I.1. Equations (I.2) to (I.6) are valid for SI units as well as British gravitational units. For SI units, the constant in Eq. (I.7) should be 0.04 rather than 0.53. The constant 0.261 in Eq. (I.8) remains the same. The constant 2.06 in Eq. (I.9) becomes 0.156, and the constant 1.05 becomes 0.08.

where [illegible] = 4206 for saturation temperature [illegible]

$$\Delta T = 0.0024 \ldots P_s T_s \quad (A.19)$$

The length units cancel in Eqs. (1.7) to (1.10); hence any unit of length may be used.

Because the curves shown in Fig. 1.1 are nondimensional, they are valid for SI units as well as British gravitational units. When using SI units (that is, N, kg, K), the g_c term does not appear in Eq. 1.1. Equations (1.2) to (1.6) are valid for SI units as well as British gravitational units. For SI units the constant in Eq. (1.7) would be 0.04 rather than [illegible]. The constant 0.201 in Eq. (1.8) remains the same. The constant 2.06 in Eq. (1.9) becomes 0.156 and the constant 1.85 becomes [illegible]

INDEX

Ac motors, 69–70
Acceleration error constant,
156–157, 159
Actuating signal, 2–4
Actuator:
hydraulic, 55–61
pneumatic, 61–64
Adder (summer), 238–239
α contours:
on direct polar plot, 412–416
on inverse polar plot, 469–470
on log-modulus plot, 431–432
Amplifiers:
hydraulic, 55–61
operational, 237–239, 250–251
pneumatic, 61–64
Analog computers, 235–254
computer diagrams, 239–243
direct programming, 239–245
initial conditions, 242
integration, 238
multiplication by a constant,
237–238
operational amplifier, 237–239,
250–251
potentiometer, 249–250
scale factors, 242–245

Analog computers:
simulation, 250
summation, 238–239
time scale, 245–250
Analogies, 24–35
direct, 24–26, 30–35
inverse, 24–26, 31–35
Angle of arrival, 212, 222
Angle of departure, 210–212, 222
Angle condition, 201–202,
205–206, 221
Asymptotes:
intersection point, 202–204
of log-magnitude plots, 397–408
of root-locus plots, 202–204, 221
Asymptotic response, 548–551
Attenuation, 461, 463
Auxiliary equation, 188–190

Balanced valve, 55
Bandwidth, 423–425
Best, Stanley, 559
Block diagrams, 3–5
algebra of, 71–72
of general system, 78–79
Bode, H. W., 400

Bode diagrams, 400–405, 451–452
Boxcar generator, 357
Break-away point, 204–206,
212–214, 222
Break frequency, 399
Break-in point, 212–214, 222
British gravitational system, 29–30

Canonical form, 277–284
Capacitance, electrical, 15–16
Cascaded networks (*see* Series compensation)
Characteristic equation, 115
(*See also* Characteristic function)
Characteristic function, 115,
164–190
of closed-loop control system,
183–185
effect of external disturbance on,
183–185
predicting transient response from,
181–186
relation to system stability,
181–190
of sampled-data systems, 349–360
zeros of (*see* Zeros of characteristic function)
Charge, 16
Closed-loop control system, 2–4
characteristic function of,
183–185
standard terminology of, 78–79
Command signal, 78–79, 88–96
Comparator, 2–4
Compensated isochronous control,
107
Compensation (*see* Internal feedback; Series compensation)
Computer-controlled systems,
380–387
Contactor element, 496–498
Control elements, 2–4
Controlled variable, 2–4, 78–79
Controller, 90–108
proportional, 99–103
plus derivative, 108
plus integral, 106–108
Convolution integral, 154–156
Correlation of transient and
frequency response, 416–422
Coulomb friction, 510–511
Critical damping, 174
Cross-over frequency, 453–454, 465
Curl of a vector, 538–539
Curl equations, 539

Damped natural frequency, 172–181
Damper:
rotational, 14–15
translational, 12
Damping ratio,173–178
Dashpot (*see* Damper)
Dc motors, 64–68
Dead band, 486–494
Dead zone, 486–494
Decade, 398
Decibel, 398
Decrement, logarithmic, 177-178
Degrees of freedom, 23
Delta method, 514–515
Derivative controller, 108
(*See also* Controller)
Describing function, 485–502
dead zone, 486–494
frequency sensitive, 498–502
on-off element (*see* On-off systems)
with phase shift, 496–498
use in stability analysis, 490–496
Difference equations, 355–356,
367–371
Differential equations, 114–120
solution of: analog computer,
239–245
classical, 114–120
Laplace transform, 120–147
state-space, 296–313

Digital-control systems, 366–387
computer-controlled systems, 380–387
discrete data systems, 366–376
sampled-data systems, 376–380
Direct analog, 24
Direct polar plots, 396–397, 409–412
Direct programming, 260–262
Discrete data systems, 366–376
Disturbance, external, 2–4, 78–79
Droop controller, 102
Dual of mechanical circuit, 38

Eigenvalues:
distinct, 279–284
repeated, 291–294
Eigenvectors, 524–525
Electric motors (*see* Motors, electric)
Electrical components, 15–16
Equalization (*see* Series compensation)
Equilibrium, 96–99
(*See also* Steady-state analysis)
Equilibrium flow, 556–560
Error constants, 156–160
acceleration, 156–157, 159
positional, 156, 158
velocity, 156–159
Error signal, 2–4, 78–79
Euler's equations, 125–126
Evans, W. R., 196
Experimental determination:
of frequency response, 404–405
of gain constant, 406–408
of time constant, 404
of transfer function, 405
Exponential hold, 361–362
Exponential response, 60–61
Exponentially decaying function, 124
External disturbance, 2–4, 78–79, 183–185

Feedback control system, 2–5
general block diagram, 2–5, 72, 78–79
Feedback elements, 4, 5
Feedforward elements, 4–5
Filters, 356–362
Final value theorem, 132–133
First-order hold, 360–361
First-order system:
frequency response of, 393–400
transient response of, 59–61, 117, 141, 145–148
Flapper valves, 61–64
Floating controller, 105
Fluid analogs, 32–35
Flyball governor, 73–74
Focus, 527–530
Force-current analogy, 25
Force-voltage analogy, 24
Forced response, 282–284
Forcing function, 115
Format method, 542–551
Frequency of oscillation, 172–177
natural: damped, 172
undamped, 173–177
Frequency response, 392–433
closed-loop, 412–422
correlation with transient response, 416–422
determining gain constant from, 406–408
experimental determination of, 404–405
of first-order systems, 393–400
obtaining desired M_p from, 425–433
open-loop, 412–422
representation: by means of inverse polar plots, 468–477
by means of log-magnitude diagrams, 397–405
by means of log-modulus plots, 431–433

Frequency response:
  representation: by means of polar plots, 396–397, 409–412
  of second-order system, 401–404, 416–421
Frequency-sensitive describing functions, 498–502
Friction, coulomb, 510–511

Gain adjustment:
  from direct polar plots, 425–431
  from inverse polar plots, 470–472
  from log-magnitude diagrams, 406–408, 451–452
  from log-modulus plots, 431–438, 449–450
Gain constant, 397–408
  experimental determination of, 404–405
Gain margin, 448–454
General programming, 264–266
Gibson, J. E., 539
Governor, flyball, 73–74
Gradient of a scalar function, 537–539
"Grounded-chair" representation, 19, 21, 22

Heaviside operational notation, 6–11
Hydraulic integrator, 56, 103–105
Hydraulic servomotor, 57–61
Hydraulic systems, 55–57
Hysteresis, 496–498

Impedance:
  electrical, 17
  mechanical, 19, 20
Impulse function, 122–124
Impulse response, 185–186
Inductance, electrical, 15–16
Initial conditions, 139–145
Initial-value theorem, 133, 139–144
Integral controller, 90, 98–99, 103–105
  (*See also* Controller)
Integrators:
  analog computer, 238
  hydraulic, 56, 103–105
Integrodifferential equations, 145
Internal feedback, 467–468
Inverse analog, 25
Inverse Laplace transformations, 121–123, 139–141, 165–172
Inverse Liapunov method, 545–551
Inverse polar plots, 468–477
Inverse z transforms, 342–344, 355–356
Isochronous controller, 105
Isoclines, 512–517, 525

Kalman, R. E., 384
Kochenburger, R. J., 485

Lag compensation, 461–465
Lag-lead compensation, 465–467
Lambda matrix, 278
Laplace transformation theorems, 126–144
  change of scale, 131–132
  final-value, 132–133
  initial-value, 133, 139–144
  linearity, 132
  multiplication: by e^{at}, 131
    by t, 130–131
  real differentiation, 128–130
  real integration, 132
  real translation, 126–128
Laplace transforms, 120–160
  for arbitrary functions, 154–156
  for common functions, 121–133
  definition, 121
  general procedure, 145–151
  inverse, 121–123, 139–141, 165–172

Laplace transforms:
of sampled-data systems, 332–336
for state-transition matrix, 303–304, 310–311
table of, 123, 127
LaSalle, J., 531
Lead compensation, 454–460
Leake, R. J., 542
Lefschetz, S., 531
Lhopital's rule, 124
Liapunov, A. M., 531
Liapunov's direct method, 530–551
Limit cycle, 495–496, 535
Linear algebra, 277–296
Linear control systems, 43–44
Linearization, 43–54
of nonlinear functions, 43–51
of operating curves, 51–54
Linvill, W. K., 362
Liu, R. W., 542
Loci equations, 217–219
Log-magnitude diagrams, 397–408, 451–452
Log-modulus plots, 431–433, 449–450
Logarithmic decrement, 177–178

M contours, 412–416, 469–475
on direct polar plot, 412–416
gain adjustment, 425–433
on inverse polar plot, 469–475
on log-modulus plot, 431–433
Magnitude condition, 201–202, 205–206, 221
Malkin, I. G., 536
Manipulated variable, 90
Mason, S. J., 272
Mason's gain formula, 272–277
Mass, 12–13
Mass-spring-damper system:
parallel, 21
series, 13–14
Mechanical components:
rotational, 14–15, 21
Mechanical components:
translational, 11–14
Minimum-phase systems, 405
Minor feedback loop, 71, 76
(*See also* Internal feedback)
Motors, electric, 64–70
ac, two-phase, 69–70
dc: armature-controlled, 66–68
field-controlled, 64–66
M_p adjustment:
on direct polar plots, 425–431
on inverse polar plots, 470–472
on log-modulus diagrams, 431–433

Natural frequency, 173–181
Newton's method, 213–217
Nichols, N. B., 431
Nichols plots, 431–433
Nodes, 522–525
Nonminimum-phase systems, 405
Nyquist, H., 439
Nyquist stability criterion, 439–448, 475–477

On-off systems, 485–489, 496–498, 518–520
Open-loop control system, 2–4
frequency response of, 412–422
steady-state characteristics of, 98–99
transfer function of, 397
Operational amplifier, 237–239, 250–251
Operational notation, 6–11
Optimum response, 384–387
Oscillation, frequency of, 172–177

Parallel combinations, 17–21
electrical elements, 17–18
laws of, 17–21
mechanical elements, 19–20

Parallel compensation, 467–468
Parallel programming, 262–263
Partial-fraction expansion, 116–119
for distinct roots, 116–117, 166
for repeated roots, 118–119, 167
Peak frequency, 403
Peczkowski, J. L., 542, 545
Pell's method, 513–514
Pendulum, 529–530
Percent maximum overshoot, 178–181
Perturbation method, 80
Phase margin, 448–454, 459–460
Phase-plane method, 506–520
in feedback systems, 515–520
isoclines, 512–517, 525
portrait, 507–511
trajectories, 507–511, 522–530
Piecewise continuous functions, 151–154
Pilot valve, 55
Pneumatic systems, 61–64
Polar plots:
direct, 396–397, 409–412
inverse, 468–477
Poles, 440
Positional error constant, 156, 158
Positional servomechanism, remote control, 68–69
Positive definite functions, 534
Positive semidefinite functions, 534
Potentiometer, 249–250
Process controllers, 382–384
Programming, 260–266
direct, 260–262
general, 264–266
parallel, 262–263
series, 263–264
Proportional controller, 91–94, 99–103, 136–138
plus integral, 106–108
(*See also* Controller)
Pulse function, 122–124
Pulse-transfer function, 346–349

Quadratic forms, 547–548
Quadripole, 190

Ramp function, 131, 151, 156
Raven, F. H., 121, 141
Reference input, 2–4, 78–79
Reference operating point, 13–14, 19
Regulator, 5
Remainder theorem, 213–217
Reset controller, 105
Residue method, 335–336
Resistance, electrical, 15–16
Resonant frequency, 403
Rise time, 178–181
Root-locus method, 196–228
construction techniques: angle of arrival, 212, 222
angle of departure, 210–212, 222
angle condition, 201–202, 205–206, 221
asymptotes, 202–204, 221
break-in point, 212–214, 222
breakaway point, 204–206, 212–214, 222
location on real axis, 202, 211–212, 221
magnitude condition, 201–202, 205–206, 221
summary, 211–213, 221–222
determination of stability from, 196–200
equations for, 217–219
roots of characteristic equation, 196–200
sensitivity analysis by, 225–228
transient performance from, 196–200
variation of parameters, 220–225
Roots of characteristic equation, 115–116
from root-locus plot, 196–200
(*See also* Characteristic function)

Rotational mechanical components, 14–15, 21
Routh, E. J., 186
Routh's stability criterion, 186–190, 206

Saddle point, 526–527, 530
Sampled-data systems, 331–366
  characteristic equation for, 350–354
  difference equations in, 355–356
  filters for, 356–362
  impulse response of, 345–348
  Laplace transforms in, 332–336
  root-locus plot of, 352–354
  Routh's criterion for, 351
  transient response of, 349–362
  z transforms in, 333–349
Saturation, 490, 494–495
Scale factors, 26–29, 242–245
Schultz, D. G., 539
Second-order systems:
  frequency response of, 401–404, 416–421
  transient response of, 173–181
Seismic instrument, 434
Sensitivity analysis, 225–228
Series combinations, 17–19
  electrical elements, 17
  laws of, 17–19
  mechanical elements, 19
Series compensation:
  phase lag, 461–465
  phase lag-lead, 465–467
  phase lead, 454–460
Series equalizer, 454
Series programming, 263–264
Servomechanism, 5
Settling time, 178–181
SI units, 29–30, 47–49
Signal flow graphs, 270–277, 304–307, 311–313, 370–371
Simulation, 250
Singular points, 520–530
Sinusoidal function, 124–126
Sinusoidal response (*see* Frequency response)
Speed control system, 72–78
Spirule, 205
Spool valve, 55
Spring:
  mechanical, 11–12
  torsional, 14
Stability, 181–190, 439–448
  determined: from characteristic function, 181–186
    from impulse response, 185–186
    from Liapunov's method, 535, 550–551
    from Nyquist criterion, 439–448
    from root locus, 196–200
    from Routh's criterion, 186–190
  in inverse plane, 475–477
State-space design, 318–324
State-space methods, 260–270, 296–318
  determination of transfer function from, 313–318
  programming in, 260–266
  solution of differential equations by, 296–313
  system design by, 318–324
  system representation by, 266–270
State-transition matrix, 298–307
  methods for obtaining, 300–307
    classical, 300–302
    Laplace transform, 303–304
    signal-flow-graph, 304–307
State variables, 261–262
Static loop sensitivity, 196
Steady state, 88
Steady-state analysis, 88–96
  of derivative controller, 108
  of integral controller, 90, 98–99
  of proportional controller, 99–103
    plus integral controller, 106–108

Steady-state constants, 90–96
Step function, 60, 122
Step-function response:
  of first-order system, 60–61
  of second-order system, 175–177
Synthetic division, 216–217
Synthetic-sampler method, 362–366
System representation, 260–270
  closed-loop systems, 266–270
  direct programming, 260–262
  general programming, 264–266
  parallel programming, 262–263
  series programming, 263–264
System type, 408–422, 442–448
Systems:
  closed-loop, 2–4, 412–422
  equivalent unity feedback, 408–409
  open-loop, 2–4, 397, 412–422
  types of, 408–422, 442–448

Tachometer, dc, 68, 69
Thermal analogs, 30–32
Time constant, 60–61
Time scale, 27–29, 245–250
Transfer function, 165
  experimental determination of, 405
  of open-loop control systems, 397
  from state-space representation, 313–318
Transforms (*see* Laplace transforms; *z* transforms)
Transient response, 114, 164–186
  from characteristic function, 181–186
  correlation with frequency response, 416–422
  from differential equations, 114–120
  of first-order systems, 59–61, 117, 141, 145–148
  from frequency response, 416–422
  from Laplace transforms, 165–172
Transient response:
  from root-locus, 196–200
  of second-order systems, 173–181
  specifications, 178–181
Transient response specifications, 178–181
Translational mechanical components, 11–14
Transmittance, 225–226, 270–277
Type, system, 408–422, 442–448

Undamped natural frequency, 173–181
Unity feedback, 3–4
  equivalent systems, 408–409

Van der Pol equation, 554
Variable-gradient method, 539–542
Variation of parameters, 220–225
Vector loci, 396–397, 409–412
Vector loci plots (*see* Polar plots)
Velocity error constant, 156, 159
Vibrometer, 435
Viscous damper (*see* Damper)
Vortex, 527–528

Walking-beam linkage, 57–59
Ward-Leonard system, 67

z transforms, 333–349
  inverse, 342–344, 355–356
  table of, 334, 342
  theorems, 336–342
Zero-order hold, 357–360
Zeros of characteristic function, 166–173
  complex conjugate, 168–172
  distinct, 166–167, 172–173
  repeated, 167–168, 172–173
  (*See also* Characteristic function)